2-19

❧ *Reliable* ❧
KNOWLEDGE

Scientific Methods in the
Social Studies

Revised Edition

HAROLD A. LARRABEE

HOUGHTON MIFFLIN COMPANY · BOSTON

To Doris, Eric and Sylvia
who helped

❧ Contents

57107

✄ Foreword to the Revised Edition

To Voltaire is attributed the thought that "men will continue to commit atrocities as long as they continue to believe absurdities"; and that remains the theme of this book. For men will continue to believe absurdities until they improve their thinking, especially about human social relationships. Long before Sir Charles P. Snow discovered "The Two Cultures," this volume's original edition was calling attention to "the gulf between the sciences and the humanities," and was offering a program for doing something about it. One bridge across the gulf, it suggested, might be a better understanding of their common goal in knowledge, namely reliability, underlying a plurality of approaches or methods.

In its pristine form, *Reliable Knowledge* sprang from several decades of teaching an introductory course entitled "Methods and Problems in the Social Studies" at Union College in Schenectady, New York, where it had the benefit of criticism by colleagues and students too numerous to mention. Before that, there was the inspired teaching of men like Professors C. I. Lewis, R. B. Perry, W. E. Hocking, F. J. E. Woodbridge, Irwin Edman, and above all John Dewey. More recently, its author has learned much from his erstwhile colleague at Union, Professor Sven R. Peterson, and from two of his own successors in the department, Professors Rollo Handy and Paul W. Kurtz.

The passage of nearly twenty years does not change appreciably the principles of logic, but if their illustrations are up-to-date in one generation, they sometimes become out-of-date in the next. This book's first version appeared in the wake of World War II, and naturally contained echoes of that conflict, now only a memory of the middle-aged. Such examples have largely disappeared in this revised edition, along with Chapters 16 and 17, which have been omitted for lack of space.

Quite unexpectedly, this volume's original edition proved to be a useful textbook in an astonishing variety of courses in many sorts of colleges and universities. Thanks are due to teachers in many departments for suggesting improvements. The chief new developments in the methods of reliable knowing and the testing of knowledge have been connected with the linguistic and computer revolutions. British and American philosophy, as everyone knows, has fairly been swamped by linguistic analysis, while the so-called behavioral sciences have encountered a similar wave of mathematical theories. The chief revisions, aside from many new illustrations, have been made in Chapters 3, 7, and 12. The labor of revision has been immensely lightened by the priceless and complete coöperation of Doris Kennard Larrabee.

H. A. L.

Schenectady, New York

v

INTRODUCTION

1. The Lack of Reliable Knowledge

ON THE EVENING of October 30, 1938, over one million Americans were frightened by a radio broadcast which they took to be an on-the-spot description of the landing of an invading force from the planet Mars at the town of Grovers Mill, New Jersey. Many of these listeners packed up and left their homes, either to flee or to fight the invaders; others prayed or gave way to hysteria; while thousands of them flooded radio, newspaper, and police offices with frantic telephone calls.

The innocent cause of this "tidal wave of terror which swept the nation" was a Mercury Theater on the Air adaptation of H. G. Wells's fantastic *War of the Worlds*, conceived, produced, directed, and acted by Orson Welles from a script by Howard Koch. The original English locale of the novel had been changed to New Jersey; and a high degree of realism was attained in the early minutes of the performance by the skillful utilization of the news-bulletin technique. Yet, to an informed listener, the names used were obviously invented; and announcements were made at the beginning, in the middle, and at the end of the program that it was a dramatization of Wells's novel.

What was the matter with the million or more Americans who gave way to panic on this occasion? Why did they not "know any better" than to accept as fact what some four or five million of their fellow listeners were able to recognize as fiction? No sooner had the excitement subsided than dozens of explanations were offered by editorial writers, columnists, and commentators. The victims, they said, were neurotic, or congenitally stupid, or ultra-suggestible, or scared by Munich, or just extremely ignorant. Indeed, some of the theories advanced to account for the aberrant conduct of the terrified were almost as wide of sanity as the behavior itself. But there were a few exceptions: not every critic went wild with eagerness to explain what had happened. Just as some who heard the broadcast retained their self-possession and judged it for what it was — exciting, spooky, Halloween-season entertainment — so a number of the calmer students of human nature refused to indulge in the extravagances of the glib elucidators. Instead, they kept their heads, held their tongues, and set about the task of analyzing the causes of the furor as objectively as possible.[1]

Looking at the two sets of failures, that of the victims to size up the broadcast for what it actually was, and that of the journalistic explainers to point out the genuinely influential reasons for the panic, it is easy to see that they

[1] Hadley Cantril *et al.*, *The Invasion from Mars* (Princeton, N.J., 1940). With the assistance of foundation grants, Professor Cantril and his co-workers of the Princeton Radio Project were able to organize and carry through this study, based mainly on systematic personal interviews with 135 persons, 100 of whom had been frightened by the broadcast, within four weeks of its occurrence.

have a number of symptoms in common. On both levels there was a failure of critical judgment in a problem-situation. Beliefs were accepted without sufficient testing of their foundations in fact. Men jumped to conclusions on inadequate evidence. They were unable to choose correctly among a number of possible interpretations of unusual events. Most of the people who were frightened by the broadcast, as Professor Cantril's sample revealed, either did not question the face value of some of its parts at all, or else were unsuccessful in their attempts to decide which interpretation, the realistic or the fictional, was the proper one. They acted without thinking, or on the basis of thinking that was too little and too late. The same things were true of the cocksure commentators who had all the answers ready almost before the questions were asked. In a way, they were even more culpable than the victims of the original panic. The latter were bewildered, and admitted it; while many of the former were confused without knowing it, being sure that they knew a good many things which later turned out to be false.

Now to exercise good judgment in a difficult situation takes knowledge that is "grounded in evidence or tested experience."[2] It was the lack of an adequate supply of relevant and dependable knowledge that, as much as anything else, made the victims of the Wells-Welles drama appear so sheepish on the morning after, and some of its explainers look equally embarrassed following the publication of *The Invasion from Mars*. Of course we are still very far from knowing all there is to know about the whole incident, but it is probable that we now know enough to make a repetition of it unlikely if the lessons of the Princeton inquiry are heeded by broadcasters, educators, and all others who influence the popular state of mind. That we possess a certain amount of tested knowledge does not, unfortunately, guarantee that it will be utilized.

Of one thing, however, we may be sure: if we do *not* possess knowledge, we cannot use it. So our first task is to remedy that lack as far as it is humanly possible to do so. That is what this book is about. It is concerned with the art of getting reliable knowledge. It does not pretend to be a treatise on the theory of knowledge, or on formal logic, or on the subject matter of any particular field of investigation. Its aim is practical: to aid those who want to seek dependable knowledge in the improvement of their methods of inquiry. Like form or style in any other pursuit, ability in knowledge-getting is best developed by continual practice under supervision. That calls for a high degree of participation on the part of the student. Thinking is seldom improved by merely reading *about* better ways of procedure that have been used by somebody else; the learner must make them his own by actually employing them himself.

2. Preliminary Definitions

Later on in the book, a good deal will be said about the importance of beginning a discussion by clearly defining the terms to be used. It is none too soon to begin following that advice. Naturally a definition that is offered in

[2] *Ibid.*, p. 205.

advance of intimate acquaintance with a subject will convey less meaning than one which follows prolonged study of what is defined.

KNOWLEDGE

By knowledge is meant, broadly speaking, any founded intellectual acquaintance with a fact or matter, ranging all the way from the simplest perception to the most profound understanding of a complex theory. It so happens that the word "know" in English often covers even more ground than this. In both French and German, two verbs (*connaître — savoir* and *kennen — wissen*) are needed to express all the shades of meaning for which English has only the one verb "to know." William James once suggested "knowledge of acquaintance" as the English equivalent of that intimate first-hand apprehension of qualities in persons and things which is conveyed by *connaître* and *kennen;* with "knowledge about" as a suitable substitute for the more intellectual *savoir* and *wissen.* Another name for the first type is "felt knowledge"; while the second is sometimes identified as "discursive knowledge," or knowledge that is definable in the terms of public discourse.

We must remember, however, that the roots of both kinds of knowing lie in doing. The most elementary test of knowledge is ability in action: knowing how to do something. The man who knows in this primary sense is one who is capable of meeting a situation with a fully adequate response in view of all the circumstances, from the unconscious avoidance of a falling stone to the highest conscious skill of the fisherman or salesman. At his best, he is an expert with an intimate grasp of his subject matter, the man who "knows his stuff."

Yet knowledge can hardly be restricted to our ability to cope with our environment at first-hand; much of it comes to us through communication with others in the form of information, or experience at second-hand. We may read a book about camel driving in the Sahara, or see a film of seal hunting in the Arctic, with the result that we may claim to know something *about* both subjects without ever doing anything about either. If we keep away from both the Arctic and the Sahara, the extent and reliability of our knowledge may never be put to the test. Thus, a receptive individual soon finds himself flooded with discursive knowledge made up of facts originally ascertained by others and conceptualized — that is, expressed in the form of words and ideas. Every library is an immense storehouse of these accumulated experiences; and day by day and hour by hour the newspaper and television add millions of items to the gigantic total of what can be vicariously known. Most of our time in school is spent in absorbing these findings of others by reading and listening. Unless we make such materials our own by incorporating them into the fabric of our own experience, they will remain mere heaped-up scraps of information. The danger of mistaking such information, especially in the form of book learning, for the whole of knowledge is that of becoming a learned dunce, a man "who knows everything and understands nothing."

There is another element in the definition of knowledge, indicated by the word "founded." By no means everything that is communicated to us by our fellows is ordinarily accorded the name of knowledge, for we make a distinction between what a person claims to know, and what he merely conjectures or thinks. When anyone tells us, "It was raining at six o'clock this morning," or, "It is ten miles to the nearest gas station," we assume that such statements are seriously asserted, and that he "knows what he is talking about." Knowledge in this sense goes beyond a mere opinion, guess, or flight of fancy to a responsible claim that sufficient grounds for its affirmation exist. As a person sometimes remarks when challenged: "I don't just think so, I *know* so!"

We do not, however, need to worry a great deal about defining knowledge, since a little reflection about the matter will show that it is, strictly speaking, indefinable in the sense that its meaning could not be conveyed to anyone who did not already know what the experience of knowing was. To know what knowledge is, you must first know what it is to know something. In any enterprise, then, including an inquiry into the nature of knowing, one is obliged to begin by assuming the primitive experience of "knowing what knowledge is."

RELIABLE KNOWLEDGE

By reliable[3] knowledge is meant any claim-to-know that is substantiated as trustworthy for a given purpose. The question of the reliability of knowledge is usually raised when the presence of a problem arouses in the knower a demand, not only for something more than mere conjecture, but for something which shall be useful in a given situation and perhaps in other similar situations. The word "useful" in this connection should not be understood in a narrowly utilitarian sense, because the demand may spring from a powerful theoretical curiosity as well as from a pressing necessity for physical action. An Einstein, intent upon strengthening the general theory of relativity, may want to know the correct deviation of the planet Mercury from the ellipse as stated in Newton's law; or he may merely want to know what time of day it is, so that he can keep an appointment with his dentist.

Whenever, in response to such demands and for a purpose in view, alleged knowledge is offered or found in which there are demonstrable reasons for believing that some degree of confidence may be reposed, it may be regarded as in so far reliable. In practice, this means that a knowledge-claim ("I know that such-and-such is so"), in order to win acceptance as worthy of reliance, must be able to pass successfully certain tests. Some of the tests are highly exacting and precise, with the result that their requirements can be met only by the most refined varieties of our discursive knowledge known as sciences. Others, however, are only approximate at best. All of us possess some knowledge, some-

---

[3] There have been purists [cf. Lucius Beebe, *Boston and the Boston Legend* (New York, 1935), p. 189] who have objected to the use of "reliable" in any sense save "able to rely," holding that the present meaning, "worthy or able to be relied upon," calls for some such word as "rely-on-able"; but established usage amply sanctions reliable as a synonym for trustworthy or dependable, especially when applied to the testimony of a witness.

times called "native wit," that may be highly dependable, but which is only vaguely formulated in our minds, and of the reliability of which we may be unable to give any public demonstration. Like many animals, man has some inborn resources for doing "the right thing" in many situations without knowing just "how he does it" in intellectual terms. Too much reliance, however, should not be placed in this supposed native wisdom of the body. It is far from infallible. Tests at the University of Pittsburgh showed that albino rats given a free choice of fats, carbohydrates, salt and casein failed to eat enough protein to survive.

Strictly speaking, reliable knowledge should be defined as consisting of claims-to-know which can be backed up by overt evidence. For social purposes, it is not enough to know, without knowing *that* we know, and *on the basis of what* we know. Private knowledge allegedly possessed by an individual, such as revelations received in dreams or trances, may pass his own personal reliability tests, but unless he can get others to accept his criteria as their own, his verdict possesses only private significance.

Normally the demand for reliability in knowledge raises two questions: reliable on the basis of what? and, reliable for what purpose? It calls upon the knower to face in two directions: he must look backward toward the past through memory for most of his foundation material; and he must also look forward toward the future for the purposes which are to guide him in its selection and use. If he confines himself to the backward look for its own sake, he may become a mere antiquarian, satisfying his curiosity by piling up masses of tested, established, and yet possibly useless data in the form of records of past occurrences. But reliable knowledge is more than embalmed knowledge. As here understood, it is a potentially dependable resource from the past or present for future knowing or acting, even though a man may not be able to see at a given moment exactly how it is going to be utilized. Reliable knowledge is what, as we say, we can safely fall back upon in a problem-situation in order to go forward to its solution.

Reliability is plainly relative to the problem which arouses the demand for it. No knowledge is just reliable in general, without reference to the situation, and purposes to which it is relevant. Some kinds of knowledge, notably logic, mathematics, and some of the folk wisdom of the ages that is condensed in commandments and proverbs, serve a wide range of human purposes in many sorts of situations. The man who can count, and read and write, will find such knowledge useful in thousands of contingencies. But no knowledge can be guaranteed to work for everyone every time everywhere.

Furthermore, the degree of reliability that will be acceptable to a given knower in a given situation will also be relative to the extent of his aroused demand. Some inquirers are satisfied with very little in the way of evidence in support of knowledge-claims: a savage may accept a medicine man as a veritable paragon of certainty on the basis of a single wonderful cure. Other seekers after knowledge may be much more skeptical, sometimes raising their demands for complete reliability in the widest possible context to such a pitch that they reject almost all human knowledge-claims as insufficiently evidenced

The same knower may also make use of very different standards of reliability from moment to moment in different moods and settings. A judge who enforces with the greatest strictness all the complicated rules of evidence which prevail in his court, when a man is on trial for his life, will be much more lenient in a minor civil suit for damages, and may even be astonishingly gullible about the promises of glib-tongued salesmen in his private life. Highly trained specialists are notoriously easy to mislead in fields with which they are unfamiliar.

This multiple relativity means that all statements to the effect that something is reliably known should, strictly speaking, be made only with extensive qualifications indicating the degree of reliability claimed, on what evidence, for what knowers, and in what contexts. In actual practice, this would load conversation and writing with an intolerable burden of qualifying clauses. To save time, breath, and inked paper, those of us who are neither witnesses testifying under oath nor scientists writing technical papers for other scientists to read, are likely to go right on with our broad, sweeping, abstract generalizations about what we claim to know, leaving it to our hearers or readers to trim them down by making liberal discounts. Unfortunately, however, not all audiences are sophisticated enough to be capable of whittling down imposing knowledge-claims to somewhere near their proper sizes.

3. Preliminary Illustrations

The demand for some degree of reliability in knowledge ("I want to know") is one which may or may not be aroused in a potential knower by a problem-situation. That depends mainly on two factors: the interests of the knower, especially his curiosity; and the urgency of the crisis in his physical or mental environment. If the demand is aroused, knowledge-claims will be made by the knower or by others, which will then, unless accepted at face value, be scrutinized and tested to see whether or not they rest upon adequate evidence. The claims for which some proof can be offered become accepted for the time being as knowledge that may be relied upon to a greater or lesser degree in certain specific contexts. Some of them, such as chemical formulas, are believed to be reliable in a vast number of contexts; while others, such as historical datings, relate merely to a single fact or occurrence. But all evidenced assertions have a status as knowledge that is above that of mere guesses, snap judgments, unsupported opinions, or wishful beliefs.

The four examples on the following pages, selected from the innumerable actual and possible knowledge-claims made by human beings in all sorts of contexts, extend all the way from a simple individual difficulty of practice encountered by an untutored savage, to a highly complex issue of social theory raised by trained economists and sociologists, and a knotty problem of historical reconstruction of past events. In each instance, the reader should make his own rough preliminary analysis of the way in which the question of knowledge and its reliability enters, by posing, where relevant, such questions as:

a. Is the problem-situation thrust upon the knower by a pressing practical necessity, or does it arise through his own initiative? Or a combination of the two?

b. What is the nature and extent of his aroused demand, if any, for reliable knowledge? Is the latter desired primarily for the purpose of immediate action? Remote usefulness? Satisfaction of curiosity? A mixture of these?

c. Is the knower well-equipped or ill-equipped for inquiry in the field?

By temperament? By past conditioning and experience? By the communicated information of others? By the understanding of relevant general principles and methods of knowing?

CASE I. THE SICK MAN IN THE FOREST

Suppose that a man who is hunting alone in a forest suddenly feels a sharp and persistent sensation of pain in the lower right side of his abdomen. He has a strong desire, naturally, to get rid of the unpleasantness, and to prevent its recurrence.

Savage. If we suppose further that the man in question is a relatively primitive savage, without any knowledge whatsoever of the internal organs of his body save what impressions are furnished by his own sensations and emotions, his probable actions with regard to the pain will be either (1) excited trial-and-error squirmings and fumblings, (2) measures suggested by his remembered past experiences of a similar nature, or (3) customary responses dictated by the *mores* of his social group. Unlike the lower animals, he will not rely entirely upon his instinctive tendencies, but will try to supplement and correct them by what he and his kind have learned from experience. Yet the sum of that learning is pitifully small. The savage is ignorant, and he is also ignorant of the extent of his own ignorance. He does not "know what is the matter with him," except perhaps in some such rudimentary sense as: "This feels like a big-meal pain and not a no-meal pain." He is, moreover, stirred up emotionally to meet a bodily emergency, and therefore likely to attempt an adjustment to it in dramatic terms, such as attributing his suffering to the anger of a god, or associating it with whatever happened to catch his attention at the moment he first noticed it.

His chances of "doing the right thing" in the circumstances would thus depend upon either (1) his happening by sheer accident to hit upon the remedy and to apply it, without knowing anything about its relevance to his difficulty; or (2) his happening to call up from his own or someone else's narrated experience a past association of the pain and the proper remedy, again without knowing why the two were connected, or whether, perhaps, it was the remedy alone or in combination with some belief or incantation that really worked the cure. If, in the face of these overwhelmingly adverse probabilities, the savage hit upon the solution of the problem and relieved the pain, it would be by the aid of a minimum of knowledge-seeking, or none at all. Unless he was an exceptional member of his tribe, his slight demand for knowledge would terminate with the ending of the pain; and what was learned, if anything, would be merely one more haphazard association to be added to his personal or tribal repertory of remedies.

Physician. If, instead of a savage, we suppose that the sick man in the forest is a well-trained modern physician who is accurately informed about his internal organs, their functioning, and their possible ailments, a different picture presents itself. In the first place, he will meet the painful situation with an emotional equanimity which the savage wholly lacks, because as a scientist he has confidence that whatever is wrong has an explanation which does not involve a hidden world of capricious beings to be propitiated by magical practices. He has learned not to take his own internal sensations or his feelings about them at face value, but rather to interpret them as symptoms or signs of wider states of affairs in the light of his extensive knowledge of their probable significance. So he sets to work to fit them into their proper places in the larger framework of modern medicine. If he is not immediately convinced of the accuracy of his first diagnosis, he will run over in his mind a whole host of alternative hypotheses ("This may be the result of a strain, or of cramps due to overeating, or appendicitis"), deducing their consequences logically, and then looking for facts about his condition which will confirm one of the many possibilities by eliminating all the rest. In the absence of his laboratory apparatus, the latter process may be a difficult one.

His final diagnosis and choice of a remedy may, of course, still turn out to be erroneous; but they will not have been haphazardly chosen, having been selected upon the basis of a thorough and relatively objective attempt to get at all the relevant facts, and to interpret them in the light of those organized bodies of tested knowledge known as the medical sciences. Moreover, if the physician solves his immediate problem of getting rid of his pain, he will probably not, like the savage, be satisfied to leave it at that. He will have what we call a scientific interest in his own misfortune, especially if it was in any way unusual. His intellectual curiosity will demand a further analysis and study of his ailment and its apparent remedy in order to consolidate the future usefulness, in other similar cases, of the new knowledge which he may have acquired.

CASE II. THE DRIFTWOOD ON THE ICE

While on a voyage in the sealing ship *Viking* to the Arctic Ocean in 1882, Fridtjof Nansen, then an ambitious twenty-one-year-old naturalist, who had gone along to learn something at first hand about the methods of marine research, noticed a piece of driftwood on a floe off the coast of Greenland. To the rest of the ship's company, the log meant nothing. To an Eskimo, it might have meant an added stick of valuable firewood. But to young Nansen's mind it posed a problem: What kind of wood was it? Where had it come from? Before Nansen stopped thinking and investigating, he had become the last man in history "to discover an ocean"; he had come nearer the North Pole than any other human being up to that time; and he had helped mightily in the founding of a new science, that of oceanography.

His first question about the driftwood was easily answered: it was some sort of pine. That ended his concern with that particular log of wood. For this simple step of classification made available a large amount of accumulated botanical information concerning the localities where pine trees do and do not grow. Nansen now had a basis for framing a number of possible answers to his second question. He knew, for example, that there were no pine trees on Greenland, Iceland, or Spitzbergen; so those points of origin could be eliminated. There were, however, plenty of pine trees in North America, Norway, and Siberia. But the question remained: from which of these three countries could the driftwood have come by the aid of an ocean current and borne on *top* of a cake of floating ice? From his personal knowledge of the normal behavior of driftwood and floes, Nansen was reasonably sure that the log had not climbed aboard the floating ice. Therefore, it must have fallen upon the ice from somewhere along the shore. That meant, he deduced, that it had come from a land with pine trees growing near the shore, and with offshore formations of floating ice.

His next step was to try out successively in his mind the North America, the Norway, and the Siberia hypotheses. He knew that the Gulf stream came northward from the southern coast of North America, where there were pine trees, but no ice. Norway's shores were likewise pine-clad but ice-free; so both of those hypotheses could be eliminated. That left Siberia, which had both pine trees and offshore floes. The log, he conjectured, must have been brought from the eastern Siberian coast to Greenland by a hitherto-unknown drift current across the Arctic regions, which might well be one great ocean. Nansen's theory was scoffed at as absurd, although it was soon powerfully reinforced by other evidence, especially by the finding of unmistakable relics, on floating ice off the southwest coast of Greenland, of the American polar ship *Jeanette*, which had been wrecked north of the New Siberian Islands three years before.[4] In an address before the Christiania Geographical Society in February, 1890, Nansen summed up his reasons for believing that "a current flows at some point between the Pole and Franz Joseph Land from the Siberian Arctic Sea to the east coast of Greenland"; and announced his plan to prove his theory in a spectacular fashion by drifting across the polar sea in a ship carried only by the slowly moving ice pack. This "illogical scheme of self-destruction" was hailed as "sheer madness" by most of the contemporary authorities on Arctic exploration; but they were silenced by the famous voyage of the *Fram* (1893–96) from the coast of Siberia to a point near Spitzbergen, propelled solely by the ocean current beneath the ice in which the stout ship had been frozen fast. Few men have seen their theories more triumphantly vindicated than did Nansen. His train of thought and observation, starting from the driftwood on the ice, not only revolutionized the technique of polar exploration; but also established the essential characteristics of the Arctic Ocean, thus paving the way for wholly unforeseen results of great practical importance in solving the future problems of weather prediction, of the sealing industry, and of Arctic transportation.

[4] Fridtjof Nansen, *Farthest North* (London, 1897), vol. I, pp. 14–53; and Anna Gertrude Hall, *Nansen* (New York, 1940), pp. 33, 65.

CASE III. WHAT IS OPTIMUM POPULATION?

> No body of scientific knowledge could possibly be more important than one which could advise a society as to the most desirable size of its population. No set of public policies could be more vital than one which would transform this advice into reality.[5]

In these words Professor Henry Pratt Fairchild gives his estimate of the importance of a problem in social theory which arose in connection with the economic studies of John Stuart Mill, Edgeworth, and Sidgwick, following the pioneer *Essay on the Principle of Population* by Thomas R. Malthus in 1798; and which has only recently emerged from the status of an academic question to become, in some countries at least, a burning social and political issue. The main theme of Malthus and his followers was *over*population, that crowded misery which is a consequence of the spread between the geometrical increase of births and the (at best) arithmetical increase in the food supply or means of subsistence. At the other end of the scale was *under*population, the backward condition of a sparsely settled area where organized social co-operation is at a minimum. Now, although both of these two extremes meant "utter poverty," it seemed logically necessary that somewhere in the zone between "too many" people and "too few" must lie "just the right number" for a given territory, or its *optimum* (best) population.

Can a formula for a scientifically established optimum for any given society be constructed, and if so, from what materials? Professor Fairchild[6] is bold enough to offer one "for the purpose of analysis."

> If L = the land and its natural resources.
>
> EC = the economic culture, or "the whole combination of human devices and instruments of every sort whereby man is able to increase the volume and variety of the things he needs and wishes beyond what Nature would offer by herself."
>
> LL = the level of living, or "the average amount of necessaries, comforts, and luxuries enjoyed by the typical family in a group."
>
> P = the number of the population.
>
> Then $\dfrac{L \times EC}{LL} = P$ or $\dfrac{L \times EC}{P} = LL$

This is a condensed way of saying that, in a given society, an advance in economic culture, especially in production-distribution, makes possible either one of two things: either a rise in the material level of living, or an increase in the population, or it may be divided among the two. But "the maximum advantage cannot possibly be enjoyed by *both* population and level of living." For example, in numerical terms, an underdeveloped country with a population of 10,000,000 people yielding a Gross National Product of $5,000,000,000 (providing an average income per person of $500 a year) if it were able to increase its GNP by $500,000,000, would have three choices. It could keep

---

[5] Henry Pratt Fairchild, *People* (New York, 1939), p. 88. Case III is based largely upon the discussion of the subject in this book and in Gunnar Myrdal, *Population* (Cambridge, Mass., 1940), pp. 139–50.

[6] *Op. cit.*, p. 75. By permission of Henry Holt and Company, Inc.

its population at 10,000,000 and aim at giving each individual an income of $550 a year; it could keep the previous $500 standard and add 1,000,000 persons to the population; or it could make any one of a number of compromises, such as adding only 500,000 people and raising the income level to $523.80. Of course any such figures are not to be taken literally as representing sound economic thinking.

Waiving for the moment the objection that living standards cannot be satisfactorily measured in dollars, this apparently quantitative formula would seem to make it easy to calculate, for a given country, the point at which the population would ideally become stabilized because the two expansive factors: the desire for more children and that for a higher standard of living, would exactly counterbalance one another. But, on closer examination, these factors turn out to be extremely complex, subjective, and dynamic. The desire for mating and the desire for offspring, for example, are by no means identical or even stably related, especially since the discovery of birth control. And even where parenthood is influenced by rational foresight, approval of an increase in the population as a social policy, whether for military conquest, religious expansion, commercial aggrandizement, or sheer race egotism, is not the same as the willingness of individual parents to raise large families.

The symbols LL and EC are abstractions whose apparent simplicity is highly deceptive. To assign a significant quantity to the "level of living" of a population would require the construction of a composite measure of all the individuals involved, a sort of combined material, moral, and spiritual "prosperity index" for a whole society. Not only are desires for specific material possessions above the subsistence level extremely variable, even for one individual; but the problem is also complicated by religions and philosophies which exalt the values of self-denial or asceticism. What we should really need to measure would be, in Professor Fetter's phrase, the total "psychic income" of the society — the sum of all the satisfactions of all its members, less their total annoyances. That would raise the question of the quality as well as the quantity of the population. Would a society of one hundred geniuses be more valuable (and to whom and in what sense) than one of ten thousand morons? Economic culture, which includes not only all "capital" used in the production of material wealth but also the complex accumulation of skills, scientific knowledge, and social organizations which enable a given "system" to function, is only a little less difficult to quantify. Here the dynamic, disturbing factors are technological invention, both of physical and social devices which may profoundly alter production and distribution almost overnight; and the so-called ideologies and propagandas, which may bring about equally radical changes in the socially accepted patterns of value.

Not only, then, are EC and LL far from static or easily calculable; there are also difficulties with the symbol P. The latter stands for the number of the people; but what about their ages, which are so important in determining the birthrate? The whole formula assumes, moreover, that a society necessarily aims at maximum productivity. What if some or all of its members happen to prefer the least possible labor as a goal? Nothing is said about isolation from the rest of the world, which seems to be taken for granted. To what extent may the level of living of a densely populated industrial country be affected by the international division of labor and raw materials? If war makes large populations desirable, do not large populations in turn increase the chances of war, thus forming a vicious circle? Is optimum population then a world problem; and, in that case, how can the Fairchild formula be employed?

Enough has been said to show why what appeared to be a promising quantitative formulation of a logically attractive theory in dealing with genuinely important social problems turns out to be largely sterile in its application to actual situations. The quantities have never been worked out for any existing country or community. To the noted Swedish population expert, Professor Gunnar Myrdal, the optimum theory remains "a speculative figment of the mind without much connection with this world; it does not give any guiding rule for the practical and political judgment of reality." Only too plainly the hazards of bridging the gap between the theory and the facts are still too great to permit a society, much less an individual, to use the formula as a reliable basis for a population policy. Why is this?

In a word, the optimum population theory lacks practical efficacy not only because it involves so many complex and dynamic qualities that elude expression in abstract numbers or symbols, but also because it presupposes the making of a large number of highly controversial value-judgments about what is "good," "better," and "best" in human population material. The so-called "revolution of rising expectations" with respect to material goods which is shaking the world has sharpened mankind's awareness of the dilemma created by the pressure of the birthrate upon a rising standard of living. But when measures are proposed to deal with the simultaneous "population explosion" and the "rising expectations," it is found impossible to begin to prescribe the size of the best population for a country numerically until you have answered for yourself such qualitative questions as: Do more valuers mean more value? Are some values intrinsically more valuable than others? But to answer such questions, or even to decide that they are unanswerable, involves the working out of a whole philosophy of life.

CASE IV. WHY WAS LINCOLN MURDERED?

About 1928 Mr. Otto Eisenchiml, a Chicago chemist of Viennese origin, head of an industrial company and a keen student of American history, became dissatisfied with the accounts of the assassination of President Lincoln which were to be found in most American history books. There were things, he felt, which needed explaining, crucial questions which historians had not only failed to answer, but which they had neglected to ask. Although not himself a professional historian, he had been trained in scientific method in the discovery and interpretation of facts. Believing that historical research "should be undertaken with a microscope, not with a briefcase," he determined to unearth every bit of available evidence about Lincoln's death over sixty years before. He spent ten years in his quest; and what he found led him to frame a theory that was very different from the accepted account. His detailed but inconclusive findings fill what reviewer Ralph Thompson in the New York *Times* called "a fascinating, well-documented and altogether amazing book" of five hundred pages entitled *Why Was Lincoln Murdered?*[7]

Briefly stated, the conventional explanation runs as follows: Lincoln was shot from behind in the base of the brain by a derringer pistol in the hand of the actor John Wilkes Booth at a little past 10 P.M. on Good Friday, April 14, 1865, while sitting in the carelessly unguarded Presidential box at a performance of *Our American Cousin* at Ford's Theater in Washington, and died about nine hours later in the Petersen house on Ninth Street. In making his escape by a back door at which his horse was waiting, Booth broke a small bone in his leg. He was finally cornered twelve days later in a barn in Virginia; and, refusing to surrender, was shot by a sergeant after the barn had been set on fire. His motive was supposedly the personal revenge of a proud, hot-headed Southerner for the impending defeat of the Confederacy, along with an egotistical desire to enact the part of sole heroic champion of the lost cause.

But Mr. Eisenschiml was puzzled by a number of things which this accepted version did not seem to explain. The principal one was this: How had it been possible for an armed assassin to enter a crowded theater in the nation's capital city in time of war, commit his foul deed unchallenged, and then make an easy escape? Was there perhaps some "inside" conspiracy involving the very Northerners of influence who should have prevented it? If so, what motives could have accounted for their actions? Did anyone charged with Lincoln's safety want him out of the way? As his researches proceeded and the mysterious circumstances multiplied, the author's suspicions became fixed upon one man, with the result that he framed the audacious hypothesis that Lincoln's death was the outcome of a conspiracy of which Edwin M. Stanton, his Secretary of War, had guilty knowledge. Once formulated, the Stanton guilt theory seemed to him to explain many attested facts which the accepted account had left enigmatic, to say the least.

This, in brief, is what the author asks us to suppose concerning Stanton and his motives: He was the master mind of the so-called Radical Republicans who, in opposition to Lincoln's merciful plans for post-war reconciliation, wanted to prolong the conflict in order to stay in power and to treat the South as their conquered province. Lincoln was the great stumbling block which must be removed if their scheme was to have any chance of success. Possibly through Andrew Johnson, Stanton learned of Booth's plot (among others), and may have arranged to provide every reasonable opportunity for him to execute it and to escape. Although admittedly energetic, patriotic, and religious, Stanton was also ambitious, domineering, evasive, and full of duplicity. Even those students of the Lincoln period who wholly reject Mr. Eisenschiml's theory concede that Stanton's personal character "lends itself admirably" to the author's indictment. The Secretary of War was virtually military dictator in Washington at the time; and there can be no doubt that he gained added power through Lincoln's death.

Yet no shred of tangible, material evidence links Stanton with the crime.

---

[7] (Boston, 1937.) A play based on it, and entitled *Yours, A. Lincoln* by Paul Horgan, was produced in New York in July, 1942.

The existing evidence is wholly circumstantial. "It is all hypothesis," as the author admits. As he presents the case, it is a matter of the relative incredibility of any other explanation so far offered of a number of well-established facts, some of them hitherto apparently overlooked. Among them are these: (1) *Unpunished absence of the guard.* The armed policeman assigned to the Presidential box that evening, John F. Parker, had a bad record of inefficiency if not venality, having been before the Metropolitan Police Board four times previous to that date for various offenses, including neglect of duty. Eleven days before, on April 3, he had been excused from the military draft and detailed for duty at the White House at the special written request of Mrs. Lincoln, for some unknown reason. At the theater, he disappeared from his post, leaving the box entirely unguarded, and was next seen at 6 A.M. on the following day, when he brought in a woman named Lizzie Williams, whom he accused as a streetwalker, but who was discharged. On May 1, 1865, charges of neglect of duty were filed against him by the Superintendent of Police; but there is no record that he was ever tried, reprimanded, or dismissed at that time, the complaint being dropped on June 2, 1865, with Parker remaining on the force until July 27, 1868, when his conduct was so bad that he had to be dismissed for "gross neglect of duty." His name does not even appear in any official story of Lincoln's death. Why, asks the author, did not Stanton, the unforgiving disciplinarian who was ultimately responsible for law and order in time of war, see to it that Parker was tried, convicted, and even shot for his gross dereliction of duty? (2) *General Grant's "escape."* General and Mrs. Grant had been invited by President and Mrs. Lincoln to be their guests at the performance. Grant claimed later that he had accepted conditionally, if not too busy; in any event, the joint presence of the Grants and the Lincolns had been duly advertised by the theater. Grant was not busy; yet at 6 P.M. he and his wife took a train for an all-night journey in a day coach to visit their children at Burlington, New Jersey, changing cars at Baltimore and Philadelphia. Mr. Eisenschiml holds that Stanton, having further use for the general, had implored Grant to stay away; but his only evidence is the statement made in 1907 by David H. Bates, one of Stanton's telegraph operators, that he had overheard the Secretary beg Grant not to attend on that evening forty-two years earlier, a recollection partially corroborated by Grant's own cipher operator, Captain Samuel Beckwith, writing in the New York *Sun* in 1913. (3) *Stanton's direction of the pursuit.* Although Stanton, in charge of all important news items and their dissemination, learned of the murder within a few minutes of its occurrence, and Booth had been recognized as he leaped from the box and fled across the stage, the first dispatch was not on the wire for more than three hours, and the name of Booth was not disclosed until 3:20 A.M., too late for the first editions of the newspapers. There were six roads out of Washington. Stanton blocked five of them, but not the one which Booth actually took, and which the author regards as by far the "most logical." It was known about midnight that Booth had crossed the Anacostia Bridge into Maryland, but no troops were sent in pursuit; and when an energetic police officer asked for cavalry horses for his men to follow the trail, the War Department refused his request. The cavalry did not start after Booth until about daylight on Monday, two and a half days after the crime. The government's exhibit No. 1 at the conspiracy trial, a photograph labeled John Wilkes Booth, which dozens of witnesses were asked to identify, and which may have been furnished to Booth's pursuers for that purpose, was actually a picture of his brother Edwin! When, due to his injury, Booth was finally cornered in a tobacco shed at Garrett's farm by Stanton's most confidential lieutenants, there was the great confusion which resulted in his being killed in spite of orders that he was to be taken alive; yet his supposed slayer was never punished. (4) *Stanton's treatment of the suspects.* By Stanton's orders, almost incredibly cruel precautions were taken against the possibility of damaging communications by any of the prisoners who had been intimate with Booth. These measures went to the extreme of placing the heads of these suspects, except Mrs. Surratt's, in canvas hoods with holes for nose and mouth only, "for better security against conversation." Other prisoners, no less guilty in the eyes of the author, but unlikely to reveal dangerous secrets, were let off without punishment.

Many other equally mysterious circumstances make it appear to Mr. Eisenschiml that "it was almost as if an invisible guardian angel were watching over Booth's every step and shaping fortune to his favor." Could it have been Stanton? Or mere coincidence? The story of the assassination emerges from the author's inquiry "in a state of confusion." The actors in the tragedy are dead; all that remains is fragmentary documentary evidence of varying degrees of reliability: letters, reports, court records, newspaper accounts, memoirs, and biographies. The main difficulty lies, not so much in assuring ourselves of the authenticity of the facts we possess, as in the lack of enough of them to enable us to decide upon their correct interpretation. Concerning the latter, the author is far less cautious than he is in establishing his facts. Most of the competent reviewers of his book conceded that his new evidence is unchallengeable in detail; yet they rejected his hypothetical interpretation of it, the Stanton guilt hypothesis.[8] Why?

A large part of the author's case rests upon the apparent lack of any logical explanation of certain circumstances *unless* Booth had a powerful ally in high places. The attempt is then made to show that these facts can be shown to converge in pointing the finger of accusation toward Stanton. But that does not prove that the circumstances have no other possible explanation save Stanton's guilt. The author himself shows, for example, that Grant's "escape" might have been due to Mrs. Grant's reluctance, after two violent scenes in public, to expose herself to any more snubs at the hands of the unhappy Mrs. Lincoln. As for the appalling negligence and inefficiency in guarding the President, for which Stanton must certainly bear some of the blame: before the tragedy it may have been due in part to Lincoln's well-known attitude of fatalism toward threats against his life; after the sudden shooting, it may have been caused by the atmosphere of hysteria and terror. In the words of Carl Sandburg: "Up till that instant (Booth's entering the box) any one of a

---

[8] Likewise George S. Bryan, who writes in *The Great American Myth* (New York, 1940): "The whole suggestion that the Secretary of War was *particeps criminis* in the accomplishing of Lincoln's death . . . is as inapt as it is malicious."

million ordinary conceivable circumstances of fate could have intervened and made the next moment impossible. Yet not one of those potential circumstances arrived."[9]

Some of the logical consequences of Mr. Eisenschiml's hypothesis do not check with the known facts. There is evidence that Booth's plans, almost until the last minute, were for kidnapping, not murder. If Stanton knew that Lincoln was to be murdered, he would hardly have acted as he did: urging Lincoln to stay away, appearing himself upon the scene without any carefully calculated scheme of action and committing the welter of blunders there. Would he be able, furthermore, if guilty, to seal the lips and covers the tracks of every one of his co-conspirators?

None of the full-scale biographies of either Stanton or Lincoln which have appeared since the publication of *Why Was Lincoln Murdered?* have accepted the startling implications about Stanton which it contains.[10]

The question of what actually happened in April, 1865, thus becomes a matter of the relative probabilities of alternative hypotheses, only one of which, however, is presented in detail by Mr. Eisenschiml. Which theory is least improbable on the available evidence: guilt, or carelessness, or coincidence, or some other hypothesis? Note that in order to make a sound and reliable judgment of the probabilities, one would need not only a profound knowledge of human nature in general, but of the personalities of Edwin M. Stanton, John Wilkes Booth, and Abraham Lincoln, in particular, as well as of the tangled and turbulent background of the whole Civil War period in America.[11]

4. *Preliminary Comments*

In the light of these few examples, what are the prospects for the obtaining of reliable knowledge by human knowers? Even the most superficial analyses should reveal that it is not to be had for the asking. It is an arduous and endless business, this affirming that one knows something, and then being able to prove it. To succeed in it consistently, even in the simplest sorts of situations, requires both training and effort; while in the more complex, it taxes the patience and ingenuity of the race's most gifted thinkers. Nor does it, once achieved, stay finished and complete; it has to be continually re-achieved. Unless men hunger and thirst for it, they will not, except when driven by necessity, even set forth upon the age-long quest. And if they do set forth, they will meet no lack of "lions in the pathway" of their ambitions.

Without attempting to prejudge the final results of our inquiry, it should

[9] Sandburg, Carl *Abraham Lincoln: The War Years*, (New York, 1930), p. 336.

[10] See Fletcher Pratt, *Stanton: Lincoln's Secretary of War* (New York, 1953); Benjamin P. Thomas and Harold M. Hyman, *Stanton: The Life and Times of Lincoln's Secretary of War* (New York, 1962); Benjamin P. Thomas, *Abraham Lincoln: A Biography* (New York, 1952); and J. G. Randall and Richard N. Current, *Lincoln the President: Last Full Measure* (New York, 1955).

[11] For a dreadful parallel case, consider the plight of future historians in unraveling the tangled skein of events surrounding the assassination of President John F. Kennedy in Dallas, Texas, on November 22, 1963.

already be evident that there is an intimate but complicated connection between reliability in knowledge and some kind or kinds of *order*. We want reliable knowledge, usually, in order to be able in some degree to anticipate what future experience will be like. Most of our knowing, in other words, is eventually for power purposes. By getting knowledge of the way things are structurally related to one another, we hope to be able to predict and control an increasing range of events. For this purpose of forecasting what is likely to happen, some of the structures which we are able to discover are far more useful than others.

Now if either the world we live in, or our own minds and purposes, were completely disorderly, there could be no such thing as reliable knowledge extending over a period of time. But plainly this universe which we inhabit has, along with its changing or dynamic aspects, certain relatively stable or structural ones. Events occur in clusters and systems, such that we are able to recognize certain patterns which we can conceptualize and use as clues of what is to come. Similarly our minds have structure, although none of us would claim for a moment that the flickering motion picture that we call our consciousness presents us spontaneously with a completely ordered and reliable account, even of the most static characteristics of the world about us. That has to be laboriously constructed and reconstructed with the aid of such devices as language and number.

It took centuries of gradual discipline by tragic failures and occasional successes to cultivate in man a limited capacity to perceive and to express some small degree of order in the chaos of his daily experiences in what are now known as logical terms. Again and again he picked out the wrong types of mental and physical order as reliably predictive of events: dreams, portents, spectacular natural calamities or blessings. Again and again his feelings and wishes betrayed him into expecting what he wanted to see occur, only to be painfully disillusioned by the eventual outcomes.

From these rebuffs of fate arose the question in his mind: What is the relation between what George H. Lewes called "the general tendencies of things and the general tendencies of thought"? Are they identical, or convergent, or divergent? Man's first civilized guess was understandably rash and premature. No sooner had some of the early Greek thinkers made the momentous discovery that most of their reliable knowledge was verbally ordered (or orderable), than they jumped to the conclusion that all such knowledge was, *by virtue of being so ordered*, reliable as a guide to the world in which they lived. Logic was the key to the universe: to discover its rules was to gain direct access to the order at the heart of things. Being in love with the fixed, the secure, the immutable, these first Western scientists and philosophers built imposing systems out of mental materials — words and ideas — in the misguided belief that perfect logical consistency would guarantee perpetual applicability to the concrete problems of living. They mistook the structure of thought for the structure of things. They supposed that the needs of the mind, and the languages which it used in achieving knowledge, were necessarily dependable clues to the order of physical events.

Once reliable knowledge had become firmly identified with the changeless, as expressed in verbal concepts and their apparently fixed relations to one another, any serious attention to the changing aspects of everyday experience came to be disparaged as yielding at best only unreliable knowledge, or "opinion." So, having convinced themselves of the paramount importance for reliability in knowledge of the static types of verbal order, it took many additional centuries for men to discover that valid logical deductions did not, by themselves, constitute infallible short cuts to their goal; but that, in order to be adjudged reliable outside of the realms of pure thought, even the most logical of conclusions must be checked against the brute facts of daily experience.

When man has wanted to know, he has also often wanted to know right away, and has been strongly inclined to claim too much for his alleged knowledge. Human history is strewn with the wreckage of premature and subsequently abandoned dogmas. Only in comparatively recent times has man learned the hard lesson of humility in the face of the facts, combined with audacity in imagining their possible interconnections. Since the rise of modern science, reliability has still been sought in order, but, on the whole, more cautiously in those kinds of order which can be ultimately discerned in specific situations in experience rather than in those which can merely be spun out by wishful fancy or the logical intellect. The effort has been made to establish connections and to disclose relationships, not simply among concepts or ideas, but between those items of experience called facts and those types of order and system called theories or hypotheses.

This task of filling in the connective tissue called inference or proof is of course much easier to accomplish in some departments of inquiry than in others. Our experiences with the behavior of falling bodies, for example, thanks to centuries of hard, as well as brilliant, mental labor by men like Galileo and Newton, are now comparatively easy to analyze, predict, and control by means of mathematical calculations experimentally confirmed. In mechanics, by devising special situations and instruments, we can pick out the structural characteristics that will give us the right clues to what is likely to happen. But it is notoriously more difficult to acquire similarly effective knowledge about the behavior of human beings, where direct observation and measurement are incomparably harder to manage, and the number of variables to be isolated, measured, and manipulated is immensely larger. If we compare Cases III and IV with Cases I and II, for example, it will be seen at once that in the social studies, not only are special obstacles present, but that all the ordinary difficulties of reliable knowledge-getting are heightened to the nth degree. The social studies deal with unique personalities living in particular societies; and both individuals and groups are extremely complex and subject to change.

That means that the seeker for reliable knowledge in these fields faces a continual dilemma in devising methods of attack to cope with his elusive materials. If, in imitation of the physical sciences, he insists upon relentless analysis and precision in measurement, he runs the risk of mutilation and dismemberment of the living wholes which form an important part of his data. If, on the other hand, in sympathy with the approach of the artist he resorts to broad, pictorial generalizations, he may find that they are so vague that he can neither prove nor disprove them. As a result, the social studies suffer chronically from a plethora of heaped-up details without unifying meanings, and an oversupply of grandiose theories and broad concepts unlinked to adequate supporting data.

It is well known that in the physical sciences the bridging of this gulf that separates theory and practice is accomplished by the use of the experimental method. That in turn is made possible because, in a laboratory, special situations can be set up in order to display the activities of otherwise hidden structures such as atoms or genes or cosmic rays. Single factors in a controlled situation can be isolated, measured, and varied at will, while the experiment itself can be duplicated by other observers. But in the social studies the situations are far less repeatable; and it is seldom possible to change one factor in a network of processes without at the same time altering many others also. This does not make social experiment impossible or wholly unenlightening, but it does deprive that method of most of the clinching power which it possesses in the fields of the more exact sciences.

These are only a few of the formidable obstacles which confront the seeker after reliable knowledge in the social studies. Is it, however, safe to assume that very many potential knowers will demand reliable knowledge about social matters in the first place? Or that they will be allowed sufficient time and opportunity to acquire it? Or that they will be able to rise above their early conditioning enough to pursue it successfully? As for the initial demand for reliable knowledge concerning social behavior, we must recognize that it is sometimes entirely absent, or feeble, or short-winded. Even when it is strong, it is obliged to compete constantly with dozens of older and more deep-seated human tendencies. "After all," says Professor Morris R. Cohen, "the desire to attain the truth is a later and relatively undeveloped human motive compared with the more vital and voluminous motives of social approval."[12] Many men in nearly all things, and nearly all men in some things, are content and even anxious to be partially deceived. They are satisfied to act without explicit knowledge, or to accept alleged knowledge without testing it, as long as it suits their immediate needs, even though in the long run it may prove to be wholly unreliable.

Again and again we shall find ourselves forced to return to this theme: the importance of the *scope* of the demand for reliable knowledge. For human beings are constantly tempted not to bother with accurate knowing, especially when it seems possible for them to get along with such substitutes as habit or emotion. Our natural inertia favors such a course. Considerations of economy of effort incline us toward as little thinking as possible. It is easier to follow the line of the least resistance, to improvise something that will work in the immediate circumstances, something that we can "get away with," letting the long-run consequences take care of themselves. Only a fine line divides the sins of omission from those of commission in these matters. It is sometimes difficult to distinguish between the innocently shortsighted and the criminally vicious. The swindler tries to get us to accept a plausible view of

---

[12] In W. F. Ogburn and A. Goldenweiser, *The Social Sciences* (Boston, 1927), p. 453.

those few aspects of things which suit his particular purpose at the moment, and to overlook all the rest. The narrow nationalist wants no one to see beyond his own program and his own kind of people. Those are examples of deliberate refusals to face *all* the relevant facts in a situation lest selfish purposes be thwarted by too much vision.

Yet well-meaning negligence produces in practice the same sorry sort of results. Each one of us has limitations of outlook which only energy and effort can overcome. Will the effort be made, and in time? Will there be a recognition of what John Erskine has called "the moral obligation to be intelligent"? Certainly the failure to live up to the responsibilities of a creature capable of knowing at least dimly what it is doing is what accounts for many of our human tragedies and wrongs. We suffer from improvisations; and we improvise because we have failed to plan ahead, and thus we have no time to devise anything but an *ad hoc* solution. When we find ourselves in the midst of a crisis in which human values and even human lives are at stake, calm fact-finding and judicial deliberation become increasingly difficult. Few social problems can wait until "all the facts are in" or all the concepts completely clarified. Choices have to be made at once; and in making them, men are obliged to make an additional choice — between choosing on the basis of long-run considerations or on the basis of immediate returns. To refrain from choosing, in such situations, is itself a choice which may determine the final outcome. Some of our most cruel moral dilemmas arise from the conflicting claims of expediency versus principle, or of business or military practicality versus our notions of justice or right.

It is just at this point that the question of human bias enters most critically, for we are all "special pleaders" at some time or other. Everyone recognizes how easy it is to be objective or impartial about what does not immediately concern us. The difficult thing to do is to press our demand for reliable knowledge where it may hurt our own interests, conscious or unconscious. So much, indeed, are our prejudices parts of our inmost selves, that we are seldom conscious of our own subtle biases. It takes a fairly high degree of sophistication to become capable of realizing that all of us approach social issues through a dense jungle of inherited prejudices, borrowed opinions, and traditions endowed with tribal prestige. From our cradle days, we have been constantly engaged in absorbing value-tinged attitudes toward most of the common varieties of human conduct. Worst of all, we are obliged to supply from within not only the initiative that will make us aware of our prejudices, but also that which will bestir us to do something drastic about getting rid of them. Small wonder that the saying has gained currency: "To think about anything is hard work; but to have a prejudice is a pleasure." The wonder is rather that so many human beings have been able to learn to find pleasure in the arduous tasks of demanding, obtaining, and utilizing reliable knowledge.

5. *Getting Reliable Knowledge about Getting Reliable Knowledge*

Any great amount of ultimate success in the enterprise ahead of us seems doubtful enough. But even before we can get started on the long road which

may lead in that direction, another objection — this one of a philosophical nature — remains to be overcome. Our purpose is to find out all that we can
about getting reliable knowledge, especially in the social studies. That involves,
first of all, some consideration of man as a knower, in the form of an estimate
of the normal human prospects for demanding and securing something better
than guesses about social problems. Perhaps the chances are good, perhaps
they are poor. But, it may be objected, those very inquiries into knowing are
themselves forms of knowing, upon which we are being invited to begin by
placing our reliance. How are we to know whether or not they are worthy of it?
Must we not first ask and answer the "previous question," namely — what are
our chances of getting reliable knowledge?

To put the challenge in concrete form: Let us suppose that the question
is raised whether or not Mr. X is capable of obtaining reliable knowledge, or is
a good judge of it, in the field of politics. Mr. Y answers that he has knowledge
that Mr. X is not, since a faulty diet has ruined the latter's digestion and
rendered him abnormally irritable, pessimistic, and suspicious of the motives
of others. Mr. X, however, stoutly denies all this, and maintains that he is an
excellent judge of political affairs; so a Mr. Z is called in to pass upon the
respective verdicts of Messrs. X and Y about the capacities of Mr. X. Whose
testimony about the trustworthiness of Mr. X shall we accept as trustworthy?
Ultimately we seem to find ourselves in the position of judges who must pass
judgments upon their own qualifications as judges. Our predicament arises
from our human ability, since we are not only conscious but self-conscious, to
reflect upon our own reflections. We can act upon the stage, sit in the balcony
and criticize our own acting, and then stand outside on the sidewalk and
criticize our own criticism of our acting, all within a few short seconds.

But there is no need of making an insoluble puzzle out of the "infinite
regress" involved in knowing about knowing about knowing. We cannot find
out how human eyes operate in seeing without using our eyes to study optom-
etry; and if our eyesight is poor, we shall simply be condemned to be poor
optometrists. The way to find out how finding-out occurs is to make a start
somewhere, using the best judgment of which we are capable and letting the
assumptions that we cannot, apparently, avoid making in order to get started,
justify themselves in the course of our inquiry. That is what will be attempted
in the next two chapters, where some of our admittedly imperfect knowledge in the fields of biology, physiology, anthropology, social psychology, and
philosophy will be drawn upon in an effort to portray man's broad capacities
and limitations as a knower.

We must admit that we can give no guarantee in advance that such knowledge will prove to be reliable for the purpose of understanding human knowing. There is no infallible way of choosing in advance one's method of studying
anything. The only way is to make an estimate and began our inquiry. Our
forecast may be wrong, resulting in the choice of a method that is inappropriate.
How we shall come to view knowing is bound to be much affected by our
appraisal of the agent who does the knowing; and that appraisal depends in
turn upon what we are willing to accept as reliable knowledge about him. But
to regard this intricate state of affairs as constituting an *impasse* would be to

concede failure before our quest had begun. The study of knowledge has to make use of knowledge; the study of methods has to make use of methods; corroboration of each is mutual as inquiry proceeds and succeeds. An enterprise of this sort must stand or fall on the issue of whether or not it accomplishes what it sets out to accomplish. We must make our choice of what we are to presuppose in getting under way, and then hope that the results will justify our perilous selections.

FOR CLASS DISCUSSION

(The numbers in parentheses refer to the sections of the chapter)

A. It is better not to know so much than to know so many things that ain't so. — *Josh Billings* (2)

B. He that increaseth knowledge increaseth sorrow. — *Ecclesiastes* I:18. Knowledge is the only instrument of production that is not subject to diminishing returns. — *J. M. Clark*

C. Only that man knows, who knows how he knows, and can so exhibit his technique that others may know what he knows, or may know, by the same token, that he does not know. — *T. V. Smith*

D. According to Arthur Dailey of the New York *Times*, the famous Yankee catcher and manager Yogi Berra was once sent in as a pinch hitter with instructions to think while he was at bat. He fanned ingloriously, and returned to the bench muttering: "How can a guy think and hit at the same time?"
Football coaching is purely a matter of science. You can't afford to get worked up about the game because if you do, you can't think.
— *Earl H. Blaik*

E. We don't know one-millionth of one per cent about anything.
— *Thomas A. Edison*
Subjective certainty is inversely proportional to objective certainty.
— *Bertrand Russell*

F. I regard that alone as genuine *Knowledge* which, sooner or later, will reappear as power. — *Samuel Taylor Coleridge*

G. The desire to extend knowledge is a very curious demon. It is a real demon, and it drives you; it puts little sharp pins in you, and it keeps you going. But it is not easy. — *Sir Maurice Bowra* (4)

H. Intelligence is the untested hope of man in the race between education and catastrophe. — *H. G. Wells*

I. The drawback to a completely rational mind is that it is apt to assume that what is flawless in logic is therefore practicable. — *John Buchan*

J. The forceps of our minds are clumsy forceps and crush the truth a little in taking hold of it. — *H. G. Wells* (5)

K. The knowledge of knowledge itself that we possess today is weak knowledge — perhaps as weak as any we have; it stands greatly in need of desentimentalized research. — *John Dewey and A. F. Bentley*

MAN AS KNOWER: From the Outside

1. Taking Inventory

ANYONE WHO VENTURES to embark upon the study of the art of knowing as practiced by human beings is likely to find himself asking such questions as these:

> The nature of man being what it is, what are the prospects that he will demand, obtain, and use reliable knowledge in many fields of inquiry that are open to him?
>
> What, more specifically, are the probabilities that, being the sort of creature that he is, he will (1) bestir himself to inquire deeply and persistently into a given subject matter; (2) be sufficiently ingenious in devising appropriate methods of investigation; (3) refuse to be satisfied with trivial or shoddy standards of reliability; and (4) make any intelligent use of such trustworthy knowledge as he may be able and inclined to acquire?
>
> Furthermore, how has it been possible for generations of men to act and think as much as they have, and to know so little? How, on the other hand, have men amassed and preserved as much genuine knowledge as they have?

Answers in advance to sweeping questions like these are not going to be conclusive, or even moderately satisfying, but they may be useful in preparing us for what we shall discover later on. Surely if we were to launch upon the analysis of the knowing activities of another creature — of a dog, for example, we should first ask similar questions about the general nature of dogs, their apparent capacities and limitations as knowers, and even something about canine history and "culture." So with man, it will be well, before asking how he goes about the task of knowing, to take a rough inventory of his nature, reminding ourselves of the sort of creature he is, of what he is seemingly well-fitted (and ill-fitted) to accomplish, and of what the broad story of his career as a knower has been. Otherwise we shall be likely to forget some of the primary conditions of the knowledge-getting process, and either grossly to over-estimate or underestimate man's probable prowess in that difficult pursuit.

For this scouting survey and estimate, as has already been noted, we have a number of obvious qualifications and disqualifications. Each of us is himself one of the men to be studied, and carries about with him his own private sample of the species as a sort of walking laboratory for experiment. Moreover, being self-conscious to some extent, we have two main sources of knowledge of human nature: one from inside by intimate acquaintance, and one from outside by observation. Thus we are in a position to paint two portraits of ourselves: one based on direct intuition, and the other on external analysis. Each view supplements and corrects the other: we make use of our self-knowledge in interpreting the outward behavior of others by "putting ourselves in their places"; and we use their observed conduct as a check in arriving at a better internal understanding of our own.

Now this "inside information" about ourselves gives us great advantages in the study of human nature, as may be seen by comparing a textbook on human psychology with one on animal psychology. We cannot get under the skin of the animal with any assurance, as we can to a certain extent in our dealings with our fellow humans. We can only guess how things appear to the animal, or how it reacts internally to various stimuli. But we know how things appear to at least one human being, and how he reacts *both* inwardly and outwardly to many of the situations which he encounters. It is this ability to correlate our own feelings with certain intonations of voice or facial expressions, which helps us in "reading the minds" of our friends. Yet a "poker face" may offer us but scant clues to what is going on behind it; and we are always in danger of overrating the reliability of our subjective interpretations.

Private knowledge becomes a serious liability when "judging others by ourselves" results in dogmatism about human nature, or the acceptance of our own self-knowledge as a sufficient measure of the entire race of man. That approach has produced no end of one-sided estimates of human potentialities: the saint has seen all men as benevolent; the cynic has seen them as calculating; the artist, as deeply sensitive; the business tycoon, as predatory; the logician, as logical, and so on. Differences from ourselves are passed over as trivial, while likenesses are seized upon as significant. What we ourselves desire slips over easily into what all right-minded men desire, or ought to desire; while those who disagree with us are classified as perverse or abnormal. Occasionally this tendency works in reverse, as when a thwarted individual comes to regard himself as exceptional, and all the rest of mankind as *un*like himself.

Another general disposition to overemphasize one side of human experience springs from the fact that our conscious knowledge must necessarily be symbolic and "in the mind," as are, primarily, such intellectual activities as reading, studying, and discussing. Man is capable of meeting his outer environment both concretely, in his collisions with objects, and abstractly, by the aid of words, in his psychological picturings. The more civilized he becomes, the less contact he is likely to have with primary material things. Most of his problems come to present themselves in terms of verbal symbols. He plans mentally before he acts physically; and the center of gravity of his living tends to shift to the psychological level. The "intellectual" is prone to substitute verbalizing for acting, and to think that a problem is solved when he has written or talked it through to a conclusion in terms of symbols. As a result, there has developed through the centuries a strong occupational tradition among teachers and students which has exalted meditation and discourse above direct action, the mental at the expense of the physical.

2. Man from the Outside: Biology and Physiology

Libraries have been written by men about man as his external behavior has been observed and dissected; and it is futile to suppose that they can be condensed into a few pages. Nothing is more characteristic of human nature than its many-sidedness: the bewildering variety of possible avenues of approach, no single one of which is likely to lead to the whole truth about man. Any statement whatever about man's conduct in general must also be made in the face of billions of individual differences. Even the most cautious generalizer must be prepared for plenty of surprises, since human originality seems to be inexhaustible.

As seen by the biologist, man begins life as a single fertilized germ cell, "becomes a metazoan of the invertebrate type, develops the structure of a vertebrate, and ultimately becomes a mammal."[1] His resemblances to some of the higher animals are numerous. Like them he is composed of living cells, he feeds on other organic life, he grows in accordance with a smooth and largely predetermined curve, forms habits and memories, adapts himself to moderate changes in the environment, reproduces sexually offspring which are much like their parents "but not just like," and finally declines in vigor and dies. He lives, like them, against a physical environment which he strives unceasingly to master, but which eventually ends his career as an organism.

When we come to the principal differences between man and all other animals, no one can fail to be struck by the smallness of the contrasts, biologically speaking, and their immensity in psychological terms. The observer who is looking for physical differences is likely to notice only such points as the completely erect posture, the larger brain, the somewhat specialized hands and feet, and the vocal organs suitable for speech.

THE SENSES

Biologically speaking, man shares the equipment of the higher animals for obtaining the raw materials of knowledge, the apparatus of the various senses, to such an extent that the differences may be regarded as trivial. It is well known that some of the sensory organs of some animals are superior to those of man in range and acuity: the bat excels man in its sensitiveness to sound, and the dog has a much keener sense of smell. Like the higher animals, man gets little except highly localized information about the universe through the "primitive" bodily senses such as touch, taste, and smell. Like them, he gets the bulk of his sensations by way of his hearing and his sight, with sight, "the king of the senses," quantitatively far in the lead. The human eye is so sensitive that it can pick up a flash of light of one ten-billionth of an erg (an erg being the amount of energy necessary to lift one thirty-thousandth of an ounce a distance of one-thousandth of an inch). Some authorities have estimated that as much as four-fifths of all our knowledge of the world about us

[1] Harry B. Ferris, "The Natural History of Man," in George A. Baitsell, ed., *The Evolution of Earth and Man* (New Haven, 1929), p. 210.

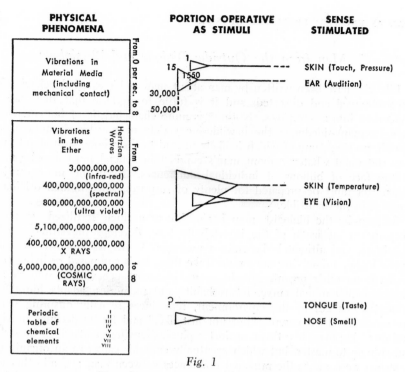

PHYSICAL PHENOMENA	PORTION OPERATIVE AS STIMULI	SENSE STIMULATED

Fig. 1

THE SENSES AND THE ENVIRONMENT

From Graydon L. Freeman, "Introduction to Physiological Psychology" (New York, 1934) By permission of The Ronald Press Company.

is based upon optical sensations. As for hearing, there are marked individual differences: the famous conductor Arturo Toscanini was said to be able to tell, from the sound, "when one of the sixty violins in his orchestra [was] bowing incorrectly, and to know exactly which player it [was]."[2] The human nose can detect as little as one-billionth of a milligram of some aromatic vapors; but the tongue, in order to get any taste sensation, needs at least a million times that amount.

When there is no change in our external environment, or, more exactly, when there is too little to pass any of our sense "thresholds," there is no sensation; and when there is too much change for our sense organs to cope with, there is no sensation either. Normally, in all our sense organs, buffers at each end of the range of sensitivity come into play in order to protect us against both overstimulation and hypersensitiveness. The functions of the organs are adapted, within limits, to the demands of the situation. Our senses act as window-filters of restricted scope, through which we are enabled to respond directly to only a very small fraction of the total changes that take place in the world about us (Figure 1). We can have no knowledge of the changes which lie outside the range of our receptors unless such changes can be magnified or

[2] John Tasker Howard, "The Orchestra Conductor," *Harper's,* vol. 175 (1937), p. 600.

focused or reduced in such a way that they can be brought within it. Man has developed an array of delicate instruments for that purpose, such as the microscope, the telescope, the telephone, and the camera plate, which enable him to observe many otherwise unobservable events.

Most of the senses, it should be noted, are linked directly or indirectly with man's motor apparatus rather than with the organs which maintain his chemical equilibrium. They form paths from the surface of the body to its controlling muscles, which enable the organism to make quick adjustments to various kinds of stimuli, especially when it is awake and on the alert. Our brains seem to have originated as clearing houses for the co-ordination of motor acts, enabling a complex creature to do many different sorts of things, but only one of them, strictly speaking, at a time.

THE NERVOUS SYSTEM

The human organism as a whole acts upon the selected aspects of its environment picked up by such senses as sight and hearing, touch and smell, and swiftly translated into the mental pictures called perceptions. These latter data become highly economical symbols for their objects, enabling the experienced perceiver to deal with his world on the basis of slender cues and clues. Images are still more simplified versions of former perceptions which enable the mind to encompass past and future in its operations. By means of concepts it can condense, in highly complex systems, vast numbers of objects and relationships.

Over all these activities are two main co-operating systems of control: the central nervous system and the endocrine or ductless glands. In point of evolutionary history, the second of these is far more ancient than the first. The nervous system makes possible both conscious and unconscious co-ordination of the organism's reactions to its external environment over a wide range; while the glands supply the regulatory hormones which may so profoundly affect its emotional balance and growth. The central nervous system of man as described by the neurologists consists broadly of two principal divisions: the cerebral cortex, and the brain stem and spinal cord. Both consist of millions of nerve cells with threadlike extensions, the cortex containing an estimated fourteen billion cells, whose possible interconnections run into superastronomical numbers. The cells and their extensions are excitable, containing stores of potential energy capable of sending electrochemical discharges to other cells, and of recharging themselves after a brief period of time. Nervous activity, which is continuous during the life of the organism, involves these minute bursts of energy of millionths of a volt traveling over the nerve fibers at a speed of about 400 feet per second, or about 280 miles per hour. The cells stimulate one another in chains and by areas: some of the discharges are set off by an external stimulus; but others seem to occur spontaneously, as in breathing and other semiautomatic activities, which seem to depend upon a cycle of breakdown and repair in the nerve fibers.

The brain stem and spinal cord have two broad functions: to carry out the plans of the higher centers, and to keep the machinery of the body running smoothly by a large number of varied reflex and regulative actions, mainly in response to external stimuli. This is the sphere of inborn and unlearned behavior which we share with vast numbers of the lower animals, where ready-made connections — prefabricated answers to our problems — apparently "know what to do" without reflection; to which are added later the acquired habits that become "second nature" by repetition.

The region in which spontaneous nervous activity is most marked is the surface network of the frontal lobes of the brain, or cerebral cortex. This superstructure is just sufficiently detached from the lower centers to permit them to take care of routine situations, and yet to "cut itself in" as a roving "trouble-shooter" when an emergency looms. For the cortex is not dominated by any one fixed kind of excitation-pattern; it is plastic and educable, so educable, that an almost unlimited number of new cell linkages is possible. It is noteworthy that, at the same time that these messages are almost endlessly various, each one that is sent over one of the incredible number of different nerve pathways (said by Dr. Robert Schwab of the Harvard Medical School to be 1 followed by 2,783,000 zeros) is individual and specific. This makes the human brain in all probability the most complex physical structure in the universe.

It is also the cortex which stores up memories, of which some of the earliest last the longest, since the time comes when a brain cannot learn or recall recent happenings, yet can remember the events of childhood. Man is thus provided with a swiftly operating organ of self-integration and recombination of mental materials which enables him both to learn by past experience and to fuse old elements into new combinations in anticipation of future possibilities.

Ordinarily the learning of new associations requires a factor of motivation or interest which creates a tension that is relieved when the lesson is learned or the problem is solved. We learn best when our interest is aroused. But if there is too much interest, our responses tend to become stereotyped. Here, as with sensations, a narrow middle pathway lies between two extremes. We shall be most effective in learning when there is enough emotional tension to arouse the higher centers to activity, but not so much that they are numbed into stereotyped responses.

THE AUTONOMIC SYSTEM AND ENDOCRINE GLANDS

Now the great source of interest is ultimately the so-called autonomic (relatively independent and involuntary) portion of the nervous system, of which the controlling apparatus is a chain of mutually co-operative endocrine or ductless glands. Where the central nervous system is concerned mainly with the body's specific motor relationships with the outer environment through the sensations, the older autonomic system occupies itself with the chemical self-regulation of what the French physiologist Claude Bernard termed the "internal environment." He referred to the fluid matrix bathing all the internal cells of the body, which is kept automatically in a remarkable state of varying yet stable equilibrium by a complicated mechanism of body sentinels and emergency devices. It constitutes what Dr. Walter B. Cannon calls "the wisdom of the body," a ceaseless stabilizing, yet defensive activating, of the organism as a whole, called homeostasis. Quite without direction from the higher centers, our body temperature is kept amazingly constant, the blood-sugar level is maintained, sharp warnings are given of the body's food and water requirements by producing the conscious states that we call hunger and thirst, and the speed of the heartbeat is stepped up to place the organism in readiness for violent struggle when enraged or frightened. Stored-up energy is thus redistributed among the visceral organs and skeletal muscles in such a way as to facilitate, on demand, the most furious action for protection or aggression. Some of the subtlest problems of mental hygiene in civilized communities result from the fact that modern man so frequently experiences the emotional upheavals designed to facilitate fighting or running away without actually doing either of those things. The unused secretions or unexpended emotions may thereupon do damage in ways that are unrelated to the original excitement.

In the task of maintaining by chemical integration these delicate self-adjustments in the internal climate of the body, a widely scattered but interdependent chain of glands, among them the thyroid, pituitary, adrenal, and sexual, play a controlling part by pouring their secretions, called "hormones" (from the Greek *hormao*, "I excite"), directly into the blood stream. Although the amounts involved have to be calculated in units of one sixty-five-thousandth of a grain, the hormones are capable of wielding an influence out of all proportion to their volume, over such matters as growth, nutrition, sex, and involuntary muscle control. The autonomic system has two divisions, the sympathetic and the parasympathetic, "often antagonistic in their action," the sympathetic acting "as a unit" to enhance and energize in emergencies, while the parasympathetic "is dominant in quiescence, and conserving and protecting the body's resources."[3] There is some evidence that the ancient part of the brain below the cerebral cortex, known as the hypothalamus, may be the co-ordinating center of some of these activities. Higher apes with hypothalamic injuries, but with their cortices intact, are said to have been changed from wild and pugnacious to entirely docile animals.

In observing the everyday behavior of a normal individual, it is difficult to realize to what an extent it depends upon his "hormone balance" at the moment of observation. Whether his temperament, to begin with, is vigorous or lethargic is largely a matter of his emotional potential and its stability, both of which are influenced by his glands. That is abundantly apparent when the latter are either overactive, or when they are removed or become inactive because of age. All of us are well acquainted with what sudden emotional crises can do to our capacities for complex and deliberate thinking, but we are not always equally aware of the less violent but pervasive influences, probably operating in rhythmic cycles, to which we give the name of moods. The brain, however, is known to be extremely sensitive to such minute changes in the

[3] Ernest R. Hilgard, *Introduction to Psychology*, 3rd edition (New York, 1962), pp. 47–8. For a table showing the functions of the two divisions, see his p. 49.

internal environment, which may take the place of external stimuli in initiating chains of thought and action. One does not have to indulge in the wilder speculations of the gland-gospelers to agree with the Canadian physiologist, Dr. J. B. Collip, that "slight changes in subjective feelings, in thought, and in the actions of normal individuals from month to month, from day to day, and even at times from hour to hour, may be logically explained as the result of the reactions of the higher centers to slight changes in the internal environment." This is not to deny but to affirm that the higher centers ordinarily dominate the lower. If, because of my body chemistry, I feel inclined to be lazy, I may nevertheless decide to do something about my laziness, although perhaps in a lazy sort of way. A chemical change, in other words, usually presents a problem for the cortex to handle, at the same time that it may affect the latter's ability or inclination to undertake the handling. In a sense, man is always trying to pull himself up by his own bootstraps, always looking for the marvelous stimulant that will be easy to take, and that will make everything else easy to undertake. Ever in search of the "royal road to a magnificent character," he has not been slow to speculate about the possibilities of "chemical conditioning" by the injection of hormones.

He has read of young female rats being offered newborn baby rats for adoption, whose almost total indifference has been marvelously transformed by a few doses of prolactin, to the point where they will "adopt as many babies as may be offered, build elaborate nests for them, and eagerly mother them." He is told that "few accomplishments in the life of the physician so closely approximate the miraculous as does the rapid improvement of a patient properly treated for thyroid deficiency." May there not be hope for other miracles of personality transformation, perhaps even for a glandular extract which will double a person's demand for reliable knowledge? Unfortunately the prospects of such painless "learning by chemicals" are none too bright. "Artificial augmentation of the thyroid hormone by gland feeding beyond the physiological need," for example, has been found to give rise "merely to a certain amount of ill-natured restlessness" rather than to an enrichment of the personality.[4]

TENSIONS AND DRIVES

In this brief survey of the two main controlling systems of human activity, we have taken for granted the activities which they control. There are excellent reasons for side-stepping the vexing problem of human motivation, which has long been the battleground of competing terminologies. Shall man's tendencies to act be dissected and discussed in terms of reflexes, stimulus-response patterns, instincts, organic needs, or vital interests? It may suffice, for our purpose, to note that, beyond the making of the simplest mechanical adjustments, human beings may be said to act, in the most general sense, to relieve a state of tension, either internally or between themselves and something in their external environment. The action which relieves or reduces the tension, from the point

[4] R. G. Hoskins, *Endocrinology* (New York, 1941), pp. 85, 95, 184.

of view of the organism, is frequently said to be initiated by a drive, although that word may, unfortunately, lead the unwary to suppose that it refers to some magical force or entity, rather than merely to a pattern of behavior resulting from a state of disturbed equilibrium.

One of the simplest examples of a drive is the diffuse organic activity set in motion by the sensations which we describe as an empty stomach for the procurement of the wherewithal to satisfy one's hunger tension. Nutrition and sex are the primary biological processes most deeply rooted in the various segments of the autonomic system; but there are others, such as muscular exercise, sleep, and elimination of waste from the body. Then there are such less strictly biological drives as curiosity, mutual aid, novelty and adventure.

How many drives or dynamic trends are to be distinguished in human nature is largely a question of the level at which one makes a survey, since a primary propensity often sends forth a number of branches from its central trunk. Roughly speaking, human nature is more plastic at the extremities than at the trunk and its roots. For, as Professors Ogburn and Nimkoff remind us: "While nature supplies the child with a set of tensions which must somehow be relieved, it remains for nurture to determine the ways in which these tensions will be managed . . . experience determines how, when, and where the hunger drive will be satisfied."[5] The principal external task of the central nervous system may be said to be just that of adjusting these primary organic needs, and the immensely larger number of secondary drives that overlay them in the adult civilized personality, to the surrounding environment, and the environment to them, with (normally) a minimum expenditure of energy.

Yet to set up complete "life adjustment" by the removal of hazards and tensions as the goal of science and technology is a dangerous fallacy. A totally efficient society of well-adjusted conformers might turn out to be spiritually barren and intolerable. The creative thinkers, the artists, to say nothing of the saints and martyrs, have not been free from stresses, but have accepted them as challenge to growth.

Our civilization tends to eliminate or reduce the tensions which threaten primitive societies, but it substitutes other and more sophisticated perils and frustrations. Fear and anxiety lead to innumerable human activities directed toward escape from danger, and the attainment of relative security, or freedom from fear. Since man is capable in varying degrees of imagining such goods and evils as well as of sensing them, he can complicate his mental horizon with all sorts of chimerical alternatives, from the most horrible nightmares to the most alluring of pipe dreams.

This means that a man of imagination has an enormous repertory of possible ways of responding to the billions of possible stimuli which may compete for his attention. But at any one moment he is going to react "unevenly" — not by doing a little of each, but by throwing his whole resources into a single line of conduct. If the latter happens to be feeding his cat, then his ability to drive a car or his attitude toward Russia will not be brought into play. Often, however, his drives will be found to conflict with one another. He may want both

5 William F. Ogburn and Meyer F. Nimkoff, *Sociology* (Boston, 1940), p. 140.

to feed his cat and to answer the doorbell. Which of the two tensions shall he relieve by action? This question itself creates a new tension which calls for a higher authority to make a decision if he is to act with vigor. It is at such junctures that the deadlocks which would otherwise paralyze us are resolved, by a weighing of the probable consequences of each course of action and of the comparative strengths of the drives and attitudes involved.

SUMMARY

Although we have considered so far only the main external characteristics of the human organism as revealed by the observations of the biologists and physiologists, already several of the first letters of the alphabet which we may use in describing man as knower have come to light. First of all, in regard to the available raw materials of his knowledge, we see that man's sensory responses supply him with only a limited first-hand acquaintance with the innumerable changes that are taking place in his own body and in the world about him. Equipped with more powerful eyes, ears, noses, or other sense organs, there is no telling how fantastically man's original stocks of sense impressions might conceivably be enlarged. On the other hand, his senses may be adequate enough to guard him from the grosser sorts of disaster: a ship captain does not have to have a sounding line that reaches to the bottom of the ocean at its deepest part, in order to avoid running upon the rocks. All he needs is one that is a little longer than the draft of his ship.

On the lowest levels, much of man's so-called thinking is mere organic response without any logical ingredients, which he shares with many of the higher animals. Naturalists assure us that "the beasts get on very well without much intelligence"; and so, under certain circumstances, does man. But, thanks to his possession of a central nervous system that is comparatively unspecified in its responses at birth, yet is capable of an enormous amount of learning, man does unimaginably more with his sensory materials than any other creature of which we have knowledge. His body stores up energy; but, what is more important, his mind stores up experience in the form of condensed symbols. Things do not have to present themselves continually before his sense organs in order for him to take them into account. The countless brain paths of his cortex, when aroused to activity, are so loosely connected that he is able both consciously and unconsciously to combine, rearrange, and systematize his own sense data and the communicated experiences of others; and hence to make new associations and meet new situations with variations upon old formulas. He is no longer limited to his biological *status quo*, as we suppose is the case with most of the animals. There is opened before him "the larger environment of the mind," the seemingly boundless fields of imagination and reflection, of the impossible as well as the possible, where he is free to wander mentally at will, spinning sheer fantasies or logical systems, just as long as he is unchecked by the necessity of bringing them down to earth by applying them in action.

Yet all this higher and more original mental activity of the free spirit is made possible, and at the same time is vitally affected by the existence of lower centers which carry on the routine life of the organism with a minimum of conscious attention. The autonomic system with its controlling glands takes care of the internal environment and of preparation for sudden emergencies; the brain stem provides a number of ready-made reflexes upon which a life of habit can be built; and repeatedly satisfying activities of the cortex become "canalized" until they are virtually mechanical. It is as if the organism economized on conscious thought by turning successful or even partially successful behavior as rapidly as possible into unconscious routine, thus giving the higher centers *more freedom*, on the one hand; by furnishing them with a wider platform from which to operate; but allowing them *less freedom*, on the other, by making it more and more difficult for them to get out of the fixed ruts of acquired habits reinforced by emotional satisfactions.

It is already apparent, then, that the structural and functional relationships of man's chief organ for the acquisition of new knowledge, the cerebral cortex, to the rest of his body are peculiar ones. His cortical activity cannot range freely in the realm of new associations unless elaborate stabilizing mechanisms take over the simpler everyday tasks of self-preservation and "consolidate" in habits the experience already gained. But it cannot escape from the beaten paths of inborn reflexes and acquired habits without the arousing factor of "interest," itself deeply rooted (originally) in the autonomic system. Yet if the emotions, which are suited primarily to coping with violent animal struggles, are appealed to, the result may be a stirring-up of the whole organism in a way that blurs the senses and deflates or inhibits all cortical activity. To become an emotional fanatic, even about the use of reason, is to cease to be reasonable. If we assume that man's hopes for the future lie in the development of his higher centers, we must take care how we appeal to the lower centers of his past life for our motivating forces. Human intelligence, never "more than a frail bark afloat upon a sea of brute nature," is in constant danger of shipwreck. Yet reason wholly divorced from emotion becomes cold, and ends in boredom and deadness.

Summarily put, in terms that are familiar rather than exact, man is so constructed that teamwork by his thoughts, his feelings, and his habits is difficult. Thinking and feeling, reason and emotion, the head and the heart, are ancient rivals for supremacy in the knowing process as well as in all other human activities; while habit is at one minute an ally of each, by lending it stability, and at the next an enemy of each, by making spontaneity and originality difficult. It is not a contest among equals in point of age: habit and feeling are immeasurably older than conscious thought. Once superimposed, however, the more recent capacity of reason tends to curb and sterilize the ancient passions. But, even after centuries of civilizing, the blood, as we have learned to our sorrow, is capable of being aroused to overthrow the usurping intellect and to re-enslave it. Man is born to external and internal conflict, not to static contentment. It is the constant ebb and flow of the battle between our reason and our habits and emotions that makes us characteristically human. At the same time that we bemoan our condemnation to a divided life of struggle, we may also find it good; for without it there would be little interest or zest in living.

3. Anthropology and Social Psychology

Up to this point our attention has been centered upon the normal structure of the individual human organism. But human beings do not come into the world as fully developed adult knowers; they mature slowly, seldom reaching the peak of their intellectual powers in less than twenty-five or thirty years of growth. Neither do they grow up in isolation from other men, but rather in societies of varying sizes and degrees of complexity. It will therefore be necessary to extend our brief survey of human behavior to include those aspects which are observed and described by anthropologists and social psychologists. Not only does our task now become vastly more difficult, as we shift from the relatively uniform structure of the human body to the bewildering multiplicity of its active functions; but we also find ourselves hampered by the lack of any generally accepted fundamental concepts in the embryo sciences of man-in-society. There are many anthropologies and sociologies and social psychologies, each with its own vocabulary; so that the mere choosing of words that will convey the essential notions common to all of them is no easy undertaking.

In attempting to find our way through the maze of differing individuals growing up in societies, both primitive and civilized, to something like a recognizable sketch of man as knower, we shall steer clear of many technicalities by using the two broad concepts of *belief* and *doubt*. From the point of view of the human individual, there are the relatively passive or acceptance-prompting aspects of social life, which tend to induce unquestioning belief; and then there are the more dynamic or question-provoking phases which may sometimes lead to doubt. It may be that a composite portrait of man the believer and man the doubter may approximate that of man the knower.

SOCIAL CONDITIONING FOR BELIEF

Man begins life with poorly developed senses, a handful of inborn reflexes, and a great many undeveloped, diffuse, and flexible tendencies, including a bundle of organic tensions which he is totally incapable, for a prolonged period, of satisfying by his own unaided efforts. About all a human baby can do at birth towards his own survival is to make random thrashings of arms and legs and some mouthing and sucking movements. He can continue to live only by virtue of help from others and what he can learn from his environment. In his helplessness, the infant is utterly dependent upon others, extremely receptive toward their assistance, and completely occupied with attracting it when needed in order to minister to his principal but quite unconscious business in life, namely, rapid growth. More than any other living creature, however, the human baby is plastic in the sense of being able to profit by experience, to retain and carry over from one response, dispositions that modify subsequent responses.

In its simplest form, this process is known as conditioning. The classic experiment is that performed by the Russian physiologist Ivan Pavlov (1849–

1936), who rang a bell in the presence of a hungry dog, noting that there was no flow of the dog's saliva. Later he presented meat to the dog, and at the same time rang the bell. The dog responded by the normal flow of saliva to its mouth preparatory to eating. After a few days' repetition, the dog's mouth watered at the ringing of the bell, although no food was presented. The dog's salivary reflex had been conditioned to respond both to the original stimulus, the meat, and to the substitute stimulus, the bell, thus widening the range of his responses. He now acted as if he had learned that the bell "meant" food.

Human infants, even only a few days after birth, begin to become conditioned by their behavior; and theoretically, "any response of which a person is capable may be connected with any situation to which he is sensitive." Yet in practice the process of learning is slow and arduous, as every parent and teacher knows. Not everything we encounter conditions us to any perceptible degree. Immense numbers of stimuli impinge upon us in pairs and clusters without, apparently, making any lasting joint impressions. Nevertheless, a single association *may* condition us for months and even for years. Evidently something else besides mere temporal contiguity of stimuli seems to be needed.

It is no secret that the great aid to learning of this sort is interest. A burnt child will be likely to stay away from the hot iron which pained and frightened him for a long time afterwards, having built the iron into a system of avoidance which acts henceforth as an independent whole. Every animal trainer knows that both animals and humans learn best in the sense of being trained or conditioned when one or more of their autonomic responses, such as hunger, fear, sex, or some other so-called "vital incentive" is aroused; and the earliest learning of the human infant is saturated with such feeling-associations. At birth the baby's emotional states are probably not differentiated beyond feelings of pleasantness and unpleasantness; and during its early life only a few distinct overt emotional responses to such annoyances as loud noises, loss of support, and restraint of bodily movement are discernible. Yet with these and a few others which develop later as a foundation, the child by conditioning, plus a great deal of later selection and reconstruction of association-complexes, builds up all the hundreds of shades of feeling which constitute the repertory of his adult likings and dislikings. His heredity furnishes the materials, but his social circumstances (including himself as a reacting personality) determine the way they are patterned. Although not without a good deal of speculative exaggeration in the process, Freudian psychoanalysis has made us aware of the many ways in which emotional conditioning in childhood, by creating complexes and conflicts through repression and displacement, may alter the subsequent conduct of the adult without his being aware of it.

It is of particular importance to notice that experience not only extends the number of stimuli which arouse our drives; but that it also leads to the discovery that certain sub-activities linked to the satisfaction of the main drives are themselves highly rewarding on their own account. Thus hunting, at first merely instrumental in the securing of a food supply, becomes for many an autonomous or independent drive, no longer just a means to an end, but an end in itself. These acquired drives, which seem instinctive, although they are really the products of social habit, take their places in the total scheme of selection and mental reorganization which is constantly going on, and of which conditioning is the first crude description. We must beware of supposing that conditioning or routine repetition, even though it is "the most important single key to human learning," is the whole story. A college education is not just a matter of exposing oneself passively to external stimuli. Once we get beyond the primary stages of learning anything, our further progress depends largely upon our determination to attack and to master what has to be learned. Unless learning has become a drive in its own right, our education will stop when the pressure of our formal schooling is removed. Only those who have "taught themselves to want to learn," by reinforcing the drive by other mental tendencies until it has become autonomous, are likely to go on learning. The older a person becomes, in other words, the more he has to say about selecting what his *future* conditioning shall be; but the less he is able to do about altering the effects of his *past* choices and consequent conditioning.

For the forms and meanings which his experiences will assume, the human infant is almost completely at the mercy of the group of adults among whom he grows up. Being highly suggestible and imitative by nature, he is shaped and molded by responding to the attitudes and gestures of his parents and associates. The objects of his surroundings are seldom purely primary things; they are already culturally defined and overlaid with conventional meanings and values. There are the "proper" and the "improper" ways of doing nearly everything. The child finds his biological drives curbed and redirected; food appears only at certain hours; cleanliness may be taught; tears may be tolerated only in specific situations; and many other restraints may be imposed, which ordinarily lead to the gradual substitution of socially approved responses for those that are frustrated or disapproved, but which may result in a rebellious, antisocial attitude of aggression.

In this familiar socializing process the most important single influence by far is that of the home; but it is soon followed by that of the school and the child's own friends. Their most potent single instrument for bringing the immature human animal into line with the group is the short-cut conditioning device known as language. A striking proof of this is the difficulty encountered by congenital deaf-mutes in attaining a normal social development, being deprived of the use of those meaning-charged symbols, spoken words. By constant repetition and the arranging of spectacular and thrilling "occasions," the normal child soon becomes habituated to manifesting the appropriate emotional attitudes when words are uttered that have become "trigger-phrases." The strange and foreign ways of aliens become abhorrent.[6] As the Chinese sage Confucius pointed out some 2,400 years ago: "The nature of man is identical, what divides them is their customs."

6 For an account of the origin of race prejudices, see the chapters "Race and Culture" by Michel Leiris and "Race and Biology" by L. C. Dunn, pp. 181–218 and 263–299 in *Race and Science: Scientific Analysis from UNESCO* (New York, 1961).

Much of the ancestral lore which is imposed upon the growing child, however, will turn out to have been amassed under conditions which prevail no longer, and will therefore be seen to be irrelevant to his current perplexities, such as narrow nationalism in an interdependent world. Often it takes a long time to correct biased attitudes; knowledge that they are outmoded is seldom enough to overcome them, so that positive legal steps become essential. This is because to most people the beliefs in which they have been brought up appear so patently to be the only possible or natural or normal ways of thinking, that they indignantly reject the suggestion that their accustomed views could have been merely the products of social pressure, compulsion, or coincidence. Their social conditioning, in other words, constantly supplies them with what seem like excellent and obvious "reasons" for following their own habitual inclinations. The process is known as *rationalization:* the finding of reasons for what one wants to believe, than which there is no more prolific source of bias and prejudice. If the society happens to be a primitive one, its mythology is likely to be full of extravagant fantasy and yet enforced by rigid and unbreakable taboos. But in any society whatever, day in and day out the plastic young individual is subject to the pressures of a gigantic conditioning apparatus, the common culture, backed by social approval for the conformist and thundering disapproval for the rebel, and operating through such overlapping institutions as schools, churches, clubs, and businesses, most of which have their own additional quotas of fashions and rituals.

All this sounds disagreeably repressive, and yet the process is also a highly satisfying one. It relieves some of the tensions associated with competition among individuals; and makes possible an integrated personality with fixed attitudes toward all kinds of common situations. A primitive man does not have to shift his approach to suit a dozen different overlapping groups: if he is noisy and quarrelsome, he is free to act that way in all his social relationships, since the latter are already unified. Socialization also promises him a profit through the division of labor and of accumulated wisdom. If he will yield to the overwhelming cultural compulsives and conform to the *mores* of the group, he will be saved the trouble of working out standards and solving social problems for himself, since a large part of his conduct will have become stereotyped and virtually automatic upon the proper signal from the *shaman,* cheerleader, traffic officer, fashion editor, television pundit, or dictator. The economy of cortical effort here is apparent: through following custom, the conformist inherits all the funded wisdom-admixed-with-folly of past generations. To the extent that his education consists of "proper training" in the tribal practices, he is enabled to begin almost where his forbears left off, although on the basis of their experiences rather than his own, and perhaps under conditions very different from theirs.

There is, in addition, to anticipate somewhat our findings about human nature from the inside, a positive spiritual profit for most individuals in the satisfaction of their longings to merge themselves in a larger whole. This urge to "get out of oneself," to lose oneself in a cause, even to achieve a mystical union with the cosmos, probably has its roots in man's gregariousness and his

aesthetic side; but it is none the less a source of real satisfaction for being
nonrational in origin. Like everything else that is human, it can be ruined by
being carried to extremes; but, in moderation, the ability to see oneself in a
larger perspective — what is sometimes known as a sense of humor — is one
of the foundation stones of individual reason and sanity.

As the human individual grows up in the midst of any developed society,
then, powerful external forces combine with his internal inertia, habits, and
unadventurous desires, to induce his acceptance of whatever beliefs are cur-
rently approved by the culture patterns of the groups which are most vital to
him. "We begin," says Bain, "by believing everything." Man's natural state
is not doubt, but credulity — a combination of suggestibility in the face of
whatever is clearly and strongly presented, and the will-to-believe whatever is
personally or socially congenial. Where immediate practical necessities do not
constrain, rebuff, and disillusion him, man tends to accept as knowledge whatever fits in with his dominant wishes and desires. Among the latter are the
desire for economy of effort, for security, and for the approval of his fellows,
all of which he soon sees are most likely to be realized through the solidarity
of the group maintained by tradition.

From the cradle man finds himself surrounded by positive claims-to-know
asserted by persons who are only too evidently more powerful and more learned
than himself: "Mother knows best"; Father knows everything; the elders know
what is what; the teacher knows her subject, because society by appointing her
has said so. It is hardly surprising that in the minds of many, as Professor
John K. Galbraith points out, "It is a far, far better thing to have a firm an-
chor in nonsense than to put out on the troubled seas of thought."[7] The
child's earliest habits in knowing and in judging the worth of knowledge are
formed in an atmosphere of acceptance, submission, docility, in a word —
of authority. He soon learns that the world is a big, dangerous, and complicated place in which his own personal knowledge-by-acquaintance is hopelessly
inadequate. What then is more natural than that he should form the habit of
accepting the say-so of his fellows? Who am I, he asks himself, to question
what everybody else believes? By such mutual reinforcement, his hide-bound
conformism may develop into a genuine horror of whatever is new, strange,
alien, or in any way unorthodox. The first users of forks (Italians of the late
sixteenth century) were ridiculed as sissies; and the first man to carry an umbrella on the streets of London was attacked and beaten.

SOURCES OF DOUBT

If traditionalism were the whole story of man's long growth through the
centuries, human societies would be almost perfectly stable organizations like
those of some of the insects, or the ancient Chinese empire perhaps. Each
new generation would be content to duplicate as nearly as possible the thoughts
and practices of its ancestors with a few minute additions to the carefully followed lore of custom and ritual. Yet we find that no society is permanently

[7] John K. Galbraith, *The Affluent Society* (Boston, 1958), p. 160.

exempted from change; and that even the most primitive and apparently con-vention-bound communities have their occasional skeptics and rebels. If hu-man knowers are powerfully influenced by habit and custom, they are also subject to violent countertendencies in the form of conflict and change. Only the briefest account of the sources of doubt and deliberation is called for here, since this entire volume is concerned with the demand for something more reliable in the way of knowledge than mankind's merely conventional beliefs.

Social Sources

Even the most rigidly socialized community, where every individual action has long since been fitted into a prescribed culture pattern enforced by over-whelming sanctions in the form of rewards or punishments, cannot guarantee that its external circumstances will remain as constant as its internal adjustment to the normal state of affairs. Floods, earthquakes, wars, famines, epidemics, and climatic changes may bring about sudden crises for which there are no stereotyped solutions ready that are both acceptable and adequate. Fresh, in-ventive thinking or complete disaster may be the only alternatives. Early in World War I, the premier of France voiced his despair over the prejudices of his commanding general: "What can I do about it? General Gamelin doesn't *like* tanks."

Of a similar nature are the simple failures, on occasion, of the conventional formulas, often compounded of subjective whims and objective experience, to cope with the problems of which they are claimed to be the solutions. "When a Zulu army is cut in pieces," says the American anthropologist, Robert H. Lowie, "the mourners *may* indeed save their faith by supposing that the an-cestral spirits were offended; and that is the usual human way. But there is an alternative. From the depths of despair the survivor may hurl Promethean defiance at the core of the system itself. At the height of his emotional dis-turbance he will cry, 'The (*amatongo*) spirits of our people are good for noth-ing! Why has the whole village perished? How is it that they never men-tioned anything to us that we might understand why they were angry?' "[8]

Conflicts among social groups may, paradoxically, enhance both belief and doubt. The solidarity of the "we-group" as against the "others-group" is powerfully reinforced by patriotic emotion in the form of a comradeship of hatred against the enemy; but at the same time their experience is being en-larged, even possibly against their wills, by contact with other ways of fighting and living. In the course of history, few peoples have been able, and then only by an extraordinary degree of geographical isolation, to escape this spreading of ideas by what is called cultural diffusion. Commercial and diplomatic as well as military contacts have been prime means of shaking up old habits and preferences. To visit another country is to see one's own in an entirely new light. Not many provincialisms can survive a world tour entirely undisturbed.

Along with these failures of old folkways to meet the various stresses and strains of change and conflict, it must not be forgotten that novelty also has

[8] Robert H. Lowie, "Primitive Skeptics," *The American Mercury*, vol. 29 (1933), p. 323. (Italics his. H. A. L.)

its positive triumphs no less renowned than those of tradition. From the earliest times of which we have record, men have hit upon or have devised new combinations of things. Most of these inventors have encountered bitter opposition from vested interests. The telegraph and cable companies neither invented the telephone nor offered to buy it; the gas companies ignored the electric light; and the steam engine companies did not give birth to the turbine, the internal combustion engine, or the Diesel-electric drive. All those innovations had to be forced into use through outside competition. Yet so useful have some of them turned out to be, that industrial research and the contriving of the novel (always, supposedly, within certain limits) have gradually come to be at a premium in advanced societies, even attaining the status of occupations, themselves partly conventionalized. We have learned that single contrivances such as television or the airplane or rayon can have an almost explosive force in transforming the conditions of life; and yet, paradoxically, they often strengthen the very powers that limit the scope of fresh technical advances. The individualism of the pioneer American inventors, for instance, has collectivized most of their descendants by making mass production, standardization, and complex industrialization possible, to the point where pioneering is done, not by free-lance inventors, but, within the limits of business policy, mainly by giant corporations who hire unorthodox technologists for the purpose.

If we consider the relation of doubt to leisure, still more paradoxes appear. It was no accident that the first conspicuous doubters in Western Europe sprang from the priestly and noble classes in Athens and the Greek colonies, where slaves bore endless burdens in order that a few cosmopolitan aristocrats might question the current myths. The latter's privileged exemption from preoccupation with immediate practical concerns was the unintentional gift of those who toiled to pile up a surplus of economic goods. Yet some of these skeptics went so far as to question the slavery that made their questioning possible — thus illustrating a paradox that still bothers conservative donors of funds to institutions of inquiry: surplus funds enable keenly analytical minds to be developed to reflect . . . about surplus funds! Leisure classes rely upon custom and tradition for their continuance, and yet they are constantly breeding doubts which may lead to their own destruction.

It has been truly said, however, that "when a man is down and out he has no use for logic." Socially accumulated surpluses of energy and goods are essential to make leisure (and logic) possible for at least a few individuals, but they do not guarantee that the leisure will be used either to create or to destroy more leisure. It is another of the paradoxes of human nature that the mechanical genius which has produced intricate tools has thereby enabled millions of men to live in comparative comfort by pushing buttons and turning switches without further practical incentives to develop any mechanical genius of their own. Thought, judgment, and skill are passionately devoted to producing gadgets that are not only "labor-saving" but also "brain-saving," i.e., they render further thought, judgment, and skill relatively unnecessary. It is true that men cannot give themselves wholeheartedly to the persistent and disinterested pursuit of knowledge unless they have leisure; but to give them the leisure does not mean that they will automatically pursue it. As the revised proverb runs: "You can lead a girl to Vassar, but you can't make her think." Whether leisure will spell idleness or reflection depends mainly upon the attitude of the individual.

Individual Sources

What are the factors which operate against wholly stereotyped actions and beliefs in the structure of the human individual? In man, as in a number of the higher animals, several of the primary drives have become arranged in polar fashion, being paired in opposition to one another, at least in the sense that only one of each pair can prevail at any given moment of time. Some examples are: approaching-avoiding, activity-repose, gregariousness-solitariness, and domination-submission. This means that there is built into human nature the necessity for choice, since one of the paired tendencies must be restrained or inhibited, at least momentarily, if the other is to be left free to function.

When two such inconsistent tendencies are stimulated equally and at the same time, action becomes suspended in a state of vacillation, as when we cannot decide whether to stand and fight or to run away. Now we may, of course, escape from the uncomfortable quandary of indecision by an impulsive or a purely conventional choosing of one or the other of the alternatives, or we may be able to dodge the issue entirely. But the moments of delay at a temporary "dead center" between two courses enable a man, *if he chooses*, to "stop and think," to deliberate, to weigh and consider imaginatively the possibilities of the available alternatives. Anything, therefore, which checks either automatic responses or headlong plunges into impulsive action favors the chances of reflection, suspension of judgment, thoughtful comparison. Man most often gets his start on the road to new knowledge by encountering and recognizing ambiguous or problem-situations; and he is able to do so partly because he is built for hesitation as well as for the making of snap decisions. It is somewhere between extreme urgency and extreme apathy that he does most of his effective thinking.

But if he who does not hesitate at all is likely to act blindly or rashly, he who hesitates too much is lost in another sense. For it is unfortunately true that this stopping to question and to compare the probable results of imagined courses of action may itself become a habit carried to excess, resulting in that fatal "puzzling of the will" which "sicklied o'er with the pale cast of thought" Prince Hamlet's "native hue of resolution." That is the palsy which is supposed to be the special affliction of the intellectual in a warring world that calls for quick decisions, thereby disqualifying him for positions of command because he cannot make up his mind to act.

There are, however, two different attitudes leading to the postponement of hasty action, which need to be carefully distinguished. The first is an excessive vacillation called *asthenia* or *abulia*, which comes from the lack of enough "psychological force" (in the language of the French psychologist Pierre Janet) to enable a person to face a problem-situation, think it through, and decide upon a course of action. To do all those things requires the maintenance, over a comparatively long period, of a high degree of tension by mobilizing one's energies, and yet the preservation of a certain proportion between the force and tension. Weak, lazy, or unstable individuals may either lack the energy in the first place, or be unable to mobilize it, or be minus the control necessary to keep it from being crudely discharged in tantrum-like responses. To make a deliberate choice, especially between unpleasant alternatives, takes an amount of strength which not all individuals possess.

The second attitude is quite the reverse of the first: it is an undue persistence in carrying through a thorough mental examination of all the relevant possibilities, coupled with a resolute refusal to act until "all the facts are in," and a clear preponderance of well-founded reasons for choosing one of the alternatives has been demonstrated. It takes seriously Colonel Davy Crockett's famous advice during the War of 1812, "Be sure you're right, then go ahead!" making use of a much more conscientious interpretation of "sureness" than the Kentucky bear hunter's. This extreme prudence may set too high a standard of proof or precision in the light of the need of *some* action in the circumstances. It may indeed "give lectures on the refinements of navigation while the ship is close to the rocks." But, while it may indicate a distaste for commitment in action outwardly resembling asthenia, instead of being based on laziness, it represents an extreme degree of habitual mental work requiring exceptional resolution. It was Pierre Janet who pointed out that man alone among the animals "invented work." It is not a primitive psychological trait, as some have supposed. Our strange habit of working all the time has been constructed by borrowing from other human tendencies. Yet so well has Western man in the temperate zones learned his lesson of industry, that he finds enforced inactivity positively painful. In 1954 three Canadian psychologists paid several college students $20 a day to do absolutely nothing, lying all day on a comfortable bed with their sense organs shielded from any stimulation. Few of them could stand more than two or three days of it, the upper limit of endurance being six.[9] Outwardly viewed, the results of the two attitudes, excessive laziness on the one hand, and excessive fussiness on the other, may seem to come to the same thing — inordinate caution leading to the indefinite postponement of action; but in terms of inward motives they are very different. Plainly the art of making tentativeness fruitful in knowledge instead of merely corruptive of efficiency in action must avoid both extremes.

4. Knowledge and Knowing

In surveying the factors which lead to belief and those which lead to doubt, there has already become evident a need for distinguishing between knowledge, the finished product, and knowing, the dynamic activity. For we have observed that the very knowledge which has proved itself reliable in a certain

[9] Donald O. Hebb, A *Textbook of Psychology* (Philadelphia, Pa., 1958), pp. 173–74, describing the experiments of W. H. Bexton, W. Heron, and T. H. Scott.

limited historical context has often become a barrier to any further knowing. Old knowledge blocks new knowing, both in the individual and in society. As Nietzsche declared: "Many a man fails to become a thinker for the sole reason that his memory is too good." Such a person may conclude that it is easier to be learned in the wisdom of others than to be intelligent on his own account.

In any society, what is accepted as known is what has supposedly withstood a good many tests, and has been organized into a symbolic system which is assumed to enshrine the essence of past successful conduct for future use. Knowledge in this sense, as John Dewey pointed out, represents what has been already "settled, ordered, disposed of rationally." People come to think of it as the ground already won and consolidated, perhaps at a great cost in human effort. Why, asks the conservative, should there be any need to conquer it all over again?

Now if conditions never changed, further knowing would indeed be superfluous. The "wisdom of our ancestors" would suffice, and any attempt to "know better" would be presumptuous. Thus, the individual doubter who tries to keep aloft the banner of inquiry in a society which believes itself already completely sophisticated, finds himself assailed as a disturber of the peace. The skeptic, the radical, the unbeliever — all these have traditionally been bad names. They may be lucky to survive the cries of "Throw him out!" or "Crucify him!" or "Systematically ignore him!"

But the very pretensions that are urged on behalf of the settled knowledge of any given day and age are what eventually expose its inadequacies, and clear the way for fresh and original thinking. The consecrated gleanings of the past cannot be made to serve as ready-made solutions of all the problems of the present and future. What was thought to be settled, once and for all, turns out to be quite unsettled. To look only backward is a recipe for extinction; man finds that he must alternate glances toward the past with glances toward the future. Past knowledge appears in its true role of point of departure rather than terminus of the thinker's quest.

Thus, man the knower, when viewed from the outside, appears in two different guises, as man the settler of questions on the basis of past knowledge, and as man the unsettler of those same accepted solutions in order to push on to the asking of better questions. From the point of view of knowledge as accomplishment, he is the conservative consolidator of society's accumulated wisdom in the form of elaborate systems of symbols and techniques. As the guardian of social gains, he supplies an invaluable element of stability for all further attempts to deal with the changing world. But his very devotion to the known may be an obstacle to further knowing. For man the knower is also man potentially the adventurer, the "growing edge" of his society. Here he plays the thankless rôle of radical doubter of accepted knowledge, but only in order that he may eventually reconstruct it upon a firmer foundation.

FOR CLASS DISCUSSION

A. If you wish to know yourself, observe how others act. If you wish to understand others, look into your own heart. — *J. C. F. von Schiller*   (1)

B. On the physical side we come of fairly good and vigorous mammalian stock — from an old family of vertebrates that have boasted . . . many a strong back and crafty paw, and many a sensitive nose and ear. On the mental side we are just simply precocious — we are the prize exhibit in the Greatest Animal Show on Earth. Nothing like us except the dazzling instincts of birds and bugs. — *Harlow Shapley*   (2)

C. Endocrine enthusiasts commit their fallacy of exaggeration chiefly because they do not distinguish between *personality* and *temperament*. They do not realize that there is a great difference between simple temperamental correlates of endocrine action (excitability, apathy, fluctuation of mood, etc.) and the much more intricate, cortically dominated, traits of personality (e.g., egotism, aestheticism, pride, and suspiciousness). — *Gordon W. Allport*

D. A lawyer was pleading before an English judge, Lord Bramwell, that his client had had an "irresistible impulse" to steal an umbrella; whereupon the judge interrupted to ask the defendant whether he would have taken it in the presence of a policeman. On receiving a negative reply, Lord Bramwell remarked, "In other words, the impulse was irresistible in the absence of a policeman." — *Foster Kennedy*

E. It is probable that few men would control their lusts if their only means of control were their capacity to think. — *E. Jordan*

F. Krishnalal Shridharani, a high-caste Hindu who came to the United States on a scholarship, relates that when he first walked into an American cafeteria he had to pull a sandalwood-scented handkerchief from his pocket and hold it to his nose and eyes. For, right before him on a steam table, was a large chunk of beef "with fat hanging on it and bones protruding" — just about as appetizing to a Hindu as "prime ribs of baby."   (3)

G. By searching the ancient regulations of Oxford University, a student found that he was entitled to a pint of beer as refreshment while cramming for a final examination. He was so persistent in demanding his pint that the authorities finally furnished it; and by the same set of regulations fined him five pounds (about $14) for not wearing a sword. — *The Lancet*

H. We think so because other people all think so;
Or because — or because — after all, we do think so;
Or because we once thought so, and think we still think so;
Or because, having thought so, we think we will think so.
                                        — *Henry Sidgwick*

I. As Einstein has pointed out, common sense is actually nothing more than a deposit of prejudices laid down in the mind prior to the age of eighteen.
                                        — *Lincoln Barnett*

Nothing is more curious than the self-satisfied dogmatism with which mankind at each period of history cherishes the delusion of the finality of its existing modes of knowledge. — *Alfred North Whitehead*

J. Doubt, not belief, is the positive process. Whatever is not doubted is believed. — *W. B. Pillsbury*

I respect faith but doubt is what gets you an education. — *Wilson Mizner*

K. The mass of men must be leavened by individuals who are self-moving, who do not habitually conform, who question not only the conclusion but the premises and the character of the evidence, who raise disturbing doubts, who imagine unexpected theories . . . who are not afraid to be wrong, and do not become panicky if they are alone. No doubt this is a recipe for producing a large number of cranks and fools. But they must be endured for the sake of the indispensable few who, as Montaigne put it, dare to breast the wave and do not roll with the tide. — *Walter Lippmann*

♉ 2 ♊

MAN AS KNOWER: *From the Inside*

1. *From Dreaming to Scientific Inquiry*

ALREADY OUR PANORAMIC SKETCH of man the knower as observed from the outside has unavoidably made use of a good deal of knowledge obtained from the inside; and the reverse is bound to be true as we undertake a similar broad survey of man as he sees himself in his own consciousness. Here all the perils of error, already great, in generalizing from our own particular inside knowledge are multiplied. Yet without some advance plotting of the principal landmarks of consciousness, it is only too easy to get lost in the mental wilderness. The contours that we shall attempt to draw on the public map of the private mind must, however, be constantly checked against the reader's own inner experiences.

Where to begin? Fortunately some clues from our previous survey of man's biological and psychological equipment are already at hand. The very distinction between man from the outside and from the inside indicates that a human being is capable of two modes of orientation in knowing: he may focus upon the external world through the senses, using his body as a sort of instrument; or he may be content to observe "the inner life of the mind." It should be noted that the two orientations usually require different amounts of mental tension and physical exertion; and are dominated by two different directing principles: the one apparently centered in the cortex, and the other in the autonomic system. Since the organism acts as a whole, the distinction between the two principles is largely one of emphasis. Freud has given to the one directed toward objective external fact-finding the name of "reality" principle, calling the one concerned with subjective internal valuing in accordance with our wishes and desires the "pleasure" principle. Among civilized men the latter, according to Freud, is held in check by conventional conditioning acting as the "censor" of consciousness. Unsuitable impulses are sent back to the unconscious or "suppressed," but they may reapply for admission to consciousness after being "sublimated" in disguises which are socially acceptable.

The two principles are by no means necessarily at odds with one another. Emotionally toned interest, the heart of the "pleasure" principle, is also needed, as we have seen, for any persistent exercise of the "reality" principle; and yet is capable of confusing and distorting as well as of sustaining it. The cortex is plainly our best instrument of discrimination in dealing with the "coercion of the world" outside us, and yet it seems to operate mainly at the

46

call of our interests, which, if undisciplined, may be highly impractical. Whether a given knower will elect at a given moment to follow the primrose path of the "pleasure" principle rather than the rocky road to "reality" will depend upon his original nature, his acquired habits of feeling and thinking, and his appraisal of the situation that confronts him.

Since it takes a greater degree of tension and effort to mobilize our interests in support of the "reality" principle, especially for any length of time, there are those who hold that the average human being, naturally economical of energy when not deeply stirred, will resort to "realistic" thinking only under the pressure of practical necessity, relaxing back into "pleasure" thinking at the first opportunity as soon as the emergency is over. Given no problems which must be solved, no obstacles to be surmounted, the normal individual will get along with a minimum of "realistic" thought. But an even greater danger lurks in man's subjective confusion of the two principles by means of the process known as rationalization. It must be remembered that the practice of reasoning realistically acquired its great prestige in Western civilization only recently. It took literally centuries for hundreds of man's originally playful, pleasant, irrational actions to be harnessed to serious or useful purposes. But today, rationally purposive actions have become the accepted, civilized standard, even to the point where we may feel that we ought to be able to give a serious reason for being occasionally playful!

Civilized man, in other words, has acquired a fear of not being thought reasonable, and, in order to cope with it, has developed an astonishing repertory of rationalizations for the purpose of convincing himself and others that, in following the "pleasure" principle, he is actually following the "reality" principle. Because he wants to believe himself to be logical, he persuades himself that the things he yearns to believe have some foundation in actuality, and that what he does not want to believe is really false. As John Locke wrote in a letter to Anthony Collins: "To be rational is so glorious a thing, that two-legged creatures generally content themselves with the title." But they do want the title; and the effort to claim it has been the cause of endless, and often innocent, self-deceit. That state of affairs should put us on our guard against taking our own inner protestations of disinterestedness at their face value. "The first step toward self-knowledge is self-distrust."

Many children unfortunately come to regard hard thinking of any kind as something unpleasant, a duty imposed upon them by parents and teachers, rather than as a challenge to achievement. Hence it is to be avoided rather than sought. The immature mind comes to regard intellectual tasks as punishments rather than rewards, and fails to make the transition from an infantile resentment of duty to the adult acceptance of it.

Attention directed to our own consciousness at any moment reveals that we are "thinking," — that is, a stream of mental states merging into and out of one another in rapid succession is passing through our mind. These states not only vary enormously in content, but in the kinds and degrees of order which they manifest in their complex and dynamic interrelationships. It is probably a mistake to use the expression "state of mind" for something which reaches out beyond itself and exists by changing, much as images dissolve into one another on the motion picture screen. The human mind has been compared to a "self-moving kaleidoscope," in which we can discern recurring patterns; but to succeed in arresting its movement at a given instant is not to isolate something called a state, out of numbers of which the whole is somehow pieced together.

At one extreme among our varying conscious experiences stand the chaotic emergences from deep and dreamless sleep into night- and day-dreams; while at the other are the intricate manipulations of interlacing chains of systematic reasoning checked against external evidence called scientific inquiries. In between the two lie all manner of mental compromises and combinations among logic, habits, memories, and whims. A swift glance from one extreme to the other may disclose some of the principal variables in man's inner life which affect his qualifications as a knower. It must be remembered that any analysis of thinking as seen from the inside is not a neat affair of fixed and separable classes of objects to which we can point, but a matter of subtle shadings, blurred boundaries, and lightning changes.

2. Night- and Day-Dreams

Sleep, viewed outwardly for the moment, since he who is asleep cannot observe his own deep slumber, is a state of bodily and mental relaxation in which motor activity is at a minimum, but during which sensory and cortical responses to very strong stimuli continue. We go to sleep by successive stages, first shutting off most of the external sensory stimuli by sheltered inaction, whereupon the brain is largely restricted to internal activity based upon stored-up memories. What the sleeper lacks, as we say, is any apparent interest. The uninterested student in class is well on his way to slumber; while the tired soldier on guard, and desperately anxious, may stay awake for days on end. The dreams of sleep, to return to our internal perspective, are composed of sensory elements from our past experience usually jumbled together in absurd patterns on faint clues from our sense organs or the cortex itself. In falling asleep we tend to rearrange our recent experiences in new relationships, sometimes resulting in "inspirations" which are difficult to recall. Our dream experiences, freed from the usual limitations of time and space, may nevertheless seem "real" enough at the moment; yet ordinarily they are strangely lacking in any genuine emotional interest, appearing to be cut off or estranged from the waking world. The extraordinary happenings in dreams do not surprise us until we awaken and begin to analyze them; although occasionally a person is aware that he is dreaming, and thus is not wholly "taken in" by the illusory character of his dream. Dreams may be, as Freud has suggested, the guardians of our sleep, in that they generally succeed in shunting off the stimuli, which would otherwise awaken us, into harmless channels cut off from the motor system, and hence from our consciousness. Dreaming is also the special pleasure of those who find themselves frustrated and oppressed in the waking workaday world; while both sleep and dreams are despised by those who, like excited children, cannot bear to miss a moment of maximum consciousness.

What is missing in most dreams of sleep is any directive or critical factor which can check the flow of images and appraise them by imposing an external standard of comparison. Without some such supervision, absurdities are allowed to run riot, guided only by loose associations and conflicting wishes and habits; so that the sane and logical waking mind may find itself reduced to a shambles of incoherence and contradiction. The moral censor also takes a vacation when we dream; all sorts of wishes that are repressed in our waking hours may come to frank or symbolic fulfillment, so that the contents of dreams are notoriously nonrespectable.

To be awake, on the other hand, is to be to some extent alert, attentive, tense, wary, suspicious, repressive of those elements of consciousness which are not connected with our immediate or remote interests. It is a state of relative readiness to discriminate and to react selectively in the situation in which we find ourselves, or may find ourselves, keeping our wishes alive but in check, and our emotions (unless we must go "all out" in some action) under still stricter discipline. It is a laborious condition of higher tension, guided by recollections of the past and forecasts of the future, concerning which ones of our lower tensions are to be relieved by action. Man learned its value by harsh experience, which convinced him that he had better be on his guard against surprises from his environment; that he could not live by his dreams or his wishes alone; and that therefore, in dealing with the often hostile world about him, the "pleasure" principle was hardly adequate. For the mastering of his environment, some sort of order or system was essential. Otherwise he could not cope with the bewildering variety of the testimony of his inner and outer experiences, and especially with some of the discrepancies between what he saw in his dreams and in his waking moments. But, in his first crude attempts at constructing such an order, he made the almost fatal mistake of picking the wrong clue. He trusted the vividness of his uncontrolled inner impressions and their allied emotions, rather than the stability of his less spectacular everyday experiences. He let his attention be seduced by the glitter of the unusual and the exciting, and came to regard dreams, strange voices, and marvelous coincidences as sources of trustworthy knowledge *par excellence*. The normal was too dull and commonplace to be significant — a delusion which still corrupts our journalism. Thus man became entangled in a web of complicated superstitions and dramatized projections of gods and spirits from which he is still endeavoring to free himself.

But we are getting ahead of our story. The first step from dreaming to scientific inquiry is from the dreams of sleep to day-dreams, which actually occupy a very large share of the waking hours of all of us. In a state of revery, we are awake, at least in the sense that we know that we are "bemused by too clement dreams," but we are "absent-minded." The play of our fancy is ordinarily under the loose control of the "pleasure" principle, and has no conscious bearing upon any fixed, specific object beyond itself. Our mind is allowed to wander away from the present situation into pathways of memory and imagination that are emotionally congenial. "Such thoughts," as John Dewey says, "are an efflorescence of feeling; the enhancement of a mood or a sentiment is their aim; congruity of emotion, their binding tie."[1] The typical day-dream is a means of escape from the irksome perplexities of the present to an imagined situation in which obstacles vanish or are easily overcome. It is a form of self-glorification in which our wishes reach the fulfillments they are denied by the actual world: we achieve personal beauty, mental prowess, romantic adoration, earthly sainthood, or sometimes personal revenge on enemies, or recognition after death which has been denied in life. The day-dream is our own privately produced prototype of a soap opera or a Hollywood "B" picture.

3. Intermediate Types

FANTASY IN ART

From the day-dream it is but a short step to the many varieties of artistic invention for the purpose of enjoyment or aesthetic appreciation: especially the fantasy or non-realistic story, play, or picture, in which we are invited to identify ourselves with the thought and actions of imaginary characters, and so are "taken out of ourselves" for a few hours. Such creations may be fairly described as artificial day-dreams: they save us the labor of devising our own stream of plot-connected images leading to a wish-fulfilling dénouement. Unless we are abnormally critical, such fantasies as *Alice in Wonderland* or a Mickey Mouse cartoon are permitted to make up their own logic as they go along, for they are self-contained worlds that make no claim to credence beyond their own boundaries. No one is going to base any of his beliefs or actions in the workaday world on the knowledge to be gained from the exploits of Donald Duck. Since they are all in fun and not in earnest, it is enough that Donald stays in character in an imaginary world that is sufficiently like ours to be recognizable. All that we demand of such phantoms is that their actions be guided by a familiar emotional patterning.

COHERENT INSANITY

Yet a man who lives his whole life by emotional congruity of the single-tracked variety without regard to the world of his fellows, we call insane. Escape can be carried so far that the inner world takes the place of the outer. When the deranged individual takes his distorted fancies for facts, and acts upon them, he cuts himself off from the rest of humanity in a "private world" of his own. In many types of insanity this private universe is highly coherent and logical in its own terms. The unfortunate individual who firmly believes that he is Napoleon may govern his every action by the strictest possible adherence to the logical consequences of his belief. Quite literally it may be said that his only trouble is that he cannot get other people to admit that he *is* Napoleon. What he has omitted to do is to check his premises against the world in which he and his fellow men are living, to enlarge his demand for

[1] John Dewey, *How We Think* (Boston, 1910), p. 4.

knowledge beyond the circle of his own conceits, so as to be able to come to some working agreement that will enable him to get along with his neighbors. Just as long as he fails to do this, it does him no good to insist that he is reasoning clearly and validly from his deepest convictions.

It would seem that making up one's own mind too thoroughly is a good way to go out of it. There is a point at which sheer clarity begins to yield diminishing returns. As G. K. Chesterton once said: "A lunatic is one who has lost everything but his reason." The remark should remind us that there is more to this business of sanity than mere system, especially when one's initial premises are narrow, as they usually are. Extreme emphasis upon the logical coherence of one's own limited ideas may result in an *idée fixe* accompanied by a compulsion neurosis — that is, in an insane obsession. A second and equally important ingredient of sanity is the willingness to accept solutions which are less than perfectly tidy in order to achieve at least a rough agreement with one's fellows about a common outer world. The normal mind is not one which is automatically in complete agreement with itself, like a smoothly running machine or a super-dictatorship. It is far more like a committee muddling through to compromise decisions after wranglings that yield no wholly consistent formulas, and that leave all of the members somewhat dissatisfied with the results.

It will be noted that so far in our inside exploring of human nature, we have been concerned with conscious activities that (1) require little or no tension or effort on the part of the knower; and (2) have little or no reference beyond themselves to the world in which he has his physical existence. Although they may be productive of new combinations of ideas, even occasionally of brilliant inspirations, dreaming and fantasy-weaving seem to come most readily to the relaxed and passive mind. We do not associate them with the effort to concentrate that marks our so-called "serious" thought. Dreams of sleep, although they may be preceded by intense study, arrive unbidden and proceed *ad lib*; while day-dreams are supposedly the mere idling of our mental machinery in its waking hours. Even artistic creation of the non-realistic sort is frequently described by poets, novelists, and composers as something over which they have little conscious control: ideas just come to them from nowhere, characters suddenly begin to speak for themselves, and plots to unroll without assistance.

4. Reflexes, Drives, and Habits from the Inside

There is another vast tract of human activities that require little conscious direction and effort, but which do refer beyond themselves to the world outside. These are the reflexes, drives, and the habits and conditionings with which they are soon overlaid. All of them may be lumped together for our purposes as relatively automatic impulses traceable to our original endowment as modified by our experiences. In Professor Hocking's phrase, they may be said to constitute the "original charter of our body's behavior" as amended by experience.

One does not get far by asking how a reflex looks to us from the inside, since many of them operate without appearing in consciousness at all, while others register inwardly only when they are delayed, hindered, or interrupted. Of a vast amount of what goes on within our bodies we are normally unaware. "To some of our acts there attaches mind," as Sherrington puts it, "to other of our acts there does not." As the automatic rigidity of an action increases, our consciousness of it diminishes. In the words of James Ward: "Where certainty is most certain, we are least aware of it." Where we can do no more about a process, mind apparently forsakes it. Above the reflex level, however, those of our primary drives which are inborn appear in consciousness as spontaneous "natural" desires accompanied by emotions and linking a perception with an action (or series of actions) which has the quality of *obvious interest*. To ask why the sight of a lake should interest a man who has been thirsty for days is as pointless as to inquire why the same body of water appeals to a duck as something in which to swim. They are both just built that way, and that is all there is to be said.

Drives which do not immediately find expression may be seen from within as cravings, which usually take the form of an unpleasant feeling, such as hunger, together with an envisaged state of satisfaction, such as the enjoyment of a square meal. But the latter element may be extremely vague, as in the stirrings of sex in adolescents, or even absent, with the result that the person experiencing the craving is restless and inclined merely to change whatever he is doing until the want is allayed. An extremely strong craving may become neurotic or compulsive, ending as an obsession which distorts a person's entire behavior, unless it is satisfied (perhaps in a sublimated form) or restrained by a stronger combination of desires.

Just how our drives find concrete expression is largely a matter of social patterning. For example, both pugnacious and sympathetic activities are capable of being aroused in connection with sex; but the actual variety of human *mores* decreeing the proper attitudes in different situations is immense. Once such patterns have become habitual and deeply ingrained, however, they take on the same "instinctive" obviousness as reflexes, accompanied by a diminishing consciousness in their exercise. Established bonds (old shoes, old friends) become "second nature," and appear to be as necessary and unquestionable as those of the "first nature" which is ours by inheritance. We catch ourselves performing stereotyped actions, and marvel at our literal "absence of mind." Since acts which are many times repeated are felt less in consciousness as time goes on, familiarity may breed indifference if not contempt.

Down the channel of an inborn primary drive or instinct, says Professor Hocking, "the current of life rushes with exceptional impetus; once committed to it, we reach our highest pitch of personal self-consciousness, our greatest sense of power and command."[2] So strong, indeed, are some of these natural impulses, once any opposing tendencies have been overcome, that a man who has been carried away by them may come to regard them as somehow external and alien to himself, as when a soldier in the midst of battle finds his fear or rage reactions sweeping him willy-nilly along unchosen paths. In such

[2] W. E. Hocking, *Human Nature and Its Remaking* (New Haven, Conn., 1918), pp. 30–31, 43.

moments of terror or exaltation he may feel both most and least "himself" — most himself in the intensity of his experience, and least himself in having so little control over it. He may even come to fear and to condemn the scarcely resistible violence of the very passions which yield him the keenest satisfactions.

Readiness to act, as seen from the inside, is thus revealed as closely related to what we call belief or conviction. A believer, we say, is one who is consciously prepared to accept the risks of action. Persons who long for the confidence and decisiveness in action which go along with intense convictions are sometimes advised: "Act as if you believed, and you will believe." That, of course, is precisely what all of us begin life by doing: we act unconsciously on the basis of what may, much later, become conscious belief based on reliable knowledge; and it is that inevitable state of affairs which constitutes the human "primordium of universal credulity." We are "born believers" because we are born actors. Doubt is something which we have to achieve; and usually we have to be driven to achieve it, sometimes at a considerable cost to ourselves. Positive doubting is a skill which has to be acquired; and human children, no matter how anti-suggestible they may be, are necessarily unskilled doubters pitted against the massive forces of social orthodoxy. Early in life, and under the overpowering influence of the surrounding culture, they frame their elementary notions of what is real, possible, probable, desirable, and so on, as a casual accompaniment of their social activities. From the grip of such primary customs and beliefs they seldom wholly escape, for they live by them until and if they are disillusioned by the results. What ensues is generally not the discarding of all of their previous ideas, but a partial revision or recombination which seems more likely to be suited to the changing circumstances. Still less drastically do most persons eliminate the traditional from their overt actions, no matter how much they have been forced to change their minds. This accounts for the lag in the discarding of many old rituals and superstitions by people who consider themselves intellectually enlightened.

INTUITION

Closely allied with our primary inborn reflexes and our drives with their accompanying emotions is a primitive way of knowing called intuition. It is an apparently unanalyzable operation furnishing our conscious mind with a conclusion which comes so quickly that we are unable to observe any preceding process of inference. We find that we have made a leap from a state of uncertainty to certainty in the form of a direct grasp or broad synthetic "sensing" of a situation. This takes the form of a guess or "hunch" which often yields a feeling of complete subjective certitude for which, it seems, no reasons need to be given. By intuition, for example, we may believe that we comprehend or gain insight into the personality of another, without being able to offer any supporting analysis or evidence. The intuitive knower is not self-critical of such directly attested knowledge, because it seems to be beyond all criticism.

When challenged for proof of his naïve unargued assumptions, the intuitionist is likely to retreat into the fastnesses of his private knowledge, or to appeal to accepted "common sense" — that is, to supposedly universal habits of thinking: every normal person *must* feel that the earth cannot move, that stealing is wrong, and so on. These things are "self-evident" to any "normal" person. But unfortunately, as Cohen and Nagel succinctly express it, "it is difficult to find a proposition for which at some time or other 'self-evidence' has not been claimed. . . . It is well known that 'self-evidence' is often a function of current fashions and of early training. The fact that we feel absolutely certain, or that a given proposition has not before been questioned, is no guarantee against its being proved false. Our intuitions must be tested."[3] The tests of intuitions, however, are not purely intuitional, but rational and analytical. We cannot validate one intuition by the simple expedient of calling in another intuition. In order to draw the line between mysticism and delusion, between the false prophet and the true, it is always necessary eventually to invoke the aid of discursive reason. Intuition has to be safeguarded, lest it result in mere wishful imaginings; and it is, unfortunately, incapable of safeguarding itself.

5. Problem-Solving and Intellectual Curiosity

Mind seems to have developed originally as flexible guidance of bodily movements. Human beings are distinguished from other forms of life by their extraordinary capacity to use instruments in the performance of bodily acts which are attentive, prolonged, and unified. *Homo faber,* or man the artificer, has exploited his environment by means of plans of action which have become wider and wider in scope. To do this successfully, he has been obliged to extend the range of his consciousness of the world about him. Seen from within, these planned acts are characterized by an integration of the mind which we call a person's intent or will. The latter involves a deliberate focusing or concentration of all the individual's resources: the senses, the autonomic system, and the central nervous system as controllers of his muscular reactions — all are placed at the service of his dominant thought or "main idea" of the moment.

Any such mental unifying of behavior to meet an external situation on a level where many alternative choices are possible is an achievement which calls for a high degree of effort. There can be little doubt that man was first driven to make the attempt by problematic situations — that is, by obstacles and blockages in the course of his existence which habit and impulse could not immediately remove. Viewed from the inside, these perplexities, when inescapable, are marked by all the discomforts which attend an upheaval of settled ways of acting — by tension, inhibition, and a usually painful suspension of judgment. The inner side of doubt is as uncomfortable as the inner side of belief is comfortable. When we doubt, our old and smoothly running patterns have to be broken up and new ones devised. At the moment we may

[3] Morris R. Cohen and Ernest Nagel, *An Introduction to Logic and Scientific Method* (New York, 1934), p. 195.

have no fresh alternatives at hand; and the result may be the temporary crippling of our effectiveness in action. Youth has abundant time and energy to make the long series of such habit readjustments from home to school to adolescence to college to vocation to military training to marriage to parenthood and so on. But middle age rebels, and turns conservative. It takes too much energy to keep on remaking oneself. The odds against further upsetting departures from the emotionally satisfying features of the *status quo* have become too great. Yet some mature minds do occasionally break away from their habits, curb their more violent impulses, and overcome their natural inertia enough to think reflectively without immediate compulsion, and even to go out in search of new and baffling difficulties. That would indicate that the laborious activity of the higher centers not only possesses great survival value, but has also become a drive on its own account by acquiring satisfactions attaching directly to itself.

To understand how that has come to be, it may be helpful to go back to a consideration of the nature of living things as contrasted with the non-living. The roots of our pleasure in extending and complicating our consciousness for its own sake may lie in the primal urge of all life to respond to an obstacle, not by quitting or accepting, but by resisting, pushing, yielding a little, and then pushing again to find a way around it. Stones stay where they are put, and await their gravitational fate. But living things possess enterprise and the urge to control their environment: plants grow by budding out in search of nourishment; frustrated animals indulge in many kinds of wildly random activities which are sometimes rewarded by success; and men seek to heighten the intensity of their living in many ways, one of which is the maximum extension of the range and richness of their consciousness.

As for problem-situations, they must have been faced by many forms of life long before man's appearance upon the evolutionary scene. To the lower animals, however, they were merely baffling obstructions to be met by random trial-and-error aided by those crystallized forms of ingenuity called instincts. Man met them with something new: a conscious mind to which they appeared as problems susceptible to analysis and having possible imagined solutions. Perhaps even more important, he met them with an internal urge to know. Lloyd Morgan may be right in saying that "the primary aim, object, and purpose of consciousness is control"; and yet through the centuries human consciousness came to set other goals for itself. While enforced problem-solving probably first jolted man out of the ruts of custom and prejudice, as soon as the pressures of constant crises were lifted somewhat from the minds of a few fortunate and gifted souls, the problem-type of thinking developed an attractiveness on its own account. These men began to see problems before they were thrust upon their attention by practical necessities: they went out to meet mental perplexities a good deal more than half-way. At first, there were only a few of these thinkers with an appetite for the abstract, and the number of those among them who have made any substantial contribution to human thought has never been large. The capacity to increase the human fund of manageable abstractions, moreover, has not often been accompanied by an equal skill in bringing about their utilization in practice. Meanwhile the rest of mankind have continued, except in their inquisitive childhood days, to avoid the burdens as well as the delights of reflective thinking, and to live largely by impulse and custom, asking few questions because they suppose that they are already in possession of all the essential answers.

In some such way the natural curiosity coupled with natural suspicion, which man shares with many of the higher animals, became expanded and intellectualized here and there into human wonder. No doubt an element of playfulness entered: more and more things became mysteries worth solving for the sake of the pleasure involved. For some, there may have been added the factor of aesthetic delight in contemplating grandiose solutions of such gigantic problems as the nature of the cosmos. Our word "theory" comes from a Greek expression which means a seeing or beholding, a vision that yields understanding. The first philosophers and scientists developed this craving for understanding for its own sake sufficiently to make it their dominant life purpose, not unmixed with other aims. Reflective thinking, long the servant of innumerable practical interests, now became the master in a domain of its own. The psychology of this declaration of independence of practice is still obscure; but there can be no doubt that if, as Professor W. P. Montague has phrased it, "man began to think in order that he might eat," some men at least, "have evolved to the point where they eat in order that they may think."[4]

Most of what man knows can be seen to be closely connected with his ambitions to dominate his world. His knowledge has been mainly concerned with the things which he has wanted to do. But one of the things that he has come to want to do is to know for other purposes besides action, "for the love of the theory," for the satisfaction to be gained from knowledge itself. His inner demands for reliable knowledge, while first aroused by immediate necessities and guided by all manner of human interests, have come to embrace more and more remote considerations until sometimes, in "pure" or apparently "useless" research, they have lost touch with all but theoretical difficulties. Thus the types of order (mathematics, formal logic, and others) which have been found useful in establishing and testing the reliability of many kinds of knowledge have acquired an absorbing interest for some thinkers upon their own account. Why, they have asked themselves, do just these particular systems of order "work" for our major purposes in the world in which we live? To find the answer to this question, some of these philosophical inquirers have turned their attention to the inner workings of the mind, in the effort to discover a clue in the criteria which it brings to the interpretation of whatever it encounters. By so doing, they have hoped to be able to distinguish between what is given *by* our minds and what is given *to* our minds when we experience anything, and thus to account for our common ordering concepts through our possession of similar mental powers of discrimination. They have sought to solve the problem of order by means of an exhaustive internal study of "the way the mind must act" in knowing: forgetting that while the *form* of knowledge may be determined in part by the equipment of the knower, its *content* must come from "outside" sources which are presumably independent of the knowing mind.

4 William P. Montague, *The Ways of Knowing* (New York, 1925), p. 158.

Others have turned toward the systems of knowledge which men have actually been able to construct and demonstrate, hoping to find the clue in some ideal unification of all that is said to be known. Under the influence of human habits and biases favoring simplicity and symmetry, they have set up for all thought the goal of a single all-embracing perfect system of propositions, each of which entails and is entailed by each of the others.[5] But whether one's preference is for minute analyses of the knower, or for grand architectural systematizations of the known, in either case it is apparent that the craving for reliable knowledge may become an insatiable theoretic passion which grows by what it feeds on. "To seek to know," remarks Professor Blanshard, "is to put a question to the nature of things. How do we tell when that question is answered? Why do we accept one answer rather than another? The conditions are determined from within, but for us, not by us; what would satisfy the animal mind would not satisfy the human, and what would satisfy a poor intelligence would not satisfy a more exacting one. *The character of the question asked and the quality of the answer accepted express and depend on the questioning mind.*"[6]

There are some human minds, we know, in which the yearning for a complete, impersonal, and consistent system of knowledge is a strong and even dominant desire. But the fact that they make this titanic demand upon the universe in no way guarantees that the latter will turn out to be amenable to such ordering, especially in terms of a single type of system. They *may* be asking too much. That a man can set up a goal, and ardently desire to reach it, is no proof that it is attainable, even in theory, much less in practice. The philosopher George Santayana has observed that "The resources of the mind are not commensurable with its ambitions."[7] Our minds do their work in economical ways, by processes of unification and convergence; and for us to understand a thing is to be able to see it in its place in a larger setting. But we are hardly justified on that account in insisting in advance that, to be reliably known, everything must fit into a single pattern or design. Possibly we are in a world consisting of several types of order which resist inclusion in any one scheme of our mental architecture. Most men, it is true, ask too little of their knowledge in the way of coherence on the grand scale; but nevertheless it may be possible that some men ask too much.

6. Man as Knower: Crucial Issues

To return to the questions which were posed at the beginning of Chapter 1, it may be that we are now in a better position to know where to look, at least, for the answers. For it is evident that man is a creature who, if he wants knowledge for any reason, is obliged to use himself as a far-from-perfect instrument in getting it, and then may neglect to use it effectively. Demanding,

[5] E.g., the entire argument of Brand Blanshard's *The Nature of Thought*, 2 vols. (London, 1939).
[6] *Ibid.*, vol. I, p. 489. (Italics mine, H. A. L.)
[7] *Interpretations of Poetry and Religion* (New York, 1900), p. 2.

obtaining, and using are the pivotal matters in determining the outlook for reliable knowledge as far as man is concerned.

THE DEMAND FOR KNOWLEDGE

What are the prospects that a human knower will demand some degree of reliability in his knowledge in a given context? That, we can see, will depend mainly on such factors as his hereditary mental equipment (high or low native intelligence), his temperament (cautious or adventurous, emotionally balanced or excessive), and his social conditioning (for belief or doubt), on the one hand; and the external circumstances (stable or changing), which he chances to encounter in living, on the other. The two main elements favoring the demand for reliable knowledge are: externally, a moderate abundance of problem-situations brought about by changes and conflicts in the environment; and, internally, many diverse interests, including an interest in problem-solving that will supply initiative for seeking out and even for creating problems for their own sake. The two chief destroyers of demand are: externally, a simple, stable environment in which primary drives and acquired habits can successfully supply most human wants with a minimum of conflict, or one so continually shaken by violent crises that calm reflection is impossible; and, internally, a state of contentment with dreams or beliefs accepted on intuition, authority, or social suggestion. In a settled, convention-ruled social order, as Professor Ely Chinoy points out: "Common-sense knowledge can become an obstacle to scientific inquiry . . . " because of "a tendency to regard as natural whatever is widespread and conventional in one's own society."[8]

It is often pointed out that human beings, no matter how well or how poorly equipped they are by nature for the gaining of knowledge, rarely develop and use more than a fraction of their mental capacities from lack of motivation. Some authorities estimate that the amount of brain power actually utilized by most individuals rarely rises above 10 per cent of their potential. The extent of the normal disuse of thinking power appears when, under the pressure of an emergency or a burst of inspiration, a person does in a few hours or days a piece of intellectual labor that would ordinarily require weeks or months.

But to speak of the demand for reliable knowledge means little until we determine its scope and persistence. The minds which have stood out above the generality of mankind have not been favored by the possession of any extra organs or senses which are denied to ordinary men. The people we call geniuses are notable rather for their wider range of consciousness, their greater sensitivity to a variety of experiences, their capacity to reorganize systematically data drawn from many sources and perspectives, and their ability to concentrate on intellectual enterprises extending over long periods of time. Almost inevitably, it seems, the adjectives which we use in describing such minds are those of space and size: deep, broad, roomy, penetrating; as against shallow, narrow, and limited. The wider the field of a man's experience, whether at first-hand or through the eyes of others, whether sought for or forced upon

[8] Ely S. Chinoy, *Society: An Introduction to Sociology* (New York, 1961), p. 5.

him, the more unlikely it is that he will be satisfied with knowledge that will "work" only within a narrow compass; and therefore the more likely it is that he will persist in his efforts to discover effective principles of a broader and broader generality. Conversely, the man who lives a restricted life, both physically and imaginatively, will be prone to ask for little beyond the scattered formulas that meet his needs for day to day.

Which comes first in these matters: the demand for more and better knowledge or the broadened social experience? Do children go to school because they want to learn, or do they want to learn because they go to school? The answer is, of course, that the influences are reciprocal: if a person is to persist in the quest for reliable knowledge, both factors must be present, and interact. There must be a potential hunger or combination of hungers in the individual; and it must be aroused and consolidated by his experience. Formal education is not absolutely essential if the person is unusually inquisitive and determined; but so great is the volume of available material today in most of the fields of learning that some sort of rigorous apprenticeship in the techniques of inquiry is indispensable. Mastery of a subject matter may seem to come quickly at the moment when it is achieved, but its acquisition is a cumulative process which may take many a weary year. This is because knowledge, to be usable, must not only be extensive in scope; it must also be internally well organized. The latter is mainly a matter of short steps and gradual accretions. The extent to which it can be done *for* a person, by means of textbooks, handbooks, manuals, and digests, is limited. Our minds, like our bodies, grow for the most part slowly by alternating periods of exercise and rest. In lieu of taking bodily exercise ourselves, we may hire another to massage us; but most of our mental exercise, if it is to be of any value, has to originate within. There are no real short cuts to the intellectual command of any subject. Centuries of educational experimenting have discovered no substitute for the inner initiative that sustains patient day-to-day study under constant criticism.

The great trouble with human nature, as far as the demand for reliable knowledge is concerned, is that it seldom, if ever, presses its inquiry to the point of ascertaining the whole truth that is relevant to a given situation. Knowing takes patience; and man is one of the most distractable of beings. Under the influence of haste, laziness, social pressure, or the pleasure principle, he is too often content with the half-truths which suit his momentary desires. A person will sometimes loudly profess that he seeks to know the whole truth, but will carry his inquiries only up to the point where they begin to threaten his more insistent interests. That policy reduces the human arsenal of inquiry to a misused weapon of one man's personal career. How rare is the thinker who, like Charles Darwin, takes special pains to "make a memorandum without fail and at once" of "every published fact, new observation or thought" that is *opposed* to his own ideas! Even those who do seek to learn the whole story, no matter how unpleasant it may be, are sometimes genuinely puzzled to know whether or not they have reached their goal, since no one can tell them in advance how much knowledge will have to be demanded in order to get to the bottom of a given problem.

What demands will be made for reliable knowledge, and about what matters, by most of the members of a given society will depend to a very large extent upon the cultural climate which prevails in it. Each age and each culture has its own characteristic notions of what knowledge is, what plausibility is, what proof is, and so on. Ancient beliefs about what exists, what is possible, and what is probable amuse us greatly. We cannot see how anyone could have been so naïve as to accept them. We forget that the basic presuppositions of society about the nature of the world, of life, and of man are constantly being modified, and that those are what determine the scope of most men's intellectual demands. A society which is dominated by a thoroughly disillusioned belief in the futility of everything except inner self-perfection will take for granted a conception of reliable knowledge which is quite different from that of one which rests upon an optimistic belief in progress through scientific enlightenment. The quantity and quality of knowledge men demand depends upon their philosophy of life, and that, like everything else that is human, is forged from the materials of inborn temperament and social circumstance.

THE METHODS OF OBTAINING KNOWLEDGE

Assuming that the demand has been made, what are the chances that the human knower will be equal to the task of devising ways and means of securing the reliable knowledge that he seeks? Since this whole book is about methods, little has been said about them in advance. A few hints, however, may be gathered from our preliminary survey. As far as the raw materials of knowledge are concerned, we have noted that man's senses give him direct access to only a part of the changes going on about him, and then mainly through a single channel, the eye. When it comes to interpreting his sensations, he has gradually learned that the clues to the structure and the interrelationships of things are not to be found on the surface, but have to be dug out and brought to light by the co-operation of all the senses and the aid of many indirect and elaborate techniques and devices. Here a fertile imagination is of the highest value; yet is must also be disciplined, since flights of fancy based upon superficial analogies and whims have misled millions for centuries because they were not, and often could not be, checked against experience.

The interpretation of the conduct of other men, which is the chief task of the social studies, is at one and the same time made easier and more difficult by man's ability to interpret his own conduct from the inside. For he has learned from his own attempts at self-knowledge something of the huge human capacity for innocent self-deceit, to say nothing of the deception of others. If, in order to avoid the perils of personal bias, he insists upon using only the highly impersonal and objective methods which have proved their worth in the physical sciences, he may find that they are totally inadequate in dealing with the behavior of personalities. But the worst difficulty of all in dealing with human individuals is the multiplicity of the possibly legitimate methods of study. Each method has its enthusiastic supporters, and with

reason, for each can boast of genuine usefulness in dealing with some particular phase of the personality. It goes without saying that our task is not to
select the single method which makes all the rest superfluous, but rather to
know how to make use of any or all of them to the maximum degree of
profit in terms of understanding. Hardest of all, perhaps, is to remember that
all our methods, whether from the outside or from the inside, are but different avenues of approach to an understanding of the same subject matter
— the living, thinking human being.

Some of the common ways of knowing are predominantly analytic, being
concerned with the subdivision of what we are studying into as many carefully
distinguished parts as possible; while others are synthetic, being designed to
bring about a fruitful patterning of the parts in larger wholes. Each variety has
its partisans: the admirers of synthetic thinking praise its scope and grandeur,
pointing out that analysis, as John Stuart Mill remarked, "has a tendency to
wear away the feelings"; while the lovers of analytic thought no less fervently
laud its clarity and precision, dispraising synthesis as necessarily vague and
sketchy. We should expect, then, that charges would be made that some
methods of knowing employ too much imagination, and others too little; that
some insist upon too much devotion to traditional formulas, and others too
little; that some place too much emphasis upon precision in the use of the
apparatus of inquiry, and others too little; and that some involve too finicky
an attitude of self-criticism, while others manifest too lenient an attitude. The
great advances in method, it is true, have often been made by feats of intellectual daring performed by men who seemed utterly contemptuous of many
of the established rules; and yet they have had to be followed up by the
infinite patience of an army of obscure investigators. Some men see only a
little, but with great clearness of detail; others see much more, but only in
outlines that are blurred and indistinct. The cause of advancing knowledge
has been well served by both types of minds; but only when their separate contributions have been merged in later and greater minds that have been able
to see *both* far and clearly.

THE USE OF KNOWLEDGE

Let no one suppose that it is to be taken for granted that the demand for
and the ascertainment of reliable knowledge in any field automatically guarantee that such knowledge will be put to profitable use. It is one thing to discover
the cure for a disease, but it is sometimes another to induce your patient to try
it. For years it has been known by doctors that the dreadful Oriental scourge
called beri-beri is the direct result of a diet of fish and hulled white rice. If
people would only change to a diet of fish and the cheaper unhulled brown
rice, beri-beri would disappear. But dietary habits are not easily or swiftly
changed by argument, especially in countries with a relatively low level of
public enlightenment. Even in more sophisticated circles, it is one of the
melancholy reflections of all students of government that the typical resting-
place of an expensive report of a fact-finding commission is a shelf in a cellar.
Scientists never tire of reminding us that our knowledge in dozens of fields

is miles ahead of our will and ability to apply it. Every time we pass a library, we should recall how much more knowledge men have on tap in books than they manage to utilize in action.

Once more we are brought up against the paradox in the relationship between our knowledge and our interests. If the getting of knowledge is dominated by too strong an interest in its use, as for instance the investigation of the part played by alcohol in automobile accidents by either a distillers' institute or the W.C.T.U., the results are likely to be unreliable. When political parties organize "bureaus of research," no one expects their products to be models of scientific objectivity. But, on the other hand, the price of rigorous impartiality may be the divorcing of the inquiry from *anybody's* interests. That will mean oblivion unless a substantial number of the population have cultivated an interest in disinterestedness. Social research is forever in a quandary: shall it accept the overenthusiastic support of interested parties with axes to grind, or shall it struggle instead to overcome the indifference of potential donors to projects which do not promise dramatic results?

The same dilemma haunts many judicial inquiries into past events. Let us suppose that a gross injustice is going unpunished because it is known to only a few participants.[9] Barring accidental discovery, will it ever become known? Will there be sufficient demand for an investigation? The question really is: Does anybody care? But some may care too much, and, bent upon obtaining vengeance, may themselves pervert the facts in the process.

Our usual resources for meeting such contingencies are twofold. The first is to bring out systematically all the private interests involved, no matter how one-sided, in the hope that by a process of cancelling out the differences there will be left a trustworthy remainder. The French have a proverb: *"C'est du choc des opinions que jaillit la vérité"* ("It is from the clash of opinions that the truth spurts out"). The second method is gradually to multiply the number of agencies and individuals who possess a paramount "interest in disinterestedness," who will inquire in behalf of an ideal reliability, and who will declare their findings without fear or favor. The development of courts through the centuries, together with such semi-judicial institutions as universities and newspapers, represents perhaps the proudest achievement of civilized man.

But it has been the ordeal of the twentieth century to witness the demand for knowledge widely subordinated to its use by the militant national state. The Nazi boast, *"Wir denken mit unserem Blut"* ("We think with our blood"), meant not only that their methods of making decisions were avowedly emotional and irrational, but also that the capacity to make them was confined to those of the same racial origin. The reliability of knowledge was identified with party reliability. There followed such colossal nonsense as the doctrine that there is a separate science for every race, an Aryan physics and a non-Aryan physics, and so on.

[9] As in the famous case of Captain Alfred Dreyfus [see Jacques Kayser, *The Dreyfus Affair* (London, 1931) and *The Dreyfus Case*, edited by Donald C. McKay (New Haven, Conn., 1937)]; or, in fiction, the war novels of Arnold Zweig: *Education Before Verdun* (New York, 1936) and *The Case of Sergeant Grischa* (New York, 1928).

Even in the countries which have escaped such evils, teachers of the social studies are accustomed, in times of crisis, to being reproached for having underestimated "the passionate unreasonableness of mankind," and for having sapped the zeal of the young by overemphasizing objectivity. When firm convictions are at a premium, they are accused of having fostered nothing but doubts. To the extent that they have failed to convince their students that critical thinking is an art to be used to forward ultimately judicious action and not to impede it, such charges may be justified. Any kind of education which emphasizes thought without action, which isolates ideas from deeds, is bound to produce some intellectuals with minds as hollow and brittle as empty egg-shells. The outcome of reflection, if it is not to be "idle thought," should indeed be commitment in action.

But not all the values are on one side of the argument. Teachers of the social studies also find themselves attacked for "bringing controversial issues into the classroom" when they attempt to link their instruction too closely to current social developments. In calling for "nothing but facts" and the exclusion of "mere opinions," however, their critics forget that, in most of the social studies, the most significant facts *are* violently conflicting opinions. There are perils in both extremes; it does not do to come too close to actuality or to flee too far from it. We ought not to expect, at any rate, to have everything at once: all the maximum profits of calm deliberation *and* those of impetuous action; *both* the fruits of meticulous care in testing our knowledge, *and* those of eager zeal in applying it. There is a place in any society both for those who cultivate the leisurely and detached refinement of methods of knowing, and for those who make possible their effective application. The important thing is to keep each group of specialists from arrogance in dismissing the claims of the other, in order that both may co-operate in the common cause of enlightenment.

There are times when men of action must take the lead, when criticism must be subordinated to the swift giving of commands; and there are other times when the leadership should swing to men of calm deliberation. It is a mistake for any society to go to excess permanently in either direction: to develop no generals in times of peace, and to cultivate no philosophers in times of war. Nothing is to be gained, in the long run, by taking sides without taking thought; or by taking thought without taking sides. But we are not obliged to choose between those two extreme alternatives, as if a critical sense excluded decisive action, and the ability to act in a crisis precluded reflection. Man the meditative knower and man the zealous doer can become man the intelligent artist in living, by a flexible balancing of thought by action, and of action by thought.

FOR CLASS DISCUSSION

A. As we come to manhood, the logical side of our brain is developed; and the faculty for logic is ever foe to the faculty for romance. It is only in our sleep, when the logical side of our brain is at rest, that the romantic side is at liberty to assert itself. — *Max Beerbohm*   (1–3)

B. Those who dream by night in the dusty recesses of their minds, wake in the day to find that it was vanity; but the dreamers of the day are dangerous men, for they act their dreams with open eyes, to make it possible.
— *Lawrence of Arabia*

C. It is the beginning of all poetry to abolish the law and method of the rationally proceeding reason and to plunge us once more into the ravishing confusion of fantasy, the original chaos of human nature.
— *Friedrich von Schlegel*

D. All power of fancy over reason is a degree of insanity. — *Samuel Johnson*
The delusions of the ill-balanced and the beliefs of the orthodox are more closely akin than is usually recognized. — *Macfie Campbell*

E. The heart is wiser than the intellect. — *J. G. Holland*
The head is always the dupe of the heart. — *La Rochefoucauld*
The great conservative is the heart. — *Nathaniel Hawthorne*

F. Thinking is, or ought to be, a coolness and a calmness; and our poor hearts throb, and our poor brains beat too much for that.
— *Herman Melville*

G. Many young scientists today don't know how to think. They learn in class that certain things have been done in certain ways, and cannot visualize any other methods. — *Harold Cassidy*

H. Thinking is the hardest work there is, which is the probable reason why so few engage in it. — *Henry Ford*   (5)
There is no expedient to which a man will not resort to avoid the real labor of thinking. — *Sir Joshua Reynolds*
The brain in general seems an organ to maximize comfort rather than consistency. — *E. L. Thorndike*

I. When Jomini, who was then a major, wrote a book giving away Napoleon's methods of winning battles, Napoleon forgave him, saying: "The old generals who command against me will never read it, and the young men who will read it do not command."   (6)

J. The world has always been, is now, and ever will be ruled by brains, and the fight between progress and conservatism is to decide, not whether sloppy sentimentality or selfish tyranny shall get the upper hand, but what order of ideas brains shall serve. — *E. L. Godkin*

K. The fundamental reason for the discrepancy (between rational control of physical force and of social relations) is that the forces of Nature have been discovered and applied by a few exceptional individuals, whereas every effort to ameliorate human relations has been frustrated by the fact that society cannot be transformed without the compliance of the masses.
— *Carl L. Becker*

⤳ 3 ⤳

FORMAL LOGIC: *What Follows from Premises*

1. Short Cuts to Certainty?

NO ONE CAN SURVEY the long history of man's failures and successes as a knower without being struck by the discrepancy between the pretentiousness of most human knowledge-claims and the small amount of evidence actually available with which to back them up. Not only are most men, as we have seen, credulous by nature and inclined to accept whatever beliefs are first urged upon them strongly, clearly, and repeatedly; they are also dogmatic and assertive — that is, their affirmations about what they know with certainty are continually outrunning any proof that they are inclined or able to offer. This appetite for certainty tempts them to take the nearest short cut to the goal of apparently reliable knowledge. This is especially true of men who are constantly being called upon for decisive action: the intense conviction that they are absolutely right in their beliefs enables them to adopt and to pursue bold policies with vigor and persistence, where doubts and a divided mind might lead only to delay and confusion.

Humility about one's knowledge, or the admission of one's ignorance, is then a late lesson which man learns only at the cost of innumerable blunders. We begin life in the deepest ignorance, which is ignorance of our ignorance. Yet knowing little or nothing is seldom any obstacle to being confident in everything. It took an extraordinary individual named Socrates to boast, as early as the fifth century B.C., that he was the wisest of the Greeks, because he alone knew that he knew nothing. Even modern scientists have been slow to acknowledge that the true measure of their knowledge is their awareness of how much remains to be known. Says Dr. Abraham Flexner: "No scientist, fifty years ago, could have realized that he was as ignorant as all first-rate scientists now know themselves to be."[1]

Nothing is more dangerous than generalizing about the thinking of men who lived many centuries ago; yet it seems safe to say that primitive peoples the world over have tended to accept as reliable knowledge whatever has been handed down from their ancestors as tribal customs or folkways. Customs are ready-made generalizations about conduct: they "lay down the law" with or without supporting "reasons" for their observance. They are beliefs which are lived by; the tribe has survived, presumably, by following them; therefore they must be right. Thus, man's first formulated "universals," such as "All flesh of a certain sort must be avoided," or "Repeating this prayer correctly

[1] *Universities* (New York, 1930) p. 17.

will bring rain," were practical imperatives which were strongly believed and implicitly followed by virtually all the members of a community. Just as habit-forming aided the individual, these fixed rules about what "was done" and what "was not done" lent stability and order to communal living. Whenever it was necessary for the group to act as a unit, such unwritten laws backed by irresistible sanctions could be used to coerce any recalcitrant objector.

Of course, we are inclined to be contemptuous of the "reasons" which were usually given for conforming to the accepted practices, regarding them as circular ("It's done because it's done") or grossly superstitious; but the important thing to note is that, in the atmosphere of authority, no reasons were really necessary. Anthropologists who have studied so-called "primitive" peoples have often called attention to the apparent spontaneity and sureness of their group decisions, as in the administration of justice, in spite of the absence of any legal machinery. The group's swift verdict is the practicing of a concrete habit, and not the deducing of the consequences of an abstract legal principle. Their behavior is dominated by a tacitly understood and firmly accepted pattern or premise, from which it "follows" inevitably. The particular case is seen to fall under an unquestionable generalization which does not need to be explicitly formulated, much less to be precisely defined. All that comes later.

This may help us to understand why the history of man's conscious quest for reliable knowledge in the Western world began as it did, and why it took so long for what we call scientific method to develop. Sometimes we may wonder why men were not more patient and humble in acquiring and claiming knowledge, why they did not begin by adding fact to fact in order to confirm a few modest generalizations, and by cautiously labeling as knowledge only what their carefully tested evidence could support. What we forget is that, for thousands of years, man was schooled under heavy pressures and penalties in a very different method of knowing. Where fixation of belief for confident group action was most important, he could hardly be blamed for taking what seemed to be the most promising routes to it. Thus for uncounted generations men grew up in communities which took it for granted that they already possessed a great deal of reliable knowledge in the generalized form of customs, rules-of-thumb, proverbs, laws, and commandments about the things that mattered most in life. People who are absolutely sure of such general truths come naturally to think of reliability in details as chiefly depending upon what follows from what they already assuredly know. If everyone regards it as self-evident and unquestionable that blasphemers against the gods ought to be put to death, then the correct disposition of an individual case hinges merely upon whether or not "this man is a blasphemer."

This dogmatic approach or habit of thought, once formed, is difficult to break, since it possesses the great advantage of complete assurance about a few highly economical "fundamental" convictions or principles on which a strong character may be based. The unswerving consistency of a man's actions with his announced beliefs is regarded as a sign of the highest virtue, and those of his actions which cannot actually be fitted in have to be rationalized. Doubt, hesitation, tentativeness, attention to exceptions — all these are denounced as subversive and reprehensible. Everything in a society of this sort seems to conspire to make men dogmatic and cocksure about the broad knowledge-claims which provide them, when challenged, with the premises of their actions.

The atmosphere of the periods of the history of Western Europe known as ancient and mediaeval may be fairly characterized as permeated by authority and the dogmatic approach to knowledge. Always remembering that there were shining exceptions, we may say that men on the whole were convinced that they possessed a supply of absolutely reliable principles or axiomatic truths upon which firm structures of detailed knowledge about the world could be built. The main outlines or "plot" of the cosmic story being already known, it remained only to fill in the gaps, where necessary, by speculative elaboration. It was not strange, then, that men were first attracted to tests of knowledge which concerned the processes of deduction from already accepted general principles, rather than to those which dealt with induction from particular instances. Thus it came about that, until well into the modern period, logic was almost universally understood to consist of the rules of valid deductive reasoning from premises that were already known to be reliable.

2. The Ancient Greeks and Abstract Generalizing

Professor F. J. E. Woodbridge of Columbia used to remark that "the ancient Greeks taught themselves how to think, and have taught all the rest of us in the Western world." What he referred to, of course, was the "miraculous" advance which was made by a few gifted Greeks of the fifth and fourth centuries B.C. in the art of formulating in language abstract general principles covering many concrete particular instances, such as: "All gods are immortal," or "No slave can be a citizen." These thinkers set the fashions and coined the vocabulary of logic for a good two thousand years; and it is mainly to them that we owe the technique of conceptual thinking that underlies all our Western science and technology. So accustomed are we to thinking in abstract "ideas" or class-concepts rather than in individual items or cases, that it is almost impossible for us to realize that things might have been very different in Western Europe if the Greeks had not happened to perfect this particular mathematical type of logic. But a glance at Oriental habits of thinking in fluid allegories and rhythmic patterns like the figures of a dance, as in Hindu and Chinese logics, should be enough to convince anyone of the immense debt which we, as thinkers, owe to the Greeks.[2]

The pre-Greek civilizations, notably the Egyptian and Babylonian, accumulated a certain amount of detailed knowledge in the fields of geometry (earth measurement) and astronomy (star classification), but their learned men seemed for the most part to be content with their specific measurements and tabulations without generalizing from them to form what we call theories about natural events. A famous example was the discovery by the Egyptian rope-

2 Cf., part II, chap. II, "Comparative Logic" in Paul Masson-Oursel, *Comparative Philosophy* (New York, 1926).

stretchers, who measured land boundaries and the deposits of Nile mud, that a triangle with two sides measuring three and four units had a third side measuring five units. But the Greek Pythagoras (580–500 B.C.) went on to make that discovery into a theorem expressing the abstract relationship of the sides of *any* right triangle whatever: the famous statement of the equality of the square of the hypotenuse and the combined squares of the two sides.

Once begun, Greek philosophizing, or the critical cultivation of the love of wisdom through both scientific and humanistic inquiries, swiftly reached the heights in the work of three giants of the intellect: Socrates, Plato, and Aristotle. The first of the three, Socrates (470–399 B.C.) spurred men on to seek underlying forms or concepts by his tireless questionings concerning commonly used words and their meanings. Plato (427–347 B.C.) carried this tendency further in his Academy, exalting the study of pure mathematics as a theoretical discipline of the mind without reference to its application to buying and selling, trading and building.[3] Plato and his pupils also aided in the clarification of terms by arranging ideas in chains of decreasing generality, subdividing at each step, such as: beings are corporeal and incorporeal; corporeal beings are animal and non-animal; animal beings are rational and non-rational; and so on. By this method, working down one side of the ladder of subdivisions, they were able to define a man as a rational, animal, corporeal being.

Aristotle (384–322 B.C.) sought not only to organize all the knowledge of his day which had been gained by observation, but also to connect it with the speculative achievements of his famous master, Plato. Accepting the prevailing view that all knowledge arises out of pre-existing knowledge, he strove to demonstrate how we are justified in placing the various classes of things in such descending orders as Plato had sketched. This, he believed, could be done by relating the two classes of things in question to a third class: animals are organisms having sensation and the power of independent locomotion; and so are men; therefore, men belong under the wider class, animals. This view took it for granted that every individual thing in Nature had its proper place in some species, which was included in some wider genus, which was in turn included as a species in some still higher genus. The task of the scientist was to see that everything was put in its proper place in the gigantic system of pigeonholes within pigeonholes which Nature was assumed to be.

In addition, Aristotle wanted to supply the pupils of his school, the Lyceum, with a series of handbooks of the art of public disputation or dialectic, in which they, as politically ambitious young Athenians, desired to excel. In the dialogues of Plato are many examples of the kind of public argument which was then in fashion, in which Socrates is made to play the part of the ques-

---

[3] "It was to be a study of abstract forms and not of objects embodying these forms." Raphael Demos, *The Philosophy of Plato* (New York, 1939), p. 287. Greek mathematics reached formulation as a purely deductive science, given certain axioms and postulates, in Euclid's famous *Elements* (about 290 B.C.). So incomparably superior was Euclid's system to any other product of human thinking up to that time that, as Professor C. J. Keyser points out, "men were dazzled by it, blinded by its very brilliance, so much so that . . . they failed to see its chief significance was, not geometric, but methodological." *Thinking About Thinking* (New York, 1926), pp. 26–27.

tioner who skillfully elicits from his fellow disputants a series of yes-or-no answers which eventually entangle them in logical contradictions. Aristotle endeavored to place this art on a solid basis by showing how a reasoner could both avoid the fallacies of his opponents and oblige them to accept his own valid conclusions.

What he and his later pupils provided was an *Organon* (or instrument) for the speedy testing of the deductive consequences of possibly damaging admissions when clearly stated in terms of classes and put together in pairs. It was a logic of deductive consistency in the use of language, designed to make the prospective disputant aware of the traps and pitfalls to which an apparently harmless verbal admission might lead. Its primary aim, says Minto, "was as practical as a treatise on navigation or 'Cavendish on Whist.' "[4] One began with already admitted assumptions, and then, by following the rules, one demonstrated their inescapable consequences in the realm of discourse for every rational human being.

The close connection of this kind of logic with man's increasing use of and dependence upon language is obvious. As long as he was relatively inarticulate, man's acts were checked for the most part by their immediate consequences. If the primitive hunter made an erroneous inference, he generally paid for it on the spot. But as human beings came to put a larger and larger proportion of their ideas into thoughts and words rather than into physical practice, they found, as John Dewey has pointed out, that "where there is no directly appreciable reaction of the inference upon the security and prosperity of life, there are no natural checks to the acceptance of wrong beliefs." In the absence of natural checks, artificial ones had to be devised, unless erroneous beliefs were to multiply unchecked. Greek logic was, in part at least, the new freedom of abstract thought and language trying to police itself.

Thanks to Aristotle's genius, his testing instrument was remarkably mature and complete. The Wise Men of Greece had hardly begun their first gropings toward the free use of abstract thinking before the beginning of the sixth century B.C., and yet, by the third century B.C., the technique of deduction by the relating of fixed class-concepts had apparently been worked out so comprehensively that it stood with only minor changes for over two thousand years. It was this seemingly finished character of the Aristotelian and Euclidean systems which induced men to believe that such verbal and mathematical theories must be identical with the patterns of physical Nature, a belief which retarded the development of science for centuries.

3. The Categorical Syllogism

Generations of students have begun their study of deduction with the classic example:

> All men are mortal
> Socrates is a man
> ───────────────
> Socrates is a mortal

[4] William Minto, *Logic Inductive and Deductive* (New York, 1899), p. 3.

Our first reaction to this is likely to be that plainly *if* the first two statements or premises are accepted as reliable, *then* any reasonable being will have to accept the third statement or conclusion, since it necessarily follows; but that actually all three are rather obvious and bring us little in the way of new knowledge. We assume that some such statement as "All men who are known to have lived are known to have died before reaching the age of two hundred years" is accepted as reliable knowledge to begin with; and also some such proposition as "Socrates is a being who may rightly be classified as a man."

But presumably we made the two statements for the purpose of determining Socrates' status with respect to mortality. We proceeded by connecting both Socrates and the state of being mortal with a third class, men, which disappeared in our conclusion. This is a familiar operation of the human mind, although generally not so systematically performed. It is useful in connecting hitherto scattered bits of our knowledge in such a way that the result can be tested. This is especially true when we are called upon to "prove our point" in an argument that does not win immediate assent. For example, let it be supposed that a question arose concerning the status of a male American Indian with respect to military service. One participant argues that American Indians are not citizens but wards of the Federal government, and hence are not subject to call for military service. Another arguer produces the act of June 2, 1924, by which American Indians were declared to be citizens, hence:

All male citizens are subject to call for military service.
All native-born male American Indians are male citizens.

All native-born male American Indians are subject to call for military service.

In such instances we are making it possible to test a conclusion by exhibiting it as the logical result of putting together either two supposedly reliable general principles, or one general principle and another particular proposition. One of the general principles happened to be lying dormant in the memory, unconnected with the other, or with particular instances which arose. It is the bringing together of the two which yields the conclusion; and that is sometimes surprisingly difficult. Looking back upon any chain of deductive reasoning, such as the final solution of a detective story, we are likely to say to ourselves: "How stupid of us not to have seen the answer all the time! It was right there in front of us: we knew perfectly well a number of separate truths that, properly fitted together, would have given us the correct result. But we failed to 'put two and two together' in such a way as to arrive at 'it.'" The skilled reasoner takes the same lot of queer, incoherent, and apparently unrelated clues, sifts out those which are irrelevant and misleading, and arranges the remainder in an unbreakable and convincing pattern. This ability to combine hitherto isolated propositions in such a way as to arrive at new, sound, and hitherto unsuspected conclusions is the mark of the keen-witted detective, the skillful lawyer, the adroit military strategist, and the far-sighted business man. Yet even the cleverest deducer cannot get his results accepted unless other equally astute reasoners can be convinced that his conclusions follow inevitably from acceptable premises. To do this, he must be capable of displaying his reasoning in terms of the class relationships which enable all who understand the rules of logic to test his conclusions for themselves.

INFERENCE AND IMPLICATION

So far, our discussion has been mainly about the process of deductive inference, which is a human activity of thinking by which we pass from one proposition to another, accepting or rejecting the latter on the basis of the former. Inferring is a temporal, psychological matter; it is something which people may either do or fail to do, and which can be done well or badly, depending upon the logical capacity of the one who does the inferring. In the presence of the same abundant evidence at the scene of a crime, for example, a layman might make no inferences at all; an untrained officer might make several incorrect ones; while an expert criminologist might make a great many correct inferences leading to the conviction of the guilty party.

In determining the reliability of knowledge that apparently follows from accepted premises, however, logicians are concerned with the rules for testing our inferences to see which ones are and which ones are not justified. Their concern is with the consistency of the reasoning. What they want to know is whether or not a given inference is valid or invalid — that is, whether or not it can be shown to follow necessarily or inescapably from the premises upon which it purports to be based. Now an inference, to be accepted as valid, must be rigorously demonstrated to rest upon an implication or necessary connection between the premises and the conclusion. If we assume that all A is included in B, and all B is included in C, that *implies* that all A is included in C, no matter what A, B, and C may happen to be, and no matter whether anyone ever happens to make that particular inference. The formal necessity is in the relations of the classes; and, once the premises are accepted, the conclusion is no longer a matter of opinion if you make any claim to being logical in your thinking. For you simply cannot accept the premises, reject the conclusion, and pretend to follow the rules of logic, all at the same time. But, if someone tries to convince you that all A is included in C on the grounds that all A is included in B, and *some* B is included in C; it can be pointed out that the conclusion is not implied by the premises. You can accept the premises, and yet escape the conclusion.

Implications are thus structural relationships between propositions; they are just there, whether or not we bring them to light and use them in the making of valid inferences. If in the heat of an argument I state that "All owners of firearms ought to register them," then I imply that Mr. X, who owns a shotgun, ought to register it, although neither I nor anyone else may ever have occasion to draw that particular inference. "We make," say Professors Lewis and Langford, "an inference upon observation of a certain relation between facts. Whether the facts have that relation or not we do not determine. But whether we shall *be observant of* just this particular relation of the facts and whether we shall *make that relation the basis of our inferences* are things which we do determine."[5] Once we have made our selection from the "extraordinarily large number" of alternative relations, and have established the precise meanings of the ones we have chosen to use as the premises of our inference, then their implications follow, and can no more be disputed, if correctly deduced, than the corollaries in a system of mathematics. We have all had the experience of admitting the truth of certain premises in a dispute without realizing, at the moment, their logical implications, and then discovering, too late, that we had inadvertently committed ourselves to the acceptance of some unwelcome conclusions. Men may and do quarrel endlessly about what relations shall be selected in the first place, and about the initial reliability and exact meaning of those which they choose as premises; but, once they have come to an agreement upon those points, the validity of their subsequent deductions can be checked with entire accuracy by anyone who is able to make a thorough analysis of the implications involved. Formal logic in its many branches deals with this analysis of implications. It is not concerned, as logic, with anything but the relations of the classes or propositions, the formal structure of the reasoning. It cares nothing about the material contents of the propositions, even though the reasoner may care a great deal about them.

Hence formal logic can examine seriously an argument which is completely absurd, such as:

> Some boneless turnips are square-wheeled bicycles
> All boneless turnips are drunken hyenas
> ―――――――――――――――――――――――――――――――――
> Some drunken hyenas are square-wheeled bicycles

> All sniks are murps
> Some worgs are not murps
> ―――――――――――――――――――――
> Some worgs are not sniks

In both of these examples, the meanings, if any, are hilariously at odds with existence; and yet the relationships of the classes, if there were such things, are perfectly clear and the conclusions are formally valid.

In order to test our reasoning by the rules of logic, it is therefore necessary in most cases, as Reichenbach has pointed out, to "reconstruct" our actual thought in the form of premises and conclusion. Men seldom think consciously by the rules of logic, which, strictly speaking, usually apply only to reconstructions of their thoughts. Like mathematics, which turns observations and measurements into numbers, and then manipulates the symbols to reach a result, formal logic takes instances of everyday thinking, and, where possible, turns them into sentences called propositions, and then into symbols for the purpose of demonstrating the validity or invalidity of the conclusion.

[5] C. I. Lewis and C. H. Langford, *Symbolic Logic* (New York, 1932), p. 258. (Italics theirs, H. A. L.) See also M. R. Cohen and E. Nagel, *op. cit.*, chap. I, 1–3.

ANALYSIS OF THE CATEGORICAL SYLLOGISM

The kind of deductive argument considered to this point, consisting of two related premises and a conclusion, is called the categorical syllogism. The word syllogism comes from the Greek "discourses together," while categorical means here "directly asserted," and not relative or hypothetical. Since this type of syllogism has been studied for centuries, a complete elaboration of its rules and exceptions fills many pages in the elementary deductive logic textbooks, to which the interested reader is referred. We shall be concerned only with the main outlines of deduction in order to show how, in general, it is possible to test formally any argument that is capable of being expressed in syllogistic terms.

If we examine a typical syllogism, such as:

All unearned income is taxable	M	P
All dividends are unearned income	S	M
All dividends are taxable	S	P

it is apparent that our argument yields a valid conclusion about the relation of the subject term of the conclusion (S), the class "All dividends" to the predicate term (P), the class "taxable things" by means of a third term (M), the class "unearned income," which does not appear in the conclusion. "Unearned income" in this example is what is called the *middle term* of the syllogism, since it is the mediating factor which brings the *minor term* (always the subject of the conclusion) into the asserted relationship to the *major term* (always the predicate of the conclusion). It is called *major* because the class of things mentioned in the predicate is ordinarily wider and more inclusive than the class in the subject, called *minor*.

Note that all three terms are classes of things, and that the reasoning proceeds by relating two of the classes to one another by means of a third. Each class is treated as homogeneous throughout on the assumption (known as the *dictum de omni et nullo*) that whatever can be asserted or denied of the whole of a class can be asserted or denied of a part of it. That is what distinguishes the logical class from the statistical group. "All students are athletes" does not mean in logic that all who are more-or-less students are more-or-less athletes; it means that all who satisfy the definition "students" also satisfy the definition "athletes." It becomes evident that if we are dealing with defined classes of things and their relations of inclusion and exclusion, it becomes of supreme importance to know whether, in a given instance, we are talking about *all* of a class or only *some* of it. In everyday speech we seldom bother to make that point wholly clear ("Englishmen are stolid"; "Wise men smoke Chokies"); but in logic we must always specify whether we are talking about all of a class (if so, the term is said to be *distributed*) or merely some of it, meaning "at least some" (when the term is said to be *undistributed*). It must also be borne in mind that the assertion "Some politicians are honest"

A: Universal affirmative

> *All* students *are* players. (All S is P)
> The class of students who are not
> players is empty.

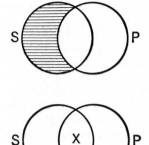

I: Particular affirmative

> *Some* students *are* players. (Some S
> is P)
> The class of students who are
> players is not empty.

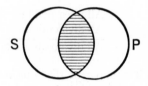

E: Universal negative

> *No* students *are* players. (No S is P)
> (Or, *All . . . are not . . .*)
> The class of those who are both
> students and players is empty.

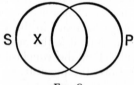

O: Particular negative

> *Some* students *are not* players.
> (Some S is not P)
> The class of students who are not
> players is not empty.

Fig. 2

does not carry with it, in logic, either any affirmation or any denial that "All politicians are honest." On the basis of "some," we know only that "at least some" are honest, and nothing either way about the rest. Propositions about a single individual: "George Washington was a general," may be treated logically as "all" or universal propositions, since the one man comprises the whole of the subject class.

Our first task in analyzing any argument syllogistically is therefore to state the meaning of each of the premises and of the conclusion in correct logical form — that is, as a relation between two classes which do or do not overlap. Not all the statements of which language is capable can be squeezed into this formula without doing violence to some of their shades of meaning. But if reasoning is to be tested in the syllogistic manner, its terms must be exhibited as related in one of four (and only four) possible ways: by total inclusion, partial inclusion, total exclusion, or partial exclusion. These are known respectively as A, universal affirmative; I, particular affirmative; E, universal negative; and O, particular negative propositions. Using the classes "students" and "players," and representing their relationships by circles in the manner originated by John Venn,[6] we have the possibilities shown in Figure 2.[7]

In the diagrams (Figure 2), the shaded areas indicate complete absence or emptiness (as in A, there are no students who are not players); the presence of the cross indicates that there are at least some instances in that area (as in I, there are at least some students who are players); while the unmarked areas both inside and outside the circles indicate that the given data tell us nothing about the subclasses which they represent (as in O, we do not know whether or not there are some students who are players, or whether or not there are some players who are not students).

From the point of view of distribution, the four types of propositions arrange themselves as follows:

	Subject	Predicate
A: All students are players	Distributed	Undistributed
I: Some students are players	Undistributed	Undistributed
E: No students are players	Distributed	Distributed
O: Some students are not players	Undistributed	Distributed

It is perhaps easier to remember that the only terms which are distributed are the subject terms of universal propositions (A and E) and the predicate terms of negative propositions (E and O).

MOODS, FIGURES, AND RULES OF THE SYLLOGISM

With these four kinds of propositions at our disposal, we may now begin to put them together in threes to make syllogisms; and a quick calculation will show that there are sixty-four different possible combinations, or moods, from AAA, AAE, AAI, etc., to OOE, OOI, OOO. But this is only the beginning, since the three terms (major, minor, and middle) may be arranged in four different orders, or figures, for each of the sixty-four combinations, or a total of two hundred and fifty-six moods in all. Happily only nineteen of the traditional two hundred and fifty-six are both valid and important. Using "students" as subject term, S; "members" as middle term, M; and "players" as predicate term, P;[8] the following are examples of the moods which yield valid conclusions:

[6] *Symbolic Logic*, 2d ed. (London, 1894), chap. V.
[7] Identical classes, such as: "All sons of the king are princes," and "All princes are sons of the king," may be treated as a special perfectly reciprocal variety of A, total inclusion.
[8] For convenience in identifying the terms, classes with names commencing with "s," "p," and "m" are used, but that is merely coincidental.

In the first   A — All members are players   E — No members are players
figure (4)   A — All students are members   A — All students are members

M   P   A — All students are players   E — No students are players

S   M

S   P   A — All members are players   E — No members are players
     I — Some students are members   I — Some students are members

     I — Some students are players   O — Some students are not players

---

In the second   E — No players are members   A — All players are members
figure (4)   A — All students are members   E — No students are members

P   M   E — No students are players   E — No students are players

S   M

S   P   E — No players are members   A — All players are members
     I — Some students are members   O — Some students are not members

     O — Some students are not players   O — Some students are not players

---

In the third   A — All members are players   I — Some members are players
figure (6)   A — All members are students   A — All members are students

M   P   I — Some students are players   I — Some students are players

M   S

S   P   A — All members are players   E — No members are players
     I — Some members are students   A — All members are students

     I — Some students are players   O — Some students are not players

     O — Some members are not players   E — No members are players
     A — All members are students   I — Some members are students

     O — Some students are not players   O — Some students are not players

---

In the fourth   A — All players are members   A — All players are members
figure (5)   A — All members are students   E — No members are students

P   M   I — Some students are players   E — No students are players

M   S

S   P   I — Some players are members   E — No players are members
     A — All members are students   A — All members are students

     I — Some students are players   O — Some students are not players

---

E — No players are members

I — Some members are students

O — Some students are not players

Total (19)

There are five other possible combinations that are valid, but which yield "weakened" conclusions in comparison with some of the above nineteen, and so are usually neglected. In the first figure, for example, AAI is a weakened form of AAA:

A — All members are players

A — All students are members

I — Some students are players

That is, it seems trivial to conclude that *some* students are players, when we are warranted in concluding that *all* are. Similarly EAO in the first and second figures is a weakened form of EAE:

E — No members are players   E — No players are members
A — All students are members   A — All students are members
―――――――――――――――――――――   ―――――――――――――――――――――
O — Some students are not players   O — Some students are not players

and AEO in the second and fourth figures is a weakened form of AEE:

A — All players are members   A — All players are members
E — No students are members   E — No members are students
―――――――――――――――――――――   ―――――――――――――――――――――
O — Some students are not players   O — Some students are not players

We have now a positive although rather cumbersome method of testing the validity of any syllogistic argument: (1) state each of the three propositions in logical form; (2) determine from the position of the major, minor, and middle terms which figure of the syllogism is being employed; and (3) see whether or not the argument in question comes under any one of the valid moods.

In practice, however, not many persons are likely to take the trouble to master and to apply so complicated a method of checking. It is usually easier to resort to one or both of two negative tests to determine whether or not a given syllogism is invalid. The first of these is the Venn diagram method applied to three classes instead of two, as previously. This can be done by drawing three overlapping circles representing the three terms of the syllogism, S, P, and M (Figure 3). Using the minus sign to indicate "no," and reading across from left to right, there will then be seven enclosed areas or subclasses, as follows:

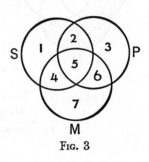

Fig. 3

1. S, — M, — P   Students who are not members and not players
2. S,   P, — M   Students who are players and not members
3. P, — S, — M   Players who are not students and not members
4. S,   M, — P   Students who are members and not players
5. S,   M,   P   Students who are members and players
6. P,   M, — S   Players who are members and not students
7. M, — S, — P   Members who are not students and not players

Proceeding as before, any syllogistic argument can be plotted on the diagram by shading the areas which are stated in the premises to be empty, placing a cross in those which are stated to be occupied by at least some instances, and leaving unmarked the areas which are left unspecified. Three rules, however, must be observed:

1. In diagramming an argument consisting of one universal and one particular premise, the universal premise must be diagrammed first.

2. In order that there may be no uncertainty as to what area a cross applies, whenever that area is cut by a line, the cross is placed on the line.

3. The Venn diagram test does not apply to the nine valid moods of the syllogism in which a particular conclusion is drawn from two universal premises (the five weakened moods and AAI, EAO in the third and fourth figures).

The following examples show how the test operates when the reasoning is valid:

1st figure   A — All members are players   All M is P
             A — All students are members   All S is M
             ‾‾‾‾‾‾‾‾‾‾‾‾‾‾‾‾‾‾‾‾‾‾‾‾‾‾‾‾‾‾   ‾‾‾‾‾‾‾‾‾‾
             A — All students are players   All S is P

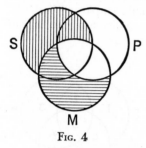

FIG. 4

We begin by shading all the area of M that is not P, in accordance with the major premise (Figure 4). Then we do the same for the minor premise, shading all the area of S that is not M. The conclusion, which can be diagrammed separately if desired, is plainly seen to follow from the premises (there is no area of S which is not included in P).

3d figure   I — Some members are players   Some M is P
            A — All members are students   All M is S
            ‾‾‾‾‾‾‾‾‾‾‾‾‾‾‾‾‾‾‾‾‾‾‾‾‾‾‾‾   ‾‾‾‾‾‾‾‾‾‾
            I — Some students are players   Some S is P

By Rule 1 above, the minor premise, since it is universal and the major premise is particular, must be diagrammed first (Figure 5). This is done by shading the area of M that is not S. A cross is then placed in the area of M that is P to indicate that it contains at least some instances. The conclusion, that at least some S is P, is seen to follow validly.

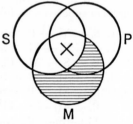

FIG. 5

The second negative method consists in applying the seven rules of the syllogism. They apply to all the moods; and if any one of the rules is violated, the syllogism is invalid.

Three Terms Rule

Rule 1. A syllogism must include three and only three terms, used throughout in the same sense.

Distribution Rules

Rule 2. The middle term must be distributed at least once in the premises.

Rule 3. No term may have a greater distribution in the conclusion than it had in the premises.

Negative Premises Rules

Rule 4. From two negative premises, no valid conclusion can be inferred.

Rule 5. If one premise is negative, the conclusion must be negative.

Particular Premises Rules

Rule 6. If one premise is particular, the conclusion must be particular.

Rule 7. From two particular premises, no valid conclusion can be drawn.

COMMON RULE VIOLATIONS

The most frequent transgression of the rules concerns Rule 2, and is called the Undistributed Middle. Political campaigns are especially rich in examples of it, such as: All Communists favor peaceful coexistence; My opponent favors peaceful coexistence; hence my opponent is a Communist. What has quietly been inserted is the very different premise: *Only* Communists favor peaceful coexistence.

Almost as dangerous is the violation of Rule 3, known as Illicit Process, said by Jevons to be easier to commit and more difficult to detect than any other syllogistic fallacy. If we argue that: All Buddhists are pacifists; No Methodists are Buddhists; thus No Methodists are pacifists; we distribute (that is, use in its widest sense) in the conclusion a term, "pacifists," which was not distributed in the premises. We have taken out in our conclusion more than we put into our premises. Nothing, perhaps, is more characteristically human than this tendency to try to extract more than one puts in; and nothing does more violence to the first principle of deduction.

Students are often puzzled about applying the rules to arguments employing assumed or unstated premises. Normal human talk is full of what Justice Holmes called "inarticulate major premises." "I do not say that my opponent has been wrong about every issue," says the campaign orator, leaving it to his audience to reach the conclusion through innuendo. The technical name for this incomplete form of reasoning is *enthymeme*.

Caution must constantly be observed in interpreting both "All" and "Some" when either is accented. To say: "*All* you fellows are not cowards," indicates that some are not, and suggests that some are. To say that in an accident: "*Some* of the passengers were injured" conveys the notion that some, *but not all*, were injured, whereas in logic "some" does not exclude the possibility that all were injured. To assert that "*Some* hippogriffs are poisonous" seems to say that "Some hippogriffs, *and there are some*, are poisonous." It requires an effort to remember that in formal logic, as in mathematics, the question of the existence of what is being talked about is always left unsettled.

Another source of confusion is any sentence beginning with the words "Only" or "None but." "Only males are fathers" does not say that "All males are fathers," but only that some are, and furthermore, it excludes the non-males. Hence it is simpler to avoid the awkwardness of two propositions by transposing the subject and predicate to read: "All fathers are males."

4. The "Laws of Thought"

The traditional syllogism does not represent the way men normally think, but rather a means of testing, retrospectively, whether they have thought validly. It is a formulation of the rules of deductive thinking of the Aristotelian variety which must be found to have been observed, intentionally or not, if the conclusion is warranted by the premises. This whole process of testing rests upon three famous assumptions known as "The Laws of Thought," which are:

The Law of Identity: A *is* A; or, a thing is what it is throughout a given argument. Meanings are not subject to change without notice.

The Law of Contradiction: A *is* not not-A; or, one cannot consistently assert and deny the same thing at the same time.

The Law of Excluded Middle: A *is either* B *or* not-B; or, of two contradictory judgments exhausting the possibilities, if one is false, the other must be true.

It will be seen at once that these "laws" are taken for granted by men who argue in the framework of our Western intellectual tradition. The poet, however, can ignore the Law of Contradiction with impunity, as Walt Whitman did. "His allegiance," says Professor Loewenberg, "is not primarily to the rules of thought."[9] Many Oriental thinkers reject either-or thinking on the ground that ultimate reality is both-and. Ever since Hegel, and especially since the rise of Existentialism, the Law of the Excluded Middle has been almost continuously under attack in Western thought.

5. Modern Logic of Propositions

In spite of the great historical importance of the syllogism, and its potential usefulness today for legal and business reasoning about stable classes of things, logicians no longer regard it as constituting the whole of deductive logic, or even as possessing prime importance. Some of them look upon it with positive disdain as dealing with too narrowly restricted an area of thought: the categorical relations of classes. Under the influence of the new mathematics of Georg Cantor (1845–1918) and others, school children are beginning to do their formal thinking in terms of the Theory of Sets instead of classes. "A set is a collection of definite objects of our perception or of our thought," and is composed of elements.[10] All sets whose elements can be put into one-

---

[9] J. Loewenberg, *Reason and the Nature of Things* (La Salle, Ill., 1959), pp. 29–30.

[10] Breuer, Joseph, *Introduction to the Theory of Sets* (Englewood Cliffs, N.J., 1958), p. 4.

to-one correspondence with each other's elements are said to be equivalent and have the same cardinal number, such as five fingers, five toes, and five men on a basketball team.

Modern logic and mathematics, which take turns trying to swallow one another, embrace many varieties of deductive inference. One of the most important is the truth-value calculus of sentences or propositions which are either true or false. The truth or falsity of any statement which has meaning is considered to be its truth-value.

To move from the syllogism toward the logic of propositions, one changes the ordinary class-relation proposition A: "All students are players," to read: "If X is a student, then X is a player." It was the English mathematician George Boole (1815–64) who paved the way for this advance by devising an algebra for logic in his *The Laws of Thought* (1854). He used the symbol zero, 0, for the concept of an empty class. This enabled him to write down such a proposition as "There are no ghosts" (using G for the class "ghosts") as $G = 0$. Then the proposition: "There are men" (using M for the class "men") became $M \neq 0$. By adding the notion of the complementary class (for example, G′ stands for "All the things in the universe which are not ghosts" and M′ for "All that are not men"), Boole was able to express the four fundamental propositions of the syllogism as follows:

A   All students are players $SP' = 0$
E   No students are players $SP = 0$
I   Some students are players $SP \neq 0$
E   Some students are not players $SP' \neq 0$

The Boolean two-valued algebra has been supplemented and enlarged by a logic capable of dealing with more complex relations among propositions.[11] Truth-tables, some of them very elaborate, have been drawn up to deal with them. Among the simpler varieties is that which states the truth-values for the two propositions p and q, assuming that for each of them only two truth-values are possible: either true or false. It should be noted that in this form of logic there is no allowance whatever for propositions which are ambiguous, doubtful, or debatable.

If p is	and q is	Then p and q are	And p or q are
True	True	True	True
True	False	False	True
False	True	False	True
False	False	False	False

This two-valued truth-table and its further extensions have gained enormously in importance from the fact that they lend themselves to electronic handling by a modern computer. It is only necessary to assign the symbol 1 to truth, and 0 to falsity, in order to correspond with the binary notation

[11] For a much fuller treatment, see Irving Adler, *Thinking Machines* (New York, paper, 1961), chap. 8, "Algebra of Classes," and chap. 9, "Algebra of Propositions."

used in digital computers.[12] In the electronic device, when a switch is closed, the current is on; when it is open, the current is off. These states correspond to the truth and falsity of any proposition; and a circuit can be designed for any desired truth-table.

DEDUCTION BY MACHINERY

The formal relationships of the syllogism were bound sooner or later to be first diagrammed and then "mechanized." The first man "to use a mechanical device as an aid to reasoning" may well have been Ramon Lull (1236?–1315). But the first logic machine, strictly speaking, was probably the "Demonstrator" built by Charles, third Earl Stanhope (1753–1816), British statesman and scientist.[13] The pioneer in suggesting a wedding of electricity and logic was the American Allan Marquand about 1885; but the first actual construction of an electrical logic machine was by Benjamin Burack about 1936. It was designed to test the forms of the syllogism; and many other similar devices have been constructed by both teachers and students of the traditional logic.

The leader in electrifying the propositional calculus by computer was Claude E. Shannon of the Massachusetts Institute of Technology in 1937. His work laid the foundations for the many types of modern truth-value logic machines, including digital computers adapted for the purpose. The devices so far constructed operate mainly as follows: premises are fed into the machine, whereupon it scans the programmed truth-table lines one at a time. The operator notes whenever the lights (those which are on) indicate "true." In time it is believed that machines specially designed to solve problems in propositional logic will be able to operate directly without scanning. There are no theoretical obstacles to the building of machines to handle multi-valued logics. In Gardner's words, "There is no reason why any formal logic that can be manipulated with symbols on paper cannot also be manipulated by properly designed electric circuits."

Much confusion has been created in the public mind by such book titles as *Intelligent Machines, Giant Brains,* or *Machines That Think,* since many persons have concluded that computers can now undertake nearly all the tasks of human thought, including original or creative thinking. This is very far from being the case, so far that some authorities have begun to define "real thinking" as "what a computer can*not* do." A machine has no curiosity; it can "think," that is to say, only in the terms previously fed into it. It is "an organized collection of hardware," which must be instructed (programmed) by a human being, ultimately, regarding what it is to think, and what it is to

---

[12] *Digital* computers are fundamentally arithmetical, using only information coded in terms of 0 and 1. *Analog* computers, often called "electronic slide rules," introduce physical distances, amounts of turning of a wheel, or of voltages which are analogous to the numerical magnitudes to be represented. There are also *hybrid* computers employing both sorts of elements.

[13] See Martin Gardner, *Logic Machines* (New York, paper, 1958), to which this account is indebted, for the history of the subject.

think about. Once it has had its function predetermined, it can carry out its programmed operations, such as following an involved process of deductive logic, far more rapidly and reliably than human beings can accomplish them. This is "thinking" only in the sense of "fixed-rule" calculation. "A problem," says Bruce W. Arden, "is computable for which the execution of an explicit, unambiguous, terminating sequence of instructions produces a solution."[14] Machines, that is, are utterly incapable of "free decisions" or original thought. A computer "specializes in deriving conclusions (logical or mathematical) without regard to the objective truth of the starting data."[15] In the course of exploring such consequences or implications, which it can accomplish with fantastic speeds (doing work that would take a man fifty years in about ten minutes), the machine may disclose hitherto unnoticed alternatives, and so may make "discoveries" possible. But it may also spew out vast numbers of irrelevant or unimportant conclusions known as GIGO ("Garbage in, garbage out").

Where the computer excels the human brain is in its virtually infallible stored-up memory and rapidity of recall. That is why "it has been predicted that during the next twenty years the world's champion chess-player will be an automatic computer program."[16] Even the keenest human memory, that is, will hardly be able to cope with an electronic memory stocked with the correct deductive inference for every possible situation in the game of chess. The computer, of course, does not "know" what the right moves "mean"; only the programmer is aware of that.

The performance of such intricate deductions, as anyone can see, requires extremely complicated and expensive hardware. Current costs of computers range from $25,000 to over $10,000,000. As a result, their use is not warranted in dealing with small-scale operations. As Irving Adler remarks: "It is no routine matter to design a machine that can do routine thinking."[17]

Many uses have been suggested for electronic logic machines where large masses of data are available: in checking the consistency of title deeds and other involved legal documents; in the interpretation of complicated rule books; in the solution of crimes involving fingerprints and other sorts of evidence; in the unraveling of insurance tangles; in the elimination of conflicts in plane landings, train dispatching, and college class schedules; and in the logistical computations of military and industrial operations research. There is every prospect that computers will be more and more extensively employed by lawyers in searching for precedents and by physicians in the diagnosis of disease. The deductive consequences of a patient's symptoms might conceivably be worked out in the light of perhaps millions of cases.[18] Nevertheless it must be granted that most of the suggested uses of logic-machines are likely to be

---

[14] Bruce W. Arden, *An Introduction to Digital Computing* (Reading, Mass., 1963), p. 1.

[15] Edmund C. Berkeley, *The Computer Revolution* (New York, 1962), p. 13.

[16] *Idem*, p. 172.

[17] Irving Adler, *op. cit.*, p. 12.

[18] *Idem*, pp. 112–15 for an example. Russian doctors have suggested a nation-wide punch-card system for keeping a computer inventory of the country's state of health.

severely restricted by the lack of a sufficient volume of data to justify computer treatment. It may be expected, however, that some of the so-called "third generation" computers will be reduced in size and cost for the use of smaller organizations in solving their problems.

6. Formal Validity and Reliable Knowledge

The question that concerns us as knowers about all forms of deduction: Aristotelian, modern and electronic, is: what part has valid reasoning to play in the attainment of reliable knowledge? All we have established, so far, is the certainty that, given reliable premises and valid reasoning, we are obliged, if we value consistency, to accept the conclusion as reliable.

But what about our initial premises? What if they are unreliable, or "materially false" to begin with? Can the formal validity of the conclusion in any way assure that our premises are true of the world in which we live? Consider the syllogism:

All Presidents of the United States have been married men
James Buchanan was a President of the United States
James Buchanan was a married man

We recognize at once a valid AAA syllogism in the first figure; and our major premise is *almost* materially true. But, unfortunately for our argument, James Buchanan never married. Our formal reasoning is valid enough, but one of our premises is false, and our conclusion is false.

At this point the reader is likely to leap to a dangerous conclusion, namely, that since true premises and valid reasoning are bound to yield true conclusions, any other combination automatically results in falsity. Using "true" and "false" in this context as convenient equivalents of "reliable" and "unreliable" in our world, there are four possible combinations:
zwna

	Premises	Reasoning	Conclusion
1.	True	Valid	True
2.	True	Invalid	?
3.	False	Valid	?
4.	False	Invalid	?

Exploring these alternatives, the second (True-Invalid) is extremely likely, of course, to yield a false conclusion. But, since the conclusion does not have to follow validly from the premises, it *can* be true, thus:

2d figure   A — All Japanese are Orientals   True
            E — No Caucasians are Orientals   True
            E — No Caucasians are Negroes   True

The reasoning is patently invalid, and yet the conclusion is true. False premises and valid reasoning, as in the third alternative, are also likely to produce false conclusions, but not necessarily so. For example:

1st figure	A — All Mexicans are U.S. citizens	False
	A — All native-born Iowans are Mexicans	False
	A — All native-born Iowans are U.S. citizens	True

Given the premises, which are false, the conclusion, which is true, nevertheless follows validly. The same happy accident of material truth can even overtake invalid reasoning from false premises, such as:

4th figure	A — All alligators are ostriches	False
	I — Some ostriches are shellfish	False
	A — All squirrels are rodents	True

By this time it should be apparent that the fact that valid reasoning from true premises is the only way that we can be *sure* of reaching true deductive conclusions is no proof whatever that it is the *only* way to do so. Any one of the other three combinations can yield material truth, in spite of the fact that they are overwhelmingly likely to result in falsehoods. This should enable us to separate, once and for all, our thinking about formal logic, which deals wholly with consistency or validity, from that about the material truth or reliability of our premises.

It would be the height of folly to interpret all this as an argument against the value of validity in our deductive reasoning. For unless our reasoning *is* valid, our chances of getting reliable knowledge deductively are very small indeed. Nevertheless, the fact that our reasoning is valid is no guarantee whatever of the truth of the premises we have chosen. We must not confuse the question of the reliability of our procedure with that of the reliability of our premises. When the latter issue is raised, the formal logician is silent. It is his task to display the exact consequences of given assumptions, irrespective of their material truth or falsity. The necessity of accepting the consequences hinges upon our previous acceptance of the premises; and, if we reject the premises, no amount of formal logic can oblige us to accept their consequences. Premises must stand on their own feet. If they are materially true, certain valid and true conclusions can be shown to follow inexorably in accordance with the rules of formal logic. But other valid and true conclusions, and sometimes some of the same ones, can be shown to follow just as inexorably from premises which are materially false. To be sure that we have reasoned validly is not enough. The final verdict concerning the reliability of knowledge that is claimed to have been established by deduction must always be primarily a question of the reliability of the premises, and only secondarily, after the former has been established, a matter of the formal validity of the reasoning.

7. Deduction Then and Now

Looking back over the long history of the human quest for dependable knowledge, we can see why the deductive method has become associated with the working out of the consequences of finished or pre-existing knowledge, rather than with the discovery of new truths. For centuries, men felt no lack of apparently reliable premises in the form of customs and folkways. When, at the hands of a few precocious Greeks, the accepted social habits began to be questioned and reasoned about verbally, more and more people had to be convinced by argument rather than merely overawed by authority. Argument that is not emotional browbeating is discourse directed toward the making of inferences. To win a rational argument is to secure the assent of others by bringing about admissions which lead to other admissions. Among the disputatious Greeks, this usually meant in practice that one's hearers had to be shown that the particular case under discussion fell within a general principle which had been admitted by all the parties to the debate. What won the argument was the demonstration: — you have admitted these premises, therefore you are obliged to admit this conclusion. Aristotle codified the rules for checking the relations of such conclusions to their premises, and thereby supplied the arguers of his day with a means of avoiding some of the rhetorical tricks of their opponents. He was not furnishing them with the rules of the art of thinking or with the language of debate, but rather with artificial devices for testing "what admissions lead to." By mastering his technique of checking logical consequences, and by applying it to the scrutiny of whatever purported to be rational argument, they could at least avoid being coerced into accepting invalid conclusions.

THE SCHOLASTIC ATTITUDE

It is impossible to overemphasize the difference between Aristotle's own intentions and those of some of his admirers in the later Middle Ages, by whom he was idolized as "the philosopher" in spite of his pagan beliefs. Although he became famous as the formulator of the canons of deduction, Aristotle himself was probably the most *inductively*, though not experimentally, minded of the Greek philosophers. Unhappily his mediaeval successors did not share his insatiable thirst for every variety of facts as well as for all-inclusive theories. To them, his philosophical system, embracing both the methods of thought and most of the scientific knowledge available in his era (and theirs also), seemed so complete that it could be accepted as authoritative in all matters not settled by Holy Writ.

Aristotle is not to be blamed for the blind dogmatism of many of those who came after him, whose purposes and demands were very different from his, and who misused his deductive logic to silence doubters and to prevent any serious attention to concrete facts. What they were seeking was an error-proof method of settling the only really important controversies, which were theological, in the light of the incontestably true premises which their religion supplied. They thought that they had found the final rules of "the grammar of thinking" in the syllogism, which dealt with rigid relations among fixed concepts, thus affording a handy guide to the fixed system of classes in nature. The ironical result was that what originated as a handbook for the guidance of eager Greek inquirers became, in mediaeval hands, a mighty engine for the coercion of heretics. Using some of the worst of Aristotle's blunders in the physical and biological sciences as authoritative, these wordy doctors retarded further advances in those subjects by applying the rules of his logic to the deduction of the consequences of old errors.

Aristotle's "instrument," in fact, reached its greatest prestige and popularity in the thirteenth century A.D. The Scholastic theologians of that period, led by Saint Thomas Aquinas, were in search of knowledge leading to salvation, and they were convinced that they were already in possession of an ample supply of it in the form of premises drawn from such unimpeachable authorities as the Bible, the Church Fathers, and such writings of Aristotle as did not conflict with the divine decrees. There were truths of revelation beyond all argument, which human reason was incapable either of discovering or demonstrating.

Since all the knowledge essential for salvation was already available, the chief task of human learning was application. The believer, already in the possession of the Truth with a capital "T," was simply concerned to deduce its consequences correctly. Today we marvel at the lack of interest shown by mediaeval thinkers generally in scientific facts. We forget that for them Nature was, in Whitehead's phrase, "overwhelmingly dramatic." Having, as they firmly believed, "inside information" of utter reliability regarding the plot of the cosmic drama and the ultimate purpose of things, the particular processes by which the ends were to be reached seemed to them to be comparatively unimportant.

This deductive approach to human problems also had important social consequences in an age when ardent believers sought to make their religion universal. Deductive logic in the hands of authoritarians bent upon religious or political uniformity, or both, became a powerful instrument of coercion to be wielded against dissenters. For reason was confined to one side of the argument. It could not be used against the premises, which were declared to be beyond its scope. But it could be used to crush, in the name of logic, any deviation from the accepted dogmas. Ecclesiastical and civil judges took their premises from the books of law, and applied them syllogistically to individual cases. Think how many hundreds of thousands of wretched epileptics and insane persons were hung or burned to death with good conscience and perfect logic because it is written in Exodus XXII:18: "Thou shalt not suffer a witch to live." If that premise is accepted as unassailably true, then in an individual instance it is only necessary to determine, by deductions from other equally certain premises, that "this old woman is a witch." The logic, once the premises were granted, was impossible to challenge without upsetting the whole notion of human rationality; while the premises could not be questioned without overthrowing the whole social fabric of Christendom. Small wonder that so potent a means of insuring social conformity was abused to the point where men began to rebel at the consequences, and thus to question the reliability of the premises.

MODERN VIEWS OF DEDUCTION

From our point of view, the mistake of the mediaeval thinkers was not in developing and refining the traditional syllogism, but in cutting it off from induction, and in harnessing it exclusively to the task of filling in the details of a single system of religious dogma, the main outlines of which were already known by revelation. Yet by insisting upon the ultimate rationality of the universe, although veiled in part to the mind of man, the mediaeval Schoolmen paved the way for a different kind of deductive system based upon measurement rather than upon Aristotelian classes of things. When, at the Renaissance, thinkers began to turn their attention to physical Nature for worldly purposes, they retained the Scholastic standard of reliability in knowledge — inclusion in a unified rational system. But the axioms of the system were now mathematical instead of theological; and there was a new insistence upon checking their consequences against the concrete nature of things as discovered by observation and experiment. To the old coercion of men's beliefs by what must follow from accepted premises, there was added the new coercion of the stubborn facts. Besides the inescapable order in the ways conclusions could be shown to be related to premises in rational thinking, there was the newly discovered regularity in the nature of things. How were the two orders related? Modern science has had the difficult task of adjusting the claims of the rival systems and their methods of assaying knowledge: the deductive habit of using tight chains of abstract logical reasoning, and the inductive demand for fidelity to concrete observed fact.

Only the outline of the combined method which moves from induction through deduction to induction need be foreshadowed here. Deduction has been demoted from its high position as handmaiden of dogma, and has assumed the lowlier task of assisting in the development of hypotheses. Yet without deduction, most of our present scientific preoccupation with facts would be fruitless, since we should be unable to fit them into systems. To realize how powerful a tool deduction can be for the revelation of structures hidden beneath the surface of things, it is only necessary to mention the immense part played by mathematics in all our technical thought. The planning of rockets, missiles, satellites and space vehicles and the vastly complicated machinery for their guidance and detection requires a volume of mathematical calculation in advance which only computers can supply in time for effective use.

A powerful factor in changing the role of deductive systems in modern thought has been the discovery that the world of these formal relations between meanings, thoughts, or sentences is enormously larger than the traditional logic had led us to suppose. We know now that the syllogism represents only one choice among many possible alternative ways of drawing conclusions. We are aware that there is an endless array of logics and mathematics, each one a timelessly valid partial account of the possibilities, and each one completely consistent throughout in its own terms, but not all of them equally useful for our intellectual purposes. Far from there being any single cosmic standard of what constitutes valid inference, there are, instead, an indefinitely large number of relations which can be arranged in many deductive systems.

The traditional logicians were right in maintaining the absolute and unchanging rigidity of many of the formal relationships which they had discovered, once their premises had been accepted as reliable. But they were fatally wrong in supposing that the same absolute lack of choice prevailed in selecting the original premises of their arguments, or in deciding which of their implications should be explored. Modern man has some choice in these matters, among an immense wealth of implication-relations set forth with a refinement far beyond the dreams of an Aristotle or an Aquinas. Contemporary logic is prepared to demonstrate "all the things you can say in a language if you know the syntax and not a single word of the vocabulary." Thus it places at our disposal a constantly expanding science of consistent forms enabling us to manipulate an endless number of related possibilities.

But the greatest shift of all has been away from treating premises as dogma to regarding them as hypotheses to be tested. By assuming that his initial premises are no longer established certainties, but tentative postulates, the modern scientist is furnished by deductive logic with an extensive repertory of their valid implications to be checked against the observed facts. The resulting systems of knowledge upon which modern man places the greatest reliance, the exact sciences, are indeed those which are the most closely knit deductively. But this is not because of any absolute conviction that their initial premises are rocklike or beyond dispute. On the contrary, it is the deductive cross-buttressing of the entire system that gives us confidence in its original premises.

This hypothetical or postulational use of deduction has won its way with great difficulty, however, in those fields, like the social studies, where the store of finished knowledge is still commonly supposed to be large, and where many minds still work according to the dogmatic deductive pattern. In the so-called routine occupations, thousands of people do little more than apply deductively the rules, formulas, recipes and prescriptions worked out by others. This policy affords a mental economy which saves them the effort of treating each individual case in the light of a large number of systematically connected possibilities, as tentativeness in deducing would require. If such a person's premises happen to be false, he will merely be practicing what Joseph Wood Krutch calls "the art of going wrong with confidence."

If, on the other hand, we are humble about the reliability of our already acquired knowledge, we shall not try to build solid proofs by means of formal logic upon the shaky foundations of self-assumed or self-proclaimed authority. We shall refuse to make consistency an instrument of coercion and confinement of human thought to orthodox and conventional pathways which must not be questioned. We shall stop insisting that the patterns of our theory-making must necessarily constitute eternal laws of the nature of things.

Pre-modern logicians erred in mistaking the validity of their instrument, the syllogism, for the reliability of its premises; and we may even be obliged to guard ourselves against a similar fallacy which might be called "computer scholasticism." Deductive conclusions obtained at great cost from vast masses of data are likely to take on an imperative air. We must never fail to recall that most ancient and prevalent of all the pitfalls of deductiton: the belief that it is possible to get more out in the conclusion than we put into the premises.

No doubt deductions by logic-machines will acquire prestige as they become more common. But it must constantly be pointed out that what goes into them in the way of premises must first be made "computable," that is, it must be transformed into a set of symbols which are the result of analysis and simplification. They are parts, not wholes. They represent binary alternatives entering into combinations with other symbolic abstractions. The machine that receives the symbol registers its presence only in ways it has been instructed to do. But when a human being is made aware of what the same symbol stands for, his whole mind may reach out in many unpredictable (and original) directions. A logic-machine has no awareness of meanings; it "thinks" only along narrow and predetermined pathways. That is why it is so difficult to get "ideas" out of a computer.

It must also be remembered that the alternatives with which a digital computer deals are true-false only. But the humanities and social studies are full of ambivalent and ambiguous situations which do not lend themselves to that sort of either-or, black-or-white reasoning. They abound instead in nuances, in shades of gray. The analog computer can deal with some of them, but its analogies are purely quantitative, and may be misleading. There should be, then, no abject surrender to the authority of the machine-made deduction until its premises have been carefully scrutinized. We must still avoid the tyranny of the logical instrument. It would be ironical indeed for twentieth-century science to have escaped the bonds of religious dogmatism, only to fall into the clutches of tyrannically manipulated logic-machines.

In fleeing the evils of deductive dogmatism, however, we should not deprive ourselves of the virtues of deductive reasoning. That the two things, dogmatism and deduction, have been historically associated for centuries is unfortunate, because a revulsion from dogmatism about premises has often been accompanied by a complete disdain for logical rigor. The attempt is made to excuse sloppy thinking on the ground that one must not be dogmatic. Such a policy can be disastrous, for one does not avoid implications by ignoring or misreading them.

We should not make the mistake of asking too little of formal logic, just because we are determined, and rightly, not to ask too much. Instead, we should strive to develop free conceptualizing in new directions in the hope of producing novel patterns of possibilities (hypotheses) which may be elaborated, in some cases by computers, and then brought to bear experimentally upon ever-widening ranges of facts. In this way, deduction can be made an essential part of the inductive-deductive-inductive method of free inquiry.

Thus we may be able to combine its rightful rigidity of form, once its assumptions are determined, with the needed flexibility of postulational thinking.

FOR CLASS DISCUSSION

A. What is the first business of one who practices philosophy? To part with self-conceit. For it is impossible for anyone to begin to learn what he thinks he knows already. — *Epictetus*   (1)

B. People untrained in logic can detect a formal fallacy in a syllogistic argument once the argument is set out. But a fallacious argument that would not mislead an intelligent child, provided that it is stated barely, in a few sentences, may mislead all of us when stated at length in a long book, or when wrapped up in much verbiage, or when combined with appeals to our passionate interests. — *L. S. Stebbing*   (3)

C. The first steam vessel to cross the Atlantic carried, as part of its cargo, a book which "proved" that it was impossible for a steam vessel to cross anything, much less the Atlantic.   (5)
    — *Edward Karsner and James Newman*

D. The end aimed at by formal logic, and attained by the observation of its precepts, is not truth but consistency. — *John Stuart Mill*

E. Formal logic can provide an elegant reconstruction of knowledge already acquired, but it throws little light upon the procedures actually followed to acquire it. — *Abraham Kaplan*

F. Logic never persuades, though it may show that persuasion has been legitimate; it never aids the work of thought, it only acts as its auditor and accountant general. — *A. J. Balfour*

G. The task of logic is to serve as a spiritual hygiene, cautioning men against the disease of intellectual confusion. The logician by himself has no remedy to offer. — *Rudolf Carnap*

H. Computers must be told where to find information, how to use it, what to do with it, and what to do next. Extremely detailed steps must be prepared for the computer even for the solution of simple problems, and they must be expressed in a language that the computer can understand.   (7)
    — *Management Review*

I. The famous epigram about the Bourbon kings of France: "They learned nothing and they forgot nothing" leads to a parallel epigram for computers: "They will learn anything and forget anything." — *Edmund C. Berkeley*

J. A world of perfect technicians is the aim . . . a dreary and boring world, where there is nothing but man and his mastery over nature, including his mastery over other technicians through his scientific management of them. Perfect hierarchy, perfect organization, total efficiency; but no spirit, no freedom, no joy, no humor, and therefore no man. — *Dr. Charles H. Malik*

K. The history of philosophical doctrine shows that, in the course of centuries, men have been able to prove almost everything . . . "All proofs," said the philosopher Alain, "are for me clearly discredited." Actually, one *can* prove everything if the words one employs are not clear and precise.
— *André Maurois*   (8)

L. Mediaeval man thought that truth had been revealed to him, so that he was spared from its wild pursuit; the reckless energy that we give to seeking it was turned in those days to the creation of beauty. . . . — *Will Durant*

M. "European logic," says Fenollosa, "is a tyranny; its thought is a brickyard stacked with little hard baked units called concepts, instead of something living, with delicate balance of overtones." — *Virginia Moore*

N. Persons who distrust deductive reasoning are apt to use it unknowingly and therefore carelessly. — *Henry Hazlitt*

EXERCISES IN THE SYLLOGISM

Test each of the following arguments for formal validity after stating it as a categorical syllogism, and indicating whether each premise and the conclusion is an A, E, I, or O proposition. State whether the argument is valid or invalid, and if invalid, what rule of the syllogism is violated. (Optional: diagram the premises by the Venn circle method.)

1. Some good musicians do not play classical music; because no jazz performer plays classical music, yet lots of jazz performers are good musicians.

2. All well-financed candidates are successful, but this candidate is not well-financed, so he will not be successful.

3. Indians are sometimes Alaskans, and all Alaskans are proud of their state; so, some who are proud of their state are Indians.

4. Only reactionaries support this legislation; Senator Z is not a reactionary, because he does not support it.

5. Some Communists are employed in government agencies; because all Communists are security risks, and some security risks are employed by government agencies.

6. Some bank presidents have not been to college, and some men who have been to college are failures; threfore some failures are bank presidents.

7. Nearly all children like fairy tales, but John is no longer a child, because he does not like fairy tales.

8. Many farmers oppose subsidies, and all members of this party oppose subsidies; so, some farmers are members of this party.

9. Several passengers were injured, but no salesmen were passengers; hence, some of the injured were not salesmen.

10. Great discoveries in the past have met with opposition, extrasensory perception has met with opposition; therefore it is a great discovery.

≫ 4 ≪

TOWARD SCIENTIFIC METHOD:
Observation—"Get the Facts"

1. The Long Way Around

How a few men in Western Europe came to abandon the confident but excessive use of the short cut of deduction from supposedly assured premises as the main road to reliable knowledge and to take what was then the long way around — by combining deduction with induction — is too lengthy a story to tell in detail here. On the whole, it was a process of becoming more and more dissatisfied with the inaccuracy and sterility of the conclusions which were reached by means of the hair-splitting refinements of the syllogism as applied to the established mediaeval system of allegedly absolute truths. As long as the disputes remained verbal, in the realm of theology, the deductive method seemed adequate; but when it was applied to physical Nature, using premises from the Bible or Aristotle, its defects became apparent. Many of the conclusions of the later Scholastics about matters of fact were ludicrously false, such as the notion that women must have two more teeth than men, a wholly valid deduction from one of the more fantastic conjectures of Aristotle, which had been accepted as gospel truth. That such futile bandyings of words yielded no new discoveries about their environment did not trouble the savants of the fourteenth to the sixteenth centuries. They were content with the relatively passive intellectual satisfaction which comes from contemplating the already known and organized. Their sole anxiety was to preserve unblemished the logically ordered unity of the verbal system enshrining the religious and aesthetic values upon which they believed that the whole world order, here and hereafter, was based. If an alleged fact of sense perception resisted incorporation in the finished system of knowledge composed of Christian theology and Aristotelian science, then so much the worse for the fact!

Such contempt for the "mere facts" of this world is so foreign to our ways of thinking that it takes a deliberate effort on our part to recapture the authentic spirit of mediaeval learning. Men's eyes were fixed upon heaven: knowledge of God was the only knowledge worth having, since, it one possessed it, all other knowledge was superfluous; while, in its absence, all other knowledge was vain. Why spend time in tedious researches into earthly things? Nature was regarded as a mere temporary stage setting for the Drama of Salvation, the plot of which was outlined in the Bible and the Aristotelian system of Saint

Thomas Aquinas, where all things terrestrial and celestial were assigned their appointed places in the divine plan.

"The modern world," says Professor Joseph Jastrow, "rose out of a reformed logic."[1] But the reformed logic rose from demands for new and different qualities in knowledge. It was only when men dared to ask new sorts of questions in a different spirit that the inadequacy of the old answers became fully apparent. This occurred when the undercurrent of worldliness which the clerics had denounced as pagan and disreputable could no longer be restrained, and the new humanistic attitude of the Renaissance became increasingly respectable. Instead of the monastic ideal of perfection beyond life, men began boldly to assert and to pursue the more immediate goal of a full existence here below. This new concern with mundane affairs "did not so much offer a new answer to the old problem of supernatural salvation as push it more and more into the background."[2]

2. The Baconian Spirit

The man who is most often associated with the attack upon the barrenness of mediaeval learning in behalf of this rising interest in knowledge "for the use and benefit of mankind" is that versatile, blemished Elizabethan genius, Francis Bacon (1561–1626). He denounced the then-prevailing method "according to which the most general principles are first established, and then intermediate axioms are tried and proved by them," as "the parent of error and the curse of all science." The deductive thinker he compared to the spider, spinning out cobwebs of learning from his premises, "admirable for the fineness of thread and work, but of no substance and profit." Because of "too great a reverence, and a kind of adoration of the mind and understanding of man . . . men have withdrawn themselves too much from the contemplation of nature and the observation of experience, and have tumbled up and down in their own reason and conceits . . . (as Heraclitus said) *'Men sought truth in their own little worlds, and not in the great and common world'* . . . whereby they are deservedly deluded."[3] "God forbid," says Bacon, "that I should give out a work of the imagination for a pattern of the universe."

Deduction had served well enough for the purposes of Scholastic disputation, and thus for the establishment of the "Empire of Man over Man." But to oblige men to conform to the dictates of authority by logical coercion was to win an empty victory in the realm of words. "The syllogism commands assent

[1] Joseph Jastrow, *The Betrayal of Intelligence* (New York, 1938), p. 131.

[2] John Herman Randall, Jr., *The Making of the Modern Mind*, revised ed. (Boston, 1940), p. 131. Chapters VI–X contain an excellent account of this period.

[3] Francis Bacon, *The Advancement of Learning*, bk. I, V, 6. (Italics his. H. A. L.) Francis Bacon, Baron Verulam, is not to be confused with the Franciscan monk, Roger Bacon (1214–94), who was one of the forerunners of scientific method and who also attacked "four stumbling blocks which hinder well-nigh every scholar: the example of frail and unworthy authority, long-established custom, the sense of the ignorant crowd, . . . and the pretense of wisdom."

to the proposition, but it does not take hold of the thing." It is powerless to extend knowledge; it bears no fruits for human betterment; and so "men despair and think things impossible."[4] But not Francis Bacon; he was no defeatist, repudiating this world as hopeless except as preparation for another, and resigned to the sterile admiration of what was already believed to be known. The world as a fit habitation for human beings was not finished; it was hardly begun. Everything remained to be done; and everything *could* be done, provided men would drop their attitude of helplessness and abject dependence, and bestir themselves. The way "to endow human life with new discoveries and powers" was to extend man's knowledge of his world. Over and over again Bacon summoned mankind to arise to new tasks and new conquests, not the fruitless "Empire of Man over Man" but the fruitful "Empire of man over Nature" — the deliberate attempt to control human destiny in this world by adding to the knowledge that is power in the service of man. Men should stop fighting one another, and turn their united efforts against their common enemy, unsubdued Nature. They should join hands in seeking "the knowledge of causes, and the secret motions of things; and the enlarging of the bounds of human empire, to the effecting of all things possible."[5]

3. The Empirical Approach

This new set of aims and demands upon knowledge — discovery for the sake of human progress — called for a new approach and a new method of knowing, an *Organon* different from that of Aristotle, which Bacon proudly and prematurely offered under the title of *Novum Organum* (1620). Knowledge, he asserts, "is not an opinion to be held . . . but a work to be done." The way to do that work is first of all to rid one's mind of all prejudices and fixed preconceptions (he calls them "idols"), and then to observe Nature humbly and constantly with a profound respect for what she has to teach. The mind must be brought into direct contact with what it is to think about, and it must acknowledge no obligations whatever except to follow the evidence wherever it may lead. "We can conquer Nature by first obeying her."

Here is a new source of authority in knowing, a new court of appeal: respect for what William James called "the irreducible and stubborn facts." Deductive logic in Bacon's time had done "little else than enslave the world of Nature to human thoughts, and human thoughts to words." The time had come to turn the tables: there is a better way of disciplining human minds — by counseling men to bow to the instruction of experience. Man's new mistress in knowing is to be Nature as revealed by inductive observation. He is to become her "servant and interpreter," but only in order eventually to master Nature for his own purposes. The new mode of attack called for the breaking down of the ancient tradition of the gentleman's aloofness from useful manual labor. The scientist must not hesitate to soil his hands with unfashionable fact-grubbing,

[4] Francis Bacon, *Novum Organum*, Aphorisms XIII, XCII.
[5] Francis Bacon, *The New Atlantis* (World Classics ed.), p. 265.

and even with carpentry and the mixing of chemicals in the course of his researches. Polite dabbling in parlor experiments would hardly suffice. It took several centuries for Europeans to accustom themselves to the idea of a new and useful intellectual aristocracy, an *élite* composed of hard-working scientific technicians.

In the years which have elapsed since Bacon's summons, however, the empirical approach to knowledge — the willingness to be instructed ultimately by experience and to let "fruits and inventions be, as it were, sponsors and sureties for the truth of philosophies" — has become the dominant intellectual attitude in Western science and philosophy, as well as in the everyday living of increasing numbers of men. Today the seeker after reliable knowledge is more than likely to take it for granted that the first step in any inquiry is to "get the facts" by observation. He assumes that he must begin and end his quest for knowledge by a candid recognition of the concrete conditions that are to be found confronting him in experience, without any preconceived ideas which cannot be altered by what he actually finds.

There are wide disagreements, of course, about the most effective methods of acquiring and testing our knowledge of different sorts of subject matter, but the essential agreement among those who share the empirical approach (as against those who do not) is on the issue: *where to look for a decision* in such disputes. The empiricist looks toward subject matter; his opponents look toward the process of thought. To the former "it is facts which coerce thinking and not thinking that coerces facts. . . . Subject matter is that which alone can validate any choice of method . . . it is our inevitable subject matter that compels the adoption of a suitable method."[6] Instead of the intellectual arrogance which insists that facts must conform to our thinking about them, this view substitutes an attitude of humility before our subject matter — a free and voluntary acknowledgment of "the majesty of the facts."

4. The Inductive-Deductive Method

Freedom from the bondage of authority and humility before the ultimate facts, however, do not mean passiveness or inactivity in knowing. We cannot get reliable knowledge by waiting around until Nature gets ready to instruct us through experience. The important facts about our universe neither smite us in the eye, nor do they analyze themselves. Even Bacon, who expected too much from induction and who reacted much too strongly against all "anticipations of Nature" as premature, realized that man must exert himself strenuously in order to get beneath the surface of things. The mere amassing and describing of data does not by itself constitute a science, although many hasty readers of Bacon have gathered that impression from his works. If the extreme rationalist is like a spider spinning out theories from within, the extreme empiricist is to be compared, he tells us, to an ant which piles up useless heaps

[6] Sterling P. Lamprecht, "Empiricism and Natural Knowledge," *University of California Publications in Philosophy*, vol. XVI, no. 14, pp. 78, 83.

of facts. Better than either the spider or ant is the bee, which selectively gathers pollen and transforms it into honey for the delight of man.

In another famous metaphor, Bacon compares "simple experience, taken as it comes," to "a mere groping, as of men in the dark. . . . But the true method of experience, on the contrary, first lights the candle, and then by means of the candle shows the way; commencing as it does with experience duly ordered and digested, not bungling or erratic, and from it educing axioms, and from established axioms again new experiments." Nature may even have to be put to the torture, like an unwilling witness against herself, in order to extract her inmost secrets. Bacon expected such investigation to be "laborious to search, ignoble to meditate, harsh to deliver, illiberal to practice, infinite in number, and minute in subtlety." He predicted that in order to furnish induction "well and duly for its work . . . greater labor will have to be spent on it than has hitherto been spent on the syllogism."[7]

As for Bacon's own work, there is some truth in Harvey's famous gibe that "The Lord Chancellor writes philosophy (science) . . . like a Lord Chancellor." Bacon's secretary tells us that the great Elizabethan "was wont to complain that he should be forced to be a Workman and a Laborer in science when he thought he deserved to be an Architect in this building." He was "the magnificent demagogue of science," leading men back from the fallacies of telling Nature to the wiser policy of asking her — the man, in short, "who rang the bell that called the wits together." So, although his conception of scientific method was extremely crude and suited only to the earliest definition-framing stage of research (since, unlike Aristotle, he had to codify his *Organon* before and not after its procedures had been extensively tried out in practice), and although his own very limited use of it was unfruitful, Bacon proved to be an excellent prophet and the true "rediscoverer of the art of discovery" in the sense that he predicted the immense usefulness for human welfare of a return to induction.

DEWEY'S ANALYSIS OF REFLECTIVE THINKING

The geniuses who took the first great steps forward in modern physics were not Baconian empiricists, but mathematical rationalists like Galileo and Newton, who showed how deduction and induction could be fused in a single hypothetico-deductive experimental method. They took their departures from observations which suggested new theories, the latter being elaborated mathematically in terms of "ideal cases," then checked against carefully measured observations. This combined method of induction and deduction received its classic modern formulation in terms of stages in John Dewey's *How We Think* (1910). In his analysis of a complete act of reflective thinking, defined as the "active, persistent, and careful consideration of any belief or supposed form of knowledge in the light of the grounds that support it, and the further conclusions to which it tends," Dewey distinguishes five stages or steps:

7 Francis Bacon, *Novum Organum*, Aphorisms LXXXII, CV.

I. *A felt difficulty* — the occurrence of something perplexing in our experience.

II. *Its location and definition* — observation that makes clear what the difficulty is.

III. *Rise of suggestions of possible solutions* — hypotheses.

IV. *Their mental elaboration* — deductive reasoning-out of the consequences: *if each* of the hypotheses is accepted, *then* it follows that . . .

V. *Further observation or experiment* — leading to acceptance or rejection on empirical grounds.

This is another way of saying that our demand for reliable knowledge is usually aroused by something which we recognize as a problem or difficulty. We come to a "fork-in-the-road-without-signs" situation, normally in our external environment, although it may be a purely intellectual puzzlement. Our first task is to clarify the problem by observation: "What is the difficulty?" If it concerns the external world, we must start with our feet firmly upon the ground of observed fact, otherwise we shall waste our time on illusions and pseudo problems. But what facts shall we observe? Only those which thrust themselves upon our attention? Without some anticipatory notion or tentative hypothesis, we shall lack a directing factor in our knowing: we shall have no way of telling what facts to look for, or whether the ones we observe are relevant to our inquiry.

So, while the quest for reliable knowledge most often begins in induction (in the broad sense of some item or items of experience), it soon rises to the region of mental guesses, hypotheses, or tentative solutions. By means of a flash of insight, perhaps, we are enabled to take a short cut to one or more possible orders or systems which may lie behind our observed facts. As soon as these are clearly formulated, mental ordering becomes important, and deduction comes into play. One by one our suggested solutions become the premises of deductive elaborations which alone make it possible to test or verify them. Some will be eliminated, as not in accord with the facts of the case. If we have been both ingenious and fortunate in our hypothesis-making, one of them will remain, having withstood every test, including consistency with the rest of our systematic knowledge, as well as compatibility with all the relevant facts. Perhaps the most prolific source of trouble in human thinking is the short-circuiting of the process of inquiry by conclusion-jumping. Instead of having the patience to observe carefully, and then to consider and test more than one solution to the problem, the impulsive thinker goes swiftly and, he thinks, surely, to the conclusion.

Dewey's five steps should not be regarded as mechanical or separable phases in thinking, all of which must appear in our consciousness in just that order in a given case. The first two of them, and even the first three, may be hard to unravel in some instances, such as in driving a car in heavy traffic, where our first conscious thought may be the possible solution of a problem that we have not yet located or defined. Once initiated, a problematic process of reflection may sometimes go on intermittently for years and even decades. With a little practice, however, the Dewey pattern can be discerned in most examples of thinking that deserve the name of reflective, such as the four cases in the Introduction.

5. What Are Facts?

The first stage of the combined method of induction and deduction has two main aspects, either of which may be considered first: observation — "get the facts," or hypothesis — "but what facts?" The two phases cannot be separated; and we shall begin by emphasizing observation rather than hypothesis. To consult experience is plainly to get the facts. But what are facts? The answer seems easy: facts are . . . just facts. The word "fact," however, has come to have a good many meanings, all the way from the broad sense of a factually supported theory ("Evolution is a fact") to the narrow notion of a single event ("It is a fact that this pebble is in motion"). To avoid unnecessary controversies, it will be best to start with the ordinary meaning of fact.

What we usually think of as a fact is something known to us directly in experience. It is what is appealed to as the ground for some human assertion or judgment. It is the stuff of evidence; it is the foundation or primary datum upon which a claim to knowledge rests. When we use such expressions as: "To get down to the facts . . .," "Now the fact of the matter is . . . ," we call attention to some lower or more fundamental stratum upon which our assertions rest. To talk about "true facts," as people often do, is redundant: facts just *are*. They cannot be false. To demand the facts is to signify our intention to find out what it is that we are obliged to take account of — that is, to move away from the sphere of the merely possible: guesses, conjectures, and fancies, toward actuality — "the world as it really is."

Now if we are to make this appeal for confirmation of our knowledge with any success whatever, it is apparent that there must be present in human experience, no matter how chaotic or variable it may be in other respects, *some* elements or factors that are relatively stable and orderly. These may be physical or mental or a combination of both. Rocks are facts, but so are the obsessions of insane people. Recent experiments have shown that a bull can be kept within a field by a fence consisting of a single electrically charged wire, provided he has been conditioned by one or more shocks from it. Such a fence is no less a fact, although it consists of the physical wire, its charge, *and* the mental state of the conditioned bull (inferred from his behavior), than an ordinary steel fence which is so strong that no bull whatever could escape from it. Whatever in experience is compelling, coercive, inescapable — whatever cannot be conjured into and out of our world at will — deserves the name of fact.

"Facts," as Smollett and many other writers have remarked, "are stubborn things"; or, as the poet Burns put it, "they downa be disputed." The brute facts, as they are sometimes called, are what, in a thorough inquiry at any given time, or especially over a period of time, we cannot seem to get rid of; they are more or less blunt indications of states of affairs to which we are ultimately obliged to adjust ourselves in order to get along in the world. They can, of course, be temporarily obscured or glossed over with fictions, romances, and all manner of pretenses by the tender-minded, or even in some instances completely ignored. Men have deliberately refrained from inquiry; they have been deceived by illusions; and they have deceived themselves times without number ever since there have been human beings on earth. There are some matters concerning which it does seem as if the old saying *"Mundus vult decipi"* ("The world wishes to be deceived") were still true. Witness the comment of President Barnard of Columbia, himself a scientist, in 1873: "Much as I love truth in the abstract I love my sense of immortality still more, and if the final outcome of all the boasted discoveries of modern science is to disclose to men that they are more evanescent than the shadow of the swallow's wing upon the lake . . . give me then, I pray, no more science. I will live on in my simple ignorance, as my fathers did before me; and when I shall at length be sent to my final repose, let me . . . lie down to pleasant, even though they may be deceitful dreams."[8]

But the will to believe what is pleasing, whether or not it is contrary to fact, must always battle with the counter-will to find out what is so; and there is abundant evidence that, in the long run, even apparently "vital lies" display poor staying powers. The facts, as we say, have a way of catching up with their most determined ignorers. Men, in other words, are forced to inquire objectively into some matters if they wish to survive and to satisfy their dearest desires. It may, of course, literally take centuries to dispel a universal acceptance of the existence of witches, sea serpents, and vampires as facts of physical Nature instead of as illusions, or facts of abnormal psychology. Certainly we should expect that many of our present opinions concerning matters of fact will look just as silly to the wiser men of a few centuries hence.

What we shall be looking for, then, in all our attempts to "get the facts" by observation in any field of inquiry, are the ultimately compelling elements or factors in the ever-flowing stream of human experience, which may form relatively stable bases for human knowledge-claims. Experience acquaints us with the world as our whole organism reacts to it; but understanding in its primary stage of observation of facts interprets our experience by finding form in it or giving form to it. The relatively constant elements in our experience may be due to the outside structure and functioning of the physical world or to the inside structure and functioning of human minds, or to an interaction of all those factors. It is not a matter of discovering absolute anchorages for knowledge which shall be eternally immovable, but rather of trimming down gradually the unmanageable areas of change or flux.

Facts are living, growing, changing affairs with cores of sufficient relative permanence to enable us to count on them in inquiry and to utilize them in confirming or rejecting our hypotheses. That means, as Dewey points out, that

[8] Quoted by Sidney Ratner, "Evolution and the Rise of the Scientific Spirit in America," *Philosophy of Science*, vol. III (1936), p. 115.

our search for reliable knowledge through what is broadly known as scientific method will usually begin and end with the process of analyzing out of the flux or experience its relatively coercive aspects for us as knowers, whatever and wherever, in the line of our interests, they may happen to be. We should not expect all facts to be of the same type, or all equally accessible, or all equally easy to establish as "factual" by a single standardized method. As George Boas remarks: "Facts should not be considered in isolation from the method of determining them, from the system of belief in which they arise."[9] Some facts lend themselves to scrutiny by instruments; some can be stated in exact quantities and precise measurements; some are capable of being expressed in words and sentences; while others, no less coercive and inescapable, are almost impossible to put into language of any sort. Some facts are also more plastic than others, at least in the sense that we are sometimes able to escape their coercion by changing our interest or dropping our inquiry. Pragmatists in philosophy emphasize this capacity of ours to determine, to some extent, what some of the facts we experience shall be *for us*; while Realists are inclined to stress the structural elements to which our knowing must inevitably conform.

6. Private and Public Facts

If facts are the coercive aspects of experience which we are able to "carve out" by analysis — that is, by relative isolation in a changing background or context, how shall we undertake the task of observing them? What method shall we use in dealing with the different kinds of experience for different purposes, always remembering that it is seldom the isolated fact in which we are ultimately interested, but rather its rôle in confirming or rejecting our tentative generalization or hypothesis?

INTROSPECTION

In our preliminary survey of man the knower as seen from the inside, we discovered the immense potential wealth and variety of the contents of any human consciousness when viewed as a "private world," without reference to anything outside itself. Minds that are both sane and insane entertain, as we know, all manner of fleeting sensations, dreams, memories, feelings, speculations, intuitions, and so on. The method by which the facts of one's private mental life are observed is called introspection. Fortunately its possibilities have been thoroughly explored by pioneer psychologists, so that its limitations are now generally recognized. Indeed, almost anyone can grasp the reasons for the essential awkwardness of subjective observation. For if I attempt to watch my own fugitive mental processes with a view to analyzing them, I find that I must, as it were, stand aside sufficiently to avoid obstructing and distorting them by "self-consciousness." To do this, I must let them run their natural

[9] George Boas, *The Inquiring Mind* (La Salle, Ill., 1959), p. 90, and chap. IV, "Facts," *passim*.

course, and then pause and view them retrospectively, i.e., in memory. Since any mental state lingers on vividly in memory for only a few seconds at most, it is next to impossible for me to make any accurate observations of inner processes that extend over longer periods. Introspection, therefore, while it can deal with simple sensations such as after-images and the like, and can reveal in our minds the presence of a great many kinds of complex mental operations, is unable to cope with the latter with any precision.

It is possible, however, for a person to set up his own private tests of what he regards as coercive in his own introspected experience, and to insist against all challenges by others that such-and-such is a fact *as far as he is concerned*. Mystical revelations may be held to be authoritative by the individual to whom they come, in spite of all the arguments of the scoffers. Carried to an extreme, this may cut the person off from his fellows as insane; but milder cases of alleged private knowledge are extremely important in the fields of art, religion, and even in politics. In my private world, I may assert that I am having a sensation of yellow, or a feeling of warmth, or a vision of eternal bliss, or a direct assurance that I am being called upon to save my country. Are these subjective or objective? Are they facts indicative of states of affairs in physical Nature, or simply facts about my states of mind?

Now it is hard to see how anyone else can know better than I do what I am in fact experiencing. Yet the capacity to experience does not necessarily carry with it the capacity to express or to analyze one's experiences. We know that men are notorious self-deceivers, to say nothing of those who deliberately misrepresent the private feelings of which they are well aware, e.g., the malingerer who, to escape military service, assures the examining physician that he is suffering from sharp but invisible aches and pains. Even the most honest patients are seldom able to tell their doctors exactly how they feel; while to diagnose the ailment of a man who is suffering from delusions is extremely difficult. Legal cases involving attempts to prove in court that a certain amount of pain or indignity was suffered, especially pain of the sort called "mental anguish," present great psychological and logical obstacles. The "secrets of the heart" make notoriously slippery evidence; and a callous jury may place a value of only six cents upon the "established fact" of a breach of promise to marry.

Thus it would seem that the private facts which pass an individual's own tests and are accepted by him as reliable knowledge are beyond the power of public examination either to credit or to discredit, except by some inference from conditions that are open to public observation. When another person's finger is cut by a knife, we suppose that his pain is like one that we have experienced in a similar situation, although we cannot verify our inference directly. Yet, we do not, for that reason, abandon our bungling attempts to guess the contents of other minds on the basis of our own experiences. We have a large vocabulary for describing these correlations between inner states and outer actions: "You look as if you were tired, angry, elated, despondent . . . . " But the "as if" is important, since you may be feigning fatigue or anger or elation. All our correlating (of your mental state with my remembered mental state via my observation of your outward behavior) is subject to a great many kinds of error.

What makes this matter of private knowledge of such crucial importance is the fact that within its scope lie some portions, at least, of all of our most profound experiences of value, and the seat of all of our ultimate bases of appraisal. The things by which and for which men live and die have final residues which are private because they lie beyond the possibility of expression in words or deeds. Lovers make momentous decisions on the basis of wordless intuitive estimates of each other that neither of them can coherently express. Many a religious mystic and romantic poet claims to "know what he knows" by intuition or direct assurance from within. If he is called upon to validate his personal feeling of certainty, he is likely to reply that the experience upon which it is based is wholly "ineffable" — that is, incommunicable, and therefore unimpeachable by anyone else.

But there are far more important although less spectacular instances of the central rôle of private knowledge than these. Any man's thinking, whether he is a scientist or an artist or an engineer or a poet, is bound to be governed to a great extent by what Professor C. J. Ducasse has called his "criterion of interestingness." The hard-boiled positivist who refuses to pay serious attention to any fact which cannot be tested publicly by sense perception, and who finds the dreams of the mystic so much moonshine, is applying his own criterion of interestingness; and so is the mystic who dismisses the public facts of science as trivial. Their respective preferences for different orders of fact lie at the very fountainheads of their inquiries, in the primary demands which they make upon knowing. Various overt consequences can be shown to flow from accepting the different criteria. But, if one chooses to accept the consequences, neither criterion can be "refuted, demonstrated, or shown to be more or less probable" than the other. We have arrived at the inner citadel of men's philosophies: the area in which originate the criteria which govern the rest of our choices; and some part of that region is marked "Private. No Admittance."

There are some particular fields of human inquiry, such as the physical sciences, in which private facts are relatively unimportant, since the goal of investigation can be reached in terms of publicly verifiable data. But there are others, such as the social studies, in which supposedly objective and scientific conclusions are repeatedly upset by a missing "x" which has apparently been overlooked, and which is sometimes characterized as "sheer human perverseness." What has been forgotten is that, while the facts of the exact sciences are preponderantly public facts, those of the social studies are mixtures of public and private facts. In the laboratory sciences, the tests of reliable knowledge are public tests of common perception, by means of which private criteria can be largely eliminated. But in the social studies, it is not so easy to distinguish between what is objective fact and what is subjective attitude. Private criteria mingle with public; introspection and external observation aid and abet (and sometimes contradict) each other. Worse still, whatever the social studies observer may succeed in distinguishing as his own subjective attitude may also be an objective fact of prime importance. The observer is not only a part of what he observes, but the very way in which he makes his observations is also a part of his results. To refuse to acknowledge this state of affairs results in the absurd blindness of "sterile intellectualism."

Where the two sets of standards, the inner "demonic" and the outer "scientific" (in Sir Arthur Eddington's terms) do not conflict, there are fewer difficulties. But where they do, it is fatal to exclude either the sympathetic understanding or the quantifying intellect. The problem is to come to a working agreement by "making allowances" from one point of view or the other. The mystic may try to banish exact science or place it at the service of madmen bent on megalomaniac dreams of world conquest. The overzealous scientist may assume that he has got rid of "demonic" activity by reducing it to his formulas, only to discover that he has overestimated the extent to which human irrationality can be systematized. It is far better to recognize the disturbing presence of the private facts of inner motivation in the picture of human conduct from the very beginning than it is to discover them, in the end, in a mysterious discrepancy between the predictions of "behavioral science" and the ways in which men actually behave.

7. Approximate Coincidence Observations

Private facts revealed by introspection do not yield socially reliable knowledge for the simple reason that, unless they can be expressed publicly (thereby ceasing to be wholly private), no two observers can ever have any solid basis for assurance that they are knowing the same thing at the same time. There is nothing tangible for them to agree or disagree about, nothing which logic can take hold of, much less succeed in deciding, because there is no sound way of telling just what is at stake. Private facts may be challenged by anybody, but can be defended by nobody, except in the sense that when my private knowledge is doubted, I can defend it to myself by considerations which are convincing to me, but which may prove nothing to anyone else. The seeker for reliable knowledge is usually relieved, therefore, to get away from this shadowy sphere of private knowledge to the other extreme — the clear, daylight world of public fact so familiar to all students of the laboratory sciences.

Here at least, he says to himself, is something objective, in the structure of things, which men can grasp and agree upon. Here we shall find the really coercive, the genuinely stable elements in human experience, the facts nobody can successfully challenge, the universally admitted conclusions that are trustworthy if anything is. Private facts are one-man knowledge; but public facts are every man's knowledge, tested by criteria which do not depend upon the peculiarities of any single individual. In the language of the laboratory, private knowledge is dominated and corrupted by the "personal equation" of human variability; while in the public knowledge called science, the personal equation is reduced to the smallest possible degree.

Consider any one of the familiar operations in a laboratory which terminates in the establishment of a scientific fact: the length of a rod, the balancing of two weights, the time consumed by a given process, the comparison of two sounds or colors. Whether or not any complicated instruments are used to supplement the sense organs of the observers, ultimately in each instance each observer comes to rest in a simple basic judgment of coincidence or the lack of it: this rod is (as far as he can determine) just as long, or longer, or shorter than that one; these two weights do or do not balance, and so on. This fundamental decision may be made by any one of the senses, or by several of them combined. Crude examples from our everyday experience are the comparison of two watches in order to tell the time, the fingering of coins in a pocket to tell whether we have two dimes or two pennies or one of each, or the recognition of two automobiles as being of the same make by the shape of their hoods. But whether we use the rough distinctions of common sense or the extremely precise readings of sensitive gauges and cross hairs, the final step is the same: *This does or does not approximately coincide with that.*

Note that the coincidence does not have to be perfect in order to serve as the basis for a wide agreement among observers. Most of the exact measurements of science are advanced, not as final figures which are never to be corrected, but as the latest products of the method of successive approximations. The latter consists of indefinitely repeated measurements by more and more refined techniques of observation, giving rise to a group of slightly differing results which cluster about a moving center in what is called the normal curve of error.[10] How far the refinement must be advanced in order to be acceptable in any given instance depends upon the demands of the observers. Ten surveyors measuring a quarter-mile running track might not agree within several inches, and yet everyone would be willing to regard the track as approximately a quarter of a mile in length. Yet, in a bacteriological investigation, a discrepancy of a millimeter might upset all the results. This calls attention once more to the factor of demand on the part of the knower at the very heart of the fact-finding process.

Once such a coincidence is carefully observed, we expect it, if it is to qualify as scientific knowledge, to be reproducible by others and to be confirmed by them. Any normal observer anywhere, who turns his attention to it, will report the same result. That does not mean that all human beings are capable of making coincidence observations with the same degree of fineness. But it does mean that all "normal" human beings are sufficiently alike to make possible wide areas of agreement within recognizable margins of error due to individual differences. There is, admittedly, some circularity in the use of "normal" here, because we use the ability to make coincidence observations as one of the tests of the normal observer.

8. Public Facts as Our Most Reliable Knowledge

We seem at last to have reached the goal of the most reliable knowledge that is accessible to man for purposes of action, mastery, and control of his world. It is achieved whenever any individual succeeds in winning virtually unanimous social acceptance of something in his experience as a scientific fact — that is, as an item that can be tested publicly by means of approximate coin-

[10] See Chapter 12, Section 6.

cidence observations carried out by normal observers according to conventions which have proved serviceable in similar instances. It consists, when analyzed, of something sensed, concerning which there is a substantial agreement among independent inquirers who have not been coerced by violence or threats or indeed by anything except the "hard data" of the experience itself. It ends the particular inquiry that aimed at discovering what was inescapably there; it clinches that argument, and provides the basis for a knowledge-claim.

But it should be clear that this does not mean in any given instance that we have arrived at knowledge which is absolute or beyond doubt. We cannot even say figuratively that we have reached bedrock, and can now build up structures that will rest upon absolutely reliable knowledge. All normal observers may bring in approximately the same sense reports about a given fact, and yet there is always the possibility that we are the victims of a gigantic "conspiracy to deceive." At the same time, we are justified in saying that, in our world, there is no human knowledge that is *more* reliable for purposes of action than that which approximate coincidence observations by many witnesses yield. To doubt *all* instances of that kind of knowledge is to refuse to credit not only the evidence of our own senses, but that of all other human observers whom we regard as normal — that is, as sharing roughly our own interests, demands, and sense-equipment. For this basic knowledge of socially tested public facts, like a bareback circus rider precariously poised on two galloping horses, rests upon elements of relative permanence in two changing realms: (1) in living human knowers, and (2) in the evolving environments with which they find that they must deal.

What happens when all such observers are able approximately to agree upon a fact is that a number of these stable elements appear and correspond. On the side of the observers, their interests, demands, past experiences, and sense organs are sufficiently similar, while on the side of what is observed, the material is sufficiently lasting, to enable them all to direct their attention upon and to single out of its context a specific item of experience concerning which all of them are willing without extraneous influence to make about the same statements with regard to its relation to the rest of experience. If either set of factors, subjective or objective, fluctuates too rapidly, we shall have no commonly accepted facts in that field. When we are able to agree on a fact, however, our agreement usually extends beyond our perception of it to its status with respect to other facts. Even the simple acceptance of the whiteness of a piece of chalk as a perceived fact normally includes an agreement that, in all sorts of perspectives and amounts of light, the object will behave with a certain consistency upon which we can rely. In knowing facts for purposes of action, then, we are not content to register them in isolation. We are not interested merely in discriminating sounds and shapes and colors for their own sakes, as in intuitive aesthetic contemplation. What we want to grasp is their meaning or import through their structures and relations to other facts and meanings — the ways in which they can or cannot reliably be expected to fit into all the sorts of future situations and contexts in which we are or may become interested.

JUDGMENTS OF FACT AND JUDGEMENTS OF MEANING AND VALUE

Live facts lead us on to some of their possible meanings; dead facts are those which are meaningless as far as we are concerned. Ordinarily we do something with whatever material we take the trouble to perceive. If we have a sudden sensation of a peculiar noise, we strain our sense organs and rack our memories to "place" (perceive) it; then normally we go on to ask, "What does it mean?" or, "What has it to do with me?" Facts are what we have before us coercively; meanings are what facts take on or acquire when we do something, or think of doing something, with what we have before us. In a problem-situation, facts are never isolated or complete in themselves. They are, as Dewey says, "operational" in that they serve as evidence by fitting together and interacting with other facts to form tentative patterns of meaning, thereby becoming possible "facts of the case."[11] Two observers investigating the same situation with approximately the same purposes in view may possibly agree on both the facts and their meanings, and even their values. But if the two observers have different purposes, then they may agree on some of the facts, and disagree flatly about their meanings and values. It is impossible to lay down a rule about what is fact and what is meaning in advance. It can be determined only by knowing where we stand and what we are doing.

That is why judgments of fact are so much more stable than either judgments of meaning or of value. Let us suppose that an owner and his friend are trying to decide which of two statues supposed to represent "The Chase" is more suitable for a spot on a hunting estate. The statues are just alike, except that one is six feet in height and the other is eight feet. It is conceivable that the two judges might temporarily disagree about the sizes of the statues in different settings and lightings, but the *fact* that the second was taller than the first could be easily and conclusively established by an accepted yardstick or by placing the two statues side by side. Suppose, however, that the owner's friend remarked, "I don't see why they should be called 'The Chase.' They do not signify that to me; and I don't believe that they will mean that to anybody else, either." A dispute might then ensue over the *meaning* of the statues in the context "signifying 'The Chase' to potential guests of the owner who might see them," which might hinge on the recognizable significance of a certain type of costume or posture. The number of persons sufficiently alike in interests and past experience to agree on the statues' meaning would probably be much smaller than the number of those who could make approximate coincidence judgments about the fact of their relative heights. An even more violent argument might center about the question which of the two statues, the larger or the smaller, was the more beautiful in the given setting, and therefore the greater in aesthetic *value*. Here the variability of subjective attitude, even in the same person from day to day or hour to hour, might be so great that it would take centuries of trial to establish a marked preference based on generations of competent observers. Even then, some individual might honestly declare the other statue to be more beautiful in his eyes.

11 John Dewey, *The Theory of Inquiry*, (New York, 1938), pp. 112–14.

Great care must be taken to distinguish between what we claim to observe as fact, where our dominant interest is in describing the object, and the added elements of meaning and value, or what is to be "made of" the object in terms of all our relevant interests. Yet we must remember that meanings and values are also facts, in the sense that it may or may not be a fact that an object has a certain meaning or value *for a certain observer.*

GETTING AT THE FACTS

Our ways of establishing primitive public facts go back to the method so well learned in babyhood, manipulation of the objects concerned: handling, shaking, smelling, tasting, and so on. We try things out in more than one setting or perspective to see whether or not their characteristics, as far as we are able to grasp them, are stable enough to serve as bases for prediction about their status as facts in future situations. Is this shiny yellow piece of jewelry made of pure gold? To find out, we may not only look closely at it, we may also feel it, bite it, weigh it, test its reaction to other objects, and even have it chemically analyzed. If it passes all the tests in common use among those gold-handlers whose criteria are similar to ours, then we may expect it to function as gold in all future contingencies.

Now, while the ultimate tests of facts are approximate coincidence observations, it does not follow that the latter must be crude and unaided sense perceptions. The exact sciences have long since ceased to rely upon the unassisted senses for their basic materials. Not only are human sense organs limited in range and in fineness of discrimination; they are also subject to fatigue and adaptation, causing variations in successive observations by the same observer. Scientists have sought not only to extend the range but also to eliminate some of the fluctuations in human observation by constructing thousands of immensely intricate instruments made out of relatively permanent materials, such as metals, glass, and so on. These telescopes and microscopes and stereoscopes and cyclotrons enable a properly trained observer to make ever more and more precise coincidence observations through finer and finer measuring devices, such as those which magnify objects to as high as one hundred thousand times their natural size, and those which separate films only one molecule in thickness.

Another type of "instrument" for bringing to light the particular coincidence observations that are significant and worth making for the purpose of gaining insight into the hidden but stable structures of things is the scientific hypothesis, or theory, of which more will be said in the next chapter. Modern physics begins and ends its experiments with direct coincidence observations: light flashes, pointer readings, sounds, and so on. But most of its investigations are conducted in quite different terms, sometimes called fictions or constructs, such as proton, neutron, atom, mass, wave, quantum, or velocity. Violent controversies have raged about the "reality" of these devices, and the degree to which their construction is or is not forced upon the knower by the nature of things. But the important matter to note at this point is that, whatever their status in the scheme of existence, these derivative "facts" function as convenient and effective tools for the interpretation of the primary data of science. The various atomic theories, some of them largely mathematical, have enabled physicists and chemists to use their powerful instruments of precision to look for facts which would otherwise have gone unnoticed, and which have turned out to be of great importance. About such systems of symbols, Einstein has remarked: "It seems that the human mind has first to construct forms independently before we can find them in things." While the ultimate, primitive, and indisputable facts of any science rest upon approximate coincidence observations, that does not mean that a science can be constructed by random gazing at whatever our senses can observe. Large numbers of our most critical scientific observations would never have been made at all if it had not been for the guidance of men's attention by elaborate hypothetical systems of symbols worked out by geniuses of the imagination. Direct sense perceptions are finally decisive in matters of fact; but what direct observations we shall make, and what they will decide, are often determined in turn by the indirect methods of abstracting, conceptualizing, and hypothesis-making.

9. The Technique of Scientific Observation

Waiving for the present any detailed examination of the direction of observation by an hypothesis, we shall attempt a summary of the main conditions of scientific observation in those fields where it has been most successful in establishing public facts, the so-called exact sciences. That will necessitate a few brief reminders about the elementary psychology of the normal human observer.

ATTENTION IS PRIMARY

To observe any fact whatever, we must first pay attention to it, and this usually requires sustained and voluntary effort on our part. The uninteresting or unobtrusive is ordinarily the unobserved, unless we exert ourselves to observe it. This commonplace fact has a number of important implications for good scientific observation. In the first place, whatever concerns us directly is more likely to attract our attention than that which affects others. Furthermore, there are two kinds of stimuli which have a great initial advantage in securing our attention: (1) the smashingly obtrusive, which thrust themselves irresistibly upon our attention by presenting vivid or startling changes to our sense organs (and on which the crude attention-catching phase of outdoor advertising is based): loud noises, lurid color contrasts, and stunts of all sorts; and (2) the intrinsically interesting, which appeal to our innate wants, such as the smell of food or alluring pictures of the opposite sex. To attend to these things requires little or no voluntary effort on our part; indeed, to resist or to ignore them is rather what calls for specific effort.

Now it is apparent that if, left to our own devices in infancy, we paid attention only to what forced itself upon our notice in the manners above-mentioned, we should remain childishly ignorant of all but the most superficial aspects of the world about us. Most of the observational material of the sciences does not consist of the obvious or the spectacular features of our environment; quite the contrary is true. We have learned to our sorrow that many of the processes which affect us most vitally — the changes in weather conditions, the growth of disease germs, the work of termites, the undermining of credit structures or of international peace — do not catch the eye of our native interests or single themselves out forcibly for our attention. They have to be patiently investigated by someone who has learned to concentrate upon things that may be, intrinsically, dull and uninteresting.

A large part of the process of human education consists of just this learning to rise above the animal level of noticing only what is natively irresistible. The child is schooled to pay attention, perhaps for hours on end, to vast numbers of things which an uneducated boy or girl would find totally blank and unappealing. This requires the gradual development of artificial or acquired interests by a process of transfer, usually involving extraneous rewards and punishments. Students who are not naturally gifted with a great deal of curiosity do not spend long hours observing in a laboratory without artificial spurs, such as tests, grades, and degrees. Few men have the patience of the famous English scientist Sir John Lubbock, who tells in his autobiography of watching a single ant continuously from six o'clock in the morning until a quarter to ten at night. The ant worked without intermission for the whole period; and so did Sir John. Similar feats of intense concentration can be performed by adults under the influence of artificial interests such as the desire for money or notoriety. In Thorndike's words: "Man can learn and do what he wants to learn and do whether he likes it or not."[12] But of course liking does help, especially in sustaining attention against competing distractions.

What we have to remember in approaching the problem of scientific observation is that its preparatory stage is attention; and that human attention is a matter of intense competition among innumerable stimuli, some of which have, as it were, "unfair" natural advantages in getting and holding the center of the stage. In addition to the limitations of our sense organs, there is also the limited span of our attention at any one moment to be considered, as well as its tendency to shift rapidly from one part of any given field to another. Of all the data that our limited senses bring us, we cannot, strictly speaking, focus our attention upon more than one thing at a time. Observation is thus, from the very start, a process of selection. We are not likely to sustain our attention upon the selected segment of the changing total field long enough to observe a fact unless we have either a native or an artificial interest that is strong enough to resist the lure of distracting influences.

Many of the greatest discoveries in the history of the sciences have been

[12] Edward L. Thorndike, *The Psychology of Wants, Interests, and Attitudes* (New York, 1935), Chapter IX contains a description of experiments in learning false dates, false biographies, writing with the eyes closed, and typing words backwards.

made by chance observations of seemingly unrelated details which were seen to be significant.[13] Among them were Galvani's discovery of current electricity, Pasteur's of immunization, Oersted's establishing of the connection between magnetism and electricity, and Fleming's finding of the therapeutic capabilities of penicillin.

Far from being a simple matter of passive mirroring of what is before us, then, scientific observation on any significant scale will be bound to call for a high degree of active concentration of attention, preferably with an end or purpose in view. We must seek with our sense organs if we are to find; and yet, paradoxically, if we seek too zealously we shall be in grave danger of finding what we seek, whether or not it is genuinely there.

PERCEPTION IS SENSATION PLUS INFERENCE

"About dusk one evening I started across the campus toward the gymnasium, but stopped with surprise before the body of a dead deer lying in the middle of the roadway. It was in the hunting season, and my first thought was of the deer I had seen recently being carried on hunters' automobiles — one must have fallen off accidentally. I stepped closer in order to investigate, and found that the rather shapeless dark brown mass which I had taken for a deer was actually a burlap bag and a large piece of brown paper, which had blown across the road together."

This everyday example of an error in reporting a simple fact should remind us that sensations are but a small part of the process of accurate observation. It is not our sensations, but what we make of them that counts in knowing. In the above illustration, the knower's sensations were all right in themselves (although somewhat weakened by the gathering darkness), but his further response in an effort to interpret them was erroneous. He worked up the sensory material by selection and combination into the wrong pattern: "This is a deer," instead of the right one: "This is an old bag and a piece of paper." To perceive correctly is not only to sense but to "size up the situation" by inference as quickly as possible. The sizing up, however, is not nearly so automatic as the sensing; and the margin of error is enormously greater. To be alive as an organism is just to be able to make and to profit by such errors. Chemical substances by themselves cannot commit blunders of this sort. As Samuel Butler once suggested: "If oxygen could go wrong and mistake some other gas for hydrogen, and thus learn not to mistake it any more, we should say oxygen was alive."

Now plainly if our most reliable knowledge consists of approximate coincidence observations, and if these in turn rest upon correct perceptions, then it is of the highest importance to know under what conditions we may expect the latter to be most trustworthy, and what safeguards are necessary in order to insure that the conditions are maintained. For unless we can interpret our sensations by referring them to publicly acceptable frames of reference, social

[13] No less than twenty-six instances are given by William I. E. Beveridge in *The Art of Scientific Investigation* (New York, 1950), pp. 27–40, 156–62.

co-operation will become impossible. It should be apparent that, in dealing with perception, we have to do with an activity which both isolates and combines sensations. It is a "unitary response to an isolated assemblage of stimuli" which yields what we take to be a fact, as for instance when we recognize a face or voice. But there is the further problem of deciding whether the face is a picture, a wax model, or a living person; or whether the voice is an imitation, a phonograph record, or a "real" person who is speaking. In the human infant, even the simplest perception is a great achievement, requiring an intense concentration of attention and frequent repetition of the stimuli in order to get to know the persons and objects which are finally isolated from the "big, blooming, buzzing confusion" (in William James's phrase) of its consciousness. But human children soon become practiced perceivers: they respond by cues and clues: "That noise was a car; that pressure is the arm of my chair; that red light means stop," and so on. Artists know that, in order to make us see what they want us to see in their paintings, they need only to manipulate light and shade in such a way as to offer the essential sensory cues. A caricature of a well-known person, for example, gives us just enough hints to enable us to fill in the rest of the picture for ourselves. As Goethe put it: "We see only what we already know."

In this way most of our perceptions come to be inferences based upon our past conditioning and our hopes and fears for the future, set off by meager sensory signals. Once our environment becomes fairly stabilized, we are chronic "observers" of far more than we bother to sense with any fullness. If you begin at the time you awaken in the morning, and follow the course of your perceptions for several hours, you will be astonished to find out how few of them are based on anything more substantial than hints that familiar surroundings are still there, and that the usual changes are still going on. This tendency of ours to steer by a few old signposts is another example of the human desire to economize on effort. But it can get us into all kinds of trouble. For we are continually tempted to suppose that we have observed something, when as a matter of fact we have only inferred it on the basis of insufficient evidence. When we have strong desires, combined with just enough sensory material to work with, it takes unusual restraint to keep from plunging ahead to observational conclusions. This is particularly true in dealing with such complex matters as "trying to read the mind's construction in the face," in Shakespeare's phrase. With an excess of confidence we make our inferences on the basis of clues which we have used successfully in some instances, forgetting that, in a genuinely novel situation, what we need is a clue to something which we have not yet perceived.

If we are to understand the most common sources of error in observation, it will be well to analyze some of the fundamental ways in which our inferences go astray. Psychologists are not agreed about the exact nature of the part played by patterns derived from past experience in molding our perceptions; but it is obvious that their influence upon our interpretations, even of the simplest object, is very strong. In Figure 6 it is difficult, to say the least, to see the three dots as other than the corners of a triangle, although they might

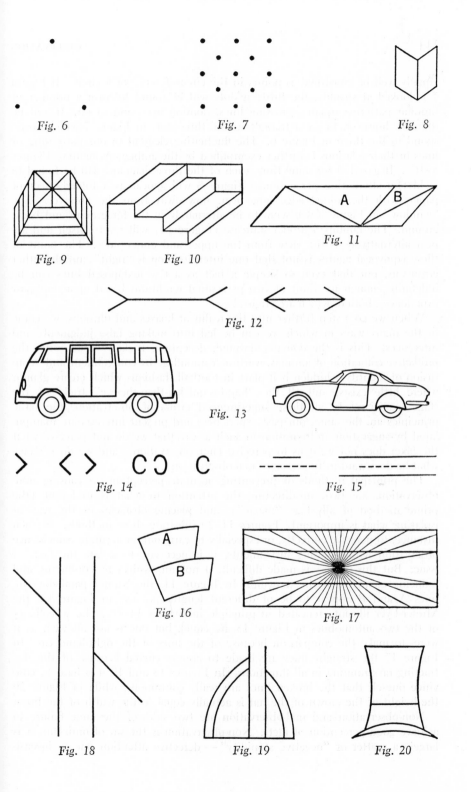

Fig. 6

Fig. 7

Fig. 8

Fig. 9

Fig. 10

Fig. 11

Fig. 12

Fig. 13

Fig. 14

Fig. 15

Fig. 16

Fig. 17

Fig. 18

Fig. 19

Fig. 20

equally well be construed as points in the circumference of a circle. If Figure 7 is looked at steadily, the thirteen dots will be found to form a number of familiar patterns: squares, crossing lines, domino fives, and so on. It will be difficult, however, to see a triangle in the three dots in Figure 7 which correspond to the three in Figure 6. The fluctuating element in our patterning of lines in their relations is further exemplified by the ambiguous figures (Figures 8–10). If gazed at for some time, each of the three diagrams will be found to yield two alternating perceptions. Figure 8 will appear as a folded sheet of paper, with the folded edge now near, now away from the observer. The "window" in Figure 9 will seem to be alternately in the foreground and background. The famous Schröder staircase (Figure 10) will reverse itself and appear alternatively as the view from the upper and under sides. The point of these equivocal figures is not that one interpretation is "right" and the other erroneous, but that even so simple a fact as a few juxtaposed lines can be indefinite enough to admit of two perceptual renditions based upon our past experiences, both of which are "right."

When we go a step further into the realm of hoaxes and illusions, we come to the many ways in which we can be led into making false judgments and inferences. This is the domain of fraud, deception, trickery of all sorts: the protective coloration of animals, wartime camouflage by concealment and "confusion of identity," hidden ball plays in football, fashions which create glamor where little exists, and all the "hand-is-quicker-than-the-eye" tricks of the stage magician. In all these superinduced errors of observation, the basic principles are the same: our past experiences and present interests are manipulated by suggestion and emotion in such a way that we do not perceive what the faker does not want us to perceive (non-observation), and we do perceive what he does want us to perceive (mal-observation).

The principal methods of preventing accurate perception, or causing non-observation, are two: misdirecting the attention to what is irrelevant (the prime method of all stage "magic"); and placing obstacles in the way of isolating what is important. Figures 11–20 illustrate these methods. In each instance, to perceive correctly, or especially to carry out an accurate coincidence observation without using instruments, it is necessary to isolate the facts at issue. But this process is made difficult, if not impossible, by conflicting and seducing elements in the drawing. In Figure 11, the Sander parallelogram, lines A and B appear to be of different lengths, as also in Figure 12, the Müller-Lyer illusion, repeated in principle in Figures 14–16. The wheelbases of the two automobiles in Figure 13 are equal, but one is not allowed, as it were, to make the comparison because of the lines of the right-hand car. In Figure 17 the straight lines are made to appear curved because of the distracting rays running in all directions. In Figures 18 and 19 it is hard to convince oneself that the broken lines are really continuous; while in Figure 20 the height of the crown of the hat is actually equal to the width of the brim.

Non-observation and mal-observation are two sides of the same failure to achieve good perception of facts. Non-observation is the sin of omission; it is largely a matter of "negative stupidity" — defective attention due to insensitiveness, carelessness, haste, preoccupation, overconcentration, or the sheer blindness which refuses to take cognizance of unwelcome truths. The swindler is happy if he can limit the field of our attention so narrowly that we do not notice the discrepancies which would reveal him for what he is. Even governments have gone systematically into the business of keeping unwelcome facts out of the range of public observation. It is never enough to be sure that we have observed a few of the relevant facts correctly. The question is: Have we observed *all* the relevant facts that a reasonable regard for the brevity of human life permits? The cures of non-observation are obvious: we should cultivate an ever-broader sensitivity to what we attempt to observe; and we should be especially careful and alert to perceive all those things to which our interests tend to make us blind.

Mal-observation, on the other hand, is the sin of commission. It outruns the data, distorts what is there, and adds what is not there, sometimes manufacturing evidence out of the whole cloth of the imagination. Parts are shifted about to conform to one's previous habit-patterns or temporary "mental set," such as the "proofreader's illusion" which makes it difficult for an author, who knows what he is trying to say in print, to detect typographical errors in his own book; or the mistake of the fleeing burglar who takes the uniformed fireman for the policeman whom he dreads. When mal-observation is induced deliberately, it is therefore usually preceded by a "preparing of the mind" to make false inferences, as when a propaganda report that "parachutists have landed and are at large in the vicinity" is used to induce people to misinterpret any strange sight or sound to the extent of firing on their own defenders. When mal-observation under emotional stress is carried to extremes, we have obsessions, collective hallucinations, solemnly attested visitations by ghosts, spirits, demons, witches, Hindus climbing ropes into thin air, radicals or reactionaries lurking behind every bush, and whatever else can be conjured into apparent existence by skillful suggestion playing upon the hopes and fears of men.

Philosophers and psychologists differ in their theories of error, chiefly about the sources and status of illusory "objects"; but there is remarkably little disagreement about the way to test an observation in practice to see whether or not we have erred in making it. The test is more observations, either simultaneously or successively. We may check a given experience by the testimony of other observers who were present: "Did you see what I saw?" Or we may test it by reference to the rest of our experiences, through memory of the past or through repetition in the future. Or we may combine all these tests. A stream of water may appear to a whole audience to pour forth from a magician's silk hat; but some of them are aware from previous experience that water is virtually incompressible, and so will conclude that they are being deceived. The most firmly attested facts are those which are open to verification by any normal observer at any time anywhere, such as those concerning the physical behavior of falling bodies, shadows, and the like. An alleged miracle is an event which defies reconciliation with the rest of our experiences: it challenges inclusion in the form of a new and reorganized belief about the ways in which things behave, or else rejection as an illusion. In civilized communities, we have reached the point where nearly all men in practice accept the same rough standard of physical factuality in their public relationships, such as trials and lawsuits. Where the level of the group's skepticism is fairly high, the burden of proof is on the describer of wonders, whose modern defensive slogan has come to be: "Believe it or not."

OPTIMUM CONDITIONS FOR OBSERVING PUBLIC FACTS

It should now be possible to outline the most favorable conditions for the establishment of a publicly perceived fact, remembering that it will rest upon coincidence observations which are confirmable by successive approximations on the part of any normal observer. These conditions, as they pertain to the observer, are often grouped under the three headings: physical, physiological, and psychological; but a more careful analysis must include another group of requirements which relate to what is to be observed. There are thus four main sets of conditions — those pertaining to the

(1) *Nature of the Subject Matter.* It must fall within the range of normal human sense organs aided by instruments: it must not be too large, or too small; or, if a process, too rapid, or too slow; it must be stable enough to support human attention, and not so chaotic as to resist all patterning. It must, in a word, be perceivable — that is, isolable and combinable. The subject matter must also either permit simultaneous observation by a number of independent observers, or else it must be substantially repeatable. Furthermore, if it is such that it is altered by being observed, there must be some way of determining the nature and extent of the disturbance, in order to make allowances for it.

(2) *Access to Subject Matter* (or Physical Conditions, including instruments). The medium between subject matter and the observer (atmosphere, glass, or whatever) must be clear and non-distorting; the background must permit isolation without confusion; and the observer must be located at a vantage point where his sense organs may reach maximum efficiency.

(3) *Observer's Sensory Equipment* (or Physiological Conditions). It must be physiologically "normal," neither congenitally defective (color-blind, tone-deaf, etc.), nor crippled, nor temporarily handicapped by illness, fatigue, excitement, drugs, or intoxication.

(4) *Observer's Perceptual Equipment* (or Psychological Conditions). It must be capable of alert and sustained attention; it must include sufficient past experience with similar subject-matter, yet not be routinized enough to prevent a fresh approach; it must be free from strong interests and personal prejudices relating to the subject matter; and it must be on guard against all the perils of erroneous inference.

Whenever we attempt to carry out controlled observations by establishing a laboratory, or "laboratory conditions," it will be seen that the four above requirements are exactly those which we attempt to meet. Given sufficient resources, it is not difficult to construct a laboratory for the study of the ordinary data of physics or chemistry or geology. Biological and medical laboratories offer more complicated problems, since the artificial conditions begin to affect the materials. When we come to "laboratories" for the study of social behavior — business, crime, genius, and the like — the term loses its exactness, for too many of the optimum conditions prove to be unattainable in practice.

10. Complexity of Observation in Social Studies

The "facts" of the social studies concern men who are living or have lived in societies. They are the stable aspects of such matters as buying and selling, the rise and fall of empires, ruins of ancient cultures, heroic exploits, leisure activities, propaganda devices, and religious beliefs. All these affairs are mixtures of public and private facts, of observable outward behavior and hidden motives and preferences. The latter are not only not directly accessible to public examination, they are also extremely fluctuating and often inexplicable even to those who experience them directly, since many of the determining factors in conduct do not immediately appear in consciousness without disguise. Thus, while we may establish by approximate coincidence observations the most elementary facts of the outward behavior of individuals (such as: A did not vote this year; B paid $100,000 for this rare book; C was graduated from medical school), in order to penetrate to even a fragmentary knowledge of inner motives and relationships (how and why did A come to neglect his duty, etc.), we are obliged to rely upon precarious inferences.[14] These latter will be drawn from either (1) our own inner states accompanying similar external behavior in similar contexts, often only imagined at best, or (2) our doubtful interpretations of the subject's imperfect verbal description of what he claims to have experienced. To the average white man, the Eskimos seem to live a life of "inconceivable brutality," yet a sophisticated Frenchman, Gontran de Poncins, became convinced after many months in their company that their inner, spiritual life is one "of infinite subtlety, full of shades and gradations, of things sensed and unexpressed."

Facts, it has been pointed out, are whatever stable and coercive elements can be isolated and combined within a context: this country among the countries of the world, this city within this country, this group within this city, this individual within this group, this act of this individual, and so on. Much will depend upon the level at which and from which the fact-finding takes place: a street crowd seen from a plane may be moving slowly southward, yet an isolated individual in it seen from the ground may be running swiftly northward. A single act of a member of an international trade union may be contrary to his own settled policy, his settled policy may be opposed to that of his

[14] Consider, for example, the paradox presented by the problem of determining the whole truth about the assassination of Lee H. Oswald, alleged murderer of President Kennedy, in a Dallas police station on November 24, 1963, which was "observed" by millions on television.

local union as a whole, yet may be in accord with his union's national policy, and at the same time opposed to its international one. In the social studies the time factor is also of unusual importance. One must never forget that, when we are concerned with human beings, data are dated. What holds in one year, one month, one week, one hour, may not remain reliable in the next. There are indeed some kinds of alleged knowledge that, as Whitehead once remarked, "keep no better than fish." Relativity has helped us to become accustomed to thinking of facts in these "moving" terms, as "facts for observers in space-time contexts."

Each fact in its own context and on its own level can be abstracted or viewed by itself in artificial isolation, while in a wider context and on a higher level it may appear quite differently. Apart from a given purpose, we cannot say that there is any one context or level in which a fact must be observed. There are many interrelated sorts of isolates that are possible: a battle can be seen as the struggle of nations, general staffs, armies, brigades, regiments, companies, squads, individuals, arms of the service, weapons, diets, morales, ideologies, or what you will. All social studies observers in devising their methods are therefore plagued in varying degrees by two kinds of questions. The first is this: In what contexts and on what levels can they most usefully isolate and combine their facts? What shall they choose as the primary bases of their observations: order in time? in place? in genesis? or in nature as a social process? Shall they talk in terms of such patterns as culture, institutions, types of social situations, academic subjects, classes, movements, or individual traits? The multiplicity of legitimate groupings and points of view for various purposes, to say nothing of their interrelations, is truly staggering. That state of affairs generates in some minds a desperate desire to simplify matters by insisting upon the absolute primacy of certain kinds of facts, together with the methods which are appropriate for observing them, such as the view that all the significant facts of the social studies are "spiritual" and knowable by intuition, or the counterclaim that they are entirely "material" and accessible to sense perception. But, instead of endeavoring to rule great masses of fact out of consideration in advance, it is more sensible to be as clear as we can about our aims in knowing, and then to look for stable elements in the flux of social existence wherever we can find them, using whatever ordering conceptions turn out upon experiment to fit both our subject matter and our purposes.

The second question is: How can the social studies avoid the confusions which arise through selection and abstraction, when facts which have been isolated in one context and on one level are transposed without warning to other contexts and other levels where different qualities are important? One of Balzac's characters points out that, chemically considered, human tears are composed of "a little phosphate of lime, chloride of sodium, mucin, and water"; but that would hardly satisfy a psychologist or a poet. The behavior of a dignified banker in his office and the same man attending a world's series baseball game may be startlingly dissimilar. The principal remedy for such fallacies is the use of a technical vocabulary of observation, or some other form of reminder of the particular perspective from which, and context in which, a fact has been observed.

It might seem as if individual differences among observers would render common findings of fact in the social studies impossible. It is true that each man sees both with the eye of his own past and with an eye to his own future. It is only by an effort of the imagination that he is able to see things from points of views other than his own, and perhaps even to "see himself as others see him." Yet both his past and his future are molded by the societies in which he lives. Just as we correct our judgment of a physical object in the laboratory by multiplying our observations of it, using all our senses and many perspectives, so we may correct our estimate of a social situation by multiplying observers and comparing their verdicts. Individual peculiarities of outlook about everyday affairs can usually be cancelled out by the ordinary method of agreement in group discussion, as we recognize in our use of the jury of twelve persons to decide disputed questions of fact in our courts. One or two members of a jury may be handicapped by habit or prejudice or blind spots, but the group, by the pressure of common opinion, is usually able to discount such abnormalities.

Where a greater difficulty arises is in the setting-up of the criteria by which a given society determines the normal conditions of impartial or accurate observation. Long-shared social perspectives, such as language habits and group fashions in feelings or ideas, are unconsciously accepted as the obvious standards of all right-thinking men, when they are often merely local prejudices. If the whole community assumes that "no member of that race can be believed under oath," then it may be impossible, within that particular group, to arrive at any just evaluation of evidence given by observers who have been discredited in advance. When a locality is aroused and in emotional agreement about an alleged crime, we do not even trust a jury to be impartial, so we provide for a change of venue to another county where a more objective judgment can be rendered.

One of the most devastating military surprises in history, the attack on Pearl Harbor by the Japanese on December 7, 1941, was largely made possible, in the judgment of a careful reviewer of the evidence, by the failure of "efficient and loyal men" who failed to perceive the significance of a wealth of intelligence information because of "the very human tendency to pay attention to the signals that supported current expectations about enemy behavior. . . . Apparently human beings have a stubborn attachment to old beliefs and an equally stubborn resistance to new material that will upset them."[15]

Just as in testing our observations, we seek confirmation by widening and varying our experiences with the object, so in setting up our criteria of observation, and in constantly retesting them, we need to extend our range of relevant experiences to the fullest possible extent. As finite human beings, we can never reach the ideal omniscience and universal sympathy to which complete disinterestedness aspires. But the fact that we are able to become partially aware of our own limitations of personality, family, class, and nationality is a strong hint that such relativisms are by no means fatal to a high degree of reliability in knowledge. The same fact, however, yields the equally pointed suggestion

[15] Roberta Wohlstetter, *Pearl Harbor: Warning and Decision*, (Stanford, California, 1962), pp. 392–93.

that, in observing what goes on about us, and especially in deciding what is worth observing and how it should be tested, we are strongly and vitally influenced by a host of superstitions, stereotypes, and labels which affect our fundamental "criteria of interestingness."

FOR CLASS DISCUSSION

A. On most of the issues facing the nation and the world, I don't think most of us have the facts. They are available, but too few of us take the trouble to go out and try to find out what the facts are. — *Willard Abraham*
   All wish to know, but none want to pay the price. — *Juvenal*   (1)
B. In Roman medicine, the great figure was Galen . . . he was essentially a dogmatist — "he knew everything" — and he laid down an immense number of dogmatic precepts which dominated the medical thinking of the Dark and Middle Ages, and which served largely to perpetuate error.
   — *Hugh Cabot, M.D.*
C. If, then, the final happiness of man does not consist in those exterior advantages which are called goods of fortune, nor in goods of the body, nor in goods of the soul in its sentient part, nor in the intellectual part in respect of the moral virtues, nor in the virtues of the practical intellect called are and prudence, it remains that the final happiness of man consists in the contemplation of truth. — *Saint Thomas Aquinas*
D. To make men perfect was no part of Bacon's plan. His humble aim was to make imperfect men comfortable. — *T. B. Macaulay*
E. Galileo's letter to his fellow astronomer Kepler (1610): "How I wish we could have one hearty laugh together! Here at Padua is the principal professor of philosophy, whom I have repeatedly and urgently requested to look at the moon and planets through my glass (telescope), which, with the obstinacy of a glutted adder, he refuses to do. Why are you not here? What shouts of laughter we should have at this glorious folly! And to hear the professor of philosophy at Pisa laboring before the Grand Duke with logical arguments, as if with magical incantations, to charm the new planets out of the sky."   (3)
F. Certain statements about human nature become, as it were, common property and so are accepted as self-evident. In the same way painters for ages painted shadows black, and it was not until the Impressionists looked at them with unprejudiced eyes and painted what they saw that we discovered that shadows were colored. — *W. Somerset Maugham*
G. A fact is a compulsory experience established by common agreement which is indicated by approximately similar behavior with reference to it. . . . For the individual, every experience singled out by attention is a fact: a rock, a river, a star, a dog, mankind, the self; warmth, fever, pain, fear; an earthquake, night; a ghost, a unicorn, a pink frog. — *Frederick Barry*   (5-6)
H. A scientific fact is a piece of impersonal knowledge. — *W. H. George*   (8)
   The solid ground of Nature is a delusion. — *James R. Newman*

I. Motto said to be in letters of gold on the walls of Pavlov's laboratory out-side Leningrad: "Observation and again observation."

J. The human understanding is most excited by that which enters the mind at once and suddenly, and by which the imagination is immediately filled and inflated. It then begins almost imperceptibly to conceive and suppose that everything is similar to the few objects which have taken impression on the mind. — *Francis Bacon*   (9)

K. It is not that the picture magazines don't make life interesting; they make it too interesting . . . everything is lifted to the level of spectacle: bright, chipper patterns are found where none exist. . . . I am tired of wading through chorus girls to get at facts. — *Samuel Grafton*

L. Inspector Alleyn of Scotland Yard, a fictional character in Ngaio Marsh's *The Nursing Home Murder:* "Any faithful account of police investigations, in even the most spectacular homicide case, would be abysmally dull. . . . The files are a plethora of details, most of them entirely irrelevant."

M. One wonders whether the rare ability to be completely attentive to, and to profit by, Nature's slightest deviation from the conduct expected of her is not the secret of the best research minds and one that explains why some men turn to most remarkably good advantage seemingly trivial accidents. Behind such attention lies an unremitting sensitivity. — *Alan Gregg*
In the field of observation, chance favors only the prepared mind.
                                                            — *Louis Pasteur*

N. Nature will tell you a direct lie if she can. — *Charles Darwin*
Motto of the United States Army Camouflage Section: "Seeing *was* be-lieving."
The old saw that seeing is believing does not characterize the scientific men-tality, but its opposite. The task of inquiry is largely one of discovering what it is that needs to be done so that we *can* believe what we see.
                                                          — *Abraham Kaplan*

O. In a story by Anatole France, two mirrors, one concave and the other con-vex, accuse one another of distorting the truth.   (10)

P. The solid facts of social life are the facts of the imagination.
                                                          — *C. H. Cooley*

Q. The branches of science most important in a study of the physical world are, in order of fundamentality, physics, chemistry, and biology. It happens that the mind is so constituted that human interest in the subjects is in reverse order. . . . — *C. C. Furnas*

EXERCISES ON OBSERVATION

Analyze each of the following cases in terms of the optimum conditions of observation (Section 9 of Chapter 4), pointing out in exactly what respects the conditions are satisfied or fail to be satisfied, and why. Where relevant, indicate how much of the observation is sensed, and how much is inferred.

1. Snowflakes placed under a microscope melt too rapidly to permit the

study of their crystal patterns. Dr. Vincent J. Schaefer, then at the General Electric Research Laboratory, covered a snowflake with a drop of a solution of formvar, a transparent plastic resin, which dried to form a permanent cast of the snowflake crystal encased in a film about eight one-hundred-thousandths of an inch thick. The snowflake can thus be photographed and studied at leisure.

2. It has been claimed that a baseball does not really curve, but that the so-called curve ball thrown by a pitcher is an optical illusion caused by the rapid change of perspective as it approaches the eye of the batter. Dr. Lyman J. Briggs, Director Emeritus of the National Bureau of Standards, Washington, D.C., conducted wind-tunnel experiments with professional pitchers, and showed by photographs that, in the 60 feet from mound to plate, a ball thrown moderately fast (100 feet per second) can be made to curve up to a maximum of 17.5 inches if it is thrown with a spin that will turn it over from seven to sixteen times during its flight, because of the difference in air pressure on the surface of the ball as it turns.

3. Eerie moanings and wailings heard only in the dead of night and assumed to be the cries of living creatures had residents of the San Jacinto Valley in California driving for miles to locate them, until they were found to come from the high-speed fans in blowers of orchard dusting machines operated on walnut ranches only at night when it was calm, and not audible close at hand.

4. What accounts for the apparently larger size of the rising moon as compared with its size when high in the sky? Some have held it to be an optical illusion caused by the bending of the light rays in the atmosphere surrounding the earth. But two University of Wisconsin psychologists, Drs. H. Leibowitz and T. Harman, conducted experiments indoors and outdoors with adults and children in judging the size of objects at eye level when overhead. They found that a disc always looked smaller when overhead; that adults underestimated its size by an average of 16 per cent, and children by 50 per cent; and that the younger the child, the greater the illusion. They concluded that they were dealing with a perceptual illusion caused primarily by inexperience in judging the size of distantly viewed objects overhead.

5. After an amputation, patients often seem to feel pain located in the amputated limbs.

6. In his book *Through China's Wall*, Graham Peck describes the behavior of the Chinese near Mongolia, who had never seen automobiles before, although they were familiar with airplanes flying overhead. Their first reaction on hearing the sound of engines was to stare upward looking for the approach of a plane. When after a while one of the crowd would chance to look lower, the commotion over the metal monster was "always immense. . . . At one place they decided it was some sort of immature train; in another they thought it was made of turtles."

7. Late in March, 1952, three daring robbers looted an armored truck of $681,000 in the town square of Danvers, Massachusetts, and escaped. It was, said a newspaper account, "a sleepy, relaxed morning with the warm sun and earthy smell of spring hanging over the square. In the perfect setting for day-

dreaming, apparently none of the few motorists and pedestrians who must have passed the scene while the looters worked, noticed anything untoward taking place. More than twelve hours after the robbery, police and FBI men had been unable to find a single witness who had noticed anything unusual in the square either before or during the robbery."

8. When the Wright brothers made their historic flight at Kitty Hawk, N.C., on December 17, 1903, no reporter was present, and only one newspaper, the *Norfolk Virginian-Pilot*, gave it more than the briefest mention. Not for five years did New York papers send correspondents to cover their activities. In 1925 Orville Wright said that the failure to credit the accomplishment "was mainly due to the fact that human flight was generally looked upon as an impossibility, and that scarcely anyone believed in it until he actually saw it with his own eyes."

9. In 1912 Charles Dawson, a lawyer-antiquarian of considerable repute, sponsored by Arthur Smith Wood, Keeper of Geology at the British Museum, presented before the British Geological Society the skull of "Piltdown Man," which he had discovered in Sussex in 1911. The fossil cranium and ape-like jaw were widely accepted as constituting "dawn man," the so-called "missing link" between man and his ape-ancestors. A few scientists were skeptical; but in 1913 a French archaeologist picked up a significant eyetooth fitting the skull in the Piltdown gravel; and in 1914–15 Dawson produced a club carved of fossilized elephant bone and eighteen other bits of prehistoric animal bones. Dawson died in honor in 1916, and in 1938 a memorial to him was erected at the Piltdown site, with addresses by noted scientists. But in 1949 fluorine tests cast doubts on the antiquity of the jaw; and in 1953 nitrogen tests showed that at least ten of the eighteen animal bones were unquestionably frauds imported from Tunis and Malta. "Piltdown Man" is now regarded as the greatest scientific hoax of all time, perhaps not the work of Dawson himself, but certainly devised by a person highly skilled in geology, archaeology, anatomy, and chemistry.

10. In the spring of 1912, the city of Washington, D.C., was visited by Rodman Law, known as "the human fly" for his ability in climbing the fronts of buildings by clinging to small indentations and projections. Law drew a large crowd by successfully ascending the front of the Raleigh Hotel; and an evening newspaper ironically suggested that he try the Washington Monument. The next afternoon an excited group at the Capitol were seen looking toward the Monument with cries of "He's part way up!" A black speck about the size of a man was plainly visible about one-third of the way up the 555-foot shaft. Thousands of people gathered in the streets and converged upon the Oval to get a closer look. Wild rumors and explanatory theories (he was using rubber suction-cups, etc.) flew thick and fast. One newspaper even issued an extra stating that "Rodman Law began the ascent of the Washington Monument today at 1:28 P.M., barely eluding the grasp of a policeman who tried to stop him." Those who reached the base of the Monument soon discovered that they could see nothing. The explanation: it had rained the night before, wetting the side of the Monument facing the Capitol, all of which, by some

freak of nature, had dried except one block of stone. The latter had remained dark; and somebody with his mind full of Law's feats of acrobatics had done the rest.

11. Since 1947, alleged flying saucers have become "the major myth of the space age," in spite of the fact that large numbers of the "unidentified flying objects "have been shown to be mirages, meteors, weather balloons, refractions of ice crystals, refueling bombers, seagulls, plover, and some of the numerous satellites now circling the heavens. Nevertheless devout "saucerians" steadfastly believe that visitors from outer space have been seen to arrive via space ship, although no such vehicle has so far been spotted by our tracking stations continuously in operation since 1957.

12. The first discovery of diamonds in England in the Thames valley near Reading was reported by geology students from Reading University, who turned up five low-grade stones in a gravel pit near a former bed of the Thames, a find at first confirmed by Professor Percival Allen of the university's department of geology. He later explained that the stones had been planted as a publicity stunt to promote a charity drive during the students' annual carnival or "rag," and that he had gone along with the hoax during a television interview.

13. "An honest and fair appraisal of any strike requires careful diagnosis. No one can reasonably assume that these stoppages are entirely the fault of labor. The mere fact that a picket line is more dramatic than a decision of a board of directors does not relieve us of the obligation for clear and fair analysis." — From a speech by Sidney Hillman, Associate Director of the OPM, April, 1941, as reported by the New York *Times*

14. To audit the books of a large corporation is to verify the accuracy of the accounts by comparing them with physical evidences that they are correct, such as vouchers, inventories, accounts receivable, and monies on hand, in order to eliminate fraud. But how far should an auditor go, according to "best accounting practice," in assuring himself of the physical existence of what the accounts purport to represent? Should he see, touch, smell, taste, or hear the stock on hand, or the amounts owed the firm? In the McKesson & Robbins drug firm scandal, in which the president of the firm conspired with a few other persons to embezzle millions through false and imaginary inventories, the SEC report severely criticized the firm's auditors, Price, Waterhouse & Co., because they "did not corroborate the company's records by actual observation and independent confirmation through procedures involving regular inspection of inventories and confirmation of accounts receivable." The auditing company attempted to defend itself by claiming that "the procedures for whose omission we are now criticized were regarded as optional at the time, we were expressly instructed not to follow some of them, and we were not instructed to follow others. . . . Furthermore . . . the determination of the scope of our audit was delegated to the president of the company, who has now proved to have been the keystone of the intricately organized conspiracy."

❧ 5 ❧

"BUT WHAT FACTS?"[1]—*The Rise of Hypotheses*

1. Theories without Facts, Facts without Theories

OUR QUEST FOR RELIABLE KNOWLEDGE has so far yielded two broad pieces of advice: "Think logically," in the sense of "Deduce validly" (Chapter 3), and "Observe carefully" (Chapter 4). Yet neither one by itself seems adequate for the attainment of our major human purposes in knowing. By a scrupulous regard for the rules of formal logic, we can construct mentally a great many consistent systems made up of principles and their implications; but their formal validity proves nothing whatever about their foundations in the facts of our world. Similarly, by concentrated effort we may succeed in bringing about the optimum conditions for establishing specific facts, only to discover that they do not seem to be worth the trouble of attesting, since they lack significance. This state of affairs has sometimes led to the pessimistic conclusion that "Nothing that can be proved is worth proving." Formal consistency in thinking by itself is barren because it does not "take hold of the thing." It does not tell us whether or not the classes and terms which we relate to one another validly have any existence outside the realm of our discourse. On the other hand, to strive directly to get a grip upon the thing by observation calls for its isolation in a limited context in such a manner that any qualified observer anywhere may be able to confirm it. Since unreliability in observing arises mainly, not from differences in our sensations, but from erroneous inferences, the less inference that is involved in making an observation, the greater its probable reliability. This has meant in practice that many of our most dependable facts are also our most isolated (and often trivial); while most of those which are richly charged with significance are notoriously unreliable.

There is little point in debating which of these two extremes is worse: theories rich in internal significance but ungrounded in fact, or facts that are inconsequential because they are unrelated to any theory whatever. An elaborate theory, too rigidly held, is almost sure to result in the omission or distortion of facts which do not fit into it; while the lack of any theory means the piling up of facts which lead nowhere. What is far superior to either theories without facts, or facts without theories, is obviously that happy combination of fact and theory in which the facts are illuminated by the theories, and the theories are tested by the facts. The scientist Tyndall called it "the incessant marriage of induction and deduction." It is the bringing together of hitherto

[1] "Begin with collecting the facts? Ay, but what facts?" Morris R. Cohen, *Reason and Nature* (New York, 1931), p. 76.

125

"He doesn't know anything except facts."
James Thurber in "The New Yorker."

isolated facts in frameworks constructed by the mind of man and vindicated by experience. It is the growing of healthy connective tissue between some of men's dreams and their inescapable circumstances; it is not simply what men find in the world, or simply what they make of the world — it is "a mixture of fact and hypothesis, datum and interpretation, the objective and the subjective, acceptance and refinement, acquiescence and transformation — in a word, of what men *find* and what they *make*."[2]

2. The Direction of Inquiry

Throughout the preceding chapter it was emphasized that the treatment of an important element in observation was being postponed, namely, the directing factor of "what we are looking for" when we observe. The advice to "get the facts" is not a blanket injunction to expose oneself to anything in the way of experience that may come along. It leads at once to the query: "But what facts?" Certainly if facts and theories are to be fitted together in such a way as to yield reliable knowledge, "just any old facts" will not do, nor will "any old theory" do either. Relevant facts do not label themselves as relevant. That is an element which must be added by the knower. Unless he is a mere random collector of odds and ends, the seeker of knowledge cannot go through life merely looking *at* things; he must be looking *for* something; and that means active inquiry with some directing factor in control.

Yet to look for something too assiduously is to run the grave risk of selecting only those facts which will fit our preconceived theory or dogma. A physician who was himself an enthusiastic oarsman, for example, once launched an investigation to prove that intercollegiate four-mile rowing did not harm the hearts of its participants. His desired conclusion directed his search in such a way that

[2] G. P. Adams *et al., Knowledge and Society* (New York, 1938), p. 382. (Italics theirs. H. A. L.)

only the facts favorable to it were admitted as evidence. There is little doubt that an equally impressive case against four-mile rowing could have been made out by selecting only the facts on the other side. According to the terms of a bill introduced in the Massachusetts House of Representatives in 1940, that state would have been authorized to conduct an inquiry into the effects of tobacco on the human body, but no teacher who smoked would have been permitted to testify or express an opinion before the investigating commission. Undirected fact-finding is futile, but such dogmatic focusing upon a foreordained conclusion is fatal.

It has taken humanity many centuries to discipline itself to follow the middle way between uninspired fumbling, on the one hand, and overeager "anticipation of Nature" on the other. The middle way is the substitution of hypothesis for dogma; it is the tentative or provisional suggestion of possible patterns in a given situation, rather than the arrogant insistence that some one particular order must be imposed. It is a modest reaching-out of the mind to explore the actual in terms of the possible by means of imagined mental constructs, which may, when put to use, clarify the confusions with which the thinker is confronted. It is guided, in its fitting of hypothesis to fact and fact to hypothesis, by what Dewey calls a "sensitivity to the quality of the situation as a whole . . . that regulates the selection and the weighing of observed facts and their conceptual ordering."[3]

To say that hypothetical formulations are modest does not imply that they are not at the same time daring or adventurous; their modesty consists, not in their unadventurousness, but in the moderation of the claims which are made in their behalf. Hypotheses differ from dogmas and even from assumptions in being explicitly tentative in character. They are not advanced cocksurely as something unquestionable or to be taken on faith. On the contrary, they are offered "for what they are worth," as possible solutions to be put to the test of experience. All hypotheses may be said to have two common characteristics: (1) they go beyond the given to a possible patterning or arrangement or interpretation of it; and (2) they do so provisionally, with a definite view to ultimate confirmation or rejection after testing.

3. The Functions of Hypotheses

All living is venturing, and any judgment which we may make, even including those of fact, may be regarded as hypothetical in the broad sense. Having the sensation of a moving point of light in the night sky, we may wonder: "Is it a firefly? A kite on fire? An airplane running light? A falling star?" Now it may be that we shall swiftly be able to determine to our satisfaction, by the aid of an accompanying sensation of sound, that the hypothesis of an airplane light is the correct one. But, if that happens, we shall have allayed only a mild curiosity about "placing" the sensation, concerning which we may not have any further interest. Given stronger demands for knowledge, we might press on to further hypothetical judgments of facts intermixed with their meanings

3 John Dewey, op. cit., pp. 70–71.

or bearings: the color of the light as an indication of the probable direction of the plane's flight; the direction as an indication of its probable destination; the destination as an indication of the probable type of plane; the type of plane as an indication of probable company policy; the company policy as an indication of the state of aviation as an industry; and so on. Note that we should then be moving away from simple naming or describing toward what we generally mean by explanation.

Hypotheses are sometimes classified as descriptive and explanatory, although no clear line divides the two. In the early stages of our acquaintance with any subject matter, we make our first attempts to order it by rough descriptive groupings of things by likenesses and differences in their behavior. We learn that fire will burn, stones will sink, diseases will kill. The process of observing things soon becomes full of interpretation and inference based in part upon these rudimentary groupings of our past experiences in the form of descriptive hypotheses. The child whose first encounter with an animal yields the pleasant experience of fondling, accompanied by the name of "kitty," is likely to try the same name and treatment on a second animal, which may turn out to be an angry dog instead. Gradually, however, the young human being masters the correct names of everyday objects, together with a sufficient knowledge of their important qualities to enable him to get along in the world.

But the inquiring mind is not content to stop at naming or classifying or even describing its environment. It asks for something more than mere unimaginative empiricism; it craves explanation. It refuses to be put off with statements that coal burns because it contains a "principle of combustibility," or that rubber bounces because it is full of "resiliency." It sees that such statements are equivalent to "coal burns because it burns" and "rubber bounces because it bounces." From classifying things according to the ways in which they behave, the scientist presses on to frame, if possible, explanatory hypotheses which state wider principles in accordance with which they (and related phenomena also) may be found to behave as they do. It may be that stones sink because they weigh more than the water which they displace; or it may be that diseases kill because bacteria consume the food of vital cells.

To explain in this sense is to make behavior understandable by exhibiting the relationships of observed elements and factors to one another in ways that are already familiar or can be made familiar to us. Sometimes the explanation proceeds by breaking a situation down into its past causes in terms of elements which we have reason to regard as incapable of further analysis. That is the mode of explanation which is most in vogue in the physical sciences, although some of their explanations are much more complicated than their original problems. But sometimes the behavior of organisms becomes incomprehensible unless we take account of the future, as when an organism acts in such a way as to perpetuate its species, even at the cost of its own existence. Much harm has been done by insisting that there is only one "true" or valuable mode of explanation, and therefore only one admissible sort of explanatory hypothesis, namely, one which analyzes a situation in terms of its component parts as related in generalizations or laws. There are as many kinds of explanation (and thus of explanatory hypotheses) as there are types of curiosity about events. Some kinds, men have learned, are much more fruitful than others; and some are almost certainly misleading for most human purposes. But until we have had enough experience to know what it is we are looking for in knowledge, we should extend a tentative welcome to any sort of explanation which promises to enlighten us.

The great superiority of the scientific type of explanatory hypothesis, which uses a generalization or law, over the descriptive hypothesis which merely classifies, consists in the way in which the former enables us to extend and unify our knowledge. A scientific hypothesis offers a general principle which connects the behavior of classes of things, and which may be capable of being extended to cover an indefinite number of additional instances. Of course it may be very useful to hit upon the solution of a problem descriptively, to find out that certain pains, for example, can be cured by the application of heat, or that certain crops will grow well only if rotated. In terms of knowledge, however, all that such a discovery amounts to is that we can do those things successfully without understanding what it is that accounts for our success — like an ignorant savage who has been taught to run a tractor by pushing levers and buttons, but who is helpless when it fails to work. A civilized man wants in addition to know *how* he solved his problem, so that he can do the same thing over again if he is confronted by a similar situation. But he is usually even more anxious to know *why* his particular solution worked, because the understanding of "the principle of the thing" may enable him to solve an indefinite number of related problems. A scientific physician may frame an explanatory hypothesis, such as the germ theory of disease, in connection with the specific ailment of a specific patient, and find that he has not only cured the patient of that illness, but has also revolutionized almost the whole of the art and science of medicine.

Why, then, are many scientists so wary of claiming to explain anything, often declaring that their task is only that of describing the world as they find it? The reason is that, historically speaking, men have had to learn by sad experience to curb their appetites for certain varieties of *premature* explanation. They were so eager to explain everything right away, without completing the task of careful description, that they rushed to set up broad, cosmic, dramatic "reasons why" all things behaved as they did, in terms of their own desires and purposes. That policy filled the world with gigantic spirits, gods, demons, and assorted forces which were supposed to manipulate events. All earthly happenings were ultimately to be explained by reference to the future intentions (in terms of the intellects or personal caprices) of such inscrutable beings. Those who, like the Scholastic theologians, believed that they knew the general plans of these personal powers were thus in a position to offer explanations of everything important in absolutely final terms. So strong was the reaction against all imaginative explanation of this sweeping sort, when modern science discredited many of its conclusions, that some scientists renounced all explanation as tainted with the appeal to mythical entities, and called for the rigid restriction of inquiry to organized description. This, as we shall see, is largely a question of what will satisfy our demand for explanation; and there is no reason for prescribing the exact boundaries of description and explanation in advance.

4. Sources of Hypotheses

If the hypotheses in which we are most interested are provisional possible explanations, where do they come from? Not from mere acquaintance with the subject matter, since there are some instances of people who become intimately acquainted with subject matter without ever bothering their heads to understand it. There is the pathetic story of the railroad man whose job it had been for fifty years to tap car wheels with a hammer, and who, on being given a dinner and a badge in honor of his half-century of faithful service, said that there had been one question which he had long wanted to ask: "Why tap car wheels with a hammer?" Plainly some imagination is essential. Yet hypotheses, to be useful, must not be wild guesses detached from actualities. The answer would seem to be a rare blending of imagination and past experience brought to bear upon a given subject matter. Hypotheses deal in possibilities. How, then, we should ask ourselves, does one get acquainted with possibilities? And how, especially, does one come to entertain new combinations of them? Patently one avenue of acquaintance is past experience. That is why we like, if possible, to consult doctors or lawers who have practiced for many years. We know that they have already explored a great many of the possibilities in the form of actual instances. Yet long experience as a source of hypotheses also has its drawbacks, for routine habits have a way of limiting and confining the possibilities entertained by the mind to those which it has already experienced.

For that reason the hypothesis-maker must add to familiarity with the subject matter the vital spark of originality; the capacity to explore imaginatively new and undreamed-of possibilities in search of ideas "not yet wordable," and to fuse old elements in novel combinations. The explanatory hypothesis is sometimes described as a leap in the dark; often it takes a kind of rash intellectual courage and freedom from convention. Francis Bacon was so afraid of this unleashing of the free imagination that he argued that "the understanding must not therefore be supplied with wings, but rather hung with weights, to keep it from leaping and flying."[4] As we should express it, the ideal source of fruitful, relevant hypotheses is a fusion of the two elements, past experience and imagination, in the *disciplined imagination* of the scientist.

THE FACTOR OF IMAGINATION

If, in order to become fertile makers of hypotheses in any field, we are told that we must discipline our imagination, must we not already possess an active imagination before we can discipline it? What if we do not possess such talent? Some authorities tell us that intellectual fertility is "given" and cannot be

[4] Francis Bacon, *op. cit.*, Aphorism CIV.

cultivated: some individuals possess it, others do not. There is an old bit of proverbial advice to writers: "Better to compose with fury and correct with phlegm, than to compose with phlegm and correct with fury." Is the "fury" of creative imagination simply a natural gift possessed by individuals in varying degrees, or is it something that can be acquired?

All human beings seem to be capable of reviving some of the material of their sense perceptions, at least in a passive sense, and so of entertaining "imagined" ideas. When this process of mental reproduction is entirely unchecked by any reference to a standard of criticism, such as the external world, we have what Hobbes called "the wild ranging of the mind," that completely unhindered play of fancy known as "free association." In the dreams of sleep, and sometimes in day-dreams, odds and ends of past experiences from many different contexts may become jumbled together in new and bizarre combinations. On a purely chance basis, very much as a great poem *might* conceivably result from an explosion in a print shop, one of these haphazard dream-associations *might* turn out to be a "great idea." That is the eternal hope of the lazy sort of inventor, who is always expecting some day to hit upon the hitherto undreamed-of gadget that will make him a millionaire. For centuries, of course, dreams have been regarded by the superstitious as important sources of revelations and prophecies; but we do not any longer expect much in the way of fruitful hypotheses from such chance associations, or even from the playful, wish-fulfilling sorts of mildly controlled association that are dominated by the "pleasure principle."

Yet there is something important to be learned concerning the scientific use of the imagination from these wilder varieties of fancy. It is the necessity of "letting oneself go" imaginatively in the early stages of any inquiry, the positive need of a certain amount of reckless daring in breaking away from one's established habits and of getting out of the ruts worn by one's past experiences. It is the willingness to take risks, to make leaps in the dark, to try unlikely and apparently absurd mental combinations, and even to be accused of madness, by the stodgy, in company with most of the pioneers of thought. When one of the professors at California Institute of Technology asked Albert Einstein how he came to formulate his famous theory, he is said to have replied: "By refusing to accept an axiom." Certainly we shall never get started on the road to new discoveries or inventions if we are constantly oppressed by the fear of being thought a crank. The tolerating of people with what seem like "crazy ideas" is the price which men should be willing to pay for that invaluable pearl, creative originality. Caution and criticism, it is true, have an important place in determining the reliability of knowledge, but they are out of place at the hypothesis-making stage of the thinking process. The motto of the explorer of possibilities for the purpose of framing hypotheses should be the rallying cry of the French revolutionary leader Danton against Brunswick and the invaders: "*Il nous faut de l'audace, et encore de l'audace, et toujours de l'audace!*" ("We must be bold, and again bold, and always bold!")

Thus, there is at least one thing that any thinker can do deliberately by an act of will that is likely to aid in the exercise of his imagination by freeing it from the bonds of routine and habit — he can purposely strive to "think otherwise," to set aside the accepted notions which he finds himself automatically entertaining in the presence of any particular subject-matter, and to do everything possible to devise a "fresh approach." There is no guarantee, of course, that mere unorthodoxy will supply the solution; but one thing is sure — rigid orthodoxy, or adherence to the old, has never yet led to the discovery of the new. Imagination, being the most dynamic mental activity of which we are capable, demands free scope for its exercise. The first step toward imagining a new and possible explanation of anything is to free our minds, at least temporarily, from the grip of the familiar. That is why there is so often a call for "fresh blood" in any enterprise which has become clogged with men who have become stale, too accustomed to their jobs, too stereotyped in their formulas, too close to their problems to permit new perspectives. It is one of the reasons why research laboratories keep their age of enforced retirement relatively low, in the belief that few new ideas occur to men after middle age.[5]

Assuming that we have taken this first step toward releasing the imaginative factor in hypothesis-making, what next? We may be free, but free for what? At this point it is customary to declare that the process of constructive imagination, what Ribot called "inventing for an end," is a complete mystery, especially to its ablest practitioners, who "don't know how they do it . . . it just comes to them." Brilliant ideas are "happy inspirations" which seem to come as it were by magic out of the thin air, without conscious effort, to certain mortals who are thereafter set apart as "geniuses." If the latter, it is often argued, knew the secret of their own clairvoyance and could put it into words, then schools for prospective geniuses would spring up, and we should all be well on the way to becoming Newtons and Darwins.

Now while it must be conceded, given the present state of our knowledge of the human mind, that there is no lack of mystery about the nature of its "original" thinking, we can say with confidence that it is neither wholly uncontrolled, a matter of sheer chance, magic, or caprice, nor is it wholly controlled, an affair of deliberate determination or will. Great discoveries are not made on order: it does little good for anyone to resolve, at a given moment: "I shall now proceed to have a bright idea!" The exercise of will power cannot force the fusion of ideas in brilliant combinations. The harder we try by such direct methods, the less we are apt to accomplish. Yet it is equally silly to wait around helplessly for something original to turn up. Inspired ideas may seem like accidents; but they are not equally likely to occur to anyone, or to be recognized as such, if and when they do occur. We must prepare ourselves and make an effort, if we are to formulate good hypotheses. But it must not be the wrong kind of effort. What, then, is the right kind?

THE FACTOR OF EXPERIENCE

Before trying to answer in full that difficult question, it will be well to shift our attention to the other main source of hypotheses: past experience. It has often been pointed out that musical "inspirations" normally come, in any

[5] Lehman found "man's most creative years" in medicine to be 30–39 years of age. *Science*, vol. 98, p. 393.

degree of completeness, only to persons who are familiar with music; chemical hypotheses usually occur only to practiced chemists; and new engineering theories only to experienced engineers. There will always be some exceptions: lucky hits by comparative outsiders who, however, seldom repeat their successful guesses. The reason is not far to seek: familiarity with many of the possibilities and their characteristic patterns through direct contact (or at secondhand through books) gives the experienced person the tremendous advantage over the inexperienced of having a broad base from which new suggestions combining old elements *may* arise. Whether they will or not is, as we have noticed, partly a question of how well the veteran has been able to avoid becoming routinized by his years of experience.

A simple proof of this is the fact that, just as it is true that few inventions or discoveries are made by people beyond middle age, so it is equally true that even fewer are made by boys and girls under the age of eighteen. Their imaginations are "free" enough, but what they lack is the necessary concrete informational background or mastery of the materials from which suggestions spring. Careful studies of the thinking of children have shown that the chief cause of faulty reasoning on the part of those who are gifted with good general intelligence is lack of information; and that "the same child may be logical and incisive in reasoning about a question on which he happens to be informed, and yet quite illogical in reasoning about another topic on which he happens to be ignorant."[6] This is also true of the hypotheses of imaginative geniuses of the first rank in fields where they are relatively uninformed. Sir Isaac Newton actually spent the greater part of his lifetime in brooding over problems of theology, history, alchemy, and mysticism, to which he contributed nothing because his fundamental assumptions were erroneous without his realizing it.

It should hardly be necessary to add that the process of stocking the mind with an abundant repertory of suggestions is not just a matter of storing up information like so many packages in a warehouse. Still less is it a matter of accumulating abstract information *about* facts which are not realized as having any meaningful significance. If it were, then the rote-memorizers of encyclopaedias would automatically become our great inventive geniuses. When we really learn something from experience — by visiting a new country, mastering a new language, or studying a new subject — we do not just add a certain number of memories. We enlarge the range and volume of our consciousness, it is true; but we also weave the new items into old patterns by likenesses and differences, and sometimes (although less frequently than we suppose) we reconstruct the old in terms of the new. Learning on the genuinely intellectual level is not only acquisition, but assimilation. The fertile mind is one that has been widened and deepened by a variety of experiences, but it has also been internally enriched by that mutual interlacing of meanings known as integration.

This richness of stored experience is by no means a purely quantitative matter. Dynamic interconnections are what count, and not just the number of

---

[6] Report of a study of one thousand New York City school children by Dr. Arthur T. Jersild before the American Psychological Association in Minneapolis, Minn., New York *Times*, September 4, 1937.

items in the collection. This is especially true in fields, like those of the social studies, where subjective factors are so multifarious and important. Sympathetic insight and dramatic imagination are indispensable to the person who would seek to understand the endless vagaries of human behavior. There are men who "have been everywhere and seen everything" without learning much of anything about human nature; and there have been other men whose mental materials have been comparatively meager, but who have woven them into a wealth of different patterns. Much depends upon what happens to our experiences after they occur. If we are intent upon perceiving patterns in ideas, then "a pattern with a gap in it" will be a challenge to our imaginative powers. Our motto for most of them may be "file and forget"; or it may be "reconstruct and remember."

To think of the right thing at the right time is to be able to call up from the storehouse (that is also a workshop) just the appropriate combination of memories. We may be able to do this mechanically by exercising great care in ordering our experiences as they occur, much as a librarian might be able, thanks to a well-catalogued memory, to tell us at once that he had just four books bearing on a certain subject in his library. But it is far more important to be able to remember creatively — that is, by the process of reorganization, transfer, and fusion of memories that we call "turning things over in our minds." The latter is not a mere assembling of remembered facts, but more often their transposition into new patterns where they take on entirely different meanings and values as we "see things in a different light."

There is another excellent reason for the fundamental rule of most scientific laboratories, "First, get to know your material," as well as for the common practice of first duplicating all the past experiments in a particular field before going on to new hypotheses. It is the obvious one that the ill-informed man never knows whether or not his supposedly original idea is genuinely new. Think how many years of wasted effort could have been saved if all inventors had first searched the patent files before perfecting a "new" idea only to discover that they had been anticipated by an earlier contriver. Well may Professor Lloyd Morgan advise the prospective maker of hypotheses: "Saturate yourself through and through with your subject and with all that bears, or may bear upon it, and *wait*."[7]

5. Constructing the Explanatory Hypothesis

If we are to obtain reliable knowledge about the structural interrelations of things in our world, we must go beyond the mere amassing of facts, or even beyond attempts to describe and classify them by their superficial properties, and seek an underlying pattern that explains them. Explanatory hypotheses of this sort are guesses that such-and-such a principle or generalization accounts for, or implies, the facts which we are trying to understand. A good explanatory hypothesis acts as a leading principle or guide in the observation of new facts

[7] C. Lloyd Morgan, *An Introduction to Comparative Psychology* (London, 1894), p. 307. (Italics his. H. A. L.)

which can also be seen to be explained by it. For example, a man might observe that railroad rails expand in the summertime, and so do metal roofs and steel bridges. From those observations he might be led to frame the descriptive hypothesis that "All metals expand when heated." It might prove to be an extremely useful thing to know; but it does not tell him *why* metals expand when heated. Their expansion was not *understood* until Rumford, Davy, and others advanced the explanatory hypothesis that heat of all kinds is a mode of motion, and that therefore the increased amount of internal motion in a heated piece of metal accounts for the increased amount of space that is occupied by its component molecules. Thus, a vast number of facts could be seen to be organized in logical interdependence upon a general principle. Having understood the principle, once it had been confirmed by checking it against all the facts which it was originally advanced to explain, men were in a position to extend their knowledge by applying it to still other facts. Wherever they encountered expansion, they looked for heat as a possible cause; and wherever they encountered heat, they searched for expansion as a possible effect.

But how, in practice, shall we take the crucial step which projects upon new material such an explanatory hypothesis or possible patterning of facts? If it is not to be a wild guess, it must be based firmly upon the facts which it is to explain (Factor of Experience); but if it is not wild enough, if it does not leap beyond the immediately given to a new, and generally hidden, connecting principle, it will never succeed in explaining anything (Factor of Imagination). The two rules so far formulated, "Saturate yourself with the relevant facts," and "Be daring and unorthodox in the exercise of your imagination," do not take us very far in the direction of a technique of hypothesis-making. Are we therefore condemned merely to "wait" for the flash of insight which heralds the great discovery?

HISTORIC EXAMPLES OF SUDDEN INSIGHT

Consider some of the well-known advances in human knowledge which have been made by sudden insights that have seemed to come "out of the blue." Each of them now seems to us absurdly easy to comprehend; we wonder why no one thought of it sooner; and yet each was an immense intellectual achievement when it occurred. Unfortunately the human tendency to dramatize the highlights in the history of science (one more example of the way attention goes to the exciting) has been responsible for mixing fiction with fact in some of these instances, as well as for exaggerating their importance at the expense of less spectacular accomplishments. But, whether or not they actually happened as popularly believed, the following familiar stories represent the common man's conception of scientific genius in operation:

(1) Archimedes, we are told, being puzzled over the problem of determining whether or not silver had been mixed with gold in a crown made for Hiero, King of Syracuse, stepped absent-mindedly into his bath, not noticing that it was full to the brim, and, when the water overflowed, suddenly grasped the principle of displacement. Wet and naked as he was, he ran through the streets shouting "Eureka! Eureka!" ("I have found it! I have found it!")

(2) Galileo, then a young medical student, during a service in the cathedral at Pisa, noticed the regularity of the swinging of a chandelier overhead, and found that, when he timed the swings by his pulse beats, the periods remained regular although the length of the oscillations was decreasing — the principle now known as isochronism in pendulums, used in clocks.

(3) Newton's perhaps legendary sojourn at the age of twenty-three under the apple tree at Woolsthorpe, meditating about the forces of Nature which he had already studied at Cambridge, when a falling apple suggested the hypothesis (not developed until years later) that the already known principle of terrestrial gravitation extended beyond the earth to embrace the entire physical universe.

(4) James Watt's alleged discovery of the steam-engine idea while watching the steam escape from a teakettle; or better, his well-authenticated grasp of the principle of the separate condenser while walking on a Sunday afternoon in the spring of 1765 in Glasgow Green, after having worked for several years on the earlier models of Newcomen and Papin.

(5) The chemist August Kekulé's labors to understand the chemical constitution of benzene (C_6H_6), which resulted in the visualizing of the "benzene ring" of atoms during two reveries in 1854, one while riding on top of a London bus, and the other during a doze before a fire in Ghent. His advice was: "Let us learn to dream, gentlemen."

(6) Most famous of all the alleged workings of the mind while "off duty," the mathematician Sir William Rowan Hamilton's invention of the quaternions at the age of thirty-eight, which, as he says, "started into life, or light, full-grown, on the 16th of October, 1843, as I was walking with Lady Hamilton to Dublin, and came up to Brougham Bridge . . . the fundamental equations . . . exactly such as I have used them ever since . . . I felt a problem to have been at that moment solved, an intellectual want relieved, which had haunted me for at least fifteen years before."[8]

In all these examples the factors of experience and imagination are easily recognized. In each instance a person already possessing considerable familiarity with the subject matter, and motivated by a strong interest, was working on a problem without being so confined by past experience or accepted conventions as to be incapable of making a fresh approach. Each man had prepared the way by hard thinking; and yet, when the click of insight came, it seemed to happen spontaneously with an ease that contrasted sharply with the earlier atmosphere of strain and effort. The inquiry had gathered its momentum during consciousness, and also its primary materials. But, at a critical point, conscious concentration on the problem was abandoned; and yet the work of solving it seemed to go right on beneath the level of consciousness. Apparently the thinker, in Sir Walter Scott's phrase, had only to "lie simmering over things" until, in its own good time, the inspiration came, sometimes in pic-

---

[8] *North British Review*, vol. XIV (1866), p. 57. The French mathematician Henri Poincaré had three similar experiences while working on the Fuchsian functions, making one discovery while off on a trip to Constances, another while out walking at the seaside, and a third during his military service as a soldier. All three were preceded by periods of intense but fruitless study. See his *Science and Hypothesis* (London, 1905).

torial or semipictorial form. A fallow period of complete intellectual inactivity, or a change of emotional atmosphere, seemed necessary in order to set the stage for the final triumph.

There is nothing impossibly magical about all this if we recall the familiar mechanism of association which we frequently employ in trying to remember a forgotten word or name. The two processes are somewhat similar, in that both call for the co-operation of our conscious and subconscious activities. When we cannot instantly recall a name, it usually does little good to try to force the associative mechanism by an exercise of will power. Most of us have learned that it is wiser to say: "Just give me time, and it will come." In other words, allow me to stop my conscious trying, and the subconscious may complete the job at its own pace. That accounts for the paradox that the way to recall anything is to think of something else.[9] Inventiveness is also a matter of association, although of a more creative type than mere recall. Even less than the latter can it be ordered about by the conscious will. Idleness, diversion, and relaxation have a definite place in the mental regimen of the creative thinker. That does not mean that they should be used as a means of escaping the necessity of assimilating facts, or that they alone will make us great theorizers. Nor does their usefulness contradict the familiar proverb that necessity is the mother of invention. Times of war, it is true, are often fertile in new military ideas; but that does not mean that the innovations were thought out "to order" by a straight-line process of sustained reflection. Great needs supply the impetus; yet even military inventors have to give their inspirations time to mature. It may even be that the great imaginative ingenuity of many prisoners in devising means of escape is due quite as much to their long periods of enforced inactivity as to their intense emotional drive toward freedom.

PART PLAYED BY ANALOGY

Another striking thing about the classic examples of sudden insight is that most of them seemed to occur in connection with the observation of a fact which "meant nothing" to others, but which was seen by the genius to form part of a pattern which might explain it. Nansen's perception of the possible significance of the driftwood on the ice floe off Greenland was an instance of that kind of achievement. What seems to happen is that the stimulus acts as a spark to the tinder of the responsive mind, but not when the latter has been dampened by habit. The eager inquirer is prepared to act upon slender clues and hints, because previously motivated by a strong desire to imagine completed systems or patterns into which new facts might fit. Ordinary persons are satisfied with what patterns their minds have already perceived or formed: they are not on the lookout for theories which may oblige them to reorganize their comfortable habits of thought.

An hypothesis, as Professor Brand Blanshard points out,[10] is a whole-under-

---

[9] Well stated by the humorist Erasmus G. Addlepate (pseud.) in his *How to Read Two Books* (New York, 1940): "It is easier to think about something when thinking about something else, than it is to think about a thing when trying to think about it."

[10] *Op. cit.*, vol. II, p. 135.

construction; and ability in hypothesis-making is "the power to extend a partially given whole." Hypotheses are incipient orders or possible patterns imaginatively envisaged, into which missing "pieces" may be seen to fit. Are they to be attributed chiefly to the subject matter, Nature, which supplies the clues, or to the orderliness of the human mind, which does the imagining? Plainly the two types of order contribute in varying proportions. Sometimes the "partial whole" is strongly suggested by the facts as they are found in Nature. It would not, for instance, take a very brilliant imagination to note that many polar animals have white fur or plumage, and that there is probably some connection between that fact and the environment of ice and snow in which they live. But more often the inquirer must hunt for clues to possible patterns beneath their natural disguises. It does not occur to the untrained, unimaginative individual that the rusting of metal, the burning of wood, and the digesting of food, all have places in a larger chemical order, the oxidizing process.

To identify like things in spite of their surface maskings, to see the underlying similarity in apparent dissimilars — that seems to be the chief task of the man who would invent new and fruitful hypotheses in any field. But where the facts neither fall into a neat natural order by themselves, nor does the mind immediately supply a pattern ready-made, the hypothesis-maker is obliged to fall back upon that great and primitive resource of the thinker, *analogy*. He must look around for some situation that resembles the present one as much as possible, on the perhaps slender probability that a known likeness in one or more respects will prove to be a safe basis for inferring other resemblances. Analogy is "the great magazine of suggestions for puzzled minds." As Aristotle is credited with pointing out: "The greatest thing by far is to be master of metaphor." The genius is one who, in De Quincey's phrase, possesses "an electric aptitude for seizing analogies." He scents similarities of pattern in places where they have not hitherto been suspected; and, what is more, he is able to follow them up.

What we do when we use analogy in making an hypothesis is to utilize the success of a previous ordering of Nature in making a new one. We see, or perhaps only sense dimly, how the mind devised or used a pattern that "worked" in explaining a somewhat similar group of facts. Neglecting the differences, and assuming that the broad structure of events is fairly stable and uniform, we use our earlier success to aid us in shaping a roughly similar pattern to illuminate our present data. The facts themselves do not have to be similar; it is their relationships that may be seen to hold in another field entirely.

We are assisted in this activity by what might be called the fringes or overtones of knowledge: everything that we learn has slight reverberations beyond its own boundaries, and there is a kind of magnetism which brings like ideas together in the mind. Poets can wait passively for striking analogies to occur to them and then use them largely as aids in their attempts to express the ineffable: but scientists are actively engaged in the hunt for analogies of a more abstract and binding sort. "Men, taken historically, reason by analogy long before they have learned to reason by abstract characters."[11] The mind of the

[11] William James, *Principles of Psychology* (New York, 1890), vol. II, p. 363.

savage operates by analogy, but from one specific case to another. His natural mode of expression, like that of children, is the parable — the story of a concrete situation with a point of similarity to another concrete situation. He may be totally incapable of putting the point into general terms, much less of proving it by means of abstract reasoning. We shall find that this distinction is of great importance when we come to the use of analogies in history as compared with the sciences.

It is one thing, however, as William James has pointed out, for cognate thoughts to be called up vaguely by association, and it is another for the genius to notice and to analyze out the bond of identity which unites them. To be able to state that bond in abstract terms is an even greater achievement. The task of the scientific hypothesis-maker is a most exacting one: he must get his hints for hypotheses from analogies, which he must then bring out of the dim regions of intuition into the bright light of intellectual formulation in terms of abstract principles or laws.

Analogy is thus an extremely fertile source of new ideas; but it is also extremely prolific in error, having yielded a large part of the myths, allegories, parables, and superstitions which comprise the endless history of human stupidity. Some of the ancient Greeks, for example, held that sight must be explained by "feelers" which extended from the eye and made contact with the objects seen — this by analogy with our location of things by touch. Alchemy in the Middle Ages was dominated by the false analogy of man as the microcosm copying the universe as macrocosm, which led one alchemist to say: "All that is without thee is also within"; and Paracelsus to declare that "Lunacy grows worse at full and new moon because the brain is a microcosmic moon."

Nine-tenths of all newspaper cartoons are analogies: current happenings are simplified into pictures of easily understandable parallel cases. All good teaching, since it must proceed from the known to the unknown, is likely to be rich in illustrative analogies, which are easily mistaken for causal explanations. An economist in search of a concrete image to explain the circulation of money may hit upon the previous success of medicine in explaining the circulation of the blood, and ornament with figurative heart, arteries, veins, and capillaries his chart of the economic "circulatory system." What is often needed is a better counter-analogy.

The world is full of analogies which are only superficial. In many fields we have an abundance of partial analogies which offer competing hints of possible exploratory hypotheses, and we are obliged to weed out the surface likenesses in order to concentrate on the deeper and more fruitful ones. Mere fertility is is not the answer here, for what we want is the *right* analogy for our particular purpose. That calls for a systematizing or ordering principle which our mind must somehow achieve and supply. Invention, as Professor Blanshard puts it, "is the emergence in the mind of novelty under the control of system."[12] Concerning the nature of this control, there are wide differences of opinion: some philosophers regard it as an ideal order of necessity in thinking; while others attribute its action to the past experience and present interests of the thinker. Here, at the very crux of the matter — namely, what ultimately de-

[12] Brand Blanshard, *op. cit.*, vol. II, p. 162.

termines our "sagacity for the significant," as William Graham Sumner called it, or our judgments of relevance and irrelevance — our darkness is the greatest.

6. Stages in the Process of Hypothesis-Making

One reason why such great difficulties are encountered in trying to lay bare the innermost citadel of the mind's inventive power in ordering its old and new materials is that the whole business is a matter of passing back and forth between the conscious and other-than-conscious levels of our mental life. The seat of inventiveness seems to be in what Sir Francis Galton called the "antechamber of consciousness," whether we give it the name of the subconscious, the unconscious, or the fore-conscious. What seems plainly to be desirable is that there shall be a large attendance of ideas in this antechamber, and that there shall be great ease of circulation between it and our consciousness. The latter is the main avenue of entrance of ideas in the first place, and it should be extended to the widest possible range and depth. Variety is of the highest importance, for the specialist tends to have patterns which are all of the same essential type. The next thing needed is a summoning authority, or demand, in order to initiate the ordering and selecting process. Then conditions favorable to its operation, which will differ widely among individuals, must be set up. The order of procedure is "prepare — strive — wait."

PREPARATION — INCUBATION — ILLUMINATION

In psychological terms that are none too distinct, Professor Graham Wallas of the University of London divided the process of discovery or original hypothesis-making into three stages which he called Preparation, Incubation, and Illumination.[13] They may serve as a basis for a number of practical suggestions in summary form.

(1) *Preparation*, according to Wallas, "includes the whole process of intellectual education," both the filling of the reservoir of possible clues and analogies by saturating oneself with classified facts, and the disciplining of the imagination by developing the capacity to think easily in terms of systems. It is the stage of hard, conscious labor without immediate rewards, which has to be sustained by "borrowed" interests. It is the scouting and the spadework: the reading, note-taking, "applying the seat of the pants to the seat of the chair" without seeing much progress in any direction.

(2) *Incubation* is a time of deliberate abstention from conscious intellectual effort, when we relax, divert ourselves, or turn to other work, letting the subconscious take over our "prepared" material under the momentum of our search for a systematic solution.[14] It is typified by the detective who makes

[13] Graham Wallas, *The Art of Thought* (New York, 1926), chap. IV. A fourth stage, Verification, is omitted here.

[14] In 1931, Drs. R. A. Baker and W. Platt reported to the American Chemical Society the results of questioning 1450 scientists concerning "conditions under which

a thorough preliminary investigation, and then turns to his violin or his pipe. Ideas and sequences may become arranged without conscious effort, *if* the inquirer has done enough spadework and has a strong enough desire to see order emerge from the chaos of his data. Individuals will vary in the nature of the alternating activity-inactivity cycles which they will find most profitable.

(3) *Illumination*, the flash or click of insight, may come at the close of incubation, or it may be postponed until the seeker returns, refreshed, to a new attack upon his problem. Generally it is a sudden success crowning many unsuccessful trials. Sometimes it is preceded by intimations of what is to come. The amazing ease of action at the climax is likely to obscure the earlier steps, since the whole problem seems to have been solved without its laborious antecedents. That is why geniuses are such unreliable authorities upon their own mental processes, often attributing their inspirations, like Shelley in A *Defence of Poetry*, to capricious invisible influences.

What makes original thinking an art rather than a mechanical business of grinding out ideas is the fact that all these stages overlap and interpenetrate, so that the exact amount of each that should be blended in an individual's creative thinking cannot be measured in advance. Preparation, for instance, can be so thorough that it chokes off invention in a flood of previously accumulated knowledge. One of the hardest things for a person to decide is just how much to consult the views of other men in order to cultivate fresh ideas of his own. Excessive bookishness can kill originality; but excessive ignorance is no guarantee of it. Incubation also can be overdone. Anatole France's remark that "Since I studied nothing I have learned much" is only a half-truth at best, since the studying of nothing followed an earlier period of intense application, without which it would probably have been unproductive. The problem is to strike a balance between a relaxed "giving in to the facts" (or what Sir Alexander Fleming called "just playing about") and a directed forcing of data together into a logical pattern.

As a means of generating original hypotheses, a technique known as "brainstorming" was devised by Alex F. Osborn of a famous New York advertising agency. In a relaxed atmosphere, a panel assembled to deal with a specific problem is invited to throw in ideas for its solution as rapidly as they can, and with a complete absence of criticism. Quantity of suggestions, no matter how wild they may seem, is the main objective of the "storming" session; selection and criticism are left until later. Brainstorming has been strongly attacked as actually less productive than individual reflection (or "lonethink"); and tests conducted at Yale University indicate that more and better ideas were brought forward by students working alone than by the members of brainstorming groups.

Illumination, merely by reason of its sudden brilliance, furnishes no proof that it is of any particular value. Cranks and insane persons have no lack of illuminations, most of which are utterly worthless, in spite of their vivid emotional accompaniments. Illumination by no means accounts for all of our

---

creative hypotheses spring into consciousness." Nearly 200 of those interrogated reported having experienced sudden insights into problems in which they had been "intensely interested," usually in periods of relaxation following concentrated study.

useful hypotheses, since many of them have been the product of the joint labors of many minds working patiently over long periods. Those which have come to the mind of a single genius in one supreme moment of insight have usually been amorphous and sketchy upon their arrival, requiring months and perhaps years of patient refinement and elaboration before they were either accepted by the world of science or productive of useful results. Often it has been the man who labored to develop the hypothesis and secure its acceptance, and not its originator, who has received most of the credit for it.

FOR CLASS DISCUSSION

A. If one considers how many things and events there are in the world and how lengthily each might be described, one is appalled at the amount of information that might be accumulated if men were not restrained.   (1)
— *Charner Perry*

B. Science is built up of facts, as a house is built up of stones; but an accumulation of facts is no more a science than a heap of stones is a house.
— *Henri Poincaré*

C. We may stare at facts every minute of our waking day without being a whit the wiser unless we exert our intellects to build upon them or under them. — *William Minto*

Imagination is more important than knowledge. — *Albert Einstein*

D. It is but a thin, aiery knowledge that is got by meer Speculation, which is usher'd in by Syllogisms and Demonstrations. . . .
— *John Smith*, a Cambridge Platonist

E. This country (Ireland) has been ruined by dreams — vague, objectless, unrealizable dreams. . . . I have to remove myself from the vacuous, the dreamy, the perpetually inept life, and go amongst the strivers and the builders who are building up a civilization out of a realizable dream which is manifesting itself more materially day by day.
— *Oliver St. John Gogarty*

F. Science without dreams is sterile. Dreams without research and science are empty. The deed of ignorance is perilous; deedless imagination is futile. United, idea and deed may create a civilization. — *Charles A. Beard*

G. One may say broadly that all animals that have been carefully observed have behaved so as to confirm the philosophy in which the observer believed before his observations began. — *Bertrand Russell*   (2)

H. Scientific research is not itself a science; it is still an art or craft.
— *W. H. George*

There is no logical way to the discovery of these elemental laws. There is only the way of intuition, which is helped by a feeling for the order behind the appearances. — *Albert Einstein*

I. Every method is imperfect. — *Charles Nicolle*

If the first duty of a scholar is to invent a system, his second is to regard it with disgust. — *André Maurois*

J. Every great age of renaissance has been an age not so much of scholastic exactitude as of bubbling suggestions, of experiments often chimerical . . . of robust curiosity . . . of the sacrifice of a cautious discipline to sheer preoccupation with living. — *George E. G. Catlin*   (4)
Sharp, prolonged thinking is necessary that we may keep on the chosen road, but it does not necessarily lead to discovery. — *Theobald Smith*
Logic supplies form to the disciplined imagination in science, but it cannot supply the intuition that creates the valuable theory.
— *Ralph M. Eaton*

K. Every theory of the course of events in nature is necessarily based on some process of simplification of the phenomena and is to some extent therefore a fairy tale. — *Sir Napier Shaw*

L. The practice of medicine is . . . an art not a science. If a doctor's pronouncement were the dictum of Science, the Absolute, there would be no advantage in having old, experienced doctors, and there would be no need for consultations in emergency cases, for one doctor to ask another doctor, "What do you think?" — *Lin Yutang*

M. According to Dixon Wecter in *The Hero in America*, Edison told M. A. Rosanoff, who inquired about rules on joining the laboratory in 1903: "Hell! There ain't no rules around here! We're tryin' to accomplish somep'n!"

N. Science is nothing but the finding of analogy, identity in the most remote parts. — *Ralph Waldo Emerson*   (5)
According to an article by Bernice Gimbels in the New York *Post* in April, 1941, a young man got a job in an advertising agency because among some of his notes submitted in applying was this item: "Perspective. A horse looks like a violin when seen from above." What impressed his employer was his ability "to see an old thing in a new way."
. . . though analogy is misleading, it is the least misleading thing we have.
— *Samuel Butler*

O. "Millions," says Hartmann, "stare at the phenomenon before a *genialer Kopf* pounces on the concept." The genius is simply he to whom, when he opens his eyes upon the world, the "right" characters are the prominent ones. The fool is he who, with the same purposes as the genius, infallibly gets his attention tangled amid the accidents. — *William James*

P. Happy ideas come unexpectedly without effort, like an inspiration. So far as I am concerned, they have never come to me when my mind was fatigued, or when I was at my working table. . . . They came particularly readily during the slow ascent of wooded hills on a sunny day.
— *Hermann von Helmholtz*

EXAMPLES OF HYPOTHESIS

1. There is an old story about an American frontiersman who had never had any medical instruction, but who decided to try his hand at practicing

medicine. When his first patient, a blacksmith who seemed to be very ill indeed with what looked like typhoid fever, demanded some pork and beans, the amateur doctor said "All right" on the theory that he might as well die happily. The blacksmith, however, promptly began to improve, and ultimately recovered; whereupon the "doctor" made the notation: "For typhoid fever — prescribe pork and beans."

Somewhat later came another patient, a shoemaker, who seemed to have the same trouble as the blacksmith, but who, on being fed pork and beans, inconsiderately proceeded to die. The undaunted "doctor" then wrote in his notebook: "Pork and beans good for blacksmiths with typhoid fever, but not for shoemakers." All he needed to do, he felt, to discover the remedy for typhoid fever was to continue the process of eliminating the failures.

2. In China, for hundreds of years the traditional gift to the young mother who had just had a baby has been pigs' feet pickled in vinegar, and no research laboratory of today could devise a better one. Soaking the pigs' feet in vinegar releases some of the calcium in the bones to replace that given by the mother to her baby before birth.

Savages in the African forest, seeking essential foodstuffs, including calcium, eat many sorts of green leaves from shrubs and trees. When the leaves are too coarse and unpalatable, they sometimes actually burn them and eat the ashes. If you want something to think about on a rainy afternoon, ask yourself how the savages ever discovered that the calcium in green vegetables survived burning and is good for them. — Bruce Bliven in *The New Republic*, January 15, 1942. (By permission of *The New Republic*.)

3. Graham Wallas in *The Art of Thought* remarks: "Sometimes empiricism lags behind science, and sometimes science lags behind empiricism. Seventy years ago, Baron Justus von Liebig was the acknowledged leader of the chemical science which then claimed to cover the field of the empirical processes of selecting and cooking food; while the chef of the Reform Club might be taken as the leader of the empirical 'mystery' of food preparation, handed on by one chef to another, and indicated in the 'cookery books' which were so strikingly unlike the textbooks in chemistry. We now know that if, in 1855, the Reform Club chef had been asked to prepare the best dinner he could, and if Baron Liebig had been asked to order another dinner, to be prepared in the same kitchen and by the same body of cooks, the chef's dinner would have been much the better, from the point of view of health as well as of enjoyment. Empiricism was then well ahead of science in the art of cooking, and it was only in 1915, that, owing to the unrewarded discomforts endured by scores of small mammals fed alternately on margarine and butter at Cambridge, the chemists demonstrated the importance of vitamins." (By permission of the publishers, Harcourt, Brace and Company, Inc.)

4. Old books on medicine contained many stories of lunatics and epileptics who had been cured mysteriously by fevers, yet modern physicians as a class scoffed at the improbable idea that fevers could have anything to do with fighting other diseases. Dr. Julius Wagner-Jauregg of Vienna was seeking the cure of the deadly disease called paresis, or general paralysis and insanity following syphilis, which had been regarded as necessarily one hundred per cent

fatal up to that time. With a tremendous inner drive for research, great powers of observation and deduction, and an almost poetic imagination, Dr. Wagner-Jauregg seized upon the hint that some kind of fever might save a paretic. For thirty years he chased what seemed like a will-o'-the-wisp; but at last, after innumerable trials and failures, he was able to report cures in eighty-three per cent of the cases of paresis by means of his malarial treatment, and received the Nobel prize.

5. Early in the twentieth century the German meteorologist Alfred Wegener proposed a hypothesis to account for the shape and position of the continents as we know them. He was struck by the way in which the coastlines of North and South America seem to "fit" those of Europe and Africa (as in a jigsaw puzzle), and suggested that they once formed a single continent which split apart, with the pieces drifting away like icebergs "calving off" from glaciers. This "continental-drift" theory did not win wide acceptance among geologists, mainly for lack of evidence of drift or of forces great enough to cause it. But it was revived in 1963 when three Australian scientists reported that Australia was "drifting" about two inches a year.

6. Alone among the lakes of Central New York, the waters of Oneida Lake fluctuate almost continually in a peculiar manner. A rise of several inches at one end of the lake is accompanied by a similar fall at the opposite end, whereupon the process reverses itself at approximately two-hour intervals. On the analogy of water sloshing back and forth in a long shallow tub, the rocking motion, known as *seiches*, may be explained by the lake's lack of depth and its relation to the local winds. The other Central New York lakes, such as Seneca, Cayuga, and Skaneateles, run roughly from north to south; while Oneida Lake extends its length from northwest to southeast, and is swept almost constantly by the prevailing winds of the region.

7. A French chemist named Becquerel took a photographic plate which had been wrapped in lightproof paper from one of the drawers in his laboratory one day in 1896. When the plate was developed, it showed dark smudges for which he could find no explanation. His curiosity having been aroused, he continued his inquiry until he had paved the way for the discovery of radium.

8. At a waterfront fire in Brooklyn, it was noticed that several fireboats were playing streams of water on the blazing pier and also in the opposite direction into the harbor. A fire chief explained the apparently useless streams by Newton's Third Law. The throwing of streams on the fire exerted an equal and opposite effect which drove the fireboat away from it; hence the necessity of streams played in the opposite direction.

9. In *Industrial Explorers*, Maurice Holland tells of the owner of a large cannery in the Middle West who learned with alarm that his most recent pack of thousands of cans of corn, piled up in a warehouse in wooden cases, was swelling in the cans, which were beginning to bulge. He could think of no explanation except that the process temperatures had not been high enough or continued long enough. Investigation showed that neither had been the case. The canner sent for Dr. Willard D. Bigelow, director of research of the National Canners Association, who had found out in his laboratory that canned corn contains bacteria called thermopiles, which can grow at temperatures of

over 100° F., but not at lower temperatures, and which cause spoilage. Dr. Bigelow guessed that the cans had been placed in the cases without cooling sufficiently, and recommended that the cases be placed in tiers with air spaces between in order to speed up the cooling. This was done; the bulging ceased; and the bulk of the pack was saved. Mr. Holland comments: "The ordinary consulting chemist, no matter how skilled he may be, rarely has enough practical knowledge of the canning industry to be of much help in an emergency of this sort. He does not know what questions to ask the canner when something has gone wrong. Dr. Bigelow had studied all the cases of actual spoilage in canning that he could locate, even using a portable laboratory for the purpose."

10. Soldier's heart, a disease common to highly civilized men in wartime, produces a condition akin to stage fright: palpitations, nervousness, flushing, and pallor, sweating and coldness of hands and feet. Dr. George Crile of Cleveland believed that the disease was an abnormality of the human system controlling bodily energy: the brain, thyroid and adrenal glands, and the autonomic nervous system. On the analogy of the electrical circuit, he decided to try short-circuiting the bodily system by cutting a nerve center located near the adrenal glands, which were thereby enervated; and was able to report cure or improvement in 107 out of 114 cases so treated.

❧ 6 ❧

DESIRABLE QUALITIES IN HYPOTHESES

1. A False Hypothesis May Be Useful

UP TO THIS POINT, comparatively little has been said about the most important questions concerning an explanatory hypothesis — Will it explain, or help in explaining, all that it attempts to explain? Will it prove to be a theory that is not only ingenious and elegant in structure, but which also has some provable connection with the facts? Will its possible patterning of experience turn out to be actually a binding one? Will it give us fruitful understanding along with temporary mastery? For we shall hardly be satisfied, as knowers, with Paul Valéry's conception of science as a mere "collection of successful recipes."

There is no way, of course, that we can tell with definiteness, in advance of actual testing by many normal observers (to be considered at length in later chapters), whether any hypothesis will prove to be more than just a pipe dream. But there are some characteristics which have been possessed in common by the hypotheses which have proved to be most satisfactory for their respective purposes, and a list of them should be helpful, both in the framing of new hypotheses and in sizing-up their prospects in advance.

It should first be pointed out that while there have been many references to the word "hypothesis" in the singular, the ordinary procedure in solving any problem is to think of several alternative hypotheses which are then developed, sometimes one after another, and sometimes simultaneously. A tourist whose automobile stops mysteriously in the middle of a desert, a detective called in to examine the cooling corpse on the library floor, a doctor summoned to stem a spreading epidemic of a wholly new disease, a business executive faced by suddenly decreased sales — all these men will probably, because of their stores of past experiences with somewhat similar occurrences and their respective abilities as creative imaginers, suggest multiple hypotheses to account for the facts in which they are interested.

Among the many possible solutions of the particular type which they are after (to say nothing of many other possible types of explanations), they hope, of course, that they have included, or will finally succeed in including, what is usually called the "true" or "real" or wholly satisfying one. What they are after is the idea or principle that will not only enable them to get the balky car going, catch the murderer (or establish the fact of accident or suicide), stop the spread of the epidemic, or bring the sales back to a higher level (any one of which feats *might* be performed by sheer fumbling); but also to *understand* the baffling ways of automobile engines, criminals, germs, and buyers in order to prevent, if possible, the recurrence of such misadventures in the future.

They would like, of course, to march with unerring accuracy to the "right" hypothesis, test it, and then move on about their business. But they know from experience that it is sometimes necessary to imagine, test, and discard literally hundreds of possible explanations before the "true" one is reached. Dr. Joseph Rossman asked 710 inventors, "What are the characteristics of a successful inventor?" The quality that was by far the most frequently mentioned in their replies was perseverance, 503 times; followed by imagination, 207; and knowledge and memory, 183.[1] Faraday, who contributed much to our modern understanding of electricity, once wrote that "in the most successful instances, not a tenth of the suggestions, the hopes, the wishes, the preliminary conclusions [of the scientific investigator] have been realized"; while Albert Einstein once told an interviewer: "I think and think, for months, for years. Ninety-nine times the conclusion is false. The hundredth time I am right."

Since most of our problems are solved, not by the formulation and testing of a single hypothesis, but by the slow process of elimination of those among our multiple hypotheses which do not stand the test of deduction-observation, it is important to note the value of the rejected or "false" hypotheses in leading us to the "true" or acceptable one. A "very lame and imperfect theory," as Priestley said, may thus be extremely useful or good, although (and even because) it is entirely disproved. If we are sure in advance that only four men, A, B, C, and D, could possibly have committed a crime, and we are able to disprove the hypotheses that A, C, and D did it, we are well on the way to the conviction of B, although more positive evidence is needed by way of corroboration. Thomas H. Huxley once paraphrased Francis Bacon's great saying, "Truth cometh sooner from error than from confusion," and then went on to remark: "If you go buzzing about between right and wrong, vibrating and fluctuating, you come out nowhere; but if you are absolutely and thoroughly and persistently wrong, you must some of these days have the extreme good fortune of knocking your head against a fact, and that sets you all right again."[2] It may seem extreme to say that the main purpose of a scientific theory is to get itself demolished, but the history of the discipline bears that conclusion out. Science owes much to the false but useful hypotheses which, by enabling some men "to exhaust the most tempting forms of error," in Whewell's phrase, have lightened the tasks of others who have profited by their predecessors' resounding miscues. What is most to be abhorred in an hypothesis is not falsity, but the futility which springs from vagueness, fuzziness, and ambiguity.

2. Testability — Clarity

The quality that is most important in a proposed hypothesis is testability, which depends upon whether or not deductions can be made from it in such

[1] Joseph Rossman, *The Psychology of Invention* (Washington, 1931), pp. 1–41.
[2] Thomas H. Huxley, *Collected Essays* (London, 1898), vol. III, p. 174.

a way that it can be definitely credited or discredited by observational tests. Its acceptance or rejection must make a difference, when deductively considered. There must, in other words, be some way of deciding whether or not the consequences which it deductively implies are or are not actually to be found by normal observers in our world. This was recognized as early as the time of Herodotus (fifth century B.C.), who said, in reviewing the various current hypotheses about the rise of the river Nile: "The person who speaks about the Ocean [a mythical stream], since he has transported the question to the dominion of the inscrutable, does not admit of refutation." Nothing could either support or upset the mediaeval notion that the stars were moved about by angels, since nothing testable could be deduced from it. For a hypothesis to be proved or disproved, there must be consequences deducible from it which would be observationally different if it were true rather than false. The process of testing may be extremely complicated and indirect, and the chain of deduced consequences very long indeed, provided that it terminates in an ascertainable difference. It goes without saying that there may be temporary obstacles of a technical nature which prevent the immediate confirmation of an hypothesis. All that is required for testability is that it should be eventually confirmable.

Testability or verifiability in turn depends to a large extent upon the clarity with which the terms of the hypothesis are stated, a matter which will be fully explored in the following two chapters. To explain the fall of France in 1940 as having been due to "a weakening of the moral fiber of the French people" is to frame an hypothesis in terms that are almost impossible to define satisfactorily. It is like attributing all the woes of the world to men's failures "to read their Bibles enough" — the word "enough" being wholly ambiguous. Where some of the same consequences follow from two or more hypotheses, and it seems impossible to decide between them by what is called an *experimentum crucis* or crucial experiment, the trouble is generally in the failure to state them in precise terms.

3. Adequacy of Scope — Power of Prediction

An hypothesis should cover in its proposed explanation all the facts which it is intended to explain, and not merely a few of them. Many hypotheses may succeed in accounting for the same limited body of facts; the rub comes when they are called upon to cover more and more territory. One reason for the unsatisfactory state of affairs in contemporary physical theory, where two or more hypotheses in regard to the nature of light (the wave theory, the corpuscular theory, etc.) are being used in competition with one another, is their partial character: each by itself is regarded as inadequate because, although it takes care of the bulk of the phenomena of light, it leaves unexplained a few items for which the other theory accounts.

Most of the explanatory hypotheses which man has found valuable have yielded fresh predictions of facts not envisaged as within their scope when they were formulated. Auguste Comte went so far as to declare that "Prevision is the test of true theory." Certainly a prophecy made on the basis of a theory that has been framed in one context concerning events in another is one of the most spectacular methods of justification imaginable. This is especially true if the predicted event is not known to be implied by anything which we already know, or, better still, if it ought not to take place on the basis of our previous knowledge. Von Laue's discovery of the action of X-rays on crystals was the perception of a phenomenon which no one had ever seen, but which he had deduced from the fact that X-rays were short waves.

Scope in an hypothesis is not a mere matter of covering a wide range of facts in a single field, but of establishing a principle from which consequences in many fields as different from one another as possible can be shown to flow. Our highest admiration goes to the discoverers of theories, like those concerning gravitation, atoms, and evolution, which yield many different kinds of fruits. We believe most firmly in those which have brought us unexpected discoveries of hidden interconnections beneath the surface of things. As our systems of knowledge have been vastly broadened and revised by these truly epoch-making extensions, we have come to the point of being somewhat disappointed in an hypothesis which applies only to one corner of a subject, so weak does it seem by comparison. This expectation is not without its dangers, since an hypothesis should not be forced to embrace too broad a scope. Much harm has been done in science by the insistence that hypotheses which have given good results in one field of inquiry must be applied universally. Many a good hypothesis has been ridden to death by misguided enthusiasts. It is always a mistake to sacrifice specific relevance, because of a "love of big problems," in the attempt to cover too much ground.

4. Adequacy of Depth — Explanatory Power Relative to Purpose

An explanatory hypothesis should explain what it sets out to explain, and more, if possible; but, as W. H. George truly remarks: "One man's explanation may be another man's chaos." An hypothesis is a possible patterning of facts, but the same facts may be patterned in a great many different ways, within a great many possible frames of reference, yielding many different "explanations." What sort of explanation will be demanded, or accepted if offered, depends not only upon the nature of the subject matter and the "facts as agreed upon," but also upon the past experience, interests, and purposes of the demander. Let us say that a man has been killed in an automobile collision, and that hypotheses to explain his death are offered by a physicist, a chemist, an ambulance surgeon, a newspaper reporter, a traffic expert, and a sociologist — each man using the terms appropriate to his branch of knowledge. Nothing could be more certain than that the seven explanations, each satisfactory to its maker, will differ among themselves, although they may not contradict one another at any point. What will satisfy the chemist will seem wholly inadequate to the traffic expert; what will satisfy the sociologist will seem irrelevant to the physicist.

Much harm has been done by insisting that there is just one "natural" or "normal" or "absolutely fundamental" way of patterning a given group of facts, a way that is "right" while all others are "wrong." This has led to a stubborn insistence that hypotheses should be patterns on the mathematical or mechanical or animistic or theological model exclusively, with all others ruled out in advance as unsatisfactory. This is not to assert that one kind of hypothesis is just as good as another for any purpose; it is rather to claim that no one hypothesis or type of hypothesis can be said to be the only one that could possibly explain (in some sense) a given fact or group of facts. What is important is that an hypothesis should possess the explanatory power that is claimed for it — no matter how weak that power may be thought to be. We should not expect a chemical hypothesis to be adequate for the purposes of the economist, but we should expect it to explain its facts to the satisfaction of qualified chemists. This leaves open the issue whether or not the sociologists and economists of the future will demand physical and chemical explanations of their phenomena. For the present, at least, the adequacy of an hypothesis in penetrating power should be judged in terms of its apparent purpose.

5. Systematic Simplicity

Since an explanatory hypothesis is a possible patterning of facts which purports to explain them by arranging them in a more intelligible sort of order, we should expect it to be self-consistent, or free from internal contradictions. But we cannot demand that it possess that perfect and aesthetically satisfying logical structure of the purely deductive system known as "elegance." For an inductive system must start with the facts which it is eventually to explain; while a deductive system may lay down its own conditions to which the facts may or may not happen to conform. As long as facts are disregarded, the speculative imagination is free to construct the most elegant and complicated systems of abstractions without the hindrance of any particular world to which they must apply. The task of the inductive thinker is far more difficult; he has two controls, and not just one, for he must keep an eye on what is given in sense experience as well as upon the ordering concepts which he uses in interpreting it. His job is to bring together fruitfully the order that is (sometimes dimly) in his mind, and the order in his subject matter. He must start with facts, and construct imaginatively a system of interpretation that goes beyond and behind them, and whose conditions, when deductively elaborated, will turn out to be fulfilled by all his original data and, he hopes, by many others also.

Most of our new hypotheses will also be consistent with all previously accepted hypotheses which have the standing of established theories or laws; but it is folly to insist that the same should be true of truly "revolutionary" ones, such as those of Copernicus, Newton, Kant, Darwin, Einstein, or Freud. Each of those sweeping advances in human knowledge brought about a temporary upsetting of the "whole body of scientific theory" accepted at the time, but that has been followed by a reattainment of consistency upon a broader and higher level of understanding.

When two rival hypotheses, each of which explains the same range of facts, are equally adequate in depth as well as in scope, a new criterion enters. It is systematic simplicity, or logical compactness. Of two hypotheses of equal explanatory power, the simpler is to be preferred, in the sense that it explains the facts in question with greater rigor, that is, with the use of fewer independent assumptions and undefined terms. Such mathematical simplicity is very different from the superficial sort which solves a problem by oversimplifying it in terms of a devil or a mysterious force. The classic example of an hypothesis preferred because of its systematic simplicity is the heliocentric theory of Copernicus, to whom the saying *"Natura simplicitatem amat"* ("Nature loves simplicity") is attributed. The geocentric theory of Ptolemy accounted for all the visible movements of the heavenly bodies by assuming that the fixed earth was the center around which all other celestial phenomena moved in circles. To explain the erratic movements of the planets, however, Ptolemy was obliged to introduce some seventy-nine or eighty "epicycles" (circles compounded upon circles). Copernicus, by postulating the movement of the earth, was able at one stroke to reduce the number of epicycles required to thirty-four.[3] Both hypotheses did all that was required of them; and neither could, at that time, eliminate the other, since each, on its assumptions, explained the same range of facts. Indeed, it should be remembered that Ptolemy's theory enjoyed an apparent superiority from the directly empirical, common-sense point of view: the earth seemed immovable, and the stars and planets appeared to move. But the Copernican theory was systematically more elegant: the so-called principle of parsimony, or Occam's razor (William of Occam's dictum against explanatory principles which one can do without), was in its favor. Copernicus' preference for leanness over fatness in hypotheses was triumphantly vindicated by later discoveries.

6. Hypothesis-Making in the Social Studies

What we want, ideally, of an explanatory hypothesis should now be clear. It is not enough for it to be a descriptive hypothesis that "works," either by quieting our curiosity or by solving our immediate problems, or even by serving as a "successful recipe" for similar situations without our understanding why it should do so. We shall not be satisfied to be like those early French chemists who called iodine "the substance X" possessing certain properties. We demand the kind of understanding which grasps the place of iodine in the whole system of the chemical substances, and illuminates its goiter-preventing qualities, in organisms, for example, by a structural analysis of its intricate chemical-biological relationships. We want to press on to achieve a patterning of facts that will connect as many of them as possible in a deductive system yielding specific predictions which can eventually be tested by approximate coincidence observations.

The word "explain" comes from the Latin phrase *ex plicis plana reddere*,

---

[3] For a fuller discussion of the two hypotheses, see Cohen and Nagel, *op. cit.*, pp. 212–15; and Columbia Associates, *Introduction to Reflective Thinking* (Boston, 1923), chap. III.

literally, "to smooth out the wrinkles or folds." A fact is explained when it is made less puzzling or obscure by being fitted into a comprehensible scheme of things already partly known. There is no universal formula for explanation because there is no one system of knowledge possessed by all men in common into which a new fact must be fitted. A child, as we know, will often accept as perfectly adequate an explanation which an adult will reject as absurd. The Santa Claus theory of the origin of Christmas gifts does not survive the increase in sophistication which comes with widening experience. The Tibetan lamas who could not comprehend why the Mount Everest expeditions should want to climb the world's highest mountain peak were satisfied when they were offered the religious reason that the climbers wanted to get as close to heaven as possible while remaining on earth. It is probably fortunate that the holy men did not carry that particular inquiry further.

The great enemy of thorough inquiry is the acceptance of flimsy, *ad hoc* hypotheses as explanations when they are mere *placebos* to quiet the curious. As Professor Harold N. Lee expresses it, "If we decide that men fight because of a pugnacious instinct, we are relieved of the immense task of finding the actual factors, economic, cultural, political, and what not, that are involved in their fighting."[4] Physical science has pretty well rid itself of this tendency to be satisfied with invented fictions brought in to "explain away" special difficulties with old systems which would otherwise have to be torn down and completely reconstructed. But the would-be social scientists still display a penchant for the explanatory short cut.

As minds become more adult, those explanations appear most lastingly satisfactory which explain a fact by exhibiting it clearly in its place in a deductive system of the widest possible scope and simplicity. To explain anything, what we try to find is a set of harmonious propositions which can be shown to imply, with the greatest possible economy, all the facts involved. In the so-called exact or developed sciences, a few gifted individuals have extracted many of Nature's secrets by imagining such explanatory hypotheses in the form of laws, which have been used deductively for the guidance of further observations with truly amazing results. What are the chances of making similar progress in the social studies?

The first thing to note in answering that question is that when, in physics and mechanics, men rushed in with premature explanatory hypotheses in terms of analogies based upon their own feelings, or supposed cosmic purposes, or "final causes," they were forced to make painful withdrawals later on. They, meaning the Greeks and the Schoolmen, had neglected careful observation and description, and so their brilliant guesses and (often) valid deductions availed them little in terms of prediction and control. By the time of Galileo, and especially by the time of Newton, there had been enough attention to observed phenomena and their measurements to provide more adequate starting points. It is perfectly true that the great triumphs of these scientific geniuses were not the results of long processes of induction based on vast accumulations of empirical data. There were, however, just enough observations taken seriously to

---

[4] Harold N. Lee, "Modern Logic and the Task of the Natural Sciences," *Sigma Xi Quarterly*, vol. 28 (1940), p. 119.

suggest alternative hypotheses which could be elaborated deductively and tested by a few mathematically "ideal" experiments. Galileo had seized upon the essentials; Newton developed them into a consistent system; and such matters as proof in detail and application in a thousand contexts could be left to minor experimenters.

The result of this sudden and dramatic advance of physics to the status of what appeared to be a highly deductive science, with most of its principles easily confirmable by observation, was that many thinkers agreed with Bertrand Russell that "we know so much about physics and so little about anything else." Where were the Galileos and Newtons of the social studies? Might not the latter be swiftly elevated to the proud estate of reliable knowledge by the bringing-off of a similar *coup de main?* That strategy has been tried, and in two different ways, neither of which has been successful. Some have attempted to import the mechanical concepts of Galileo and Newton directly into the social studies in the hope of annexing the sciences of man to those of matter; while others have sought for key concepts of human behavior, such as power, acquiescence, brotherly love, and so on, which might play rôles analogous to those sustained by mass, inertia, and energy in physical systems.[5]

Without going into the recent changes in physics itself, which have robbed it of some of its nineteenth-century appearance of simplicity, it is apparent that the subject matter of physical inquiry, at least in its grosser forms, lends itself to testable systematization far more easily than does that of the social studies. Galileo and Newton won the quick assent of qualified observers by their ability to devise crucial experiments which dealt crushing blows to the hitherto accepted hypotheses and left their own in undisputed possession of the field. They could do this because the phenomena with which they were concerned were so largely homogeneous. The multiplicity of alternatives was on a single level: the motion of masses, with all such complicating factors as the influence of angels or the yearnings of the bodies themselves to be in one place rather than another, excluded from the picture.

As we shall presently see in greater detail, the social studies are obliged to operate with a double multiplicity of explanatory hypotheses. There are not only multiple explanations of the same happening on a single level, such as the many possible physical causes of a political assassination; there are also multiple levels on which alternative kinds of explanations of the event may be sought, such as biological, psychological, and social-cultural. Since there is nothing to prevent human imaginations from supplying an almost endless number of supposititious theories, how can there be proof by the final elimination of all but one of them?

7. Levels and Perspectives

Even in describing a single living object, there are a great number of "correct" modes of procedure, no one of which is entitled to exclude the others unless we specify one standard purpose and point of view. Some experience

[5] Discussed in greater detail in Chapter 13 below.

will bear us out, whether we interpret this black fuzzy blur as a thing, an organ-ism, an animal, a vertebrate, a carnivorous quadruped, *Felis domestica,* or our cat Smudge. For it is all of these things, and more too. Which concept we shall choose, in a given context, will depend upon our interests and our esti-mate of the people with whom we are going to try to act in concert. "Have you seen Smudge?" will be a useful question to ask only of those who share our intimate acquaintance with him; of others we shall inquire: "Have you seen our cat?" or, "Have you seen a male black cat about six months old?" If the person had never seen a cat, we should have to use concepts that were still more general.

Each description, we can be sure, leaves out something that another one includes. Which one or ones will prove to be adequate for our purpose, trial alone will tell. So with explanation: which of the many possible ones will suit us will depend upon our particular demand. This is true to some extent, even in the natural sciences, where a single event, such as an earthquake or landslide, may be studied and explained from several points of view: astro-nomical, geophysical, geological, geographical, chemical, and so on. Each sci-ence abstracts from the phenomena the aspects in which it is especially in-terested, and employs the concepts and frames of reference which it finds illuminating for the purposes which it has in view. Each is looking primarily for constant correlations among the facts on its own level, to which it is tempted to "reduce" everything else. That, of course, is folly: colors are no less colors because we use the concepts of wave motion to explain their dif-ferences.

Of these many ways of abstracting and arranging things in order to explain them, one sort — the mechanical — has excelled all others in getting rid of the time element and in becoming "pure" and mathematical. Investigators of some phenomena, such as the astronomical, are fortunate enough to be able to confine themselves to the measurable and repeatable aspects of their data, and to astonish us with their exact predictions of the behavior of comets and eclipses. Such abstract calculations are almost entirely separable from the careers of any particular physical objects. Other sciences, such as geology and meteorology, are less able to rid themselves of historical considerations. Note that none of the natural sciences is obliged to take any account of either conscious or unconscious purposing or end-seeking on the part of continents or oceans or clouds.

When we come to the social studies, as compared with these more fortunate disciplines, the contrasts are both numerous and striking. The sciences of man have brought together enormous accumulations of details; they have inherited and developed many sorts of conflicting descriptive hypotheses in the form of empirical rules of thumb, proverbs, folklore, customs, and codes; they have invented some too ambitious explanatory theories, and a few more modest ones that are restricted to a single "subject" or level; but they are sadly lacking in *testable* explanatory hypotheses which go beyond the narrow confines of a school of economics or psychology to shed light upon human social behavior in general. Thus we find ourselves without the reliable knowledge which we so desperately need in order to cope with such broad and many-sided social problems as wars, depressions, class struggles, crime, population movements, and revolutions. What knowledge we do possess is often unused for the lack of will and skill in applying it.

As they concern the framing and functioning of explanatory hypotheses, the pivotal differences between the subject matters of the social and the physical sciences may be summarized as follows.

(1) *Multiplicity of possible levels of explanation.* Social facts are potentially viewable as physical or biological or psychological or sociological (with many sublevels, as well as conceptual cross-groupings of many sizes and degrees of complexity). We may usefully arrange them in patterns by time, place, growth, motivation, influences, organization, institutional types, situational types, trends, and so on. Thus, at the very start, in framing an hypothesis, a choice of levels and scope has to be made from among a vast congeries of alternatives, with only a few of which any single individual or audience can be expected to be intimately familiar. To insist upon one of the levels or perspectives as fundamental to the understanding of what happens on all of the others is, in the present state of human knowledge, to commit a fatal error. Usable explanations in the social studies, therefore, almost invariably suffer either from vagueness and imprecision, because they try to cover too much ground; or single-sided fragmentariness, because they confine themselves to too few aspects of many-sided phenomena.

(2) *Historical (non-repeatable) character.* All facts are in one sense historical, since they can be placed on some time-dimension; but many of them, in the natural sciences, have aspects which, being highly uniform and recurrent, lend themselves to abstraction and the precise quantitative formulation of laws. An individual physical occurrence then becomes a "case of" the law. Now to generalize about battles or panics or revolutions is also to abstract certain features which are common to more than one event, but there the resemblance ceases. A social study cannot carry the time-neglecting process nearly so far. If it does, it falsifies its material. For each battle or panic or revolution has its individual, non-repeatable, historical character which must be grasped in its entirety if it is to be explained fully. To make it a "case of" some law of battles or panics or revolutions is, as Dewey remarks, "to eliminate its qualities which make it a social fact." In history, as Professor Postan reminds us: "The penalty of being sufficiently concrete to be real is the impossibility of being sufficiently abstract to be 'exact' in the scientific sense."[6] The observer is also infected with temporality, since he is not wholly at liberty, having been born when and where he was, to choose his social-historical perspective. That fact may limit the explanatory power of his hypothesis to his own cultural context, as when a history book explains a war, but only from the victor's point of view.

(3) *Partly teleological character.* Without engaging in any of the interminable controversies over purpose, we may note that man is, to some extent at least, a consciously self-patterning organism, who frames and envisages de-

[6] M. M. Postan, *The Historical Method in Social Science* (Cambridge, England, 1939), p. 33.

sirable ends, and who constantly projects and exaggerates the power of his volitions directed toward such ends. This strongly influences the use of his imagination: it leads him to advance moral or religious or aesthetic patterns of ideal order, not as tentative hypotheses, but as dogmas to be imposed, or to be made to come true by believing them; and it impels him to demand sweeping explanations in terms of a premature "Why?" directed at the whole universe, to be answered by an emotionally appealing but non-testable story or myth.

Although it is toward the past, in terms of causes, that man has looked most successfully for explanations which are testable, as a living organism he can hardly avoid facing toward the future and thinking in terms of possible effects. When he analyzes a social problem, it is not enough to be able to describe or even to explain it in terms of factors entering the situation from the past. An indispensable part of the solution is the ascertainment of the ways in which suggested plans of action will appeal (or fail to appeal) to those who must co-operate in order to carry them out. An hypothesis about a social problem which disregards the question of its own acceptance by those who must put it into effect will prove to be theoretical in the worst sense of the term.

Thanks to these sorts of difficulties, explanatory hypotheses in the social studies tend to err in one of two main directions. If their makers seek breadth of scope, they are likely to wind up in some sort of gigantic wishful abstraction or oversimplification by "reduction-to," like the Christian or Marxist or Freudian versions of human nature and history. Some one aspect of experience — climate or sex or race or technology or power-seeking or reason — is made the explanation of everything. If, on the other hand, they are content with piecemeal isolation, their hypotheses may achieve confirmation in detail, but they will be confined to provincial points of view, or to the minutiae of genuinely closed-off systems like price relationships or the data of local histories. As a result, inquirers tend to oscillate between broad and breathtaking Utopian social theories which can neither be proved nor disproved, and prosaic garnerings of trivia which lack any integrating vision. Both kinds of reflection have their usefulness; but we need more of the kind of creative connective thinking that can begin to bridge the gap between the two. If the histories of the sciences which have already achieved maturity are to be our guides, then the best first step in the direction of better explanatory hypotheses will be the improvement of our descriptive ones.

As for the much-debated issue of the priority of observation over hypothesis, or of hypothesis over observation, it should be apparent that each needs the other if inquiry is to proceed with profit. If an investigator asks a crude and superficial question, he is overwhelmingly likely to get a crude and superficial answer. But, if he is intelligent, the crudity and superficiality of his answer will lead him to formulate a better question the next time. His observations are bound to be colored by his hypotheses; and his hypotheses had better be colored by his observations. Facts are in part the product of theories; and theories are in part the product of previously discovered facts. We learn both by guessing what the facts will be, and by colliding with what they are — the colliding tames the guessing; and the guessing helps us to avoid some of the less pleasant of the collisions.

FOR CLASS DISCUSSION

A. A scientific theory is useful to the extent that suggests experiments which will help to disprove it. — *James R. Newman*   (1)
   Wrong hypotheses, rightly worked, have produced more useful results than unguided observation. — *William De Morgan*

B. Looking back over the patchwork of my life's labors, I can say that I have made many beginnings and thrown out many suggestions. Something will come of them in the future, though I cannot myself tell whether it will be much or little. — *Sigmund Freud*

C. There's an old story about a veteran public health nurse who sniffed: "I wish you doctors would make up your minds. All these years I've climbed stairs telling Italian mothers *not* to give their babies tomato juice. Now I'm climbing stairs telling them to give tomato juice."   (3)
                                                        — *Catherine Mackenzie*

D. In the elementary courses (in college) you learn the theories, and in the advanced courses you learn that they do not apply. — *Anonymous*

E. Before you try a complicated hypothesis, you should make quite sure that no simplification of it will explain the facts equally well.
                                                        — *Charles S. Peirce*
   Seek simplicity, but distrust it. — *A. N. Whitehead*   (5)

F. What a scientist regards as a good explanation, what will satisfy his demand that events be reasonably ordered and accounted for, does profoundly influence his description of the world. It determines the position from which he advances in those speculative ventures which make possible the discovery of new truth. . . . — *Arthur E. Murphy*   (6)

G. Contrast the part assigned to the works of Aristotle in a contemporary academic course on natural science and one on politics. Obviously what Aristotle said on natural history can be safely ignored by the modern scientist, but the student of politics does not show the same confidence that centuries have materially improved upon Aristotelian doctrines in his field. — *Barbara Wootton*

H. The social philosophers and the social scientists are separated by a wide gap . . . social theorists are not as a rule acquainted with many facts, and factualists tend to disdain theory . . . and also, the facts that are required for the development of a scientific theory of society are scattered over so many fields that no one individual has a comprehensive knowledge of them. — *Mark A. May*

≫ 7 ≪

CLARIFYING THE HYPOTHESIS:
Semantics—Words and Meanings

1. Preliminaries to Testing

WITH THE GOAL IN SIGHT, the temptation is strong to hasten directly toward it. But haste to prove something has long been the curse of human inquiry. Reliable knowledge is to be achieved by the attesting of observed facts, but only after first patterning them in hypotheses which, if established, may be shown to explain them. From the earliest times of which we have any record, for example, men observed the peculiar behavior of large bodies of water which we call tides. They described, recorded, and even measured the rise and fall of the water, without being able to explain it, except in some fanciful way. Careful observations by a few Greeks and Babylonians, however, strongly suggested some connection between the times of high water and the moon's position. Galileo tried in vain to devise an explanation; and Kepler framed an hypothesis involving an attraction exerted by the moon on the water of the earth, but was unable to work out its consequences mathematically. It was only when Newton offered his hypothesis of universal gravitation that the tides were explained — that is, fitted into a deductive system. Today, tide-tables are calculated for years in advance; and their predictions are verified by everyone who uses them.

As soon as a person has thought of an hypothesis or possible explanation of anything confused or mysterious, it is wholly natural for him to want to test it immediately. One of the hardest lessons which any thinker has to learn is that of patience at this point in the process of inquiry. For few hypotheses, when they first come to mind, are in shape for immediate testing. Many of our most valuable theories have had to wait for years before a decision about their probable truth or falsity could be reached. Kepler, for example, was undoubtedly aware that he was close to the explanation of the tides when he linked them in his imagination with the attraction of the moon, but he could not immediately frame his hypothesis in such a way that it would account for all the relevant facts. (It explained why the water was heaped up on the side toward the moon, but not the simultaneous heaping-up on the opposite side of the earth.) Neither could he state his theory in such a way that deductions from it could be checked by the times and amounts of the actual rise and fall of the tides. It was only when Newton's more inclusive and more precise hypothesis was advanced that the connection of the tides with the action of the moon and sun was both made more intelligible and "proved" by exact predictions which were borne out in practice.

To be testable by the deduce-and-confirm method, we know that an hypothesis must be so clearly stated that definite conclusions can be drawn from it. There must be an ascertainable difference somewhere in the world between what follows if the hypothesis is true and what follows if it is false. Otherwise, it can neither be proved nor disproved. The connection of such a difference, if one exists, with our theory cannot be pointed out if we cannot state with precision what follows validly from our proffered explanation. The physical sciences have, on the whole, been extremely successful in setting up experiments which demonstrate such crucial differences, thereby confirming (or discrediting) many of their hypotheses. But in the social studies, even granted that we start with a supply of brilliant hunches, two further obstacles confront us before we can hope to test them. Both concern the task of clarifying the meaning of an hypothesis before we attempt to make deductions from it. The first lies in the fact that the social studies are sadly lacking in generally accepted descriptive hypotheses: classifications, definitions, and units of measurement that are known, understood, and used in approximately the same sense by a large majority of investigators. We constantly try to explain *why* men behave as they do before coming to any substantial agreement about *how* they actually do behave. The second source of trouble is shared by all the branches of knowledge, but is especially demoralizing in the social studies — namely, the necessity of stating our hypotheses, both descriptive and explanatory, in words. So great are the perils of language that we may sometimes wonder, with John Locke, whether it has "contributed more to the improvement or hindrance of knowledge amongst mankind?"

2. "Words, Words, Words"

Whether language will be more of a help than a hindrance is likely to be decided by the extent to which we succeed in grasping the complex and elusive character of words. There can be knowledge and even explanation without words, as when a small child, who is trying to pry open the back of a watchcase which screws on, is set right by a more experienced person who makes a rotary motion with his extended fingers — a form of pantomime. But most of the knowledge and thought of civilized men is in the form of words, since words are what enable us to share our mental operations, to a certain extent, with others who are like-minded, like-languaged, and like-experienced with ourselves.

The broad subject which deals with words and their meanings is called semantics (from the Greek word *semainein* — to signify). The pioneer work of Lady Welby (1837–1912) encouraged C. K. Ogden and I. A. Richards to publish *The Meaning of Meaning* in 1923, with Basic English as one of its by-products. Ten years later the Polish mathematician Alfred Korzybski brought out *Science and Sanity*, which initiated the movement called "general semantics," now represented by the journal entitled *Etc.*[1]

[1] Cf. Stuart Chase, *The Tyranny of Words* (New York, 1938); Bertrand Russell, *An Inquiry into Meaning and Truth* (New York, 1940); S. I. Hayakawa, *Language*

In all discussions of language, we are using words to explain how words can be used to explain, so that whatever we may say in the way of destructive criticism lays itself open to the same attacks. Completely to discredit words by the use of words is sheer intellectual suicide. It is equally absurd to look upon the perfecting of language as the panacea for the ills of human society. Even though every last meaning in the world had been made clear, men could still find ways of getting into trouble.

Words are very powerful things, both for weal and for woe. They "rule the world" in the sense that they are the indispensable instruments of large-scale co-ordination of behavior. It does little good to be perceptive if one cannot communicate one's perceptions to others. The man with the great idea, but without the words in which to express it, is socially powerless; while there seems to be almost no limit to what can be accomplished, for good or for ill, by the man who is articulate. Words enable us to live together in a growing cumulative culture, and yet they can be used to injure and destroy. They make possible immensely valuable meetings of minds, but they can also bring about catastrophic misunderstandings.

Some of these difficulties with language come from relatively simple failures in communication, due to the inherent limitations of words and experiences, where there is an honest intent to agree upon the facts. If a Northerner tells a resident of some parts of the South to come to see him in the evening, he may arrive in what the Yankee calls the afternoon. In a single language, one word may have different meanings in different contexts; while many different words may convey substantially the same idea. Then there are factors in every situation which elude statement in any words whatever. No language has nearly enough words to express the exact shadings of all the various happenings about us; and individual vocabularies are limited to a tiny fraction of the words that are in the dictionary. These, however, are all in the nature of obstacles to clear and complete comprehension where there is the intention to make words convey information from one person to others.

Language has other functions besides the informative one. They may be grouped together as the emotive (or affective) use of words: either to express our own feelings, such as the ejaculations of joy, pain, relief, that were probably man's earliest tongue; or to arouse emotional states and subsequent action in others, such as the "trigger words" of patriotic orations, sermons, sales-talks, and other varieties of propaganda. Paulhan calls these slogan-words "condensations," since they carry powerful and explosive charges of emotion.

The fact that a sign can have both a descriptive and an emotive meaning was the basis of Charles L. Stevenson's notable contribution to the unraveling of ethical disagreements in his Ethics and Language.[2] One of the most far-reaching discoveries of the twentieth century has been that of the immense potentialities of the "loading" of language as a weapon for influencing mass be-

---

in Action (New York, 1941); C. W. Morris, Signs, Language and Behavior (New York, 1946); C. I. Lewis, An Analysis of Knowledge and Valuation (La Salle, Ill., 1946), chap. IV; and Stephen Ullmann, The Principles of Semantics (New York, 1957).

2 (New Haven, Conn., 1944).

havior. Incessant repetitions of "the big lie" in the condensed form of epithets and slogans have been shown to have almost hypnotic effects. This has begun to make men aware that the way they choose the words they address to the public really matters in ways that cannot always be foreseen.

When words are used emotively, the habitual feelings and attitudes of the user are infused into what would otherwise be neutral statements of fact, and they arouse corresponding feelings in his hearers. Professor Hayakawa makes effective use of the contrast in emotional tone between two phrases which refer to exactly the same object: "Finest quality filet mignon" and "First-class piece of dead cow." If an employer tells us, "Idleness ruins a hard worker," we feel that each word is surcharged with moral valuation. "Idleness" and "ruins" are highly condemnatory expressions, while "hard worker" is eulogistic. But if a doctor reports to us that "Unnecessary prolongation of the period of immobilization lowers the tonus of the worker's inactive muscles," we make no such emotional response. His words are technical, and almost entirely devoid of emotive coloring.

In its journals, reports, and textbooks, pure science goes to great lengths to avoid the emotional. It seeks to insure the purely communicative function of its terms by coining symbols to which it assigns precise and "sterilized" meanings. Each of the new meanings discovered in research must have a new word assigned to it. Their relations are stated in the quantitative language of mathematics, which is bare of feeling. The result is usually a jargon which is meaningless to the uninitiated, but is an instrument of great exactitude in the hands of those who have mastered the science in question. This is because the meanings of the symbols are so clearly defined within the specialized context that variations due to their use by different individuals are kept at a minimum. Even so, a violent scientific controversy sometimes results in loading the most recondite expressions with emotive significance.

In Anglo-American philosophical circles the movement broadly known as Analytic Philosophy has undertaken several varieties of linguistic therapy designed to rid traditional metaphysics and epistemology of "meaningless" or nonsensical problems, either by a close analysis of ordinary language, or by the construction of an ideal language free from emotive pitfalls.[3]

Words may thus be seen as forming a broad spectrum in regard to their emotional coloring or the lack of it. At one end will be found the ideally exact technical terms of the natural sciences, which attempt to be "monosemantic" or unambiguous. They have clear-cut boundaries which prevail in any context, and their emotional potency is negligible. In indicating size, an example would be "microscopic." But the same object might be called "teensyweensy." At the other extreme, then, we find the supercharged expressions beloved by the romantic poets, full of both passion and ambiguity, and usable in manifold contexts with endless shades of meaning. These are the "magic words," said by the French poet Soumet "to evoke by their golden flames the forms of ethereal beings which one sees in hearing them." In between the two extremes are found the words which face both ways, performing both a

[3] See Lecture Two, "Analytic Philosophy," in Abraham Kaplan, *The New World of Philosophy* (New York, 1961), pp. 53–96.

cognitive and an emotive function, such as the series: "minute, diminutive, small, little, tiny, wee."[4]

The social studies, for reasons which have already been foreshadowed, are in a particularly difficult position with respect to the language problem. They seem, by their very nature, to be condemned to struggle endlessly against the myriad confusions which result from an inevitable mixing of the informative and the emotion-stirring functions of words. There seems to be no easy escape from this dilemma. For if they are true to their subject matter — often the loves, hates, stupidities, ambitions, fears, and heroisms of men — they are open to charges of unscientific imprecision and bias. But if they become semantically accurate and technical, they may find themselves completely cut off from a sufficiently sustaining human interest and influence. This discussion will center upon the informative or symbolic function of language, since, from the point of view of knowledge, that is the fundamental power of words.

3. Signs and Symbols

Perhaps the first step in understanding the nature of words is to grasp the notions of *sign* and *symbol*. All human beings learn by experience a number of natural weather signs: dark clouds *mean* wind or rain to come; soaked ground means that rain has fallen during the night; and so on. Coming upon an apparently deserted cabin in the wilderness, we look about for "signs of life," such as the ashes of a fire or scraps of discarded trash. A sign is anything which we take as an indication of something else. It is whatever has meaning for us, whatever enables us to make an inference about what has happened or is likely to happen. If it imposes no limitation upon the course of our thought, we say that it is almost totally vague, without significance, meaningless. If, however, the Weather Bureau raises a certain kind of flag to warn the public of an approaching storm, the sign will work only if the people comprehend the agreed-upon meaning. The flag, in other words, is an artificial or conventional sign called a *symbol*, which *stands for* the coming storm. Similarly, if we find written on the wall of the deserted cabin the words, "Off hunting till Saturday, November 8," we shall, if we understand English, grasp the situation which accounts for its seeming to be deserted. The writing stands for the absent hunter.

All symbols are thus contrived or conventional signs; but not all signs are symbols. One way to state the difference, as it applies to words, is to point out that, to the higher animals, words are only signs, at best; while to human beings, they can be both signs and symbols. Take, for instance, a monkey which has been conditioned, in a manner fundamentally similar to Pavlov's dog, to approach at the sound of the word "banana." To say that the

[4] Poetic extravagance of language sometimes irks other poets, as when Tennyson objected to Wordsworth's line: "And sitting on the grass partook the fragrant beverage drawn from China's herb," saying: "Why could he not have said, 'And sitting on the grass had tea'?"

monkey has learned the meaning of the word "banana" is merely to indicate that he has formed the temporary habit of behaving in just about the same manner in the presence either of the thing (the desired fruit) or the word (audible sound) which is the sign of the thing. By repeated associations of fruit and word, the word has come to act as substitute stimulus for the fruit. To the monkey, the reaction to the word is as automatic as to the fruit. The word, to him, *is* the fruit; it cannot be said to *stand for* or symbolize the fruit, for it never occurs to him to separate the two. If the word keeps on appearing without the fruit, it will soon lose its signifying power. We know very well that the same monkey could have been trained to flee in terror at the same word "banana" if he had been whipped every time the word was pronounced; and that he could have been conditioned to approach just as gladly at the mention of the word "arsenic" if it had been uttered repeatedly along with the fruit. What things mean, then, to animals in terms of signs or signals is thus at the hazard of their experiences. They have nothing to say about determining what anything to which they respond shall come to mean to them. They do not originate meanings on their own initiative. They live in a world of things and signs of things, but not in a world of symbols.

Man possesses not only the ability to learn passively from his experience what events, gestures, and cries are to be responded to as natural signs (smoke means fire, frown means anger, "Ouch" means pain); but also to create for himself new symbols (mostly words, numbers, and designs) in unimaginable profusion. He is, in other words "the linguistic animal." If he so desires, he can take anything whatever that is discriminable and make it the symbol (or carrier, for him, of the meaning) of anything else he can experience. He can hit upon the most unlikely combinations of sounds or letters to symbolize or stand for simple events or ideas, such as "phleborhexis" to denote exactly the rupture of a vein; or he can let thousands of subtle distinctions in emotional shading be swallowed up in the single four-letter word "love."

This means that man is no longer tied down by the accidents of his conditioning. He is free to make artificial signs or symbols to conjure into verbal existence a whole series of private worlds supplied with logics, languages, and laws. A man can coin an endless variety of words, ritual gestures, colors, odors — anything that can be discriminated — and make symbols of them by endowing them with meanings and values as arbitrarily as he chooses. He can decree: let an amber light mean . . . pedestrians may cross, or fish for sale here, or no Baptists admitted; let the word *warple* henceforth mean . . . this new card-trick, or the thrill experienced by a dub golfer the first time he breaks 100. As Humpty Dumpty said to Alice in *Through the Looking Glass:* "When *I* use a word, it means just what I choose it to mean."

William James is said to have lamented, on one occasion, the fact that each individual human being was not permitted to have his own private language — that is, his own personally chosen symbols for his own stock of meanings. Each of us, to the extent of our ability as a symbolizer, could make one; but communication would be impossible unless we could also invent and agree upon a common-to-all language by means of which all our private languages could be translated. Few individuals living today have coined so much as a single new symbol that has been accepted and ratified by society, thereby adding a new word to the language, such as *kodak* and *serendipity*.[5] Yet the opportunity of experiencing what is, according to Professor M. M. Postan, "the greatest of all joys, that of inventing new names," is always open. All we need to do is to find a sufficiently common meaning which lacks a good symbol, and then to induce our fellow men to accept and use the one we have coined as their instrument for handling that meaning in their writing, conversation, and thinking. We do not have to insist in advance upon identical private meanings for all users; the test of any symbol is its ability to "deliver the goods" at a given time in co-ordinated social behavior. When a new expression becomes old and worn we call it a *cliché*; and yet all languages have to be composed mainly of *clichés*; otherwise they could not enable large masses of individuals to share their meanings.

Civilized men grow up in the midst of highly articulate families where most of the common meanings of life have symbols already firmly attached to them. Viewed at any given moment, a living language is a transient integration of symbols and meanings in certain conventional orders which have become habitual and involuntary in human minds. It is at one and the same time a social institution and a practical art in process of growth. Yet our familiar words are so inseparably fused with their meanings by long habit that, if we are suddenly transferred to a foreign country with a different language, we may be completely at a loss to make ourselves understood, and be obliged to revert to "sign language." We have come to identify the symbol with the thing symbolized. We may even succumb to the fallacy of believing that there are "proper meanings" for words in a sense that goes beyond the conventional. It may be hard for us to realize that, as John Dewey put it, "the particular sound or mark that stands for *dog* or *justice* in different cultures is arbitrary or conventional in the sense that although it has *causes* there are no *reasons* for it."[6] We may even share the linguistic naïveté of the small boy who was asked, "How did the first man who saw an elephant know it was an elephant?" and who replied, "Because it *looked* like an elephant!" Only a few words in any language have obvious "causes" that give an unmistakable clue to their meanings, having been formed in imitation of the natural sounds which they symbolize (a process known as "onomatopoeia," such as buzz, hiss, or slurp — the latter a tea-taster's symbol for his chief activity, slurping tea).

Man, then, can make his own signs and can use them as symbols, in the form of invented words which stand for, or map out mentally, or pass like coins instead of, the things or ideas whose meanings they symbolize. His great achievement is in detaching the symbol from its original context and manipulating it in new combinations and contexts without necessarily doing

[5] The first of these originated as the brand-name of the cameras sold by the Eastman Kodak Company of Rochester, New York. Horace Walpole coined the second when he wrote his friend Horace Mann about the "three princes of Serendip," who were always "finding things they were not in quest of."

[6] *Op. cit.*, p. 47. (Italics his. H. A. L.)

anything about the things to which it refers. This enables him to live in as many mental worlds as he chooses to construct, without accepting the savage's conclusion that, because he can think of a thing, it must therefore exist.

To realize, however, that there is no necessary connection between the symbol and the symbolized, that words are independent of things, takes a certain degree of sophistication that not everyone possesses. If we stop to think about the matter, we shall recognize that the structure of language does not necessarily duplicate the structure of the world about which we wish to write or talk. Words are not the same as the things for which they stand: we can eat oysters and ride in automobiles; but we cannot be nourished by the word "oysters" or be transported by the word "automobile." Most language is intended to map the actual world, but it often takes in possible and imaginable worlds as well.

"Thinking proceeds by abstraction; that is its difference from sensory perception," says George Boas. "One can think about redness without seeing it at the time of thinking, and one can see redness without thinking about it."[7]

We must also recognize that to find that a sentence is grammatical does not prove that it is logical, although thinkers for centuries after Aristotle assumed that it did. Gradually we have been forced to abandon both kinds of parallelism: words-things and grammar-logic, and to accept the partial autonomy of each of the four orders.

Yet so strong is the human tendency from earliest childhood to impute a more than conventional connection between our symbols and their meanings, and our ability to discourse and our limited capacity for logical thinking, that many of our fellows live their lives in a world primarily composed of words and talk. This is the besetting sin of the pseudo-intellectuals. They swap verbal coins with their neighbors as if the latter were the actual goods, and they assume quite mistakenly that because they are using language grammatically they must be dealing with logical and testable meanings securely anchored in existence.

4. Levels of Abstraction

Words are an immense aid to thought by enabling us to fix or stabilize a large stock of meanings, and yet to interchange them mentally in all sorts of new combinations, thereby evoking new meanings. Symbols make it easier for the limited span of human attention to take in broad patterns of significance. From a number of complicated situations with common characteristics we extract a meaning to which we apply a symbol, or word, such as white or frozen or triangle or honest. If we are in a hurry, as, for example, a stenographer taking dictation, we may substitute still another symbol for our first one, the word; or a scene-designer may write the letter "W" instead of the word "white." Such symbols-of-symbols take us farther and farther away from the full concreteness of our original experiences. The "x's" and "y's" of mathematics are shortcut ways of manipulating symbols *without* thinking of the meanings they may be standing for temporarily, such as so many bushels

[7] George Boas, *op. cit.*, p. 101.

of wheat or the area of a deck. We say that such symbols are very abstract, being far removed from the concrete things which they symbolize. The word "abstract" comes from the Latin verb *abstrahere*, meaning "to draw away from" or "to separate." All symbolizing involves some degree of abstraction or selection. To symbolize the color of a horse or a house or a flower as "white" is to leave out of account the other characteristics of those objects; but to refer to "whiteness" is to take a still further step of abstraction that leaves out the many different objects exemplifying whiteness.

There are many levels of abstraction, each selecting, condensing, and therefore omitting, some of the meaning that was included on the level just below. Uncivilized societies abound in concrete words, but seldom reach a high level of abstraction. The Zulus are said to have words for white cow or red cow, but no word for cow; while the aborigines of Central Brazil have no words for palm and parrot, although they have a wealth of concrete names for different varieties of palms and parrots. The very lack of high-level abstractions, however, may serve to protect them from some civilized nonsense in the form of abstract proverbs and superstitions. They have an immunity to what Abbé Dimnet calls "the terrible French craving for summing up complex realities in a single formula . . . or apparently illuminating foreshortening."

The harm comes, not in the abstracting, which is highly necessary and superbly useful for handling great masses of facts and experiences, but in forgetting that we have left out great numbers of individual differences, and that we are not entitled to endow our abstractions at will with mysterious powers and qualities which they cannot be proved to possess. Modern physics has demonstrated the vast utility of elaborate mental constructs or abstractions, some of which have become exceedingly remote from everyday experience. But physicists have kept their abstractions in touch with experience through constant experimental demonstrations. We accept the "fictitious" electrons and other complex abstractions because they have visible operational significance in the world of events.

The cure for "vicious abstraction" is to be constantly conscious of abstracting while we are doing it. That means, in Stuart Chase's words, "to know what level you are on, and what characteristics are left out at that level."[8] We must not forget the omitted differences which our abstractions conceal; but it is equally fatal to become so obsessed with individual peculiarities that we deny or minimize the likenesses which enable us to think in general terms. We must be just as aware of what we put into our abstractions as of what we leave out. One way to cultivate this double awareness is to retrace the process by which most of us learned the use of words in the first place.

LEARNING TO MANIPULATE ABSTRACTIONS

On the simplest level, we found out the meanings of words largely by imitation and repetition when they were pronounced in the presence of ob-

---

[8] *Op. cit.*, p. 89. What happens when one forgets what has been *included* is well indicated in Arthur E. Murphy, *The Uses of Reason* (New York, 1943), pp. 45–52 and 70–80.

jects. We may have formed the habit of associating the sound of "doll," for instance, with the sight and touch of a rubber object. Thereafter the object might suggest the word, or the word might call up the object. This learning of object-words, as Bertrand Russell calls them, is on the conditioned reflex, response-to-sign level. The child's use of words, however, is extremely loose, fluid, and wide-ranging. It tries to say everything about a situation at once. Only gradually does the child learn that words are unequal to the task imposed upon them, that common meanings must be consolidated and attached to symbols with a much more limited significance. "A child's word," writes Professor Grace A. de Laguna, "does not designate an object *or* a property *or* an act; rather it signifies loosely and vaguely the object together with its interesting properties and the acts with which it is commonly associated in the life of the child . . . so it is left *to the particular setting and context to determine the specific meaning for each occasion.* In order to understand what the baby is saying, you must see what the baby is doing."[9] Note the great importance of this "perceptual context" of words at this lowest level of abstraction.

What the child wants of language, aside from the pleasures of the sound, is to understand others and to make himself understood — in other words, to gain a degree of control over his immediate environment. So he proceeds to experiment with words to see what they are capable of doing, applying them sometimes too widely, so that "doll" may be used for anything made of rubber or shaped like his doll; and sometimes too narrowly, insisting that only his doll is really a doll. Some of these experiments succeed, and some of them fail. What he runs into, of course, is the common usage of others. By encountering a great many "not-dolls," but more than one doll, he may make a great discovery — namely, that there is one roughly standardized sound (or, better, one family of sounds) "doll," or "dawl," but *not* "ball" or "dull," which will act successfully as a symbol in many different contexts for a group or family of objects having certain abstract characteristics; limited size, resemblance to human baby or animal, and so on.

He will have released, to a greater or lesser extent, the meaning of the concept "doll" from the particular conditions (perceptual context) under which he first encountered the word. "Doll" now refers to a roughly blocked-out class of objects, and can be used, among English-speaking people, in all sorts of combinations with other words in sentences. Later in life, he may find it in Restoration comedies or gangster movies, where its meaning will depend very little upon its original perceptual context, but rather on its language context, or relations with other words. If, with the aid of dictionaries and books of reference which list the common possibilities, he cannot fill in the background, its meaning will remain obscure. This is the great source of difficulty in understanding foreign languages and the writers of past ages: we may lack either the perceptual or the language contexts which would enable us to

---

[9] Grace A. de Laguna, *Speech, Its Function and Development* (New Haven, 1927), pp. 90–91. (Italics hers. H. A. L.) Wittgenstein in his posthumously published *Philosophical Investigations* (Oxford, 1953) expounded the doctrine that the meaning of a word *is* its use, although there might be an extra something which defied analysis.

grasp the meanings that they have sought to put into words. Our worst trouble will be with metaphors, the figures of speech which take a symbol out of its normal context and make it refer to something that is roughly similar in a different context, as a novelist might describe a selfish mother's feeling toward a dead child: "She had lost her doll." Taken literally, the statement confuses us; but taken figuratively, we see how the meaning is enriched by using the word "doll" in a new context instead of the word "child" in its accustomed place.

In the process of learning the flexible use of such abstractions, however, the child carries along in memory the most vivid of the feeling-tones which attach to the word in its original perceptual contexts. If, for example, he was very much attached to dolls in his early experiences with them, it will be next to impossible for him to separate the abstract symbol from the pleasant emotion in his adult thinking. That is one reason why our first emotional associations ("Give a dog a bad name," etc.) with the labels of things can be so decisive in determining our later attitudes. Once our feelings and the words become fused, we tend to endow the symbol with all the magic of our first associations with it; and, what is more, we expect others to do likewise. Then it becomes difficult, even impossible, for us to think well of anything that bears a certain obnoxious label, or ill of anything that carries the tag of our childhood church, political party, nationality, or neighborhood. Our prejudices, as well as our intellectual judgments, operate symbolically.

"No one," says Bertrand Russell, "learns the word 'procrastination' by hearing it frequently pronounced on occasions when someone is dilatory."[10] Such symbols are "dictionary words" right from the beginning; we learn their meanings through other words, by way of verbal definitions. It is in the realm of dictionary words that we are most likely to commit the two worst crimes of abstraction: being unaware of omitted differences (that we *are* abstracting), and projecting desired characteristics into words just because their meanings are so general that it is difficult for anyone to prevent our doing so. "Democracy" and "co-existence" and "appeasement" can become loaded with all kinds of meanings and magic, as long as we are not called upon to produce any objects to which they refer. Thus we may use dictionary words as if they were object-words, in the belief that they must have some eventual concrete reference to our world simply because they can be defined. But perhaps they can be defined, only in other words; and can we be sure of *their* meanings? Many of our broad terms with emotive colorings, like "absolute mind," "perfect beauty," and "a just peace," should be recognized for what they are, not object-words, but high (and perhaps highly useful) abstractions based upon dictionary definitions.

At this point the temptation is strong to yield to the lure of that vicious phrase, "meaningless abstractions." That would be as stupid as the error against which it protests — the belief that all abstractions must be meaningful in just the ways in which they are claimed to be. Abstractions by themselves are like all other marvelously delicate instruments: they can be used both clumsily and skillfully. To create and manipulate the broadest of abstractions

[10] *Op. cit.*, p. 83. See also Charles L. Stevenson, *op. cit.*, chap. III.

in their true character, as abstractions, is to engage in perhaps the highest intellectual activity of which a human being is capable. Just because some very abstract terms which are outside the formulas of the sciences may possess emotive associations is no good reason for avoiding them entirely. The function of the "great words," as I. A. Richards points out, is "to sustain the order in our minds, an order not less essential to them than any contrasted referential order. They sustain the order of our purposes. Without that order reason and desire destroy one another."[11] Lenin swayed the Russian people in 1917 with "Bread, Land, Peace"; and in 1963 Pope Paul VI on his election declared that the themes of his pontificate would be "Truth, Justice, Love, and Freedom." It is easy to point out that such very big words refer to ends, not means, and that therefore they leave much unaccomplished.

The danger lies in the abuse of the great words by those who lack a firm grasp of the nature of the abstracting process. It is they who transform sublimest sense into ridiculous nonsense. This is possible because the high-level abstractionist has set himself free from low-level explicitness, and may neglect to return to it. If, in his lofty speculations, he forgets what he has taken apart by analysis or left behind in his selective abstracting, he may mistake the results of his verbal operations for the world as it is in experience, instead of a mere sketch map of it drawn at a given moment from a certain point of view. He may even commit the further fallacy of supposing that where words abide, meanings must remain the same. Then he will be surprised and shocked when experience refuses to confirm his imagined and desired picture; and he may even try to force the world to behave the way his abstractions behave, but probably without much success.

The remedy for such calamities, however, is not to flee abstracting like the plague, and to insist that all words used in our presence shall be object-words with whose meanings we are immediately familiar. That, unfortunately, seems to be the moral which many readers draw from the popular semantics books. To refuse to think or to discuss because one is unable to point to everything thought about would be to head in the direction of Dr. Kurt Goldstein's mental patients who, having suffered brain lesions in the first World War, were unable to "take the abstract attitude" sufficiently to use words as symbols at all, and so were obliged to think laboriously in terms of their concrete experiences. Our task is rather to perform more and better abstracting, conscious of itself and in touch with the concrete. Sometimes the fact that abstractions are easily misused is turned into a blanket vindication of the concrete fact discovered in practice as against theory of any kind. No mistake could be more costly. We have seen how single facts in isolation from theories and their validly deduced consequences are useless to prove anything whatever. Humanity has always been oversupplied with merely practical men; but it has never yet had nearly enough theorists who could enlighten concrete practice with reliable abstract knowledge.

That latter task is a long and arduous one. Naturally those who are mentally lazy shrink from the discipline required for rigorous conceptualizing, and

11 I. A. Richards in his Introduction to Hugh R. Walpole, *Semantics* (New York, 1941), p. 17. See also I. A. Richards, *How to Read a Page* (New York, 1942).

are delighted to hear its shortcomings lampooned as "words, words, words"; while they themselves, presumably, are extolled by implication as hard-bitten practical men who stick close to the facts of life. They forget that it is just as bad never to budge from direct contact with the concrete as it is to get too far away from it into the abstract. It is in the country that is lacking in men of *vision*, says Proverbs XXIX:18, that the people perish.

The happy medium is a constant, cautious shuttling back and forth between words and things. No one can afford to let either one monopolize his time and attention. The "highbrow" is prone to overdo abstractions and to neglect the facts; while the "lowbrow" is just as likely to mock at the theories which he does not understand. To condemn all abstraction and all ambiguity, just because they are subject to certain vices when used in particular ways, is just as silly as to cover them with a blanket of eulogy for their virtues in other contexts. We must never forget that thinking is an art as well as a science; and that different languages may be needed for different purposes. When we come to a consideration of the historical pattern (in Chapter 14, Section 2 below), we shall see that the part played by generalizations in history differs markedly from their rôle in science.

Our policy in regard to abstractions, then, should not be inflexible, but adapted to our purposes. When we want our meanings to be crystal-clear and unmistakable, we should not hesitate to resort to technical terms — that is what they are for — in spite of the fact that they may sound pedantic when wrenched out of context and used in everyday conversation. We should also take it for granted that if the man in the street is to share, in part, the insight of the expert, the latter's professional vocabulary will have to be translated into relatively inexact "journalese." On the other hand, we should hardly be human unless there were moments when we wanted our words to snarl and hiss as well as to purr and fondle. Such expressions, which are hardly more than betrayals of our own emotions directed upon those of others, may nevertheless blast or heal the inner consciousness of our associates. In the mouth of a skillful propagandist, they may do the work of a dozen armored divisions. Language is at least as capable of a variety of uses as gunpowder. While it is important not to confuse ritualistic compliments and rhetorical billingsgate with sober and precise statements of fact, one gets nowhere by assuming that the restriction of language to its solely communicative function would solve all of humanity's problems overnight.

5. The Double Rôle of Language in Social Studies

It is one thing to give good advice, itself expressed in abstract language, but it is another to make clear what it would mean to take that advice seriously in the social studies. Few will venture to deny that the latter, in our day, are the happy hunting grounds of vague and dubious symbols with many meanings, on the one hand, and sonorous abstractions devoid of any ascertainable connection with the examinable world, on the other. In the second half of his book *The Tyranny of Words*, Stuart Chase has gorgeous sport with the economists, the statesmen, the lawyers, the formal logicians, and the philosophers as they intoxicate themselves and their hearers with their impressive symbols: capital, labor, credit, money, inflation, socialism, freedom of contract, due process, national honor, neutrality, freedom, destiny, value, goodness, and so on. As he remarks: "The student of semantics is embarrassed with the sheer richness of the evidence that people do not know what they are talking about. . . . Words, words, words, making blab, sense, blab, blab, sense, blab; a thin white flicker of meaning on a broad black band." It is clear that if we are not to mistake "mental machinery" for "tangible events," we must constantly keep looking over the edges of our abstract symbols and asking:

> "What is really happening out there?
> How do the facts really hang together out there?
> What are people really doing out there?"[12]

To accomplish this, however, it is not enough to concentrate our attention on a minute examination of each isolated symbol. Symbols take on alternative meanings in different contexts; and if we are to grasp the context of any discourse, we are first obliged to "let ourselves go" with the speaker or writer before we can start dissecting his vocabulary. We need continually to remind ourselves that unemployment and conscription and peace are not abstract entities, but people involved in specific conditions of living, which demand the closest study before we begin to generalize, or frame hypotheses about them. "Money" is what money does; it is itself symbolic, and words about money are doubly removed from the world where concrete goods and services are exchanged.

At the same time, words interpenetrate the subject matters which the social studies discuss in a way that they do not enter the natural sciences. It does not make any difference to the sulphur in a chemical experiment whether we call it "sulphur" or "S" or "32.06" or "bodgemush." Edgar Snow, in his *The Battle for Asia*, tells of the remarkable results obtained by the renaming process in the early years of the Red Chinese Republic. For years the Chinese Communists had insisted that their communism was only a stage in the democratic revolution, but all to no avail, as long as they persisted in using the imported name "Su-wei-ai" for their councils. When they changed to the Chinese word "tsan-yi-hui," which also means council, "missionaries who formerly saw nothing but evil in the Reds now returned from brief visits to the ex-Soviets singing the praises of the 'liberals' of Yenan who had overnight 'abandoned Communism' in favor of democracy."[13]

Words bring things to pass, and so form an important part of the human behavior which the social studies use words to describe and explain. Language has directive functions: we all try at times to mold the future of society by decrees, constitutions, laws, contracts, oaths, and slogans. No matter how

---

[12] Stuart Chase, *op. cit.*, pp. 350, 358. Several other writers emphasize the ritualistic and directive character of many abstractions in the social studies. See Jerome Frank, *Law and the Modern Mind* (New York, 1930), Clarence B. Randall, *The Folklore of Management* (Boston, 1959), and the works of Thurman Arnold.

[13] Edgar Snow, *The Battle for Asia* (New York, 1941), p. 317.

aloof and dispassionate the social studies try to be, their methods alter the very things they are endeavoring to expound. The words in their hypotheses cannot be wholly prevented from interacting with the facts which they describe or explain. Let us suppose, for example, that a welfare investigator in an industrial city has been studying the status of a dozen individuals who have been without work continuously over a ten-year period, and who seem psychologically incapable of resuming any regular occupation. They differ in many respects; but among them he thinks that he discerns two patterns of meaning which are connected: the inability to hold down a job, and its apparent explanation, which is a psychological condition. He casts about for words or symbols in which to express these meanings in his report, which may serve as the basis for action or for further study.

What language shall he choose for the formulation of his diagnosis? Shall it be that of precise symbols and functional equations? Or shall it be vivid and poetically rich in overtones? Kant once said that the function of a scientific theory was "to spell phenomena in order to be able to read them as experiences." Today we realize that there are many different languages in which this spelling may be undertaken. Once a language has been chosen, there is the further problem of finding words in its dictionary for the meanings which the investigator has in mind. Of course he is "free" to coin new symbols in the hope of getting them accepted, such as: "These individuals are *nerpophrotics* because of prolonged *ipsteriosis*." But that would mean a long campaign to popularize his coinages: and meanwhile the men in question would certainly believe that they were the victims of some dread contagious disease. The mere intent that our symbols shall be without emotive coloring is no guarantee that they will function that way in minds which differ from our own. The scientific investigator may be completely disinterested, and yet he cannot assume that everyone who hears or reads his results will be equally neutral in interpreting them.

At the other extreme, our social worker might try a military metaphor, and say: "These men are industrial casualties due to economic shell shock." But that would court misunderstanding because of the sympathy which would be aroused by the emotive associations of the words. He might ponder long over the feasibility of using the word "unemployables," both because of its vagueness, and even more because of its possible reaction upon the men in question, and upon his own attitude toward them. To call a man unemployable may actually help to make him unemployable, because either he or his potential employers may be led thereby to abandon hope. Words which incorporate emotional attitudes also react upon those who use them. To give a class a name, such as "beatniks" or "drop-outs" may result in attracting or repelling prospective members, so powerful are the forces of verbal suggestion and imitation in influencing our conduct.

Thus, the investigator finds his vaunted "freedom" to formulate his hypothesis in words hedged in from at least five sides:

(1) By the relatively "independent" structure of the material or subject matter which his hypothesis must ultimately fit.

(2) By his purpose in framing it, whether descriptive or explanatory, and to what extent and depth.

(3) By the already established meanings of words in various past contexts that are known to him and to those with whom he hopes to communicate.

(4) By the accepted rules of language and of logic in stating and connecting propositions.

(5) By the ways in which the emotive and directive functions of his own language may affect the structure of the material in (1).

The first four of these restrictions apply to the wording of hypotheses in all fields of inquiry. It is the fifth which is of particular importance in the social studies.

FOR CLASS DISCUSSION

A. The art of thinking and the proper command of words are inseparable. — *Albert Guérard*   (2)

B. In the last analysis we are governed either through talk or through force.
— *Felix Frankfurter*

C. A very great part of the mischiefs that vex this world arises from words.
— *Edmund Burke*

D. Words, as a Tartar's bow, do shoot back upon the understanding of the wisest, and mightily entangle and pervert the judgment.
— *Francis Bacon*
Change the import of old names, and you are in perpetual danger of being misunderstood; introduce an entire new set of names, and you are sure not to be understood at all. — *Jeremy Bentham*

E. They [the Royal Society] have exacted from all their members a close, naked, natural way of speaking, positive expressions, clear senses, a native easiness, bringing all things as near the Mathematical plainness as they can, and preferring the language of Artizans, Countrymen, and Merchants, before that of Wits or Scholars. — From the *History of the Royal Society* (London, 1667), by Thomas Sprat

F. Scientific language gains in exactness at the cost of flexibility. A perfect scientific language would be wholly unambiguous, possessing a representative, and only one, for each possible content item and relation in possible experience. Literary and colloquial languages gain in flexibility at the cost of exactness. The ideal of a language which would fulfill the requirements of a perfect science and perfect art would be difficult to realize.
— *A. E. Avey*

G. The notion that because words of a statute are plain, its meaning is also plain, is merely pernicious oversimplification. — *Felix Frankfurter*
The notion that bad linguistic habits are at the root of our social evils and that good linguistic habits will abolish them is just as much a form of

belief in verbal magic as the primitive's faith that his enemy can be slain by an incantation. — *Sidney Hook*

H. "The question is," said Alice, "whether you *can* make words mean so many different things."
"The question is," said Humpty Dumpty, "which is to be master — that's all." — *Lewis Carroll*

I. Words are wise men's counters, they do but reckon by them; but they are the money of fools. — *Thomas Hobbes*
Concepts become like molten bullion poured into coining moulds, whence — after due rolling, punching, and pressing — they issue as legal tender for general circulation. — *C. Spearman*

J. No two languages can say quite the same thing. . . . — *Michael Roberts*
If Aristotle had spoken Chinese or Dakotan he would have had to adopt an entirely different logic or at any rate an entirely different theory of categories. — *Fritz Mauthner*

K. The mind is a connecting organ; it works only by connecting and it can connect in an indefinitely large number of ways. Words are meeting points at which regions of experience come together; a part of the mind's endless endeavor to order itself. — *I. A. Richards*

L. Language is an unscientific phenomenon grown in fits of absent-mindedness. — *Stephen Ullmann*
There be so many words in use at this day in the English Tongue, that though of magnifique sound, yet (like the windy blisters of a troubled water) have no sense at all. — *Thomas Hobbes*   (4)

M. We want words to do more than they can . . . we expect them to help us grip and dissect that which in ultimate essence is as ungrippable as shadow.
                                                                    — *Samuel Butler*

N. The ideas and teaching of theology and philosophy — that was a matter of words giving birth to words, an endless procreation growing more and more bloodless with the centuries, a science of words with a dry logic begotten of lifeless abstractions . . . the unending war of opinion — opinion that turned sometimes upon little more than the shadow cast in the mind by the shape of a word. — *Henry Bellaman*

O. There is, unfortunately, no automatic method of achieving success in using verbal patterns, and we must never assume without special inquiry that our formal verbal pattern has not led us into nonsense. . . . The true meaning of a term is to be found by observing what a man does with it, not what he says about it. — *P. W. Bridgman*

P. There can be no peace without communication — there can be no communication without honestly used words. And when we go to the funeral of enough murdered words we end indeed in the graveyard of civilization.
                                                                    — *Raymond Swing*

Q. Language may be compared with the spear of Amfortas in the legend of the Holy Grail. The wounds that language inflicts upon human thought cannot be healed except by language itself. — *Ernst Cassirer*

EXERCISES IN SEMANTICS

Analyze each of the following in terms of the appropriate sections of Chapter 7, indicating the principle illustrated by each item.

1. The Incas of Peru left records in the form of small ropes of various colors tied in hundreds of kinds of knots. It is presumed that each knot of the *quipu*, as it is called, meant something; but no anthropologist has yet been able to translate a *quipu*, or ever to say exactly what they were intended to tabulate. Some have suggested that the knots refer to financial transactions, while others lean to the theory that they relate to weddings and funerals.

2. What's in a name? that which we call a rose
   By any other name would smell as sweet.
                                    — William Shakespeare in *Romeo and Juliet.*

3. Lists of "most beautiful words in the English language": Dr. *Wilfred J. Funk:* dawn, hush, lullaby, murmuring, tranquil, mist, luminous, chimes, golden, melody. *Mr. Frank Colby* (words chosen by readers of his column): mother, cellophane, bellboy, memory, wilderness, flamingo, lavender, belladonna, melancholy, tambourine. *Mr. Edwin Markham,* poet: empyrean, nevermore, sea sands, reverberate, imperishable, ideal, Californian. Mr. *Rupert Hughes,* novelist: oriole, immemorial, threnody, tremulous, blithe, translucent, ivory, gloom, inviolate, blue. List of "ugliest words": ubiquitous, impeccable, bosom, amenities, hash, spinach, gangrene, gripe, cacophony, scram, guzzle, mange, and sap.

4. Joshua Bug advertised in the London *Times* on June 26, 1862, that he would be known henceforth as Mr. Norfolk Howard.

Mr. and Mrs. Chester A. Frankenstein of Port Chester, N.Y. petitioned the County Court to change the last name of their two teen-age daughters to Franks because of the teasing associated with horror motion pictures.

5. In Sir T. Erskine May's *Parliamentary Practice* there are listed over one hundred epithets and expressions which a House of Commons member may not use in referring to another member, among them "villain," "jackass," "cheat," "cad," "swine," "stool pigeon," "insulting dog," and "not a damned one of you opposite."

6. (a) Owing to the scarcity of Pacific ocean sardines, some canneries attempted to substitute horse mackerel, but found housewife resistance to the name, and asked permission to call the fish "California haddock." The Food and Drug Administration denied the request, saying that it could not approve "names made out of thin air."

   (b) An attempt was made to introduce the noun "electronism" (by analogy with mechanism) for any electronic device, but it failed to catch on. Dr. Simon Ramo suggests the name "intellectronics" for the lore of computers which are used to amplify human brain-power.

7. "Therefore, you clown, abandon — which is in the vulgar, leave — the society — which in the boorish is company, of this female — which in the common is woman; which together is, abandon the society of this female, or, clown, thou perishest; or, to thy better understanding, diest; or, to wit, I kill

thee, make thee away, translate thy life into death." — Touchstone in *As You Like It*

8. In his book *Rehabilitation of the Physically Handicapped* Dr. Henry Kessler notes the immense harm done by the word "cripple," and points out that defects are a relative matter hinging upon our definition of "normal." A defect which causes an actual restriction of activity or arouses a prejudice is a physical handicap. "The definition must be necessarily social and economic, rather than medical or anthropological. It defines the status of the individual in his society."

9. As propaganda against federal projects creating electric power, a group of electric light and power companies published full-page magazine advertisements entitled "How Federal Electric Power Sets Up a 'Favored Class' in America," arguing that "a favored class" of Americans get "subsidized power" denied to the taxpaying customers served by private enterprise, which is "unfair."

10. Punctuation can change the meaning of a sentence to a fantastic degree. Three professors at New York University on a WPIX television program offered as an example the sentence, "My friend Ralph has not yet married Celia," and were surprised to receive lists of thirty or more interpretations created merely by changes of punctuation.

11. A Londoner visiting America found himself confused by the meanings of the word "fix" in this country. To fix a drink, he said, was to mix it; to fix a meal was to prepare it; to fix a car was to repair it; to fix something to a wall was to attach it; to have a fixed income meant that it was steady and unchanged; to say "I'll fix him!" was to suggest revenge; and to be in distress was to be "in one hell of a fix."

12. Dr. Morton Prince once treated a neurotic patient who complained of a sharp pain in her foot. He assured her in a confident tone that it was a plain case of pododynia. Finally one day she asked: "What is pododynia?" He answered, laughing, "It is pain in the foot." She also laughed, and said: "Never mind. I feel much better already. It is a great comfort to know what it is." In the course of a few hours she was walking without limping and was free from pain.

13. In August, 1963, the Boston *Herald* declared editorially that "The term 'de facto segregation' has become a semantic barrier to equitable agreement between the Boston School Committee and the NAACP on the real and pressing problem of securing a decent education for Boston's Negro school children." The newspaper pled for the use instead, of "racial imbalance" to describe schools which are virtually 100 per cent Negro, as in New York and California, on the ground that "*de facto* segregation" implies a guilty intent not present.

14. Instead of inventing a scientific nomenclature free from extraneous associations, economics, like theology, borrows its terms from common speech, defines them in a sense different from and often opposite to their accepted meaning, erects a stone wall of logic on concealed verbal foundations, and defies the plain man to scale it. — *Lancelot Hogben*

❧ 8 ❧

CLARIFYING THE HYPOTHESIS:
Classification and Definition

1. The Need and Nature of Classification

"THE WORLD IS SO FULL OF A NUMBER OF THINGS" that the only way in which a human mind can cope with it in thinking is by grouping individual items into *classes* to which names or symbols are usually attached: knives, stamps, protozoa, plumbers, melodies, dilemmas. The limited spans of human attention and memory make it impossible for anyone to think for long in purely individual terms. A teacher or a salesman or a judge may try to remember all those with whom he comes in contact by their names and personal idiosyncrasies; but unless he has the legendary memory of a Jim Farley, he soon finds the task impossible. Most of us resort to the economical short cut which we owe to the Greeks, and assort our scattered instances in classes on the basis of as many similarities as possible (but at least one) which they seem to us to possess in common. That device enables us to think of the symbol which stands for the class, and to ignore, at least for the moment, the many detailed ways in which the individual members of the class may *differ* from one another. In other words, classifying plainly involves abstracting, since we substitute for the original richness and variety of the concrete individual items an abstract concept, idea, or label. The trouble is that we are likely to fall into the delusion that what we have omitted has ceased to count or even to exist. Constant reminders are needed in order to keep alive our sense of individual differences among hundreds of ships or soldiers or students. This need becomes more acute as our abstractions become verbal and rise to higher and higher levels, more and more remote from specific situations.

Classes of things are capable of classification by similarities into more inclusive classes of classes. A professional baseball team is a class made up of individual ballplayers; but a baseball league is a class of classes made up of teams of players. On the league level, the member teams are treated as individuals — that is, they are not further analyzed on that level. "Organized baseball" is a class of classes of classes, a grouping of leagues of teams of players, with each league, on that level, occupying the rôle of individual member. The technical terms most often used for this relation of class inclusion within a wider class are *species* for the narrower class and *genus* for the wider

178

class. The same class may be, in different contexts, both a species (as related to a wider class) and a genus (as related to narrower classes).[1]

How shall we go about this task of classifying, which is evidently the first of the spadework that must be done before we undertake the framing of good descriptive and explanatory hypotheses? Is it, in the first place, one task, or many? Do objects compel us to classify them on the basis of fixed traits marked off in Nature? For many centuries, chiefly under the influence of Aristotle, it was believed that the universe consisted of such fixed natural classes created in a hierarchy which needed only to be discovered or laid bare by human inquiry. It was supposed that the grammarians among primitive men had begun that task. The names applied to the classes were widely believed to mark off genuine and deep cleavages in the nature of things, or even to indicate eternal patterns (Plato's archetypes) which were more real than any imperfect, changing, individual instance could possibly be. But philosophical criticism soon revealed the gap between grammatical classes and the purified concepts of logic. The Greek view of the nature of classification was dealt a deathblow by Darwin's evolutionary theory of the origin of new species, with the result that many thinkers went to the opposite extreme, and contended that classifying was solely a matter of drawing imaginary lines at the convenience of the classifier. We are accustomed to thinking of classes of living things, for example, as temporary and as shading off into "twilight zones" on either side, with new classes beginning wherever the mutations amount to enough to warrant a more-or-less arbitrary "cut" in the continuous series of slightly differing individuals.

Today we endeavor to avoid both of these extremes. We recognize that the structures of objects limit, to some extent, the useful ways in which they can, for various purposes, be classified in systems. All things do not lend themselves equally well to all kinds of classifications. But, on the other hand, within the limits imposed by the nature of things there are plenty of alternatives, no one of which can claim to be the only acceptable formula. As Karl Britton expresses it: "The facts of the world do not in themselves seem to determine any classification at all: the world seems to be differentiated only by some human volition, instinct, plan."[2] Whether we shall attempt to classify and how we shall proceed, will depend primarily upon our interests. Whether we shall be successful will depend upon the materials, and our ingenuity. College students, for different purposes, may be classified by age, eye color, type of fingerprints, ability in spelling, number of first cousins, third letter of first name, amount of money on person, and so on indefinitely. Some of these possible likenesses seem to have little to do with one another, while others of them may prove to be key characteristics linked in constellations of related traits. The

---

[1] Note that the plural of the word *species* is *species*, while that of *genus* is *genera*. In biology, species has a technical meaning, namely, the lowest and most important class of living things, with genus as the next wider class.

[2] Karl Britton, *Communication* (London, 1939), p. 181. Especially true of race classifications, nearly all of them "arbitrary"; see Michel Leiris, article cited in *Race and Science*, pp. 181–90.

bases of some of the classifications seem to reside in the structure of the subject matter, while those of others appear to be located in the individual who does the classifying.

Now we cannot tell in advance, from a superficial glance at our materials, just what class-concepts will be the most useful in ordering them for the purpose which we have in mind. But we can be sure, from the past history of science, that many of the most obvious ways of assorting objects by surface resemblances are the least useful, as for example the color and taste of foods, which give little indication of their chemical value in nutrition. Neither can we be sure, at the start, how deeply our classifications may penetrate into the nature of things. Thus, all classifying is, in its early stages, tentative and hypothetical: the men who devised the first census, or the first poll of public opinion, had no way of being sure in advance just what classes, or how many, would turn out to be significant. They were obliged to guess what questions to ask, and in what classes the replies should be grouped, and then to improve their techniques as they went along.

2. A Classification of Classifications

Since there are many legitimate sorts of classifications, how shall they be classified for our purpose, which is to understand their construction and use? Since classification is a mental ordering more or less related to the independent structure of things, we should expect some classifications to emphasize the classifier, and thus to be relatively artificial, superficial, and adapted to his limited purpose or taste; while others will stress the subject matter, being more "natural," structural, and adapted to the character of the materials. In the first type, which may be called *index* classifications, the aim of the classifier holds almost complete sway over the material; while at the other extreme, in the *structural* (or natural in the sense of less artificial) classifications, the material dominates the classifier. Intermediate sorts of classifications in which the classifier usually exploits a fairly important quality of the subject matter for a purpose of his own, may be called *diagnostic* classifications.

Index classifications. In this group the purpose of the classifier dominates; and there is usually no need or desire to go below the surface of the items classified. The main object is convenient arrangement or accessibility: books are catalogued by the first letter of the author's last name in order that they may be found quickly; and we have long been accustomed to the assigning of numbers to convicts, policyholders, and soldiers. With the coming of computers and electronic accounting devices, however, the use of large and complicated numbers for identifying telephone subscribers, bank accounts, and postal addresses has enormously increased, and has even provoked the formation of Anti-Digit Leagues in some localities (not as yet tagged with numbers).

A whole "science" of filing and cataloguing has developed in this field; and we have come to demand that every book containing factual data should have an index. Classifications of this sort may rest upon any easily recognizable mark of identification; and they abound in strange bedfellows, such as:

Arc, Joan of	Lead Kindly Light	Polish constitution
Arc light	Lead poisoning	Polish, floor

An index classification is usually so superficial as to be meaningless apart from a knowledge of the purpose of the classifier, as we can see when we come across articles which bear numbers or letters applied by another person with some forgotten end in view.

Diagnostic classifications. Here the purpose of the classifier is still dominant, but more account is taken of the external characteristics of the material without penetrating very deeply or respecting them very faithfully. In this group belong the child's game of "Animal, vegetable, or mineral?" and all of the early scientific classifications (hot, cold, moist, and dry substances; Linnaean botany, etc.). Collections of objects which are not scientifically (i.e., structurally) classified usually have some ordering principle of a diagnostic nature: flowers by season, or habitat, or degree of cultivation; weapons by country of origin, century of use, or branch of the service using them. Trees in a park might be diagnostically classified from the point of view of landscaping, age, or value as lumber, depending upon one's interest at the moment. Motion pictures are often grouped on the basis of length, or cost of production, or suitability for different types of audiences. But to classify a picture as "unfit for children" is to make your opinion the basis of an attempt to keep children from seeing it. That, in turn, may be exactly what will make many immature persons want to attend. The classification will have interacted with the material classified.

The social studies are full of what might be called directive diagnostic classifications, in which the classifier, for some purpose of his own, deliberately exploits some characteristic of his subject matter, such as race or occupation or sales appeal or moral quality, in an effort to make it appear to be a structural one. Some of our most bitter legal arguments are over these directive diagnostic classifications, since they are often struggles for the control of policy disguised as quarrels over the labels of things. It is a mistake to suppose that they are to be settled, once and for all, by consulting dictionaries or legal precedents. For the question at stake is for society to decide, in the long run, whose purposes of classification are going to be served, and not what classifications are justified by the nature of things. The latter will tolerate, at least temporarily, an endless variety of different diagnostic patternings. Time and trial reveal which ones are superficial, and which ones serve the more abiding human purposes.

Structural classifications. These are also artificial, in a sense, being the product of human minds, and yet they are relatively "natural," since they seek to penetrate to the key characteristics of things, both external and internal. When Berzelius, at the beginning of the nineteenth century, proposed to divide all the elements into metals and non-metals, he could point to ten or a dozen physical and chemical properties linked together in each class: metals have high density, luster, malleability, ductility, are good conductors, form basic oxides, etc.; while non-metals have low density, little malleability or ductility, reflect light poorly, are poor conductors, form acidic oxides, etc. Yet there are some elements which are very difficult to classify as either metals or non-metals. In biology, the possession or non-possession of a backbone (vertebrate or invertebrate) was found to be accompanied by many other related characteristics. Note that most of the structural classifications which have proved most useful (the periodic table in chemistry, the analyses of sounds in phonetics, etc.) are not at all obvious on the surface, but are the fruit of the exercise of the disciplined imagination and of the most prolonged and determined study. When such a classification enables us to predict and control, not simply a narrow range of experience for a limited purpose, but the widest range of possibilities that we can imagine, we suppose that we have succeeded in distinguishing key or basic qualities. To find one of the qualities enables us to infer the probable presence of other associated qualities.

Once established by being woven into laws, we expect such classifications to be relatively stable (at least until still wider ranges of possibilities are envisaged and explored), since they depend as little as possible upon the fluctuating purposes and abilities of transient human knowers. At the same time we recognize that the boundaries of structural classifications are not permanent walls of separation which keep plants from being animals or women from being men. Many of our classes are grouped about central tendencies and shade into one another without sharp cleavages; and we should resist the tendency to classify sharply where the differences are almost imperceptible. We must not fall into the error of assuming that "Nature is as respectful of our classifications as we are"; or that of supposing either that the edges of her demarcations are as well defined as those of our scientific class-names, or that no further evolutionary changes will occur.

Structural classifications in fields where our knowledge is well-ordered also possess the valuable property of forming systems, such that the location of an item tells us something about its relations to the other items in the same system. The botanical classification of the American White Birch tree, for example, enables us to place it with respect to other trees in the same ladder of generality, thus:

Kingdom: Vegetable
Series: Flowering plants
Class: Dicotyledons
Subclass: Angiosperms
Division: Apetalous exogens
Order: Cupuliferae
Suborder: Betuleae
Genus: Betula
Species: Alba
Variety: Populifolia

This method of classification has made possible the naming of more than 890,000 species of animals (722,000 of them insects).

3. Rules and Criteria of Classification

If these are the main varieties of classification, what is a good one? That question cannot be answered without knowing: good for what? Classifications that are excellent for some purposes are worthless for others. First you must decide whether the use to which the classification is to be put demands an index, a diagnostic, or a structural classification. Having settled that point, you can then go on to formulate certain rules which apply to all classificational thinking for public use. (It must be admitted that our minds have non-logical but effective ways of classifying some of our memories for private purposes.)

Rule 1. *The classes chosen should fit the material to be classified.* Men should not be grouped by the kind of wings they have, since they have no wings. Sensations should not be classified as true and false.

Rule 2. *At each level, the classes should have a single basis of classification without overlapping.* The constituent species must be mutually exclusive. Taxpayers should not be classified as rural, delinquent, urban, and non-resident.

Rule 3. *To avoid inadvertent omissions, a classification should be exhaustive.* When added together, the constituent species should equal the genus. A classification should cover all the material it purports to classify, and it should allow for the inclusion of new data when discovered. Regulations classifying persons as married and single for income-tax purposes would appear to be adequate; but if "married" means "living together as husband or wife," then no provision has been made for widows, widowers, divorced persons, or those legally separated. All have been married; yet all, by the rules, are single. Only a classification including the unmarried and both classes of those who have been married would be exhaustive.

Classifications, like any constructions composed of verbal symbols, are likely to mislead us by their static appearance. This is particularly true of our classifications of growing things. Many organisms go through strikingly different stages of development. A butterfly emerges from the egg as a caterpillar, spins a cocoon or chrysalis, from which it emerges with wings. We are always surprised to find that a boy or girl has ceased by imperceptible degrees to belong in the "child" or even in the "youth" group any longer. Often we fail to remember that the categories themselves have a way of changing in meaning from culture to culture and from century to century. The group "children" in upper-class Victorian England was far more inclusive than it was on our Western frontier, where maturity was forced upon the young by hardships. There is a high rate of obsolescence in the classifications used by the social studies, both because the material classified and the interests behind the classifications change. It was once important, for instance, for a community to know whether each of its houses had a hitching post, a fire bucket, and a well; today the census-takers are more likely to be interested in television sets, trailers, bomb shelters, and health matters.

Although it is thus perfectly apparent that reclassifications are needed as such alterations take place, most of us are very slow in making them. There is a great lag in all of our classifying activities, partly due to our inertia and the satisfyingness of the familiar. If we are accustomed to rating Frenchmen as romantic, then the first prosaic Frenchman we encounter is likely to be discounted as an exception to the rule. Ordinarily it takes a good many of these exceptions to force us to change our habits of sorting. When our emotions are involved, the task is even harder. When a whole nation changes classifications from "hated enemy" to "befriended former enemy," great and painful upheavals in emotional attitudes result.

The mere complexity of a classification is no guarantee that it has any structural significance. A most minutely classified inventory of a great department store, or the "classified advertising" pages of a metropolitan newspaper, might possess great complexity, and yet be quite superficial. Then, too, the pattern which enables us to locate objects in a collection may be quite different from that which enables us to see the relationship of parts in a system. If we are to make good explanatory hypotheses, and are to be able to test them, we must aim at building up as many structural classifications as possible: classes, that is, whose similarities can be shown to be key characteristics linked with other important similarities. Only in that way can we expect our classificatory generalizations to lead us to other generalizations. Above all, in our classifying we must avoid the attitude of Procrustes, the legendary highwayman of Attica who laid his victims upon an iron bed, and then either stretched or cut off their legs to fit. Men have been repeatedly classified in such a fashion, once and for all — as civilized and barbarian, saved and lost, educable and hopeless; but fortunately few of these dictated parcelings have long endured.

4. Division

Not many of us are privileged, except for our own amusement, to do a great deal of original classifying of new material on an extensive scale. We are born into a world where most of the familiar things are already pretty thoroughly classified, cross-classified, and symbolized. A natural scientist thinks himself lucky if he can find a single important rock or plant or animal that does not fit into existing classifications, and so force a revision to accommodate his new discovery. In the social studies the multiplicity of different ways in which phenomena may be classified makes originality in rearrangement easy, but demonstration of utility difficult.

The problem of grouping things in classes, at any rate, does not always present itself as an affair of going from scattered facts to a general concept (classification), but as the reverse process of starting with a general concept and splitting it into usable sub-classes (division). A student of finance might conceivably compile his own classification of banks by visiting all such institutions in his neighborhood and discovering that (for his purpose) they fell conveniently into such classes as national banks, trust companies, and savings banks. But he might approach the same problem in a different way by starting with the class-concept bank, and then breaking it down into a number of smaller classes.

Since division is classification in reverse, substantially the same rules apply. In division, however, greater emphasis is placed upon making the sub-classes on each level completely exhaustive. To divide all men into white and Negro, for example, leaves out the Orientals entirely. This would not be serious in classifying the residents of a state which contained only whites and Negroes within its borders; but in a treatise on anthropology such a division would be disastrous. For this reason, an ancient logical device known as *dichotomous division* (literally: cut in two), which makes the two halves automatically exhaustive and non-overlapping, is sometimes employed. If men are dichotomously divided, a white man would doubtless begin by splitting them into whites and non-whites, then the non-whites into Negro and non-Negro, and so on. But a Negro would be just as entitled to start with a division into Negro, and non-Negro, then into yellow and non-yellow, white and non-white, and so on. The important thing about any dichotomous division is that it never omits any of the original class — men, since the remainder are always included in the negative half of the last dichotomous division. Yet the device is a clumsy one, since the positive and negative halves are seldom co-ordinate species: white men form a single relatively homogeneous color group, while non-white men may be black and red and yellow. The same would be true in dividing income-tax payers into married and non-married, since one of the other of the two halves (depending on the definition of marriage) would include the widowed and divorced.

But whichever approach we use to the problem of classes and their members, whether we start with the individual items and classify them in wider and wider groups, or whether we begin with a broad genus and divide it into narrower and narrower species, our central difficulty is essentially the same: to pick out of the flux about us stable bases or principles or key similarities which will make useful components of larger systems. No rules or mechanical formulas will tell us in advance what traits to select. Even the best of classifiers has to learn as he goes along. But, as we have seen in the whole field of hypothetical patterning, of which classification is a part, the important thing is to be thoroughly acquainted with one's subject matter, on the one hand; and conversant with, but not too attached to, the types of order which have already proved their worth in somewhat similar branches of knowledge, on the other.

5. Definition

"If you wish to converse with me," said the wise Voltaire, "you must define your terms." Otherwise, he implied, our conversation, like innumerable student bull-sessions, is likely to lead nowhere and accomplish nothing. Communication by means of words can only take place successfully if both parties attach approximately the same meanings in terms of behavior to the symbols used. Why make noises at one another systematically if nothing is happening meanwhile in our minds? Unless we have some conception of what is going on in the other man's mind, we cannot even be sure that we misunderstand one another. Talk without mutual understanding is just a means of preventing silence. That, like music, may yield certain entertainment values, but it does not advance co-operative action. If we are to understand one another, the meanings in our minds must run roughly parallel with the symbols we are exchanging, and we must be aware that that condition obtains. In a well-understood conversation, each word should call up approximately the same core of meaning in all the minds involved. Since the exact meanings of symbols depend on contexts, there must be a sharing, to some extent, of the contexts which illuminate them. To be sure that we understand, we have to know a great deal about what the other person is taking for granted: what sort of world he believes that he is in, what sort of past experiences he has had, what "language" he speaks — in the sense of the common ways in which he uses the words that come most naturally to him.

Failures of understanding may come about in many different ways. A wholly new word or symbol, suddenly introduced, will not be understood; but an old word may also fail to be taken as the speaker intended. The commonest reason for this is the vagueness and ambiguity of our symbols. Thousands of honest misunderstandings occur every day because of the fact that there is not, except in the most exact sciences, a one-to-one correspondence between symbols and meanings. Many words have more than one common meaning; while many meanings can be expressed by more than one word. Most words, except the most explicitly technical, have many shades of meaning around a central core; such as, a queen is the wife of a king, with related meanings in bee culture, card games, society, the movies, and so on. Moreover, the whole system is alive and growing as the word is used daily by millions of people in millions of contexts. All is in flux, both the boundaries and the central nucleus or nuclei.

Students of semantics have traced the many characteristic ways in which the meanings of words become altered. Sometimes the changes are in the things symbolized more than in the symbols, such as the plow of antiquity and the plow of today, or the extension of meaning of horn from animal horn to a horn made of metal. But more often the seat of the change is in the user of words. He may contract the scope of a symbol by limiting its application: "success" in Elizabethan times meant any outcome, whether good or bad; today it has become restricted to the narrower meaning of favorable result. He is far more likely, however, to do the reverse. Every time he uses a word metaphorically — that is, shifted to a slightly different context — it may acquire an additional meaning or shade of meaning. Sometimes this spreading into remote contexts occurs with great rapidity — witness the instant acceptance of Winston Churchill's coining of "iron curtain" to signify Russia's exclusion of the rest of the world.

It would be foolish to argue, as many writers on semantics seem to do, that ambiguity is all loss and no gain. Without it the bulk of our wit and humor would be non-existent, especially all puns and *double entendres*. Poetry would also vanish, since it depends upon evoking the maximum number of associated meanings, plus their overtones and undertones, in the fewest number of words. A society with a completely univocal language, one in which every word could be taken literally, since it possessed but a single possible meaning, and thus was capable of being fed into a computer, would be utterly prosaic and probably unprogressive. For we know that the vague resemblances in things, often playfully discovered through the wild use of metaphor, are excellent seedbeds of new ideas. How to make ambiguity fruitful in originality without at the same time plunging us into disastrous misunderstandings seems to be our language problem. To solve it, we shall probably have to become versatile, both poets and scientists, the masters of more than one use of language. It will not be enough to be able to employ just the clear and technical accents of pure science, or just the sublimely stirring equivocations of pure poetry. There are times for using both in their purity; but there are also occasions for utilizing a compromise between utter clarity and utter vagueness.

We want, in other words, to preserve the "good" ambiguity which enables us to do justice in our language to the changing twilight zones of our actual world, and to get rid of the "bad" ambiguity which prevents us from following those paths which are reasonably clear. Now the great foe of "bad" ambiguity is definition. The word "definition" comes from the Latin *de,* which means "concerning," and *finis,* boundary or limit. A definition is therefore literally a statement concerning the limits or boundaries of the meaning of a word or symbol. It states the relation of the defined term to other neighboring terms. A meaning can sometimes be defined as lying between two others, such as "brush-country folks — those too poor to paint and too proud to whitewash." There is, of course, no great point in being precise about the edges of a word's meaning if we do not know what is at the center or core. Definition thus has two main tasks to perform: to convey the essential meaning which is to be the common ground of understanding, and to mark out its limits with sufficient precision for the purposes in view. It is idle to suppose that a few simple rules can show how these two aims are to be realized in all instances: everything will depend on where the new understanding is to start from (in terms of already comprehended symbols) and the destination at which we expect it to arrive. Sometimes we want to know what a thing *is,* sometimes where it *came from,* and sometimes what it will *do.* On the lowest level of experience, that of the small child, definition has to proceed ostensively — by gestures which point out or enact the meaning at the same time the word is uttered, with subsequent corrections when the newly learned word is applied beyond the limits of its accepted meaning. The only general rule is to find, if possible, a common starting point, and then to use whatever devices will bring about advances toward the desired goal. Mr. Walpole lists twenty-five possible "routes" by which we may hope to succeed in defining our symbols, and then adds a twenty-sixth: "Any other kind of connection or connections, simple or complex, that you can think of."[3]

Some of the routes, however, are more important than others; and it will be worth our while to give special attention to the three most commonly used.

[3] Hugh R. Walpole, *Semantics* (New York, 1941), p. 136.

They are: (1) definition by example; (2) definition by genus and differentia; and (3) definition by stipulation. Suppose, for example, that it was agreed that "managers" could not belong to labor unions, but a dispute arose over whether plant foremen were or were not "managers." Three familiar ways of approaching a definition that might resolve the issue would be:

(1) *To give an example:* "A manager is a man like Mr. Smith over there."

(2) *To state the class to which it belongs, and the characteristics which distinguish it from others of its class:* "A manager is any person acting in the interests of an employer directly or indirectly," according to the National Labor Relations Board.

(3) *To stipulate the sense in which one proposes to use the term:* "I maintain that a manager is any person (as defined in 2) who has jurisdiction over hiring and firing, and a part in the making of policy."

It will be seen at once that these three types of definition vary considerably in the degree to which they aim at and succeed in performing the two main functions of definitions: the conveying of the central meaning, and the demarcation of its boundaries.

DEFINITION BY EXAMPLE

This variety is also called demonstrative, illustrative, or denotative definition. It is closest to the child's ostensive pointing. It constitutes the shortest route to the understanding of the meaning of a symbol, since it attaches the symbol directly to an instance of it. Everyone knows that the quickest way to learn the nouns of a foreign language is to go about with a native who points at everything in sight and simultaneously names it. One of the reasons for the rapid spread of the self-service store or supermarket is that the customer has only to reach or make gestures toward the desired article. Dictionaries move in the same direction by the use of pictures of what is defined.

Definitions by example have the great advantage of conveying the meaning of a symbol directly by producing a concrete illustration or illustrations of it, but they have a number of serious deficiencies.[4] For one thing, they are subject to ambiguity concerning which characteristics of the example (or examples) are to be related to the symbol. If someone tells me that his idea of a manager is "Mr. Smith over there," the question may still remain: "What is it about Mr. Smith that makes him a manager?" It is still necessary to indicate whether it is his dress or his air of authority or the attitude of his associates or some other characteristic which constitutes his claim to the title. Furthermore, a definition by example tells us little or nothing about the edges or boundaries of the symbol's meaning. How much like Mr. Smith does one have to be in order to qualify? Every specimen of anything has its own individual peculiarities, which need to be eliminated in a good definition of it.

[4] Some authors call them merely "empirical descriptions," reserving the term definition for statements that are completely substitutable one for the other.

What we want, of course, is a typical or representative sample which bears on its face some indication of what it is intended to be a sample of.[5]

Recently the demand for definition by example as a means of counteracting the evils of abstraction has spread from nouns to verbs and adjectives. Those who hold the operationalist point of view are loath to accept any definition of the meaning of any sort of doing which does not point out just what acts are performed. For example, "to analzye" the plot of a novel and the contents of a stomach does not require the same kind of operation; hence the meanings differ, and should have different symbols. "Strong" is used both of language and of weight lifters; yet the operations by which strength is established in the two contexts are only superficially alike. This is a demand for a language richer in the fine shadings of its verbs, adjectives, and adverbs. Carried to an extreme, it would make all abstractions illegitimate, and give us specific words for every aspect of every conceivable situation. Much can be done, however, in the operationalist direction without individualizing our symbols to a point where we would be swamped in uneconomical, detailed meanings.

DEFINITION BY GENUS AND DIFFERENTIA

For persons with a fairly large stock of words and meanings already quite well fixed and assorted, who are confronted with a symbol of uncertain meaning, the commonest traditional procedure in defining it (unless it is unique, a proper name, in which case a form of pointing may have to be resorted to) is to refer the concept to its neighboring concepts until we arrive at one in the meaning of which it shares. We do this ordinarily by placing the term to be defined under the next wider class or genus, and then by indicating the essential ways in which it differs from the other sub-classes of the same genus. This is known as definition *per genus proximum et differentiam* (by the nearest genus and the difference). It rests on the assumption that, on the whole, the meanings which are most likely to be widely comprehended are those which are based upon the broader similarities of things; and that therefore the most promising route to common understanding is upward to similarity and then downward by differences.

If we apply this method to the symbol "a manager," and look about for a class to which all managers belong, we may select "person," and go on to define a manager as "a person who . . ." But "person" is a very broad genus; there are too many persons who are not managers. We might narrow the genus down to "official" or "agent." But we should then be obliged to eliminate the officials and agents who are not managers.

Similarly, an "automobile" might be defined by this method as a "machine which . . . ," but would be more effectively placed in the genus "vehicle." There are many vehicles, however, which are not automobiles, such as wagons, bicycles, and rickshaws. Therefore, we introduce the differentia "self-propelled," which is actually included in the derivation of the word "auto-mobile" = "self-

---

[5] Note the effort, in the Introduction to the present volume, to convey the author's conception of "reliable knowledge" denotatively by offering four instances of the demand for it.

moving." But there still remain self-propelled vehicles which are not auto-mobiles: locomotives, steam-rollers, tractors, and so on. To eliminate the locomotives and the tractors, we may add a second differentia, "for use on highways"; and to avoid steam-rollers and road-scrapers, a third, "to carry passengers or goods." Our tentative definition now stands: "An automobile is a self-propelled vehicle for use on highways to carry passengers or goods." We may test it by inquiring: Is there anything so described that is not an automo-bile? Is there any automobile that falls outside our definition? Someone might object that a motorcycle, with or without a sidecar, would be wrongly included in our definition; but if we added the differentia "four-wheeled" to exclude motorcycles, it would lead to arguments about three-wheeled automobiles.

There is another reason for moving first in the direction of greater generality in our definitions, and then "coming down to cases"; instead of pointing out a single instance and saying, "That object is an automobile, and so are all other somewhat similar objects." The alert reader may already have noticed the connection between definition *per genus* and structural classification. Both are systematic. A structural classification gives us a prepared highway of as-cending genera. To define an American White Birch tree, we need only to go upward in the classification until we reach a group of trees whose charac-teristics are more familiar to us, such as the *Cupuliferae*, or oak family, and then make explicit the differentia.

This method of definition by connotation or Aristotelian subsumption (the placing of an instance or class under a higher class) works best where we are already somewhat familiar with the cores of the meanings involved, and de-sire chiefly to make their boundaries and relationships more precise. It is especially applicable in fields where our knowledge is already highly organized and structurally classified, and where there are large numbers of broad class-symbols whose meanings are not in serious dispute. It tends to induce in its users the belief, which may be wholly unwarranted, that everything to be known is arranged, or ought to be arrangeable, in a static hierarchy of classes of things. Therefore, it may have the effect of overemphasizing the class-and-member relation at the expense of such mathematical relations as position in series. The method also has definite dangers in fields where the inclusive class-symbols are dictionary words whose meanings we may mistakenly think we agree upon. It will do no good to argue over the differentia of "personal liberty" as a species of "liberty" if we start out with different meanings of the wider term. Furthermore, the demand for definition *per genus* should not be pressed too far, to the point of demanding wider classes in which to place such terms as existence, time, point, or relation. Claude Bernard quotes Poinsot as saying: "If anyone asked me to define time, I should reply: 'Do you know what it is that you speak of?' If he said, 'Yes,' I should say, 'Very well, let us talk about it.' If he should say 'No,' I should say, 'Very well, let us talk about something else.' "

QUALITIES OF A GOOD DEFINITION

A good definition is one which both conveys and clarifies with the greatest possible economy of language the meaning of the term defined. There are, however, two aspects to be distinguished here: psychological effectiveness, which may often be best achieved in a single, narrow context by a vivid example; and the possession of such logical qualities as breadth, system, precision, and conciseness. It is the latter which are important in the sort of completed definitions which may usefully be placed in a dictionary or textbook for use in the maximum number of possible contexts. A definition that is psychologically illuminating to the initiated in a restricted circle, such as the diplomat's famous definition of a lie as "an untrue statement made to a person who has a right to know the truth," would never do to place in a dictionary. On the other hand, dictionary definitions may be much too abstract to be psychologically effective in all contexts.

Nevertheless it is possible to lay down at least two characteristics which a good definition by genus and differentia should possess, and three which it should not possess. It should be:

(1) *Precise in stating the essential properties or central characteristics of what it defines.* Example: Most automobiles have gasoline engines placed in the front of the vehicle, but these differentia are not essential to the meaning of the concept "automobile," since a car with an engine placed in the rear is still an automobile.

(2) *Commensurate with what it defines, so that the term and its definition are convertible,* i.e., interchangeable without alteration of the meaning. This rule is violated whenever the definition is either broader (because of too few differentia), or narrower (because of too many), or both (because they are badly chosen). Example: A book is a collection of sheets of paper bound at one edge (it is too broad, since tablets of notepaper are not excluded; and it is too narrow, since collections of parchment and other materials, which are books, are excluded).

On the other hand, a good definition should *not* be:

(3) *Narrowly circular, in the sense that it can be understood only when we already understand the term to be defined.* Examples: "A putter is what you putt with"; "A wife is the mate of a husband." All definitions are circular in the sense that all the words used in the definitions in a dictionary are also defined in the dictionary. The difference between a good definition and a bad one in respect to circularity is, as Professor C. I. Lewis says, "in the diameter of the circle." To define a Cuban as other than "a resident of Cuba" would require oblique and lengthy references to the latitude and longitude of a certain island. Synonyms and translations should not be relied on in the final stages of definition, but in approximating the core of the meaning they are sometimes very helpful.

(4) *Obscure or figurative, relative to one's probable audience.* As an example of obscure language to the ordinary reader, we have the English comedian George Robey's definition of laughter as "a synchronized co-ordination of neurophysiological reflexes with a semi-automatic impulse of mass-inherited suggestivism." Extravagant metaphors often throw

some light on meanings, but do not define: "Logic is the Baedeker of the world of thought."

(5) *Negative where it could be positive.* This is because of the great vagueness of negative concepts. A dog in Columbus, Ohio, had to pay an inheritance tax of thirty-five dollars on a bequest of five hundred dollars from his late owner because the animal fell into the negative class of those "not related to the deceased." There are, nevertheless, some concepts which are difficult if not impossible to define in positive terms, such as: orphan, bachelor, bankrupt, underclassman, or non-combatant.

There remains the question of the supposed authoritativeness of dictionary definitions. Most of us have encountered individuals who suppose that they have settled an argument by triumphantly producing a dictionary which determines, once and for all, the "true meaning" of a disputed word. Dictionary-makers are both historians of what words have meant to their users, and upholders of accepted conventions of "good use." They are not lawgivers for all time, since they cannot predict or prescribe how their definitions will fare in the future. They have no coercive power to make words mean only certain things to everyone who is to utilize them. A dictionary should indicate clearly what words are used, and how they are used, by reputable writers. But words belong to those who use them, and not to any academy of "authorities." Nevertheless the dictionary-makers should do their utmost to indicate which words are in "good use" and which are still waiting to win acceptance by persons of taste in such matters.

DEFINITION BY STIPULATION

At the same time we must recognize that all of us are, to a certain limited extent, lawgivers concerning what words we shall use and in what senses we shall employ them. In choosing our symbols, as we discovered in the last chapter, we are hemmed in on many sides; yet there is always the possibility of an appeal to our audience in behalf of a brand-new coinage or a slight change in the meaning of an accepted word. Wherever our knowledge is not well organized and crystallized in language, as is frequently the case in the social studies, we may find ourselves not only permitted but obliged to stipulate the exact meanings of our terms as we go along. This is often done by announcing that we propose to use a certain word or symbol as substitutable for another word or phrase. Thus, at the beginning of an essay, we are free to state to the reader that we are coining a new symbol to stand for a more complicated group of familiar words, such as "rurbanite" for "a person who lives in the country and works in the city." Or we may state that "in the following essay, the word 'unemployed' will refer only to the persons out of a job, able to work, and looking for work."

Such definitions, often called verbal or nominal, cannot be disputed, in the sense that we can, if we choose to face the consequences, insist that "that is what the word means as we use it." No one can legitimately inform us that we have not "properly" defined the term, except in the sense that our definition is not the customary or logical one in view of past usage. It would certainly be a departure from custom and logic based upon custom to define "earned income" as "goods and services received by free gift from others"; yet there have been actual changes in the meanings of words which have been almost as drastic. Everything depends upon the willingness of the public, in the long run, to follow the innovator in making the switch. Just as has been observed in connection with classification, there may be a large element of directive pressure in forcing new definitions into use in the hope of preventing or forwarding certain types of behavior. Reformers tend to begin by introducing new slogans and symbols. Strong statements about the "true meaning" of religion, patriotism, democracy, or progress may be used as a means of coercing others into the acceptance of approved attitudes and the rejection of the disapproved. Struggles for power on the large scale, such as wars, may truly develop into contests over whose definitions of such broad concepts as "justice," "freedom," and "peace" shall be accepted. To possess the power to stipulate the meanings of basic social and political concepts, backed by collective sanctions, is to be well on the way to ruling mankind.

We must guard ourselves, however, against concluding that, because of our mere resolve to use words in a certain way, the relations of the things we are talking about are thereby transformed. To restrict the word "unemployed" by arbitrary edict does not mean that all persons outside our verbal definition are now no longer unemployed in the customary acceptation of the term. Their status has been changed only with respect to our particular stipulation. A hungry man is no less hungry because we decide to call his hunger by another name. This state of affairs should place us on our guard against "argument by definition" and deduction, as when it is "proved" that "there can be no morality without dogma" (because morality is so defined); or that the "profit system is wrong because a profit is something got in return for nothing."

There are large areas of the social studies which are especially troublesome with respect to definition by stipulation because of the apparently arbitrary character of many of the boundaries. In matters of law and regulation generally, we are obliged repeatedly to "draw the line somewhere" in defining hours of labor, speed limits, age groups, passing grades, housing zones, and so on. Customary usage is of little assistance, notably when we are invading a new field of reform, such as billboard regulation, where we may need to define an "aesthetic nuisance" or "eyesore." In the final location of the exact boundary in such cases, there is bound to be a large element which can only be described as arbitrary, since there are no overwhelmingly convincing reasons why the line, such as a passing grade in an examination, should be exactly at 60 rather than at 58 or 62. Yet few such lines are *wholly* arbitrary. The reasons we can give become more convincing as we inquire whether it should be at 55 or 65, and still more so as we compare 50 with 70. What *is* vital, everyone realizes, is that the line should be drawn *somewhere*; and that, when drawn, it should be as clear and unmistakable as possible. Those who fall on the wrong side of it will always complain of its arbitrariness; but that is unavoidable. The important thing is not to mistake such practical compromises for pure fiats or for pure structural cleavages. They are neither. They are tentative devices whose value is to be determined by social experiment.

Classification and definition in our day have steadily lost in importance in one direction at the same time that they have gained in another. By the sophisticated, they are no longer regarded as infallible keys to the nature of things. The universe is more complex, more plastic, and more permeated with change than the conceptualizers of earlier periods dared to suspect. It may be that "knowing is classifying," but that is hardly the whole story. The class-member relationship is by no means the only ordering principle which has proved to be useful in dealing with the intricacies of the flux. Many of the characteristics which have long been believed to justify class distinctions have turned out to be superficial, and many of the time-honored demarcations of class boundaries have been shown to be fuzzy matters of shadings and degrees. Definition has also been shown to be, on the whole, a far more arbitrary affair than it had been supposed to be; and to have many more varieties than had been suspected. The limitations of the method of defining by genus and differentia are now only too plainly apparent: it is powerless to clarify simple, unanalyzable qualities and extremely broad concepts. Arbitrary defining is slowly but surely being deprived of its coercive power in argument, as more and more listeners inquire into the sources of the definitions which they have been asked to accept on faith.

But in spite of the fact that classification and definition have been largely deposed, at least in scientific circles, from their ancient thrones as final arbiters of thought; as instruments of clarification and organization their value has become increasingly recognized as the sheer quantity of knowledge to be handled has mounted apace. Programming and cataloguing brains were never in greater demand than in the age of computers, as complexity piles upon complexity; and no man can hope to know the details of more than a small fraction of the information available. Such persons are the map makers who mark out possible pathways for the advance of the real explorers, the makers of explanatory hypotheses.

FOR CLASS DISCUSSION

A. Classification is a contrivance for the best possible ordering of the ideas of objects in our minds; for causing the ideas to accompany or succeed one another in such a way as shall give us the greatest command over our knowledge earlier acquired and lead most directly to the acquisition of more. — *John Stuart Mill*   (1–3)

B. Every class should be so constituted as to contain objects exactly resembling each other in certain definite qualities which are stated in the definition of the class. — *W. S. Jevons*

C. A mammal is a warm-blooded animal with hair on its body, which bears its young alive and suckles it at the breast. Don't worry that there is a mammal that lays eggs, and that the whale has no hair. Nature can be most unscientific. — *Roderick Peattie*

D. The appeal to a class to perform the services of a proper entity is exactly analogous to an appeal to an imaginary terrier to kill a real rat.

— A. N. Whitehead

E. Every definition is dangerous. — Erasmus (5)

Don't let us be too keen on definition . . . it was the attempt to define that split the Christian church into fragments soon after it came into existence . . . if we try to define the [British] constitution too much we may split the Empire into fragments. . . . — Earl Baldwin

F. English-speaking people are notoriously unable to think clearly because our language is like a magnificent organ on which a virtuoso can produce marvelous effects, but which is too difficult an instrument for the average man. — H. R. Huse

The line between reform and revolution, between prophecy and subversive argument, between patriotism and treason, is difficult to draw in a society blessed with free speech. — Henry Johnson

G. Indefinite expression is the best exponent of imperfect knowledge.

— Louis Pasteur

H. A definition is . . . no definition of any one thing if its terms are applicable to any one other. — Edgar Allan Poe

EXERCISES IN CLASSIFICATION

Identify and appraise the classifications in the following examples in terms of their presumed purposes.

1. In her novel In This Our Life, Ellen Glasgow has one of her characters remember her mother's "classification of human beings into persons of good or bad blood. How easy living, and especially loving, must have been when people believed, or even acted as if they believed, in such fetishes."

2. Relief investigators in Pompano, Florida, asked a client the ages of her four children. She said that she could not remember, but that she had "one lap child, one creeper, one porch child, and one yard young 'un."

3. In designing gas masks for the U.S. Army, the heads of 3,000 enlisted men were carefully measured, and classified in five types: "Tall, thin-faced, narrow-headed, mainly British and southern"; "Tall but wider face and head, Scandinavian and West North Central region"; "Short, round-faced, broad, Germanic and Slavic, Middle Atlantic and East North Central"; "Short, narrower face and head, French and Mediterranean, New England"; "Unusually broad face, non-European, Indian extraction, Oklahoma and Texas."

4. Fingerprints, "nature's infallible seal of identity for each individual," or "the only sure way to tell who is who," are classified by a system devised by the late Sir E. R. Henry of Scotland Yard, which assigns numerical values to each of the ten prints, based on arches, whorls, loops, and other key characteristics. This permits the working-out of a mathematical formula according to which each set is filed.

5. A simple system of classification for stars was originated by Professor E. C. Pickering and adopted by the whole astronomical world. Class A stars

were white, like Sirius and Vega; Class B stars were blue-white, like Rigel; the letter G stood for our own Sun and other yellow stars; while F was used for stars between B and G. But the present order of star classification is B, A, F, G, etc., because, when it was too late to change the system, the B stars were found to precede the A stars in life history (the order BAF is easy to remember, said an Irish astronomer, because it stands for "baffling"). As now arranged, the letters represent the stars classified, not by color, but by decreasing temperature and increasing redness as age-indicators.

6. In his book *Psychopathic States*, Dr. D. K. Henderson classifies them under three heads: predominantly aggressive (alcoholic, drug-addict, epileptic, pervert, and suicide), predominantly passive or inadequate (cycloid and schizoid states), and predominantly creative (in between the other two — perseverance, mental ability, "genius").

7. In 1941 the *Cross Country News* of Lubbock, Texas, pointed out that the figures regarding the population served by the country's 1,600 airports were misleading, since they showed that virtually all the 1,077 cities in the "over 10,000 population" classifications had such airports providing service for 62.7 million people. This obscured the fact that hardly one in five of the smaller communities (2,387 of them in the "2,500 to 10,000" bracket) had an airport, yet they could serve 11.7 million people. There would still be a rural population of 47.9 million without such service.

8. For the purpose of outlining a national highway financing policy, Charles L. Dearing of the Brookings Institution attempted to classify all roads "scientifically" on the basis of their chief users. He distinguished two main classes: "general purpose" and "local" highways. "General purpose highways include a large part of the state highway system, which carries 74 per cent of the traffic volume on 11 per cent of the total mileage, plus some small "feeder" roads. "Local" highways, mostly unsurfaced, comprise 64.5 per cent of the total mileage, but carry only 10 per cent of the traffic volume. The chief beneficiaries of "general purpose" roads are the motor vehicle operators of the whole country; while the beneficiaries of the "local" roads are the residents of the localities. Therefore, federal and state taxes on cars and their operators should finance the former; while the latter should be paid for locally.

EXERCISES IN DEFINITION

In the following examples, identify and criticize the definitions in terms of their apparent purposes.

1. At the request of dealers in farm produce, the Pennsylvania Department of Agriculture defined a legal bushel is contained "in a basket holding 2,150.42 cubic inches, or 32 quarts of dry measure" of fruits or vegetables, regardless of the weight.

2. In 1885 an international convention in Vienna, Austria, fixed the musical note "A" as 870 vibrations per second. In 1945 French musicians claimed that in the concert halls of Great Britain, the United States and Russia the note had been "inflated" in some instances to 912 vibrations per second, and demanded another international conference to achieve a compromise at 880 vi-

brations, still somewhat higher than was intended by the composers of classical music.

3. Since antiques were exempted from price control during World War II, it became necessary to define an antique. The Office of Price Administration said it was "an object that tended to increase in value because of age, and was purchased primarily because of its age, authenticity, rarity, and style rather than its utility." They were obliged to set a minimum age for antiques arbitrarily at seventy-five years.

4. In 1947 the Civilian Production Administration issued the following definition of a man's white cotton shirt: "It is a man's shirt, other than a work shirt or sport shirt, made in half-size neck sizes, and marked accordingly with a button and buttonhole at the collar, except on shirts for use with detachable collars, with wrist length sleeves and a minimum length of 50 inches measured from the highest part of the yoke to the bottom of the shirt."

5. A college fraternity occupying a house in a single-family zone claimed that its twenty-three members were bound together in a single family. The justices of the Appellate Division of the New York Supreme Court "declined to follow that reasoning, since the members had no blood relationship."

6. Two women appeared in Bronx Magistrate's Court on the charge of "wearing other than ordinary attire" in Van Cortlandt Park. Each had been wearing play suits that exposed three inches of midriff. The judge found the first woman, who had removed only her jacket, not guilty. But the second woman had removed a dress from over her play suit, thereby making her attire "other than ordinary." The judge found her guilty, and suspended sentence, saying: "I have to draw the line somewhere."

7. When is a coal miner "at work"? Is it "from the time he comes under the supervision of his employer," or "from the time he begins to mine coal"? The portal-to-portal doctrine is based on the first definition. Previous custom had excluded underground travel from "work time."

8. A 32-year-old midget walked into a clothing store in Stamford, Connecticut, bought a coat in the store's children's department and refused to pay the State sales tax because "children's clothing" was exempt from the tax under the law. State Tax Commissioner Walter W. Walsh contended that the tax should have been collected, since "children's clothing" legally meant "clothing for the express and exclusive use of a child."

9. A San Diego, California, woman sued for divorce on the ground that she had been married by the captain of a seagoing vessel of only forty-seven tons burden, when maritime law requires seventy-five tons or over.

10. English law assumes that when two brothers die in the same accident, the elder is presumed to have predeceased the younger. During the bombing of London in World War II, two brothers, Randolph and Edward Grosvenor, were killed by the collapse of their house in Chelsea with no surviving witnesses, and both left wills. A lower court held that Randolph, the elder, must have died first; but three judges of the Court of appeal decided that the two had died simultaneously. On final appeal, the five law lords voted three to two to sustain the lower court, admitting that high explosives had abolished the distinction upon which the law was based, but not the law itself.

11. May a child injured before birth sue those alleged to be responsible? Judge Elmer W. Ryan of Hartford, Conn. ruled in 1954 that the right depends upon the unborn infant's "viability" at the time of the accident. This means that the child was capable of life independently of its mother, usually possible by the seventh month of pregnancy. A pregnant woman named Mrs. Tursi fell down an outside stairway maintained by a Motor Lines Company. The accident occurred on September 8, 1953, and her infant son, born on October 27, 1953, was found to have sustained numerous injuries, some of them permanent.

12. What is the meaning of "board" in the expression "sharing bed and board"? A Mrs. Hawkins sued for absolute divorce in 1948, testifying that since 1928 she and her husband had had no marital relations, occupied separate rooms, and never went out together. They had, however, occasionally eaten together with their children, but without speaking to one another. A lower court judge ruled that they had shared "board" and were living together. But the Washington, D.C., Court of Appeals ruled that the essence of "board" was sociability; "not separate roofs but separate lives" destroy it.

13. In November, 1957, County Judge Harold T. Garrity of Westchester County, New York, denounced the century-old definition of legal insanity as "a fantastic semantic charade." He said that "We demand of psychiatrists that they testify as to whether or not a defendant is insane — a term of classification our medical brethren refuse to acknowledge as part of their lexicon since they deny it has any validity in their science. . . . The most superficial familiarity with the problems of mental illness and criminal responsibility renders the statutory definition untenable on any medical or legal basis. It has been preserved for more than a century as if it epitomized man's knowledge and wisdom in this field."

14. (a) A saint is a person like Francis of Assisi or Joan of Arc.

(b) A political party is a group of people who are trying to make everybody better off.

(c) An explorer is a bum with an excuse. — *Charles Miller*

(d) Language is the garment of thought.

(e) Money is whatever has purchasing power.

(f) A dole is an un-American handout to incompetents.

(g) A dormitory is a place designed to provide five or more persons with a place to sleep.

(h) A cause is that which produces an effect.

(i) An undergraduate is a college student who has not yet received a bachelor's degree.

(j) Americanization is the process by which an alien becomes an American.

(k) Social epidemics are things like witchcraft manias, financial bubbles, land booms, lynching waves.

(l) Attention is organismic orientation.

(m) Let us apply the word "propaganda" to any attempt to influence people that is not educative.

❧ 9 ❦

CLARIFYING THE HYPOTHESIS:
Causal Analysis

1. Clarity of Terms Is Not Enough

IT HAS BEEN POINTED OUT that, if we are to be able to test our suggested explanations, it is essential to see that the meaning embodied in their terms are clearly defined. Otherwise, we cannot deduce the logical consequences of our hypotheses in such a way that any normal observer can check the results. We shall be powerless either to prove or to disprove such explanations as "Crime is due to drink" or "Television has increased the reading of books," unless we can make clear exactly what is meant by the words "crime," "drink," "television" and "reading of books."

But to classify our facts and to define with care the meanings to be attached to our class-symbols or words is by no means the whole story. We need to pay attention to the verbs in our hypotheses, as well as to the nouns. We must be sure that we know what we are trying to prove when we allege that one thing "causes" or "produces" or "is due to" another. Full-fledged sentences, as we know, are not made up solely of nouns, such as "depressions, birthrate." They demand verbs, such as "depressions lower the birthrate." Verbs are what make our sentences "say something." They bring in the element of doing, of action, of linkage in processes. They supply the dynamic element without which we can rarely go beyond mere classification. They are what we must add if our knowledge is to be effective in a world of happenings, of interacting systems or complexes of events. Otherwise we shall have only dead aggregates of knowledge, static and abstract.

Whenever we write or utter a sentence, we make an attempt to take events in the world about us (or in some imagined world of our own) and pattern them in linguistic symbols. In this task of mental engineering, both in the tearing-down by analysis and the building-up by synthesis, it is apparent that the nouns are the relatively stable elements as compared with most of the verbs. By the use of nouns, we abstract and register the common characteristics among groups of individually varying items: tiger, steel, village, debit. But verbs have the much more difficult task of expressing change itself: to force, to join, to suffer, to admire. Some of them, the transitive verbs, such

199

as, the dog *chases* the cat, are full of action; others, the intransitive, such as, the dog *sleeps*, are less so. But all verbs, save those of mere classification — the dog *is* an animal — partake of some sort of change or "doing."

Now most of our explanatory hypotheses use verbs expressing the relation of cause and effect. The description of the causes of anything is what most often constitutes a satisfactory explanation of it. Since our object in making explanatory hypotheses is usually to be able to predict and control, we want to find out, if we can, "what produces what." Unless we are one of those rare inquirers motivated by sheer curiosity, we look for the causes of bankruptcies or happy marriages or fluctuations in the interest rate in order to act with respect to those matters. So it is of the highest importance, not only to define the nouns involved, in order that we may know just what we are talking *about;* but also to see clearly just what we are *saying about it* — what it means, for example, to link nouns by verbs in the causal relationship, as in "Germs cause disease," or "Trade rivalry brings on wars."

2. Brief History of the Notion of Cause

"Felix qui potuit rerum cognoscere causas" — "Happy he who could perceive the causes of things" — sang the poet Virgil almost twenty centuries ago.[1] The notion of cause and effect (the two are correlative) has had a long history, dating from man's earliest attempts to order his world in terms of stable relations among events. It has been the center of interminable philosophical debates into which we cannot enter here. What is more important for our purpose is to trace its rôle in Western thought: to see how, after being worked out in the early stages of man's thinking, and crystallized in his linguistic habits, it became refined and elevated to a pivotal place in Newtonian mechanics, only to lose some of its immense prestige in the course of recent developments in science.

ANIMISM AND POST HOC REASONING

It is now generally admitted that our highly developed sciences are a refinement and a continuation of what goes at present by the name of superstition and magic. We have come to recognize that, like ourselves, primitive man was anxious to come to terms with his supposed environment, and, to a certain limited extent, to control it. He differed from us, not so much in the general ends or aims which he had in view, as in his relatively crude understanding of what he was "up against" in Nature, in his resulting conception of the appropriate methods for getting along in the world, and in his very low estimate of his chances of controlling it.

What he did was to look for striking likenesses and dramatic linkages on the surface of the complex world about him, which he proceeded to interpret in terms of his own inner experiences, including his dreams. The result was an abundance of fantastic explanations which we call myths, the product of

[1] *Georgics,* II, 490. Probably composed between 37 and 30 B.C.

wishful imaginings unchecked by any clear standard of fact as distinguished from fiction. But, in apparently simplifying his world by these legendary accounts of it, man actually added enormously to its complexity by peopling it with all sorts of unseen beings with powers very similar to his own. Behind the visible world (although, of course, not separated from it in primitive thinking) was another shadowy world of superhuman beings — the whole forming a single society.

Early man was aware of himself as a center of force, an agent producing subsequent visible effects — felling trees, setting fires, killing animals. When he found instances of the same results that he was in the habit of producing by his own efforts, occurring in the wake of storms or lightning or disease, he naturally blamed them upon some other agent similar to himself. He was familiar with the experience of exertion followed by results; so he reasoned that results must have been preceded by exertion on the part of someone. That reasoning formed the nucleus of the primitive conception of cause. Man projected, as we say, his own personal experiences upon inanimate objects outside himself, endowing them with powers and making them "causes" (producers of effects) like himself. Effects of all sorts could be produced at points widely separated in space and time; and almost anything could be the vehicle of intervention by a good or evil spirit in the ordinary run of events. As one of the first Greek wise men, Thales, later expressed it: "All things are full of gods." This stage of the interpretation of Nature is known as *animism* — the reading-into natural objects of an *animus* or spirit or directing center of action similar to man's own conception of his "soul." A good deal of primitive religion is summed up in the prayer credited to Ajax: "Oh, that the gods would empower me to obtain my wishes!" Bargaining with the unseen powers by means of bribes and sacrifices was supplemented, as man grew bolder, by attempts to control both good and evil spirits by charms or *magic*.

The universal assumption of animism was that, whatever happened, some-*body* (rather than some*thing*) was to blame. The Greek word for cause was adapted from the word for guilt: the cause of anything was what was "guilty" of producing the effect. By the time of the early Greeks, it must be remembered, guilt was widely believed to be punished in accordance with the fairly well-stabilized principle of retribution. The distinguished jurist Dr. Hans Kelsen has suggested that our notion of cause grew out of the primitive and Greek conception of a moral order supernaturally enforced upon the natural world, in which effect *must* follow cause as reward or punishment follows a good or evil act. The principle of retribution ("An eye for an eye, a tooth for a tooth") has many striking similarities to our idea of cause: (1) the good deed or crime must precede the reward or punishment (cause is prior to effect); (2) the deed and its retribution must also be connected in space (cause and effect are contiguous); (3) good is to be rewarded with good, and evil with evil, in roughly proportionate quantities (cause must be equal to or greater than the effect, and qualitatively similar); and (4) retribution is inevitable in a world ruled by an all-powerful moral force (cause and effect are necessarily connected).[2]

[2] Hans Kelsen, *Society and Nature* (Chicago, 1943), chaps. IV–V.

Superstitions are the result of taking a short cut in explanation by seizing upon some dramatic and emotionally stirring event that precedes another in time, and calling it the cause. This fallacy, perhaps the commonest of all human errors in connection with cause, goes by the Latin name of *Post hoc ergo propter hoc* — "After it, therefore because of it" — often referred to simply as *post hoc* reasoning. It is, of course, a hasty overdoing of factor (1) above, the temporal priority of the supposed cause to its effect. If a person finds a four-leaf clover just before making a profitable business venture, he may, by *post hoc* reasoning, connect the two as cause and effect, in complete disregard of other and far more important factors in the situation. So strong is this ancient human tendency to read "cause" into spectacular temporal sequences that it usually does little good to bring up such sad cases as that of Mrs. Willmore Trotter Jones of Madison, Georgia, who has found and saved thousands of four-leaf clovers, and yet has been in five automobile wrecks, has lost three husbands, and has suffered so many misfortunes that she is known among her neighbors as "Calamity Jane." The superstitious are still likely to hold that a mysterious power is at work, but that in this particular instance it has simply backfired in some inexplicable manner.

According to the animistic version, then, cause was regarded as some sort of mysterious linkage by which one event had the power, like a human being, to produce another later event. This was the view which became firmly incorporated in the linguistic habits of civilized man. In a thunderstorm, the animistic observer probably remarked: "Jove is thundering." Today we are likely to continue to say, "It thunders" — without much thought about the nature of the "it" which has replaced the god. The verb "thunders," conveying a change going on in Nature, simply seems to us, because of our habitual mode of expression, to be in need of a subject which does the thundering. There is much truth in Max Rieser's contention: "We could think non-causally only if we could think . . . in sentences without subjects, which is impossible."[3] Our deeply entrenched language habits practically compel us, unless we constantly resist them, to turn all events into actions having a cause.

For many centuries, then, causes were personal and anthropomorphic. Man began his attempts to order the chaos of events around him by simplifying them according to the pattern with which he was most familiar: his own living activity. He knew that in his own mind, when he acted, things came to a kind of focus which gave meaning and pattern to individual occurrences, enabling him to some extent to unify his scattered experiences and thus to anticipate future happenings. Following this apparently valuable clue, man assumed that all events must be the doing of conscious, deliberate, and responsible agents like himself. Nature was a part of society; the external world was the counterpart of the internal: all things interacted causally as men interacted. But his next step was to discover that some things in Nature apparently followed a different pattern, or interacted non-personally. Some happenings seemed to occur and to be predictable without involving either a visible or an invisible someone. From then on, the de-personalizing or de-

[3] "Causation, Action, and Creation," *Journal of Philosophy*, vol. XXXVII, pp. 491–99.

anthropomorphizing of Nature advanced with rapid strides, until the new pattern of cause itself began to be applied, though not without difficulties, to man's own personal activities.

NEWTONIAN PHYSICS AND THE MECHANICAL PATTERN

It will be necessary for our purpose to skip nimbly over the centuries from the primitive animistic conception of cause to the modern non-animistic version which reached the peak of its prestige in the mechanistic physics of the late nineteenth century. The story is that of the step-by-step banishment, first of miracles, or events without natural causes, and then of personal powers from their supposed residences in natural objects or processes; and of the gradual substitution of wholly circumstantial explanations in terms of observed sequences and correlations of events. "One of the great achievements of those who utilized causal explanation," says George Boas, "was the suppression of the human equation . . . in macroscopic physics, the personal equation is not of enough importance to count."[4] The many intermediate stages are illustrated by familiar episodes in the history of the sciences, as personal causes were first replaced by relatively impersonal "forces," the latter still regarded as agents at work in things. As late as the early seventeenth century, for example, as able an astronomer as Kepler still held that the planets must be guided in their orbits by angels. Lodestones, or magnetized substances, were long regarded as the seat of some kind of "soul"; while late in the eighteenth century, the enlightened Joseph Priestley, co-discoverer of oxygen with Wilhelm Scheele, energetically defended the then common belief that combustion was caused by *phlogiston*, or fire-stuff, which passed from one body to another in the form of flame.

But, as one scientific problem after another was found to yield to the kind of analysis which left out of consideration all animistic or semi-animistic agents exerting forces, a new conception of cause emerged and swept all before it in the scientific world. It may be described for convenience as the mechanical or clockwork or billiard-ball pattern of causation, which grew out of the overwhelming success, in astronomical and physical predictions, of the Newtonian mechanics of "matter in motion in space and time." According to this view, as refined after the philosopher David Hume's famous criticisms, the cause of any physical event is *the indispensable set of conditions which are observed invariably to precede or to accompany its occurrence.*

This is another way of saying that the physicist, following the example of the technologist, felt himself justified, on the basis of something like "habit" in Nature, in imputing causes wherever he was able to observe enough uniformity in the continuous processes going on about him to permit him successfully to predict and control (to some extent) certain definite future outcomes. Given an isolated system, such as a billiard ball at rest on the surface of a table, he would say that its movement to some other point on the table would have as its causes a set of surrounding circumstances: the impact of the cue, the air in the room, the friction of the cloth, the resiliency of the cushions, and

---

[4] George Boas, *op. cit.*, p. 131.

so on. Given an exact knowledge of the regularities of behavior of all these elements, a ballistics expert would undertake to measure and predict, with ever-increasing accuracy as his measurements became more precise through successive approximations, the point and time at which the billiard ball (or any similar object in similar circumstances) would come to rest. Note that he has dropped out entirely from his conception of cause the idea of any hidden, secret power suddenly leaping forth from one thing to another, or any necessary connection between the events, since, as Hume pointed out, we never observe anything of the kind.

So superbly did this causal analysis on the mechanical pattern succeed in dealing with the heavenly bodies and with more and more complicated movements of physical objects on earth that it came to be regarded as *the* principle of causality, believed to hold for the whole of Nature, which was now regarded as essentially uniform in behavior and, in theory, entirely predictable. Newton had considered it probable "that God in the Beginning form'd Matter in solid, massy, hard, impenetrable, moveable Particles," very much on the order of billiard balls. Applied to such particles, the mechanical conception of cause yielded the conviction that "the future could be predicted if the present position and velocity of each particle was known."[5] The program of science was now clear: everything had a cause, and cause was envisaged in terms of an underlying mechanical patterning. All that remained was the selection and measurement of the proper circumstances of each causal situation. The ideal or "tight" scientific notion of cause called for the reduction by measurement of each of the conditions of an event and their interrelations to functional equations, such as the pressure, volume, and temperature of Boyle's law concerning the behavior of gases. Once these were calculated, a prediction could be made; and the necessary ingredients of a successful prediction might, if one chose, be called the causes of the predicted event.

Only one more idea was needed to set up a closed system embracing past, present, and future called "uniformitarianism." It was the doctrine that like causes produce like effects without regard to time; hence whatever causal laws are discovered today may be assumed to have operated "uniformly" over the millenia of the past, and on into those of the future. Apparently this eliminates from history many of the so-called catastrophes of which the records are numerous but inexact. It must always be remembered that uniformitarianism is itself a hypothesis which needs to be challenged, as by Velikovsky and others.

CONTEMPORARY REVISION

Even a little reflection reveals the fact that the idealized causal situation of Newtonian physics is not quite so simple as it at first appears. Or perhaps it is too simple to be universally illuminating. Why, in the first place, should the physicist consider only the cue, the air, the cloth, and the cushions as the causes of the motion of the billiard ball? What about all the other factors — the floor which supports the table, the walls which enclose the air, and so on, all the way to the sun and moon and stars? It is sometimes said that they are

[5] P. W. Bridgman, "The Recent Change of Attitude Toward the Law of Cause and Effect," *Science*, vol. 73, pp. 539–47.

conditions of the movement of the ball, but not its causes. Surely, if some of them were removed, the outcome would be altered. The mechanist would probably answer that "the state of the whole physical universe" does indeed affect every physical happening in it, but that its very stability with relation to small events enables him to isolate the billiard table, or at least the room in which it stands, and to deal only with the immediate or local conditions of the change in which he is interested.

Is just *one* condition to be regarded as *the* cause, or is it a whole series of interlaced events? Here we find ourselves thrown back upon the human factor of selection and interpretation. If we use the mechanical sort of causal analysis into sequences, we are committed to a high degree of isolation and abstraction, which works best with relatively simple, gross, inert materials in situations where "like acts upon like." But nineteenth-century mechanics went on to proclaim that all events were fundamentally understandable in terms of the changes of position of massy particles, and therefore were to be envisaged as mutually conditioning and conditioned by one another. Prediction in such a universe was theoretically possible by means of such abstractions as the laws of gravitation applied to all existing matter; but in practice the mathematical formulas were applied merely to the relations of a few manageable physical objects, with the rest of the cosmos regarded as constant, and thus as causally negligible.

"The expectation [of Newtonian physics]," says Professor Bridgman, "was that by increasing the accuracy of measurement indefinitely we would be able to make predictions about the future with indefinite precision." But, when the simple, gross, physical situation was complicated at either end, by bringing in either unimaginably small electrons, or energy-distributing organisms with memories, the mechanical version of cause ceased to enable us to predict. This became strikingly evident with the increase of precision made possible by the development of sub-atomic physics. When a single electron was substituted for the billiard ball, the expectation of increasingly accurate prediction by means of mechanical principles was not realized. On the contrary, investigators encountered situations in which the initial conditions were completely identical as far as observation could determine, yet in which the electron appeared sometimes at one place and sometimes in another. There was no longer any predictability of the individual minute event in terms of its isolable local conditions.

This surprising state of affairs found expression in the Heisenberg Principle of Uncertainty, which can be formulated in several different ways. In its application to predictability, it may be expressed as the discovery of the cost of increasing the accuracy of one kind of sub-atomic measurement in the form of decreasing the accuracy of some other kind. If a physicist attempts to measure both the position and the velocity of an electron, and increases his accuracy of measurement of its position, his measurement of its velocity becomes less accurate "in such a way that the probable value of the product of the two inaccuracies is of the order of magnitude of Planck's constant, h, divided by the mass of the electron. . . ." This is important for the electron (but not for ordinary bodies, to which the Principle equally applies), because

the mass of the electron is so very small that the uncertainty becomes comparatively large. The latter, as Professor Bridgman points out, "gets into the
situation through the act of observation . . . which interferes *by an unpredictable and incalculable amount.*"[6]

Shall we, because of these upsetting developments in contemporary physics,
abandon the mechanical pattern of imputing cause wherever increasingly precise measurements of variables in sequences enable us to predict, simply because it proves inapplicable to the motions of single electrons? What seems to
have happened, again according to Professor Bridgman, is this: "As long as
experience was confined to the large-scale things of daily life, an ever-increasing
number of phenomena could be brought under the approximate sway of the
[causality] principle; but as soon as physical methods became sufficiently refined so that we could deal with small-scale phenomena, uniformities became
less and less conspicuous, until we finally arrived at electrons and photons, the
ultimate structural elements of the physical world as we know it, where we
would expect the utmost in the way of simplicity and uniformity, but where,
on the contrary, experiment shows that uniformity in its original sense has entirely vanished." He concludes that "the burden of proof is now on the side
of those who maintain that Nature is uniform and can be described in terms
of a causality principle"; the extent to which any such principle is valid "is
solely for experiment to decide"; and that, "if it is true that there are certain
aspects of Nature which are neither controllable nor predictable, then the
obvious course is to avoid these aspects of Nature."[7]

If all we desire is to *understand* these minute sub-atomic events, then we
shall merely have the task of revising our orthodox conception of what constitutes understanding in physics by giving up our previous demand for the
discovery of uniform sequences directly linked with the immediate past. Instead of stable and isolable chunks of some kind of solid stuff, we shall have to
accustom ourselves to dealing with exceedingly complex patterns of minute
events occurring in rhythms which can be formulated only statistically. Instead of particles and simple forces acting among them, we shall need to think
in terms of fields where changes in space occur. On the basis of our observations, we may be able to predict the probable behavior of masses of electrons in
systems where *individual* events take place with no observable (much less,
measurable) connection with past happenings. This may be difficult for those
minds in which the mechanical picture of cause has become ingrained; but,
to the next generation, educated in the new physics, the notion of different
levels of predictability should offer no psychological obstacles.

On the basis of our brief survey of the history of the notion of cause to
this point, we may be in a better position to understand the present situation
in the physical and biological sciences and social studies. Until recently, it
was pretty generally supposed that there had to be an either-or choice between
the two extreme versions of cause: either a person accepted the complete uni-

[6] *Idem*, p. 543. (Italics mine. H. A. L.)
[7] *Idem*, pp. 542–47. There are also grave language difficulties, pointed out by Niels
Bohr and others, in applying to the world of electrons the forms and descriptions
originally designed for ordering the world of gross physical objects.

formity, and therefore the theoretical predictability, of all individual events in Nature after the mechanical pattern; or else one fell back into the chaos of animism with its mysterious and totally unpredictable powers at work in things. One was either a scientist or a mystical obscurantist; there was no other alternative.

Today the situation is much more complicated. Animism, at least of the cruder sort, is still banished from the physical sciences, and is still on the defensive in every department of human inquiry: impersonal things do not cause effects by exerting personal powers over them. On the other hand, the physicist Victor F. Lenzen declares that "the mechanical theory no longer provides a basis for systematic unity in physics," much less in all the sciences. The universe, he says, appears to be "a set of loosely coupled systems," some of which we are able to isolate and quantify.[8] We ought to expect to find zones of varying degrees of predictability, both of individual isolates and, statistically, of aggregates. Instead of dogmatically identifying true science exclusively with the search for mechanical causes, we should proceed cautiously in the various fields, picking our way by means of experiments which reveal just what "streaks of uniformity" in Nature are discoverable upon which predictions can reliably be based; and making allowances for gaps in our resulting systems of knowledge, some of which may be due merely to the limitations of our knowing powers or to the backwardness of our techniques of inquiry, while others may represent genuine breaches of continuity in the universe.

BIOLOGY AND THE ORGANISM

The physical sciences built up the great prestige of the mechanical pattern of causality by demonstrating the fruitfulness of treating large-scale physical phenomena by non-animistic causal analysis — that is, as quite *unlike* human beings, especially in their relations with one another. Planets and rocks and chemical elements are not to be controlled by being prayed to, cajoled, exhorted, or deceived. The way to do it, as far as man can hope to master them, is to isolate them, pick out their key characteristics by "varying one thing at a time" to see which are crucial, measure them, express the quantities if possible in equations, and then calculate their probable future states from the formula or "law" so derived. Predictions of eclipses, calculations of artillery fire, and the figuring of "safety factors" in skyscrapers and bridges are familiar examples.

The very success of this pattern of cause (as a functional relation between numerical measures of variable quantities) had an enormous effect upon the sciences of man. As Professor Frank H. Knight has pointed out, many biologists, sociologists, and economists, in their zeal to duplicate the triumphs of the astronomers, physicists, and chemists, jumped to the conclusion that "since natural objects are not like men, men must be like natural objects." In running away from animism, or the savage's mistake of reading persons

8 Victor F. Lenzen, *Procedures of Empirical Science*, International Encyclopaedia of Unified Science, vol. I, no. 5 (Chicago, 1938), pp. 41, 57.

into everything, they made the opposite mistake of reading mechanism into everything, expecting thereby to construct a social physics.

Now this naïve assumption can be justified to a certain extent by pointing out that there are in fact a number of ways in which human beings *do* resemble gross, inert physical objects whose behavior is subject to approximate prediction according to the mechanical pattern. If, for example, you want to know when a 150-pound weight dropped from a height of 10,000 feet will reach the ground, it makes no difference to your calculations (if air friction be disregarded) whether the physical object is a bomb, a bag of sand, or a live aviator. The latter, of course, calculates his time of descent before opening his parachute by the same "law of falling bodies" that astronomers use. An architect planning the passenger elevator service of an office building would (among his other calculations) compute the human loads in terms of pounds and cubic feet of space, exactly as he would in planning the freight elevators of the same building. Man may thus be treated mechanically as a physical object in many of his relationships; and those relationships constitute, for man, *the zone of maximum predictability of behavior.*

But man has other and far more interesting relationships than those of an inert physical body colliding with similar bodies. For he is also an *organism* engaged in releasing and transforming energy, the energy of sunlight stored up by photosynthesis. "The organism," says Professor Howard C. Warren, "may well be regarded as a new kind of system, whose distinctive characteristic is an ability to maintain its organic unity through dynamic interplay with the environment." It registers past experiences, and makes anticipatory adjustments. Many of its activities will not take place unless the organism is "prepared" to react.[9]

This calls for a new version of cause to fit what organisms actually do. Two biologists, M. N. Chappel and F. H. Pike, have suggested that in a world of organisms, "A cause is any event which directly or indirectly delivers energy to another event." This may be a kind of trigger action or stimulus to the stored-up energy complex of the organism. How the latter will react depends, not simply upon the releasing "cause," but upon its own structure and history up to the moment of touching off the response. Its energy may accumulate over a long period of time, and yet be discharged by what seems to be a totally inadequate cause, as when a long-smoldering resentment bursts into a violent assault. It is this selective response of the organism to a total situation, which includes parts of its own past history, that makes prediction difficult.

It will be noticed that in analyzing the causes of the behavior of an organism or living thing, we are obliged to operate *both* on the billiard-ball level with the mechanical pattern, *and also* on a "higher" level that differs from it in many respects. Organisms, all the way from tiny bacilli through plants and animals to men, are physical bodies characterized by mass and motion; and, as we have seen, some of their grosser movements can be predicted in mechanical terms. Some of the causes of what happens to them may thus be expressed quantitatively in the relations of two or more variables: if you

[9] Howard C. Warren, "The Organic World and the Causal Principle," *Science,* vol. LXXI, p. 208.

drop a 100-pound weight on a 1-pound plant, or raise its temperature 200 degrees, the plant will be destroyed; just as a 200-pound New York subway guard will probably be able to ram twenty 100-pound stenographers onto a single rear platform. But if the weight only hits the plant a glancing blow, or if the temperature only rises 50 degrees, we know that the plant may recover and may even repair the damage. As for the long-suffering passengers in the subway, they may also react to the guard's ramming and shoving in many *physically* unpredictable ways, such as by fainting, developing claustrophobia, writing letters to the newspapers, or refusing to ride in subways any more.

It is idle, then, to suppose that living and non-living things can be forced into one homogeneous mass of material which can be made to submit to a type of causal patterning, the mechanical. No two human beings, even though they may be identical twins, can be said to be exactly alike in the sense that two lumps of pure carbon may be stated to be similar. It is, as Professor J. B. S. Haldane remarks, "a great biological truth that one man's meat is another man's poison." Men differ from one another in subtle ways which make predictions about their behavior most precarious. We may classify them in "types" on the basis of their common characteristics, but even that is dangerous. A panel of doctors discussing the baffling problem of migraine headaches before the American College of Physicians came to the general conclusion that there are so many varieties of migraine that "the headache you have depends on the individual you are . . . the physician must size up the individual he is dealing with . . . there is not one cure for migraine, but many."

Organisms, in other words, are not simply kinds of "inert" physical entities buffeted about by other bodies in accordance with the generalized laws of mechanics. They are also energy-storing-and-releasing systems in varying states of tension, organized in such a way that they will respond to certain selected events going on within and about them in ways that are constantly being altered by "learning" from their own past experiences. They change in a direction which is irreversible; life is a journey down a one-way street. But those living things which possess memory are capable of condensing, as it were, vast tracts of past happenings in such a way that their "original natures" are modified thereby. Man possesses what Korzybski has called this "time-binding" capacity to the highest degree. At the same time the organism reacts in ways which manifest, at the very least, a tendency toward the restoration of its dynamic equilibrium as an ongoing whole. It is not necessary to read conscious purpose into simple matters of self-preservation; but, on the other hand, if plants and animals are mechanisms, they are very extraordinary self-repairing (within limits) machines, which act "as if" they were concerned with the continuance of their own future existences.

In order to predict the movements of a billiard ball on a table, we are not normally obliged to take into consideration its past history or future dispositions. But substitute for the ball a spider or a robin or a puppy, and the problem of prediction is immediately complicated. The mechanical pattern still applies to some of their movements. A sharp blow will undoubtedly "cause" any one of them to be swept off the table, just as it will displace the billiard ball. Computing the masses of the living things, one could even predict roughly how far off the table they would be projected by a blow of a certain force. But what will be the effect upon the spider or the robin or the puppy of a gentle prodding? Possibly none at all, since each one of them, we know, responds differently to the totality of events going on at the given time and place, of which the prodding is a single element. How each will respond depends, not only upon the single factor of the amount of the prodding, but also upon the *total configuration of events* including the internal organization of the insect's or animal's energy system and its conditioning to that moment. A puppy may have been conditioned to sit perfectly still when prodded, or to roll over, or to bark loudly. Another puppy of the same species, even of the same litter, may behave quite differently.

Professor Haldane's proverb might even be revised to read: "One man's meat on Monday may be the same man's poison on Tuesday." When an experimenter, in order to test an hypothesis, tries to make history repeat itself in an organism, he finds that it is not exactly the same history. The organism is older, or it is fatigued, or it has learned something, or it is engaged in a different train of activity. No matter how many times a milk truck was driven over the same route, it would never learn where to stop and start. But a milkwagon horse is different. If predictive generalizations of the mechanical type are to be employed, the investigator finds that he must add: "All other things being equal." But they are not equal; so "corrections" must be introduced in order to take care of neglected elements which refuse to remain constant while he is studying his chosen factors. When these corrections for differences become so numerous that they overbalance the likenesses which are covered by the abstract mechanical concepts, the time has come to introduce other patterns of causal analysis. This happens when consciousness and self-consciousness are added to organisms, as in the conduct of men and women with many specialized functions sharing among themselves innumerable experiences in all sorts of situations. The resulting complexity calls for "historical" patterns of cause in terms of selection, adaptation, and purpose on the part of partially organized wholes: human personalities.

We may regret that this is the case, and wish that one neat methodology would suffice for the causal analysis of everything knowable. As Einstein has remarked: "The supreme goal of all theory is to make the irreducible basic elements as simple and as few as possible." That is ever the hope of the systematic thinker; but we are still very far from realizing it in our understanding of human nature. Of course it would be absurd, on that account, to abandon all attempts at scientific generalization about human beings, on the ground that each historical happening was "absolutely" unique in the sense of possessing no specifiable characteristics in common with any other event. On the other hand, it would be equally a mistake to insist that the successful technique of nineteenth-century mechanics in dealing with gross physical objects must be regarded as the exclusive and universal method of obtaining reliable inductive knowledge. There are contributory conditions and sufficient conditions and (perhaps) necessary conditions, all of which go by the name of "cause."

3. Causal Focusing

For the present, at least, the social studies must be cultivated pluralistically — on more than one plane of complexity, by means of more than one pattern. This does not mean the abandonment of mechanical analysis in dealing with stable elements and uniform, measurable processes wherever they appear. If we are wise, we shall continue, in Aristotle's phrase, "to look for precision in each class of things just so far as the nature of the subject permits." But we shall not insist upon finding the same kind of regularity and exactness on each level. In seeking the causes of events, we shall use every resource of thinking which will enable us to anticipate the "next move" of something or someone by an examination of the conditions upon which it seems to hinge. Generally, we shall have been set off on our causal inquiry by having noticed a change or a difference — something that might not have happened at all, or that might have happened otherwise. We assume that if we knew all the factors in operation, the complete set of conditions and their mutual interrelationships, we should be able to anticipate future outcomes, and thus be enabled to take the requisite steps to meet them.

When we use the notion of cause to resolve a difficulty, however, it is not to the universe as a whole that we apply it. What we want to know, usually, is not what the cosmos is going to do next, but what this particular billiard ball, or airplane, or woman, or nation is going to do next. In order to find out with any accuracy, it becomes necessary to isolate the particular someone or something in which we are interested at the moment as if it were self-contained. Thus we focus our attention upon that particular stage of that segment of the immense network of surrounding conditions whose interactions, we have reason to believe, are relevant and indispensable to the occurrence of the particular state of affairs which we are bent upon analyzing. But what *is* relevant? And how much? That will depend, not only upon the "way things are" in the dynamic universe of processes about us, but also upon the purpose which we have in view, and our past experience in making similar inquiries. When there is a violent death in a country district, the practiced detective will not rest content with the causal explanation which quiets the country sheriff; while the sheriff may dig somewhat deeper than those neighbors who are only mildly interested.

Some news-minded persons will always think it sufficient to confine their inquiries to the immediate causes of an event. Answers which outline the particular concatenation of circumstances at the moment of an accident, for example, will seem to them to explain its occurrence. Everything being as it was in the universe at the moment of the crash, of course it occurred. Why delve into the history of the case? Why explore its remote bearings along the dimensions of both time and space? The ordinary journalist plays about upon the surface of events with little attention to the long-accumulating tensions which underlie the spectacular happenings. There is the next edition to catch; and he has no time to probe deeply into the antecedents of his news stories. Only occasionally does a Theodore Dreiser show what can be done by documenting in two long volumes the background of an ordinary murder case, as in his *An American Tragedy*, where he minutely reconstructs the heredity, family life, and harsh experiences of a weak young sweetheart-slayer from upstate New York.

It is possible to go to the other extreme, and to press our causal inquiry without let-up to the most remote antecedents. Conceivably, we can always ask for the cause of the cause of the cause of any event, in what is called an infinite regress, like a small child demanding: "You say that God made everything, but who made God?" Actually we satisfy ourselves at some point by concluding that our analysis has "gone far enough" to suit our purpose in inquiring. That usually amounts to the belief that we have discovered the condition or conditions *sine qua non*, or those without which the effect in which we are interested will not occur (or would not have occurred, if we are investigating a past happening). But that judgment, as we have seen, is always against a background of "all other things being equal," which stands for the unimaginably vast background of "constants" which are taken for granted, although always at our peril, since no one can absolutely guarantee their stability. In aiming a fieldpiece, we do not allow for an earthquake between the aiming and the firing; yet one might occur, and if it did, it would certainly spoil our aim.

Usually we stop at the point where we believe that by changing CH, our causal hypothesis, or supposed key condition, we can bring about a specific change in E, the effect in which we are interested. A difference in CH, in other words, will mean a subsequent difference in E; and that will happen every time that the conditions are the same. We do not seriously conclude therefrom that we have reached the ultimate cause or point of origin of the effect E. We have merely arrived at the point where, "for all intents and purposes" which we have in mind at the moment, any further tracing-back of linked differences seems unprofitable. Our demand, whether for the purpose of understanding E, or for momentary or long-run control, has temporarily been satisfied.

Now, as we look about the world, we see in physical Nature many linked sequences or systems of interdependent processes manifesting themselves in series of events. Some of the alterations of relative equilibria are relatively slow, such as a volcano in reaching the point of eruption, or a storm gathering, or the wearing away of a rock. Many of these processes can be isolated from the rest of Nature for study, since they seem to be relatively self-contained. But one day the rock wears away to a certain point and releases an avalanche; or the storm lets go with discharges of lightning; or the volcano belches forth lava. Segments of Nature itself, it would seem, come into focus at certain crucial explosive points, as when an atom loses an electron, a star bursts, or a natural dam gives way. Something that is perfectly normal within its own isolated system enters some other system with (perhaps) a catastrophically upsetting effect upon the equilibria of both. Each one of these focal happenings, so crucial from the point of view of the manifold events which follow in its train, is itself the outcome of a numberless assemblage of occurrences which preceded it. But that is no reason for denying that it is truly focal, especially if we are interested in bringing about (or in preventing) any or all of its consequences.

What we do in such instances, if we are interested in their control, is to try to prevent the processes from reaching a focal point, or "coming to a crux," by taking measures which play them off against one another, or which merge them in a wider setting of enveloping conditions. We combat natural floods and landslides by such countermeasures as reforestation and the building of diversion channels and dams. What we have to remember is that not all of the equilibria which are disturbed by collisions with other systems or their members are of the simple mechanical type of evenly balanced forces. We cannot suppose that everything in Nature tends to remain in a balanced state of apparent inertia until it is upset by some extraneous force. No doubt every possible development has restraining and forwarding conditions; but they are not necessarily equal and opposite. There are many sorts of equilibria in Nature, some of them relatively simple, stable, and apparently self-perpetuating, while others are complex, precarious, and easily destroyed. The explosion of a bomb in a field may upset innumerable interlocked cycles of chemical, vegetable, and animal growth; and yet, twenty years after, the face of Nature may have largely healed, provided that the major organic equilibria of the neighborhood were not destroyed.

But compare the explosion of the bomb with the metaphorical detonating of a bombshell of scandal which might burst from the lips of an excited person in an organized group. Here we see that a vast number of psychological equilibria of choice might be affected by a single word. The entire basis of mutual confidence of the members of the group in one another might be destroyed. Much would depend, of course, upon the strength of the cohesive and divisive factors operating within the organization at the time when the scandal broke — whether, in other words, the group equilibrium was stable or precarious. But whatever the fate of the group as a whole, we know that innumerable potential individual developments would radiate from the one rash utterance, to be met and countered by all sorts of reciprocal buffering effects. The extreme difficulty of predicting the exact outcome of any such incident reveals the immense number of alternative possibilities.

THE CAUSAL SCAPEGOAT

Both in Nature and in that subdivision of it called human nature, many of the processes which interact are not spread out evenly through the universe, but are concentrated or tied together, at least temporarily, in bunches or centers which are relatively independent of one another, but which may collide. Many extraordinary but nevertheless natural events seem to hinge upon the collisions of these systems at what we have called focal points. By such highly organized systems as human beings, problem-situations of that sort are met with actions which we call choices or decisions. When a man is knocked off his stride by unexpected developments in his environment, there are literally thousands of different things which he can and may do about it.

If, among other things, he inquires into causes, his thinking is likely, as we know, to follow some ancient human patterns. In the first place, sudden changes will attract a disproportionate amount of human interest just because his organism is geared to attend to spectacular interruptions in the ordinary course of events. Let us suppose, for example, that a railroad runs its trains for a week without incident. All of them leave and arrive on time. Everything runs smoothly within an artificial, man-arranged system of processes. Now it is hard to imagine that the board of directors, at the close of the week's business, would institute a board of inquiry to find the causes of the railroad's safe and punctual operations. It is human nature to let sleeping dogs lie. When all goes well, one lets causes alone. But that does not mean that they cease to operate.

During the very next week, however, the same railroad had three accidents, all accompanied by loss of life. A board of inquiry was promptly convened to ferret out their causes. The first catastrophe was declared to be due to a landslide started by the dislodging of a single pebble by a heavy rainstorm. The second was traced to the "accidental" grasping of the wrong lever by a switchman; and the third was enveloped in suspicions of sabotage on the part of someone in the train dispatcher's office, who issued a mysterious order which brought about a collision.

In all three instances, there was an unpleasant disruption of the "normal" system of train operation, which was immediately traced to a point at which a major redistribution of energy seemed to have taken place. That apparently decisive variation or turning point was seized upon as *the* cause which obviously "made all the difference," and which should therefore be held responsible for everything out of the ordinary which ensued: the train derailed, cars destroyed, passengers killed, homes broken up, insurance paid, dividends reduced, and so on. No doubt the public would get most excited over the possible saboteur, for he would represent the maximum of unpredictable danger of interference with the expected course of events. How could anyone travel with confidence, if train dispatchers' offices were known to be tenanted by intentional agents of disruption? But prospective travelers would not be much happier about the careless switchman, whose single twist of the wrist was blamed for accident number two. As for the "natural" landslide, they would be inclined to look around for the maintenance-of-way employee who let the pebble get into such a dangerous key position. If that trail led nowhere, they would undoubtedly blame "the weather," and, since they could do very little about that, they would declare the accident legally "an act of God."

This human tendency to seek a causal scapegoat for whatever disrupts the system in which we are interested, is easily understandable.[10] We want to be able to predict and control as wide an area of the future as we possibly can, by reducing it to some kind of manageable order. If single collisions can result in the making and breaking, not only of railroads and banks but of whole empires and cultures, we had better pay attention to them. Every war, it is

---

[10] For a more detailed discussion, see chap. VI, "Cause as Precipitant," in R. M. MacIver, *Social Causation* (New York, 1942), and H. L. Hart and A. M. Honoré, *Causation in the Law* (Oxford, 1959).

said, has its turning point; and we should all like to be present and to have a hand in that particular phase of the struggle. But how does a war reach its turning point? And how is the latter to be identified? It is only sensible economy of thought for us to concentrate our attention upon influencing the key events rather than the minor details. Yet that tendency often leads us to attempt other economies that may turn out to be unprofitable, such as those prompted by the delusion that deep-seated habits and drives can be transformed by slogans or other superficial forms of oral persuasion. To pick out causes on the basis of logical convenience, that is — whatever we judge will be easiest for us to identify and alter — is a poor rule of analysis.

This punitive type of causal focusing needs tempering in at least two directions. In the first place, it grossly neglects all the rest of the conditions which were, in the given circumstances, necessary but not sufficient to occasion the effect. The last straw, it argues, is what breaks the camel's back; although the last one weighs no more than the first straw or any other of the straws whose presence is necessary, but not sufficient, for the breaking. There may have been a dangerous spacing of trains on the railroad, which was already close to the safety limit, when the switchman's error or the saboteur's order added the last fatal nudge. This exaggerated importance of trifles in upsetting delicate balances is particularly marked in human social conduct, where a single intonation of voice may "cause" a riot, or a wisp of smoke, a panic. But we should always ask the additional questions: What were the other essential conditions which made the one condition decisive? What set the stage for the potential flare-up of the strike, the epidemic, or the war? What permitted Booth's pistol to get into place behind Lincoln's head? What enabled one scratch of Hitler's pen to set armies marching all over the world?

In the second place, no sooner have we funneled our inquiry down to the switchman's error, for example, than we find ourselves asking: How did he happen to make it? Was he, perhaps, overtired from long hours of labor, or intoxicated, or just day-dreaming? The answering of such questions obliges us to invert the cone of causal convergence, since we find ourselves embarked upon an investigation of all the relevant surrounding processes of the allegedly decisive cause, no one of which, in turn, may be sufficient by itself to account for it. The weather, union struggles for shorter hours, diet, the boss's attitude, the day's news, the switchman's entire personal history — all these things and many more may have contributed to his error. And all of them have *their* conditions. As Professor D. H. Parker expresses it: "Every focus is a point of absorption of influences that converge upon it; and from it, in turn, influences diverge, to be absorbed by neighboring foci."[11] Causal analysis of human behavior is not a linear affair of successive knots in a string, or points upon a single plane. When we select and define a situation, we discover that rays of influence radiate upon it from innumerable constantly shifting fields of force on many different levels, and *vice versa*. Each center sums up a manifold of potentialities; and there are very few of them which are invariably connected by fixed chains extending over many links. Instead, most of linkages are short, and the alternatives are many. The same outcome

[11] De Witt H. Parker, *Experience and Substance* (Ann Arbor, Mich., 1941), p. 233.

in behavior can be reached by a host of different causal pathways. That is what makes the tracing of an historical sequence so difficult. This happening, we may declare, "caused" the outbreak of war; but war might have broken out, once granted the existence of potentially antagonistic processes, in any one of a thousand ways.

We get some conception of the difficulty of precise causal analysis in social situations when a whole nation falls before the invader, and there is a demand that "the guilty ones" be brought to trial. Some of the accused, while in positions of conspicuous public responsibility, may seem to have done nothing more than act as passive channels of external influences; while others may appear as genuinely initiating or deflecting forces. Even if such an inquiry is not merely for the purpose of providing a scapegoat upon which an unhappy public may vent its wrath, there is a strong tendency to stress the importance of the dramatic trigger-releasing actors in the drama rather than the long-run influences which loaded the gun. Similarly a ruler can often get undeserved credit for maintaining order, simply because he does not allow explosive "incidents" to bring nearly intolerable conditions to a head. On the other hand, it is unlikely that we are wholly mistaken in allotting different degrees of influence to the participants in a disaster in which all (and millions more) are causes; but in which some, through the fact of organization, played a more decisive part than others.

The alternative to some degree of causal focusing seems to be complete diffusion of the explanatory process in all directions equally. That ends in making everything the cause of everything else, as in the following statement by a criminologist: "The amount of crime in the United States responds to all the factors and forces in American life . . . the criminal . . . is the product of the sum of our institutions."[12] Explained in the same fashion, the amount of disease would be attributable to our entire physical and mental environment. That kind of causal analysis sheds little light upon the antecedents of specific crimes or diseases, to say nothing of specific patients or criminals. If we could never find the cause of anything without inquiring into the nature of everything, we should probably be paralyzed in advance by the magnitude of our undertaking.

4. Illustrations of Causal Analysis

Since the task of finding the causes of human conduct involves both the sounding of the quiet depths of ongoing processes, and the following of apparent convergences toward and divergences away from dramatic foci which may be on different levels, it will call for varied methods of attack. It is not just a question of stringing crucial events together, or of probing long-run movements; but of mixtures of both. The analyses, even of a single situation, may well differ greatly in scope and depth, depending upon the purposes for which and the skill with which they are carried out.

[12] Frank Tannenbaum, *Crime and the Community* (Boston, 1938), p. 25. For a critical analysis of the many theories about the causes of crime, see R. M. MacIver, *op. cit.*, pp. 80–95.

They will, however, be found to follow one or two main patterns which may be called the mechanical and the historical respectively. Those of the first variety trace comparatively "tight" yet often lengthy causal sequences along a single level by means of well-established uniformities or laws. Their subject matter consists of "natural" physical and chemical chains, on the one hand, in which each succeeding effect acts as cause for another effect; and certain "artificial" sequences, on the other, such as the operations of the automatic machines which man has devised for various purposes. In contrast to these mechanical analyses, however, other instances will be found to require a zigzagging back and forth among the levels in short, "loose" historical sequences of individual occurrences, each of which might easily have happened otherwise.

It should be borne in mind that when human conduct, either of an individual or of a group, becomes rigid and fully predictable we begin to talk of robots and automata; and that it is when a machine breaks down that we are most likely to treat it as semi-human. There is a familiar story about a visitor to the Western frontier city who went there as the guest of a prominent politician, but who had his watch stolen only a few hours after his arrival. On complaining to his host, he was told that his watch would be on the mayor's desk within twenty minutes; and so it was. Behavior that can be controlled so swiftly and unerringly, we immediately attribute to something like a "machine" in the background. It is that kind of tight concatenation of linkages which is the aim of "mechanical" football coaches, drillmasters, and dictators.

The following examples of everyday instances of causal interpretation of events may serve to indicate some of the main outlines of the process as applied to individual instances. Note how the various inquirers break down the total network of conditions into those which they deem relevant for their particular ends in view, and then trace the causal sequence to the focus which satisfies them, disregarding other possibilities of analysis as constant and dispensable, as far as they are concerned. As John Stuart Mill remarked, "in practice, that particular condition is usually styled the cause, whose share in the matter is superficially the most conspicuous, or whose requisiteness to the production of the effect we happen to be insisting on at the moment."[13]

1. News item, New York *Times*

INCOME TAX LEADS TO FIRE

Edward H. Reynolds, 46 years old, former assistant U.S. district attorney, worked at his law office in North Tarrytown all night making out his income tax return. At 5:45 A.M. he dozed, and his lighted cigarette fell on an overstuffed chair beside his desk. A few minutes later neighbors observed smoke curling from the office windows. Firemen were called and found Mr. Reynolds overcome by smoke. He was taken to the Tarrytown Hospital, where physicians said this afternoon his condition was good. Damage to the office was estimated at $400.

[13] John Stuart Mill, *A System of Logic* (London, 1904), p. 239.

Let us suppose that three men arrive upon the above scene: an interne from the Tarrytown Hospital, the chief of the Tarrytown Fire Department, and a reporter from the New York *Times*. All of them ascertain the primary fact: a man is unconscious, overcome by smoke from a fire in his office. Each, however, makes his own analysis of the causes of the event in terms of his past experiences and future purposes, namely:

(*a*) Interne, Tarrytown Hospital

Purpose in *view*:	Recovery of patient, and increased medical knowledge.
Effect to be explained:	Patient is unconscious; respiration irregular, pulse weak, etc.
Focus:	Physiological disarrangement of functions.
Causes:	Inhalation of smoke while in fatigued condition from all night work, hunger, etc.
Uniformities used:	Medical knowledge of effect of inhalation of smoke, fatigue, etc., on adult human beings. (Note that complications might require some knowledge of Mr. Reynolds's individual "life history" in order to interpret this specific case.)

(*b*) Chief, Tarrytown Fire Department

Purpose in view:	To establish cause of fire for legal and insurance purposes, and to prevent future fires.
Effect to be explained:	Danger to life and limb; $400 damage to property; and $25 expense to taxpayers.
Focus:	Physical cause of combustion; and (more remote) physiological and psychological causes of dropped cigarette.
Causes:	(1) Contact of lighted cigarette and inflammable materials of chair. (Note that a chemist seeking to perfect a non-inflammable upholstery material might analyze this much further, even to sub-atomic level.) (2) Release of finger muscles by Mr. Reynolds while asleep.
Uniformities used:	(1) Laws of gravitation and combustion. (2) Psychological laws of sleep. (Note that account might have to be taken of Mr. Reynold's individual life history, habits, condition, etc., in order to interpret his falling asleep on this particular occasion.)

(*c*) Reporter, New York *Times*

Purpose in view:	To furnish information about current happening that will be interesting and useful to a wide group of potential readers.
Effect to be explained:	Event sufficiently exceptional to be newsworthy.
Focus:	Social-cultural connection of circumstances of the fire and the interests of potential readers through a series of foci.

Causes:	Possibility of remote linkage of minor blaze on March 4 with income tax returns then due on March 15, namely, danger to life of prominent citizen due to fatigue due to overwork due to Mr. Reynolds's handling of his income tax return problem. Implication: no income tax requiring complex return, no fire; but no serious claim is made of "necessary" linkage of U.S. governmental policy and fire damage.
Uniformities used:	Many of those already mentioned, and loose generalizations concerning social suggestion, imitation, curiosity, habit, etc.

If someone asked the interne, "How did it happen?" his brief answer would probably be something like, "Smoke and fatigue." The fire chief's reply to the same question would no doubt be "Carelessness"; while the reporter might explain that "The poor guy was up against one of those long and detailed income tax returns . . . something ought to be done about things which take all night to figure out." Still different analyses of the incident would undoubtedly be made by an anti-cigarette leaguer ("Smoking habit is to blame"), by a coffee salesman ("A cup of our coffee would have kept him alert"), by a metal furniture salesman ("You see what happens to men who stick to old-style furniture"), and many others. Each one would differ in emphasis and interpretation according to his particular experience and interest. It is not a case of one causal analysis being correct and all the rest incorrect. All of them may be justifiable, up to a point, for the purpose for which each is intended.

The analyses also differ greatly in the extent to which they view the Reynolds incident as typical of a certain kind of event rather than as standing alone. It is one thing for Mr. Reynolds to have "learned his lesson" from the misadventure; but it is quite another for the residents of Tarrytown or physicians as a class or fire chiefs or readers of the *Times* to have learned their lessons. For the prevention of further incidents of the same sort, some of the analyses are more likely to be useful than others; yet all of them taken together would be needed for the fullest *understanding* of what happened and why.

II. News item, New York *Herald-Tribune*

WEATHER FORECAST BRINGS $250,000 SUIT
New York Woman Says Its Error Caused Father's Death

Suit for $250,000 damages was filed in United States District Court by Mrs. Shirley Seid of 1075 Park Avenue against the United States on the ground that the death of her father, Emanuel Kaplan, resulted from erroneous information supplied by the Weather Bureau.

Mr. Kaplan, an officer of the Saxony Corporation, manufacturers of processed wool, was killed when his private plane crashed into Long Island Sound as he was flying from Far Rockaway, Queens, toward Salem, Connecticut.

The plaintiff charged that the Weather Bureau had told her father that atmospheric, weather and flying conditions were "favorable and safe," and alleged that the information was "erroneous, inaccurate, and carelessly furnished."

Once again the question "How did it happen?" sets off a search for the decisive factor in the crash of the plane. What led the plaintiff to place the blame upon the Weather Bureau? Her first quest was for a factor which had not been present in Mr. Kaplan's previous similar flights.

(a) Daughter, Mrs. Seid

Purpose in view:	To fix responsibility for loss.
Effect to be explained:	Crash of plane.
Focus:	Physical condition of plane, physiological and psychological condition of pilot, amount of his knowledge and known ability to use it.
Uniformities used:	Physical data regarding age, upkeep, strength of materials of plane; physiological status of Mr. Kaplan, his medical history, his competence as pilot and known habits regarding weather decisions.

In this first stage of the inquiry, the plaintiff, Mrs. Seid, assumes a whole series of uniformities which, she supposes, have prevailed in earlier flights by Mr. Kaplan; and also that they continued to hold in every respect but one, namely — his use of the information supplied by the Weather Bureau. Had the reports he received from them been accurate and carefully prepared, she alleges, her father would still be alive. Hence the cause of his death was the "erroneous" information for which some party or parties in the Weather Bureau was (or were) responsible.

Assuming that the weather into which Mr. Kaplan flew did not correspond with the description of its probable character furnished to him by the Bureau, what would be likely to be their view of the causal situation?

(b) Officials of U.S. Weather Bureau

Purpose in view:	To fix their responsibility, if any, in crash of plane.
Effect to be explained:	Role of weather information.
Focus:	Normal care and skill of employees in preparing and giving weather reports.
Uniformities used:	Normal degree of accuracy in predictions, time lapse, etc.; probability of sudden, unforeseeable changes.

Here the search for the cause of the alleged "error" branches out in two directions: (1) it is conceivable that some person or persons through lack of skill or through carelessness gave Mr. Kaplan a truly "erroneous" report, thereby misleading him into making a trip he would have not taken, had the information been correct to the best knowledge of the Bureau. This could be determined by a searching of the records and an interrogation of the personnel on duty at the time. (2) It might, however, be established that the reports were given to the pilot with the highest degree of skill and care attainable in weather forecasting, and yet proved to be "erroneous" because of factors beyond the Weather Bureau's control.

This would involve an extensive study of the state of the whole science of meteorological prediction, as well as a minute analysis of the weather conditions prevailing at the time of the accident, and during the preceding hours when the reports were prepared. Assuming that the Bureau acted in good faith and with the maximum efficiency attainable in the circumstances, the quest for "the cause" might lead to an inquiry into the amount of public confidence normally possessed by private fliers in Weather Bureau reports. Who is responsible for that? Should Mr. Kaplan as a normally intelligent person and experienced pilot have been more sceptical of their probable accuracy than he was? Did he, or did he not, somewhat overestimate the chances that the reports he received would be borne out, and if so, why? Plainly his mental "history" in these respects would be of great importance in fixing "the cause" of his accident; and the search for its causes would reach deep into the fabric of society in general.

We are now in a position to see what a person is trying to do who is bent upon resolving a puzzling situation by means of the notion of cause. He starts with a change, usually a single event envisaged on a certain apparent level: the unconscious lawyer, the blazing chair, the good news-story, the crash of the airplane. He wants either to do something with respect to it (and similar occurrences), or merely to understand it. He thinks to himself: This change would not have occurred unless . . . there had been some disturbing factor or complex of factors earlier in the game. Then, in accordance with his prevailing purpose, his past training, his imaginative ingenuity, and his persistency, he tries to connect the event with some other difference or chain of differences which can be fitted together in such a way as to form one continuous and intelligible series.

Inevitably he will proceed by comparison, for that is the only way to establish and handle differences. If he is seeking to account for the past rather than to alter the future, he will most often make a comparison of the present state of affairs with some preceding stage. The causal inquirer always has to start with some knowledge or conjecture about "what went before." If he were completely ignorant, he would be unable to make the simplest preliminary judgment about what was relevant to what. Bring to a man who has never seen either a radio or a dog, a broken radio and a sick dog, and you will find him unable, except by analogies with other things, to diagnose the ills of either one. To treat the dog, he would need to know something of its history as an organism; whereas the radio might be put together merely by consulting a diagram of its parts.

Since what the investigator is looking for is a hidden order beneath the surface of events which will give him a clue to the interconnectedness of processes, he naturally utilizes, in framing his causal hypothesis, whatever already known or alleged uniformities of behavior are available on each level in the form of classified things, qualities, patterns, formulas, or laws. These shorthand devices facilitate the diagnosis enormously (imagine what medical practice would be like if every symptom of every patient had to be treated individually in terms of his past history). Yet we have learned that there are limits to what can be accomplished by the dismemberment of individual instances into units which are uniform enough to be subsumed under a mechanical or even a statistical law.

Some of the uniformities, such as the law of falling bodies which enables the fire chief to account for the behavior of the dropped cigarette, or the laws of the rate of combustion of materials in the presence of air, are truly mechanical and on a single level. By their aid, if we classify and define our terms correctly, we can set up fairly rigid causal chains which lead directly from the effect to previous measurable states of affairs and *vice versa*. In those instances, we can usually reconstruct or re-enact that part of what happened, with substantially identical results. Knowledge of the relevant antecedents of any such event does not affect its happening or failing to happen. But there are other aspects of the fire which are not so easily repeatable. Having restored Mr. Reynolds's office to the *status quo ante*, we might ask him to re-enact his falling asleep while smoking. But he is now a person who has learned some of the causal implications of such conduct, and that is bound to change his state of mind.

When we come to the problem of Mr. Kaplan and the Weather Bureau, we are by no means dealing with the actions of a robot responding to signals, but with a sophisticated mind, an experienced flier, engaged in estimating the reliability of a set of predictions. We find ourselves trying to relive the historical events preceding the crash as the flier probably experienced them. On the other hand there is a highly organized and scientific social institution engaged in the perilous business of prophesying the future. What should we expect their batting average of successful predictions to be, assuming that they are operating at top efficiency? What has been their actual level of performance in terms of accuracy? Have we any basis for believing that it ought to be higher than it is? Were Mr. Kaplan's expectations excessive? Such questions plainly involve both the mechanical patterns of scientific meteorology and the historical patterns of complex events in the annals of Mr. Kaplan, of the airplane industry, and of the Weather Bureau.

THE TWO PATTERNS

The principal difference, then, between the two brands of uniformities which we have called the mechanical and the historical is not that the mechanical laws are abstract while the historical patterns are concrete. Both sorts of subject matter are concrete and extremely complicated; but both explanatory generalizations are abstract — that is, both the natural scientist and the humanist historian select and form concepts from the total goings-on in the world. Neither is there an absolute boundary line separating two sorts of subject matter: on one side the mechanical, and on the other the historical. It is rather a distinction among useful points of view. If one chooses, the mechanical pattern can be applied to history, even to poetry, but in those fields it simply fails to yield a rich enough harvest of returns in either understanding or control. Similarly, the historical pattern can be applied to the experiments of the physics laboratory, as it sometimes is when one takes care to preserve untouched the apparatus of some great scientist. But that accomplishes little toward the *scientific* understanding of the physical laws which he discovered.

The chief contrast in the two points of view lies in the fact that the mechanical pattern aims at carrying abstraction on a single level to the point of disregarding qualitative individuality, thus achieving wide scope on that level, and high, though limited predictive power; whereas the historical pattern aims at qualitative individuality at the cost of limited and dubious applicability, since its abstractions are, though intimate, necessarily loose analogies between non-repeatable configurations extending over many levels and time-periods. Mechanical concepts have a sharpness of outline that invites repetition, isolation, and the precise measurement of differences, while historical concepts are more like composite motion picture photographs with blurred outlines composed of the many fine lines of individual instances intricately intertwined. Yet they often deal in terms of a first-hand knowledge that is far less derived than what is stated in mechanical formulas. Their great weakness, as we shall see, is in the realm of proof. Only the strictest statements of physical science lend themselves to causal proof in the sense of sole invariable antecedent. All other causal analyses shade off into incidental circumstances which may or may not have something to do with the effect.

5. Levels of Causal Analysis

In spite of the immense complexity of the universe, it may be worth while to try to draw up a rough scheme of useful levels of causal analysis, always remembering that the lines of such a classification of materials are not clear-cut, and that each level may be further subdivided. The main criterion of the levels is the presence of fairly distinguishable sorts of uniformities permitting different degrees of predictability. On certain of the levels there are well-established uniformities which have been found to work well, but which prove inadequate when they are applied to other phenomena of greater complexity. When that happens, it is fairly safe to say that we may usefully distinguish another level. But we should be ill-advised to assume that levels are anything more than useful boundaries of points of view in inquiry; or that we know in advance exactly to what extent the laws of one level will or will not enable us to make predictions concerning the qualitied related events on other levels.

The following five levels are those commonly distinguished in most discussions of cause. It should be noted that any event on one level will be found to be analyzable on all the *preceding* levels, although not always usefully, as far as we can see at the present time.

1. *Sub-atomic physical.* Isolated electrons and photons can be constructed and studied inferentially by means of tracks, but their *individual* behavior cannot be predicted upon the mechanical pattern due to such difficulties as those exposed by the Heisenberg Principle. Theoretically, however, a single cell of

an organism (level 3) might be thrown out of balance by an as yet unpredictable event on the sub-atomic level, and that change might possibly upset the delicate balance of the whole organism. Prediction of behavior of aggregates on this level is statistical.

2. *Gross physical.* The familiar realm of physical things or bodies forming the zone of maximum predictability of behavior on the mechanical pattern. Notable for the comparatively small number of variables and the relative precision with which they can be measured.

3. *Biological.* Realm of the organic as distinct from the inorganic. The genera of living organisms all the way from the unicellular to the extremely complex multicellular, with functionally related parts co-ordinated for self-maintenance (but liable to conflict) interacting as units with the environment, including other organisms, with varying degrees of altered internal conditioning or organic "memory," thereby requiring the introduction of semi-historical patterns, yielding reduced predictability.

4. *Psychological.* Conscious individual mind-organism with immensely enlarged memory-anticipation areas of response, increased flexibility, and an environment which may include the imagined mental life of others. Here limited to individual rather than social psychology. Uniformities are mainly centered in limitations of organs, routine habits, and plans built upon alleged drives or tendencies, yielding relatively slender and inexact predictability due to enormous variety of stimuli and responses, possible mental conflicts, and constant reworking of materials. Thus there are many psychologies using semi-mechanical, statistical, and semi-historical methods of inquiry.

5. *Social-cultural.* Conscious groups which have not only cumulative habits in the form of *mores* and institutions, but which actively organize, plan, and to a certain limited extent predict, their own behavior in the form of aims, ideals, and policies. Since the cumulative continuity of culture on this level depends largely upon the active transmission of ideas and ideals through education, and since the possibilities of individual and group conflicts are at a maximum, the degree of complexity is so great, and of isolability so small, that predictability is at a minimum. History traces its types and patterns on this level, while the so-called social sciences are mixtures, in varying proportions, of the mechanical elements and laws of the lower levels, and the historical and normative elements already mentioned.

There are innumerable special problems which cannot be gone into at this point, such as those of the special relationships between the uniformities of levels 1 and 2, and between those of levels 4 and 5, where the uniformities on the higher level are statistical aggregates of units on the lower level. In general it may be ventured that each level furnishes the necessary but not the sufficient conditions for the level next above it, and so on upward; although that assumption would be disputed by those who regard the mental levels as primary and the bodily as dependent thereon. Nearly everyone would agree, however, that the lower levels limit, at least to some extent, the activities of the higher.

It will be well to remind ourselves of the common human failing of playing favorites among the levels by choosing one of them and then maintaining that it explains all the others. This is often accomplished by the simple expedient of going no further, in our hunt for explanations, once the chosen level has been reached. This is the ancient fallacy of "reduction-to," which consists in the demand that everything be explained in terms of our favorite level: atoms or organisms or minds or societies, whether or not there is any demonstrably basic decisiveness to be found on that level in a particular case. There seems to be no set of factors, for example, that has not been assigned the position of key to human behavior by someone. But so far, we may say with assurance, our knowledge of any one of the levels does not enable us to deduce all the laws of any other level from it. If it did, the two levels would hardly be worth distinguishing. The best reduction so far accomplished still leaves a wide margin of phenomena unexplained. That is true in both directions: individual psychology does not furnish us with a complete picture of social behavior; and sociology is just as impotent to illuminate all the activities of individuals.

Our wisest course, then, will be to play no favorites in advance, but to begin our explanation wherever we find our problem, using the methods appropriate to that level, and then to continue it by reference to the levels which enable us to solve it with the greatest degree of finality and fruitfulness for other problems. We should get over our fear of "hybrid" causes embracing factors on more than one level. Sometimes a man cannot think because he has eaten the wrong things; and sometimes a man cannot eat because he has thought the wrong things; and more often the two sorts of maladies interact. To correct the first difficulty, we should do well to explore the lower levels with the help of a physician or a nutritionist. To remedy the second, we should call in a psychiatrist in the hope of illumination on the higher levels. There is no reason why either specialist should disdain the advice of the other. To insist dogmatically, and in advance, that all thinking must be reduced to eating, or that all eating must be reduced to thinking, certainly is not called for on the basis of our present knowledge of either activity.

6. Review of Clarification of Hypotheses

In the last two chapters much attention has been given to the subject of preparing our hypotheses for the crucial stage of testing, or proof. All this preliminary groundwork has been necessary because the social studies, especially, are cursed with innumerable hypotheses which are in no condition to be discussed because they can neither be proved nor disproved. For the lack of sufficient care in setting up the terms and the causal pattern, hours are wasted in futile argument, with neither side being able to "prove anything" to the other. So the intellectual scene becomes cluttered up with harebrained theories which survive because they cannot be finally discredited, and which therefore demand endless though fruitless rehearsings. Any labor expended in weeding out such badly stated theories is well invested, since it saves time and energy which would otherwise be wasted in futile attempts to prove the unprovable.

An inquirer is endeavoring, in an explanatory hypothesis, to use the statement of an imagined order as an instrument for discovering and proving that all the facts he is trying to explain fit into his mental scheme sufficiently well to warrant predictions about them based upon it. In the early stages of his inquiry, the imagined order may be, and ordinarily is, rather dimly apprehended in the form of a guess or hunch. But it is one thing, for example, to suspect that a sabotage plot lies behind a series of unexplained accidents, and quite another to be able to prove it. To formulate an hypothesis is to draw up a kind of indictment of events in the hope of being able to make it stick. Care must be taken, not only with its static abstract terms (the nouns), but also with its activating patterning (the verbs). Perhaps the briefest way to test the preliminary formulation of an hypothesis is to ask oneself: Just what is it that I am trying, or being asked, to find out here? Just what alleged order in events am I seeking to test? A more detailed check can be made by asking the following six questions about the two main elements utilized in framing the proposed hypothesis:

Concerning the terms:

1. Is the symbolic reference of each term (especially its level of abstraction) plain, and appropriate to the problem and its subject matter?

2. Are the classifications used well suited to the subject matter and to the purpose in mind?

3. Are the terms free from harmful ambiguity?

Concerning the causal pattern:

1. Is it appropriate to the subject matter and to the purpose in mind?

2. Are the levels upon which the causal explanation is sought sufficiently evident, and fundamental for the purpose?

3. What types of uniformities should we expect to be able to utilize on the levels chosen?

FOR CLASS DISCUSSION

A. Cause has etymologically the meaning of *thing before.* Though, indeed, the origin of the word is very obscure, its derivative, the Italian *cosa,* and the French *chose,* means simply *thing.* In the German *ursache . . . sache* denotes "interesting or important object," the English *sake, ur* being the equivalent of the English *ere, before. . . .* We abandon, then, both etymology and philosophy, when we attribute to the laws of causation any meaning beyond that of the conditions under which an event may be expected to happen, according to our observation of the previous course of nature. — W. S. Jevons   (2)

B. A man falls ill; a remedy is given . . . in time health is regained . . . therefore, he recovered because of the remedy. . . . When men are ill, something is usually done for them; the majority recover. . . . Almost any treatment applied would, under the type of reasoning (that of the testimonial advertisement) result in a fair percentage of recoveries; hence the multiplicity of remedies. — *Howard W. Haggard*

C. We ought then to regard the present state of the universe as the effect of its anterior state and as the cause of the one which is to follow. Given for one instant an intelligence which could comprehend all the forces by which Nature is animated, and the respective situation of the beings which compose it — an intelligence sufficiently vast to submit these data to analysis — it would embrace in the same formula the movement of the greatest bodies of the universe and those of the lightest atom; for it, nothing would be uncertain and the future, as the past, would be present to its eyes. The human mind offers, in the perfection which it has been able to give to astronomy, a feeble idea of this intelligence. — *Marquis de Laplace*

D. David Hume's definition of cause: "An object precedent and contiguous to another, and so united with it in the imagination, that the idea of the one determines the mind to form the idea of the other, and the impression of the one to form a more lively idea of the other."
The agricultural investigator finds that a crop does badly *because* there is insufficient iron in the soil; that, he says, *explains* its failure. Actually, however, this causative explanatory business turns out to be a very slippery affair, and we shall be on safer ground if we confine ourselves to expressing the laws of science simply as statements of association between phenomena.
— *Barbara Wootton*

E. A coral reef which just comes short of the ocean surface is no more to the horizon than if it had never been begun, and the finishing stroke is what often appears to create an event which has long been an accomplished thing. — *Thomas Hardy*

F. Because in nature an interaction is an exchange, it is incorrect to specify one factor as cause and the other as effect. An axe, for example, in splitting wood is as much acted upon by the wood as the latter acts upon it . . . the axe "splits the wood" and "the wood splits" or "stops the axe."
— *Arthur Lapan*

G. Human behavior is hardly a thing to dogmatize about. It is too easy a way out to blame poverty, backwardness, even criminality, and all the ills that flesh is heir to, on genes in chromosomes, or on the environment or on any other isolated or isolable factor. Human behavior is a function of a number of "independent" variables . . . hereditary constitution . . . environmental impacts from childhood to any cross section in time in the life of the individual, the general cultural milieu, the physiological state of the individual, the immediate stimulating setup, *and man's conception of what he is,* as well as many other factors. . . . — *A. W. Bray*

H. In the science of medicine, which still deals largely in "causes" — the bacillus is said to be the cause of typhoid fever. Here there is one condition that is practically of more importance than such other factors as the chemical reactions of the body to the presence of bacterial poisons, the state of nourishment of the organism, etc., and so the term "cause" has remained in use . . . the other "contributory causes" are not envisaged as easily as the presence of the bacillus. — *H. H. Dubs* (3)

I. The conventional way of handling problems of human relations resembles a witch hunt. When the adjustment between individuals or groups breaks down, somebody must bear the blame. . . . — *William Foote Whyte*

J. Knowledge comes in layers. A question on any one level is dependent

immediately upon information in the layer directly beneath it; the answer
there, in turn, can be applied at the layer just above.   (5)
                                                        — *Raymond J. Seager*

EXERCISES IN POST HOC REASONING

1. Justice T. B. Horwood in the native high court at Estcourt, Natal, heard
a murder charge against an aged witch doctor who was said to have killed an
Indian and made "medicine" from parts of the corpse. He warned the assembled Zulus against the "fraudulent claims" of such witch doctors; and, before passing sentence, asked the accused if he had anything to say. The old
man muttered a curse in his own language. As he passed sentence, Justice
Horwood collapsed, and died within twenty-four hours.

2. Joan Pye, ten, and her brother William, nine, of Newark, while vacation-
ing at Stockholm, New Jersey, became lost in the wilderness of the Beaver Lake
mountain range, spent the night in the woods, and in the morning made a
little cross out of some sticks, prayed, let the cross drop to the ground, and
then followed the direction in which it fell. By this means they reached a
dirt road, where they were finally picked up by a passing driver. New York
Times headline of the story, August 30, 1941: "2 LOST CHILDREN SAVED
BY CRUCIFIX."

3. Letter to the author of a newspaper column giving advice on bringing up
children: "I read in your column where you think a child never should be
slapped in the face. I am sorry to disagree with you. I have slapped all my
children in the face and I have never seen such fine children."

4. Bill Werber of the Boston Red Sox told this story about his then-playing
manager, Joe Cronin, to a New York *Herald Tribune* reporter. "Joe was swearing at a snappy pace as he was waiting his chance to bat against Washington.
Father O'Donnell, sitting behind the dugout, heard the blasphemous oratory.
Calling Cronin, who was a friend of his, over for a minute, he said: 'Joe, you've
been swearing all day without results. Let's try a prayer.' Cronin agreed;
then stepped to the plate and hit the first pitched ball into the left-field
bleachers. The priest, an ardent baseball fan, watched the ball, and as it
dropped into the seats for a home run, he sank back, exclaiming, 'Good
Lord!'"

5. A doctor known as "Sea-water Russell," who lived near Brighton, England, in the nineteenth century, became convinced by analogy with the cures
brought about by drinking the waters at Bath and other noted spas, that similar cures could be brought about by a regimen of drinking seawater while
bathing in it. Some patients did indeed benefit, not from the seawater drinking
but from the vitamin D produced by the exposure of their bodies to the sun,
of which Dr. Russell knew nothing. As older persons flocked to Brighton to
sea-bathe, the Mrs. Grundys of the period insisted that they be swathed and
swaddled from ankle to chin, and the beneficial effects disappeared.

6. In a letter to a Schenectady, New York, paper on October 20, 1951,
entitled "Democratic Record of War," a person identified only as "V.S."

argued: "During three Democratic administrations in the past 25 years the fathers and mothers of the U.S. have sacrificed 1,495,101 of their sons to bring peace on earth, plus $396,528,603,870 and the end is not in sight. If the voters want more war, more taxes, more debt . . . they can have it by voting into power the candidates representing the Democratic party. . . ."

7. Evidence of an alleged "jinx" affecting U.S. Presidents elected in even-numbered years in multiples of twenty, of whom seven in a row have died in office: 1840 W. H. Harrison; 1860 A. Lincoln; 1880 James Garfield; 1900 William McKinley; 1920 Warren G. Harding; 1940 Franklin D. Roosevelt; 1960 John F. Kennedy.

8. Ten instances of disasters occurring to sports figures soon after their appearance on the cover of *Time* magazine giving rise to the "*Time* magazine cover jinx in sports," *viz.*—

October 5, 1931 Primo Carnera, lost fight to Dempsey.

May 7, 1934 Col. E. R. Bradley, his Derby favorite *Bazaar* loses.

August 20, 1934 *Cavalcade*, Derby winner injured, never wins again.

July 13, 1936 Joe DiMaggio, no hits, two errors in All-Star game.

June 6, 1938 Johnny Goodman, lost two Walker Cup matches, and cup.

November 6, 1939 Tom Harmon, U. of Illinois stops him, and Michigan 16–7.

May 6, 1946 Elizabeth Arden Graham, loses 26 racehorses in fire.

April 14, 1947 Leo Durocher, suspended as Dodger manager.

January 10, 1949 Ben Hogan, loses Los Angeles Open, near-fatal auto accident.

August 27, 1951 Dick Savitt, injures leg and loses in U.S. tennis. In rebuttal, *Time* magazine listed five sports figures who appeared on its cover during the same period, and who fared well.

EXERCISES IN CAUSE

The following examples are not intended for study from the point of view of *proof*, but merely as starting points for causal analyses similar to the two given in the chapter, with the aid of the five levels later distinguished.

Directions: (1) Decide upon the phenomenon or event for which the explanatory causal hypothesis is to be formulated, and indicate what level it is on. (2) State, as nearly as can be ascertained from the case, the purpose which the analyzer has in view. (3) Trace the steps in accounting for the phenomenon or event in terms of its conditions, pointing out any changes of level in the process, and what uniformities are used in each step. (4) Show what, if anything, is selected as *the* cause, and its level. *Optional*: (5) Indicate other possible causal analyses of the same subject matter, or ways in which the analysis given could be carried further.

1. In March, 1941, the Bucharest press reported that an entire village in the Carpathian foothills had been destroyed by a landslide blamed upon a herd

of goats. The goats killed a number of trees by nibbling the bark. The trees were cut down, their roots decayed, and the loose earth, rock, and shale slipped under the pressure of the melting snow, engulfing over two hundred acres of land, and leaving a hundred families homeless.

2. What causes migrating birds to migrate? "All theories of the causes of bird migration," says Dean Amadon of the American Museum of Natural History, "have serious shortcomings." Lack of food and extreme cold provide obvious stimuli; but some birds in warm climates fly north in response to wet or dry conditions. One theory holds that migrations began when the continents were closer together. But the continental drift, if it occurred, must have been so long ago that only primitive types of birds were present. Mallard ducks of non-migrating varieties were hatched from eggs in Finland, and promptly migrated southward; and anaesthetized birds transported long distances have returned home, indicating that memory is not the cause.

3. For centuries planting and harvesting were guided by the phases of the moon, but modern science has discredited such practices. It has been noticed, however, by doctors in mental hospitals that their patients make more noise and indulge in more sleepwalking at the full of the moon; and London police refer to several criminals convicted of attacks upon women when the moon was new as "moonshiners." This caused the London *Daily Express* to speculate: "Is there a moon madness? Perhaps in the human brain small granules in the nerve cells are moved about as the moon changes its position in space. The fluids in the cavities of the brain and spine may be influenced."

4. "The hardest crime to detect," said Ray Gill, Fire Marshal of Ohio, "is not murder but arson, which Webster says is 'the malicious burning of a dwelling or other structure.' With murder, you have a corpse, but a fire is different; all you have is a fire. It is up to you to prove that it's arson. On the surface, most arson fires look just the same as those accidental things. Once you figure out that it's arson, you look around for the person who did it, and the motive." Experts say that the motives are many, but that they boil down generally to four things: revenge, jealousy, greed and sex. Then there is the fire-setter who merely says: "I don't know why I did it."

5. A cartoon by Donald McKee entitled "Adolescence *à la Mode*" shows a juvenile delinquent surrounded by ten eager explainers of his behavior, viz. — *Father:* "I blame undesirable associates"; *Mother:* "Try X—— School rather than Y——"; *Aunt:* "He needs a larger allowance"; *Uncle:* "Alas, his faulty inheritance!" *Friend of the family:* "He needs a change, send him to Europe"; *Doctor:* "It's all due to the wrong diet"; *Surgeon:* "No, it's his ductless glands"; *Clergyman:* "We must persuade him to change his habits"; *Eye-specialist:* "Slight defects of vision have soured his disposition"; *Dentist:* "A few teeth out will reform him"; *Psychoanalyst:* "A traumatic fixation — he's not responsible." In a side panel, a scene in a woodshed entitled "And — in 1899" with the caption: "I'll learn ye common sense!"

6. It is sometimes argued that many of the effects which are usually attributed to the Industrial Revolution are to be traced instead to the agricultural revolution which was brought about by the discovery of such root crops as turnips. The alleged sequence runs: root crops enabled the farmer to feed his

stock through the winter and so made unnecessary the excessive slaughtering of animals at Christmas. This made possible the selective breeding of animals, and a marked improvement in the meat supply. The increased meat supply, along with the larger crops of vegetables, brought about a sharp drop in infant mortality by the middle of the eighteenth century, thus greatly increasing the population. The agricultural surplus was what enabled the added inhabitants to flock to the urban industrial centers.

7. Tenants of buildings in large cities sometimes take little interest in the efficiency of city government, since they are unable to see any visible connection between it and their rental charges. The latter, however, can be shown to depend to a large extent upon the amount of new building construction. Since construction requires investment of funds in competition with other forms of investment, it will depend upon the rate of return relative to liquidity and other factors. Poor government ordinarily means high taxes, increased insurance charges, and excessive maintenance and operating costs, thereby reducing the expected returns. The process is so slow and roundabout that the tenant, as voter, may be entirely unaware of it.

10

TESTING THE HYPOTHESIS:

The Mechanical Pattern—Mill's Methods

1. Kinds of Proof

GIVEN A WELL-FORMULATED HYPOTHESIS which passes all our preliminary examinations with flying colors, how shall we go about the serious business of testing its worth as reliable knowledge? When can we rightly feel entitled to say that it is no longer "just an hypothesis," but that it has been established or proved? And in what sense? Proof is a word which has many meanings: mathematical proof, proof beyond a reasonable doubt, proof by preponderance of evidence, and so on. In the usual sense of the term, to prove anything is to show that it is a necessary consequence of something else which has been independently accepted on other grounds.

CONCLUSIVE AND PARTIAL

Our first undertaking is to remind ourselves that we are *not* dealing, in the testing of hypotheses by the inductive-deductive method, with the type of *conclusive* proof that is found in formal logic and mathematics. In the latter kinds of reasoning, we begin with accepted premises, and we see directly, or by a series of obvious steps, how their acceptance necessarily conditions or proves their consequences *if* we adhere to the rules of valid reasoning. Each step in the proof is seen to be an inescapable consequence of what we have already taken for granted. It belongs in a system or order which has a certain structure of its own. If the premises which we have accepted to begin with are true, and our reasoning is valid, then, since we are following a necessary order, our conclusion will be true. But, as we learned in our study of formal logic, the demonstration is no better than the soundness of the original premises, which the mere validity of our reasoning in no way guarantees.

The inductive approach is obliged to be more modest in what it tries to establish. It is looking, not for an obviously necessary connection which can be wholly understood by an immediate inference as soon as it is pointed out (as in each step of a proof in geometry), but for a possibly hidden order among scattered facts by means of the mediation of imagined hypotheses. The problem-situations which it tackles are characteristically those in which we do *not* see the connections which are later found to underlie the sequences of events.

People are ill; or commerce languishes; or forms of taxation bring in unexpectedly large revenues — yet we are unable, without the aid of a theory, to be sure that we understand of what conditions the illnesses or the depression or the increased revenue are the necessary consequences. So we are powerless to do anything, except by accident, to solve our present and future problems. To do the latter by means of thinking, we have to devise some possible systems of logical connections of the *if-then* form: *if* the water-supply is contaminated, *then* the illnesses follow; *if* the milk-supply is pasteurized, *then* the illnesses do not follow; and so on.

The next step is to search for evidence both for and against our hypothesis by observing relevant facts. From a knowledge of selected particulars arranged as parts of a system, we hope to be able to show that our hypothesis holds, both of their interrelationships and of those of other particulars like them. Actually we try, in every way we can think of, to break down the imagined connection. When we are unable to do so, we may speak of *partial* proof of the hypothesis in question, but never of absolute or conclusive proof.

Some prefer not to use the word "proof" in inductive reasoning, but rather to speak of "confirming" or "disconfirming" a hypothesis. Others go even further, and refuse to speak of a hypothesis as having been confirmed by evidence, but only as "not yet disconfirmed." But common speech permits us to say of a lawyer that he has "proved his case" if he has shown a high probability that his contentions are correct, and we may use the same language of the scientist. Remembering always, of course, that scientific method yields only degrees of proof which fall below one hundred per cent, or certainty.

The scientist at best establishes only a high degree of probability that his hypothesis is reliable for certain purposes. This does not mean that his method is not rigorous. On the contrary, a scientist will strain every nerve to increase the probability that the hypothesis which he accepts temporarily is the only one that "fits all the facts." The addition of even a fraction of one per cent to that probability will seem to him to be worth no end of patient labor. But he can never be positive that his analysis of "all the facts" has been wholly adequate or complete, or that he has selected the best hypothesis for his purpose in explaining them.

A scientist doubts systematically everything that goes into his proof. He doubts his facts; he doubts his hypotheses; and he doubts whether they fit together as he thinks they do. He may think that he has established inductively a necessary connection between typhoid fever and a certain bacillus; but he can never be sure that he has observed its presence in every single case of typhoid, or that he has imagined, detected, and eliminated every other variable which could possibly be significant for the occurrence of the disease. Therefore, he cannot prove inductively that the grip of any of his hypotheses upon the facts is absolute; since (1) no human observer is infallible; and (2) no human being's knowledge of all the relevant facts about anything, let alone a command of all their imaginable patternings, is demonstrably complete.

DIRECT AND INDIRECT

Since inductive proof is thus necessarily dependent upon imperfect observation, it is important to recall the distinction between private and public facts, which is closely related to the intimacy or directness of our knowledge. We know that each individual can, if he chooses, have his own private tests of what private facts he will regard as reliable knowledge. There is a sense, then, in which we can speak of "proving something to ourselves" without reference to our fellow knowers. "Is what I am now feeling, or is it not, hunger?" is a question in the form of an hypothesis which we can address to ourselves, and answer without external reference. A busy man may have difficulty in deciding, from memory, whether or not he has had lunch; and may attempt to prove to himself that he has or has not done so, by bringing into consciousness feelings which he associates with the presence or absence of ingested food. All our accounts, or descriptions to ourselves, of our present experiences may be regarded as hypotheses of this directly verifiable sort. We sometimes grope for the right words or symbols to describe an emotional state ("I am provoked . . . no, that's not exactly it . . . I am disappointed . . ." and so on), testing the proposed description against our actual feelings, which are, of course, partly molded by the process. But only a very small part of all our alleged knowledge can be proved by this private method of direct correspondence.

The minute we enter the domain of public knowledge, making claims that we expect other knowers to accept, we find that proof becomes a different matter. Suppose that we say to another person, "I am disappointed . . ." and that person replies, "I know better . . . you are not in the least disappointed, really, you are very much pleased, and you won't admit it, even to yourself." Here we have another person telling us, apparently, that we are not having the experience we claim to be having, but a different one, and offering to prove it! He does this by an indirect method, on the basis of an hypothesis about our state of mind and its causes (bias, prejudice, self-interest, in this instance), which is different from our own, gathering his confirmatory evidence, or proof, from his observation of our behavior in the situation, his knowledge of our past history, and his estimate of our credibility as a witness about our own states of mind. A third party might, on this person's indirect evidence, accept the latter's hypothesis about our behavior as more credible than our own. But since each of these "outsiders" lacks access to our feelings for purposes of direct examination, we may, if we choose, stick stubbornly to our own private version of the matter, which they are powerless to impugn (except to others).

Indirect proof, either that a witness is lying, or telling the truth, about a private state of mind is ordinarily difficult because we are not usually, unless we know the person extremely well, in possession of enough knowledge to frame a good hypothesis about such elusive and unstable materials. It must consist of inferences based upon observations interpreted in terms of the person's past behavior and of our own similar experiences. Did a certain overt act or expression by another person betray "consciousness of guilt," or was it a natural expression of innocence? There are few acts or expressions which are displayed *only* by guilty persons. The ordinary human action is characteristically capable of many interpretations, any one of which *may* be the correct inference.

If we try to solve the problem by asking ourselves, "What would we have done in the circumstances if we had been guilty (or innocent)?" there is still a likelihood of making faulty inferences. For we are not the other person, and the best we can do is to imagine ourselves in his place. This becomes especially awkward when a good citizen is called upon to sit in judgment at the trial of an alleged criminal. For "judgment by imaginative substitution" is not likely to be accurate unless the righteous person is capable of envisaging himself vividly as a criminal. The latter process will hardly be reliable unless it is based on experience, and perhaps not even then. When a long period of time has elapsed between the human action to be interpreted and the actual interpretation, the task becomes even harder. Who will venture to describe and assess, with any pretension to accuracy, the activities of Moses at the court of Egypt, of Nero at the burning of Rome, or of Benedict Arnold in his hour of decision? That is one of the things which lends fascination to historical and biographical reinterpretation: so much of the evidence is permanently inaccessible that it gives leeway to each and every interpreter.

Besides the direct proof that rests upon our own inner convictions about the reliability of our own immediate judgments, then, there are many sorts of indirect proof of varying degrees of remoteness. One vast category of indirect proof embraces the simple testimony of others concerning their own observations, always imperfectly expressed in language and always tainted with the possibility of erroneous inferences. Yet this material is relatively accessible, as compared with another range of experience which is important for the social studies, namely, other persons' inner states of mind.

The aim of physical science, so largely realized in the modern age, is to prepare the way for a direct observation of external matters of fact by dint of rigorous preliminary theorizing. The technique of proof in such instances is the indirect utilization of the theories and testimonies of others in order to set the stage for direct observations which can be repeated at will by practiced observers under controlled conditions, yielding approximate coincidence judgments. Billiard balls can be set in motion over and over again under almost identical conditions under the eyes of innumerable observers, until virtually all doubt in practice about the most probable explanation of their behavior has been removed. Electrons, it may be argued, are just as inaccessible to direct observation as human thoughts. But there are ways of bringing electron behavior into the realm of the directly observable with a statistical regularity and repetitiousness that, so far, exceeds anything which has been accomplished in the realm of human psychology.

As soon as we reach the organic level and beyond, the conditions which we attempt to repeat are only "somewhat similar"; and the ways in which they are different are, unfortunately, very hard to detect. No one ventures to repeat experiments endlessly with the same set of laboratory animals, unless animal learning (that is, growth or change) is being studied. The animals might seem to the outward observer to be about the same from week to week, bearing no external marks of the added experiences which have been condensed in their nervous systems. But we shall be in grave danger of deceiving ourselves if we insist upon applying the mechanical pattern of proof, with its emphasis upon the repeatability of ultimately direct observations, in these areas where it must necessarily lose its grip.

2. Inductive Proof Under Optimum Conditions

With the distinctions between conclusive and partial proof, as well as direct and indirect, in mind, we may undertake the difficult task of establishing the reliability of a given explanatory hypothesis. Why should one hypothesis be preferred to its rivals? When can we say that we are entitled to consider any particular suggested solution as supported by evidence? Two things we know in advance about inductive proof: it will not be absolute, but *partial*; and it is likely to consist largely of *indirect* inferences rather than of direct observations. Sometimes, in order to decide between two hypotheses, we may be fortunate enough to make what Francis Bacon called a "crucial experiment." But the word "crucial" is misleading, since to knock out or disconfirm one or more of the hypotheses is by no means a proof or confirmation of the remaining one, unless we know that only two alternatives are possible. We can seldom be sure of this.

Since ordinarily we cannot claim to have examined and analyzed properly all the possibly relevant evidence in the case, the best we can hope to do is to show that our theory is highly probable on the basis of publicly verifiable tests. The last step in our proof will be a direct observation which can be duplicated by any normal observer, but it will have significance, as proof, only because of a long chain of indirect inferences. In the social studies, this sort of indirect-direct proof is especially vulnerable because of our normal inability to restage the decisive observation at will under sufficiently similar circumstances.

Instead of giving way to discouragement and defeatism over the immense complexities of proof in the social studies, however, it will be better to center our attention first upon the easier problems of proof in the physical sciences, where the subject matter is such that processes are roughly controllable, repeatable, and sometimes reversible, and where the mechanical pattern yields maximum predictability. If we can see clearly what can and what cannot be accomplished by the use of that pattern under the most favorable conditions, we may then observe how its rigor is relaxed when inquirers attempt to apply it to the more elusive materials of the social studies, and what other methods may be needed to supplement or to replace it.

SINGLE-VARIABLE HYPOTHESES IN "CLOSED" SYSTEMS

To return, then, to the relative simplicity of our billiard ball example — we saw that causal analysis on that large-scale physical level proceeded by the artificial isolation of the table and its immediate surroundings in the midst of a vast and changing universe treated as constant, followed by the further isolation and abstraction of certain selected factors or variables within the now "closed" physical system of table-cue-ball, such as the weight of the cue and ball, their velocities, and so on. To predict the course of the ball, and thus to account for it simultaneously, the student of ballistics frames his explanatory hypothesis by trying to select and measure the determining conditions indispensable to the particular behavior in which he is interested — in this instance, its movement from a spot on the center of the table to a position touching the rail near a certain chalk mark. What he is seeking to establish is a functional correlation between certain measurable physical conditions within a closed system, *only one of which* is altered, and the ball's subsequent behavior relative to certain fixed points within the system. If he succeeds, he will then be able to predict the result, with an increasing accuracy by successive approximations, as often as he can duplicate the original conditions.

Under ideal conditions, from the point of view of proof, the investigator will be able to point to a single variable as "the cause C" of "the effect E"; and to show that they are invariably connected and reciprocal: whenever C is present, E follows; and whenever E is observed, C will be found to have been present. But note that neither C nor E comes plainly marked or already analyzed. The inquirer must decide what interests him, and frame his causal hypothesis accordingly, splitting the continuous natural process which he has selected into two sections: the antecedent conditions or possible causes, and the consequent situation or effect. Unless this clarifying of both the terms and the causal pattern believed to connect them has been well done, then the drawing of a reliable conclusion will be most unlikely. For it is already apparent that testing involves a greater and greater refinement of the factors to be tested. It is not enough to sharpen our conception of the cause; we must also be as precise as possible about the effect, and about the linkage between them.

The entire process of induction is one of isolation and elimination. We start with the whole universe to choose from, any aspect of which, for all we know in advance, *may* be connected with the effect. By isolating our field of observation and limiting it to the least that must be included for our purpose, as in the billiard ball illustration, we rule out many conditions of the ball's behavior as either too remote or "relatively constant." If the floor of the billiard room should be suddenly tilted, the whole temporarily isolated system of table-cue-ball would be thrown into disorder; but we judge from experience that, except in earthquake centers, the chance that anything of the sort will happen is so small that the stability of the floor may be taken for granted, like the gravitational pull of the sun. We assume that, in order to achieve a causal explanation of the movement of the ball on the table, it will not be necessary to go outside the boundaries of our "closed" system. The scope of that system will be closely related to our choice of certain levels of explanation as probably adequate for our purpose. Ordinarily we specify in advance what kind of explanation we are demanding. We do not expect a lawyer to give us a medical explanation, or a physicist to talk in terms of psychology. The student of ballistics asks only for a functional correlation of physical variables on the abstract billiard table; whereas a student of "form" in tournament play would demand an explanatory hypothesis embracing both table and player and influences on both, if he should inquire: "How did Mr. Hoppe come to miss that easy shot tonight?"

The actual testing of hypotheses proceeds largely by the elimination of irrelevancies, which is a continuation of the clarifying process. The more levels that are embracd in our demand for an explanation, the more difficult it will be to "close off" our system. In the billiard ball illustration, the ballistics student has little difficulty in isolating his physical large-scale system centering about the ball on the table by declaring all but a few of the surrounding conditions irrelevant. It does not matter, for his purpose, what the color of the cue used happens to be, or what time of day it is, or how far the table is above sea level. Thanks to the relative simplicity of his subject matter, he may continue his analysis on the mechanical pattern in either of two ways, depending upon whether he is mainly interested in the prediction of the future or in the explanation of the past. He may define his effect, let us say, as "the movement of the ball from the center spot to the chalk mark over the surface of the table by the shortest possible route," and then set up several hypotheses to account for it, comprising a list of the supposedly relevant conditions, such as — it could have come about through a certain physical impact applied to the ball by the cue at a certain angle; or, it could have happened by means of a shove applied to the end of the table; and so on. Or the student might begin at the other end of the process with an imagined cause, such as the application of a certain force, and then try to calculate its probable effect.

But, no matter how he approaches the question of the behavior of the ball, he will be seeking, if possible, to fix upon a single independent factor or variable in each section of the process, which, if given a determinate value, will be found invariably to be linked with a determinate value of the other variable, the effect, *all other relevant conditions within the system remaining the same.* He cannot possibly do this by inspecting the cue and the ball, because there is no visible necessary connection between the behaviors of the two. But if he knew in advance that only five independent and distinguishable conditions were relevant to the movement of the ball, and he could eliminate four of them by showing that separate hypotheses connecting each of them with the effect entail consequences which are inconsistent with the facts, he would be justified in inferring that the four were *not* necessarily connected with the effect. But if, after trying every known method of elimination, he could not get rid of the fifth, he might also be warranted in inferring that the latter (or some part of it) was causally related to the effect. If he did succeed in eliminating the fifth, he would be forced to go back and attempt to reconstruct his analysis in such a way that it would include additional new factors, one of which might turn out to be the actual cause. It should be apparent that the whole process of proof by elimination depends upon including the "guilty" causal factor in one's list of "suspects" — the hypotheses which are to be subjected to testing.

3. Mill's Methods of Elimination

Granted that we are dealing with the sort of subject matter which permits a clear analysis of causes and effects into alternative relevant factors that are easily controllable, the most promising methods of proof are not positive but negative — the methods of elimination. They rest upon the common-sense proposition that if you want to find out whether two distinguishable things are invariably connected, the thing to do is to try your best to separate them. If C is followed by E, we cannot safely infer that they *are* causally related; but if E is observed *without* the previous presence of C, under certain conditions it is safe to infer that C and E are *not* causally related. Similarly, if we can produce instances of C which are not followed by E, we may infer the same lack of causal relationship. But if we cannot possibly separate C and E, either by producing the effect in the absence of the supposed cause, or by exhibiting an instance of the supposed cause without the effect, then the possibility that they are causally related still remains open. From our inability to eliminate, however, we cannot rule out the possibility that both C and E are effects of other causes, just as night and day, which cannot be separated, are related, not as cause and effect, but as parallel effects of the operations of the solar system. No amount of elimination proves that further refinement of analysis is impossible, as scientists have learned to their sorrow time and time again.

The man who formulated the classic methods of testing causal hypotheses of the single-variable, closed-system type was the English Utilitarian philosopher John Stuart Mill (1806–73), who acknowledged his indebtedness to the pioneer work on induction which had been done by Francis Bacon more than two centuries earlier, and to the more recent *Discourse* of Sir John Herschel in 1830. We now see that Mill expected too much from, and claimed too much for, his five famous Methods of Experimental Inquiry: Agreement, Difference, Joint Agreement and Difference, Concomitant Variations, and Residues, regarding them as ways of positive demonstration similar to deduction, rather than as indirect means of strengthening inductive conclusions by excluding irrelevant factors. This chapter will consider only the first three of Mill's methods, which are those of elimination, leaving the others to be treated in Chapter 11.

The first two methods of elimination (the third is simply a combined use of Agreement and Difference) have a single end in view, in Mill's own words — "the successive exclusion of the various circumstances which are found to accompany a phenomenon in a given instance, in order to ascertain what are those among them which can be absent consistently with the existence of the phenomenon."[1] They are not to be thought of as completely distinct or wholly alternative techniques, but rather as forming a team, since nearly all causal inquiries on the mechanical or semi-mechanical model involve the use of one or both of them. They differ principally in direction and point of attack: Agreement looks toward instances of the *effect*, stripping away irrelevancies from it

[1] John Stuart Mill, *System of Logic*, bk. III, chap. VIII, p. 3.

and thus defining it more accurately; while Difference whittles away irrelevancies from the alleged cause, thus giving it greater precision. Yet Agreement can also be used negatively to rule out some factors as *not* being necessary conditions of the effect; and Difference can point to some elements in the effect to which the cause is *not* necessary.

Both methods start from the supposition that the problem to be solved is a relatively simple one, in that the situation is completely analyzable into a small number of alternative hypotheses about the cause (CH's) which include all the relevant conditions of the specific effect E, also properly analyzed. If E, for instance, is the movment of the billiard ball over a certain path, then CH_1 might be the impact of the cue, CH_2 the shoving of the table, CH_3 the breeze across the surface; and so on. Each must be a single independent variable acting without the interference of others. *The use of the methods of elimination presupposes that this analysis has been properly performed before they are applied. The methods themselves in no way guarantee that it has been.* The actual cause of E may have been CH_4, the touch of someone's sleeve, which has not been included in our original alternatives, and which, therefore, can hardly be tracked down by elimination until it is included. We are all continually discovering that "there are more things in heaven, Horatio, than are dreamt of . . ." in our hypotheses. But we may console ourselves with the thought that if we have omitted something from our advance calculations, so, at some time or other, has everyone else who has ever lived.

Assuming that we have succeeded in including all the relevant CH's, then — Either CH_1 (our first causal hypothesis to be tested), or CH_2, or CH_3, or CH_4 — up to any number of CH's which are believed to comprise all the relevant conditions of the effect — *may* be the cause of E (the effect under investigation). Now any given CH, let us say CH_1, can be eliminated as the cause of E, provided we are able to do either one of two things: (1) point out or produce an instance where CH_1 is present, and E is absent; or (2) an instance in which E is present whether or not CH_1 is present. If we have a finite number of CH's to begin with, then their successive elimination may leave only a single one which cannot be dismissed. That remaining CH, especially in case we are unable to eliminate it by the thoroughgoing application of any method that is known to us, may be regarded as the probable cause, or as including the cause, of E, *provided that all the relevant factors were included and properly analyzed in the first place.* Since we can never be absolutely sure that all the above provisions have been complied with, proof by elimination will be only partial at best; and, should any of them have been neglected, it may be worth very little.

4. The Method of Agreement

Suppose that we wish to discover and to establish by proof the cause of the freezing of water into ice. Our first move would be to observe a number of instances of the effect: water frozen into ice in all sorts of localities and containers. We should probably notice that wherever we found that water was undergoing the phase-change from liquid to solid known as freezing, its immediate environment was cold. Thus we might frame the crude hypothesis: "The freezing of water into ice is caused by a certain 'amount' of cold." Until some such device as the thermometer was invented, it would be difficult to refine the causal factor by stating it as "less than 32 degrees Fahrenheit of heat." Assuming that we wish to test this revised hypothesis, we should proceed by inquiring whether or not the factor CH_1 (less than 32° F.) was invariably present in all instances of E (the freezing of water into ice), no matter how much they might differ in other respects.

POSITIVE USE OF AGREEMENT

In his statement of the canon (or rule) of the Method of Agreement, however, Mill went much further than that, namely:

> If two or more instances of the phenomenon under investigation have only one circumstance in common, the circumstance in which alone all the instances agree is the cause (or effect) of the given phenomenon.[2]

This may be symbolized by the use of $abcCH_1$ to represent the causal phase of the continuous act of freezing, with a standing for barometric air pressure below thirty inches, b for humidity below fifty per cent, c for normal daylight present, d for a field of electrical energy, and so on; with CH_1 for a temperature of less than 32° F. The factors, a, b, c, and d, of which there might be any number, are other circumstances that are possibly relevant to the production of E, or the freezing. Of the symbols on the right hand, E stands for the phase of the process in which we are particularly interested at the moment, the freezing; while x, y, and z represent other sequential aspects such as changes of color, volume, smell, and so on, in which we are not interested.

First instance (ice in puddle) $abcCH_1 \ldots xyE$
Second instance (ice in electric icebox) $abdCH_1 \ldots yzE$
Third instance (ice on airplane wing) $cdeCH_1 \ldots xzE$
and so on for an indefinite number of instances.[3]

Here we have an apparent instance of the applicability of Mill's canon of Agreement, namely, three instances of the "same" effect, ice, agreeing in only one respect, the presence of CH_1. All the rest of the possibly relevant circumstances: a, b, c, and d, each of which is entitled to consideration as a CH or

---

[2] *Idem*, p. 280.
[3] The three or more instances might have been any combination of initial circumstances, such as

$$abcCH_1 \ldots uvE$$
$$defCH_1 \ldots wxE$$
$$ghiCH_1 \ldots yzE$$

just so long as CH_1, *and no other relevant causal factor*, was common to all the examined instances of E. The reader should be on his guard against the "specious simplicity" of all letter formulas.

hypothetical cause of the freezing, has failed to live up to the requirements of the causal relationship, since each one of them can be seen to be present in some instances and absent in others. Now, unless some unobserved factor upon which we have not reckoned is subsequently discovered to have been present also in all our cases, it is highly probable that CH_1 (or some part of it) is the cause of E in these instances.

But we have not proved the causal connection, since it is almost impossible in practice to find even two instances of a like effect, such as the freezing of ice, which actually differ in all the possibly relevant respects *save one*. Still less have we proved, by examining a few somewhat differing instances, that a temperature of less than 32° F. is the cause of the freezing of water in every one of the billions of instances of the formation of ice. The positive use of the Method of Agreement is, therefore, little more than a scouting device, a useful technique of preliminary reconnaissance. It is a way of comparing differing instances of the effect to see whether a suspected factor is universally present, as it must be, if it is the cause.

NEGATIVE USE OF AGREEMENT

If, in the course of our examination of differing instances of the effect, we should come across a case of E occurring in the absence of CH_1, namely,

Fourth instance (ice in hot oven) *efg. . . .stE*,

then the Method of Agreement would operate negatively to exclude CH_1 as the cause of E. That follows by deduction from that part of the definition of cause which requires it to be an *invariable* antecedent of the effect. The rule for the negative use of Agreement is thus: *Nothing can be the cause of a phenomenon which is absent when it is present.* Or, stated differently, whatever is not a common circumstance of all the instances of a phenomenon cannot be their cause. Any factor in which two or more instances of an effect do *not* agree may be eliminated as causally irrelevant.

Like the positive use of the same method, negative Agreement is largely a method of preliminary observation rather than of deliberate experiment. In its broad survey of differing instances of the effect, while positive Agreement directs our attention to defining the effect and its common characteristics, negative Agreement begins the task of clearing away non-essential factors from the supposed cause by pointing to examples of the effect in which they are absent. Negative Agreement is particularly effective in excluding irrelevancies from the causes of widespread qualitative effects, where there are many scattered instances with varying circumstances, such as insect pests, crop failures, epidemics, crime waves, or concerted sabotage. It is often the only method that can be used, since there are many inquiries in which we find ourselves unable to alter the conditions at will. But where we are fortunate enough to be in a position to manipulate the circumstances, a subtler method of elimination is employed.

5. The Method of Difference

For many centuries men groped for the causes of things by the unconscious use of rudimentary forms of the Method of Agreement. They tried, in other words, to find a common circumstance in differing instances of the effect. As a result, they made innumerable errors in the form of rash and superficial judgments. Even when they hit upon the correct common factor associated with the presence of the effect, it was usually much too broad and ill-defined. A great advance in human thinking was made possible when a few bold individuals forsook this passive and hit-or-miss observation of accomplished facts for that active and systematic interference in the course of events which we call *experiment*. An experimenter is an observer who deliberately controls his conditions and manipulates them in order to record the result, anticipating, as it were, a possible development without waiting around for it to happen haphazardly. He snatches the initiative from Nature; and even puts the latter to the torture to extract her secrets, as Francis Bacon suggesed.

Everyone with the slightest acquaintance with modern laboratory science knows that its principal slogan is: "Vary one thing at a time." Or, as W. S. Jevons puts it: "The great method of experiment consists in removing, one at a time, each of those conditions which may be imagined to have an influence on the result."[4] He implies the other essential requirement of what Mill formulated as the Method of Difference, namely, that all other conditions must remain the same. Mill's canon for the Method of Difference is:

> If an instance in which the phenomenon under investigation occurs, and an instance in which it does not occur, have every circumstance in common save one, that one occurring only in the former; the circumstance in which alone the two instances differ is the effect, or the cause, or an indispensable part of the cause, of the phenomenon.

As in the use of the Method of Agreement, the terms "circumstance" and "phenomenon" refer to qualitative states or "differences in kind" rather than to mere quantitative variations or "differences in degree." It should also be borne in mind that both causes and effects may be "absences of" as well as "presences of" — the lack of a certain vitamin may cause scurvy, while the presence of a certain poison may cause death, or absence of life.

POSITIVE USE OF DIFFERENCE

Using the symbols of the previous example, the freezing of ice, the Method of Difference sets up two identical instances, and then alters (or notices the discrepancy in) *one factor only*, with a corresponding difference in the effect, thus —

First instance: klm . . . . . . qr (temp. above 32° . . . . no ice in beaker X)
Second instance: $klmCH_1$ . . . . . . qrE (temp. below 32° . . . . ice in beaker Y)

4 *The Principles of Science* (London, 1883), p. 417.

Here k, l, and m are used to indicate the contrived circumstances which the laboratory experimenter has arranged and controlled, and which may be relevant to the freezing or non-freezing of the water: k being the kind of glass of which the beakers are composed, l being the amount of the water, and m being the distance above sea level. The symbols q and r stand for the characteristics of the two samples which emerge unchanged regardless of the presence or absence of the effect, such as chemical composition and weight. What we have done is to introduce (or to observe the presence of) a single difference, the hypothetical causal factor CH_1, temperature below 32° F., with the result that a corresponding difference occurs (or is observed to have occurred) in the presence (or absence) of the effect.

Where the time element is unimportant, as in this example, it makes no appreciable difference in the application of the formula whether the two identical beakers X and Y are used simultaneously; or one beaker X at a given moment, temperature above 32° F., and the same beaker X filled with the same amount of H_2O a few minutes later, temperature below 32° F. Note, however, that when we come to deal with organisms, the time element may become extremely important, possibly to the extent of vitiating the comparison between the two successive states of the "same" living thing.

Our daily lives and the whole history of science are dotted with examples of the use of the Method of Difference, such as these: To test the cause of the rusting of iron, place two identical bright pieces, one in a vacuum, the other in a tube successively with various gases; to ascertain the cause of the deposition of dew, expose two identical metal plates at the same temperature, one being brightly polished, the other not, in the presence of moist air; or to prove the protective value of paint on a barn, apply paint to only one of two adjacent and identical sections of wall. In all these cases, what we do is "make a difference to see whether it will make a difference" in the result. Let us suppose that it does. Then we have the positive use of the method: when CH_1 is present, E is present; when CH_1 is absent, E is absent; therefore, CH_1 (or some part of it) may be causally related to E. The linkage will seem highly probable if we find that not only do we get rid of E when we remove CH_1, but also that if we add CH_1 to a given klm situation, we get, not qr, but qrE. We can say that if CH_1 is truly the single-factor cause of E, then the Method of Difference ought to give us just that positive result. But does the positive result, when it is obtained, prove that CH_1 (or some part of it) is the cause of E? Not unless we have first established (1) that all relevant factors have been considered; and (2) that our two instances differ in only the one respect.

NEGATIVE USE OF DIFFERENCE

The real probative force of the Method of Difference, like that of the Method of Agreement, is negative and eliminatory rather than positive. This may be shown in two ways:

(1) Suppose, as above, that varying our CH_1 factor gives a positive result — making a single difference does make a difference. Then it follows from our definition of cause as invariable antecedent that all the

factors *which remained the same* in our two instances are irrelevant to the effect and can be eliminated. A factor which is present whether or not the effect follows cannot be invariably related to it. The rule for this negative use of Difference is thus: *Nothing can be the cause of a phenomenon in the presence of which it fails to occur.* For example, the factor k in our illustration was the kind of glass of which the beakers X and Y were composed (or beaker X at one time, and at a later time). Since in the first instance the kind of glass was not accompanied by the freezing of ice, while in the second instance it was, then k cannot possibly be the cause of the freezing.

(2) Suppose, on the other hand, that making a difference fails to make any difference, so that the formula becomes *either*

First instance: klm......qr (temp. above 32° F...no ice in beaker X)
Second instance: $klmCH_1$...qr (temp. below 32° F...no ice in beaker Y)
or
First instance: klm......qrE (temp. above 32° F...ice in beaker X)
Second instance: $klmCH_1$...qrE (temp. below 32° F...ice in beaker Y).

Then we can eliminate CH as the cause by the rule already given for the negative use of Agreement: *Nothing can be the cause of a phenomenon which is absent when it is present.*

It is sometimes difficult to tell whether a given elimination has been carried out by Negative Agreement or Negative Difference. The essential principle, that of trying to divorce the alleged cause from the effect, is the same in both methods. What differs is the setting and the approach. Whether an example is to be classified under Agreement or Difference does not depend upon the final outcome of the eliminatory process, but rather upon the way in which it is achieved. One must go back to the starting point to see which avenue of approach was utilized. The two methods can be kept distinct if one remembers that:

The Method of Agreement always seeks a number of differing instances of the effect, hoping to find that they agree in one antecedent condition only. It pays no attention to instances in which the effect is absent. It takes notice of instances where the supposed cause is absent only when used negatively.

The Method of Difference always seeks to find or to contrive two instances, one with the effect and one without, but otherwise identical except for the presence or absence of one antecedent condition, the suspected causal factor.

6. The Joint Method

Mill formulated a canon for what he called the Joint Method of Agreement and Difference, or the Double Method of Agreement. The second name is

far less misleading than the first, since the method is not truly a use of
Difference at all. It is, in fact, so cumbersome, rare, and generally ineffective
that it need be noted only in passing.

> *If two or more instances in which the phenomenon occurs have only
> one circumstance in common, while two or more instances in which it
> does not occur have nothing in common save the absence of that circum-
> stance, the circumstances in which alone the two sets of instances differ
> is the effect, or the cause, or an indispensable part of the cause, of the
> phenomenon.*

He intended this group-comparison method[5] to be used when two instances
differing in only one respect could not be found or easily contrived. If a number of very ancient manuscripts found in dry climates are legible, while those
found in damp climates are not, then we may infer a possible causal connection between dryness and legibility without having to wait for five hundred
or a thousand years to conduct an experiment. Thus:

First set	$abCH_1 \ldots opE$	(Ms. found in Egypt, dry, legible)
	$cdCH_1 \ldots qrE$	(Ms. found in Greece, dry, legible)
	$efCH_1 \ldots stE$	(Ms. found in Tibet, dry, legible)
Second set	$gh \ldots uv$	(Ms. found in Ireland, damp, illegible)
	$ij \ldots wx$	(Ms. found in Norway, damp, illegible)
	$kl \ldots yz$	(Ms. found in England, damp, illegible)

What we have here is not strictly the joint use of Agreement and Difference,
since there are no two instances which differ *only* in a single respect; but rather
an extension of the Method of Agreement to include the observation of negative as well as positive instances. Agreement ordinarily assures us, when it
works positively, that CH_1 is present in every observed case of E. The so-
called Joint Method merely adds that it is also true in every observed instance
where E is absent, CH_1 is likewise absent. That is what we should expect to
find if the two are causally related. But it adds scant proof of that relationship, since it merely shows that in the observed negative instances there is no
case of "presence of CH_1 — absence of E," and no case of "absence of CH_1 —
presence of E."

7. Complementary Use of Agreement and Difference

It is important not to confuse the so-called Joint Method with the sort of
team play between the methods of Agreement and Difference which charac-

---

[5] Care must be taken not to confuse the Joint Method with the "control group"
frequently used in laboratory experiments. A control group consists of a set of instances *alike* in all essential respects (therefore, virtually equivalent to a single instance), which is compared, by the Method of Difference, with another set of instances
exactly similar to the first set except in one respect.

terizes most of our actual testing of hypotheses. The very fact that we frame an hypothesis in the first place indicates that we think that we have glimpsed an agreement. Our first move is usually to collect instances of the effect which are accompanied by the suspected cause. If the collected instances are alike in many respects, we shall not feel at all sure that the particular likeness that we have selected in our hypothesis is the cause we are looking for; whereas if they happen to be different in many respects (perhaps in every respect save one, though that is rare) we are able at once to eliminate the differences as irrelevant.

Having thus narrowed down the field by this preliminary reconnaissance (positive Agreement), we may then proceed to the more serious business of testing our hypothesis by attempted elimination in several ways, all of them designed to break it down if possible by showing that the alleged cause and the effect are not invariably and indispensably related. Right here lies an important difference between the spirit of the scientific inquirer and that of the mere justifier of a theory. The true scientist goes out of his way to make every effort to discover facts which will demolish his tentative hypothesis; while the defender of a theory looks only for the facts which will support it. The scientist subjects his hypothesis systematically to two main sorts of attack which it must survive if it is not to be discarded: (1) the attempt to produce an instance of the effect without the alleged cause: this may be done by finding one, negative Agreement, or by taking away the cause without disturbing the effect, negative Difference (use 1 above); and (2) the attempt to produce an instance of the alleged cause without the effect: this may be done by introducing the alleged cause as the sole difference without bringing about the effect, negative Difference (use 2 above).

Whether our approach will take the form of the Method of Agreement or of the Method of Difference depends chiefly upon the character of the subject matter. If we can separate and control all the relevant conditions, we shall usually proceed at once to set up an experiment using Difference. But if we cannot manage to find (or to devise) two identical instances (save for a single crucial difference), or if we do not want to, being reluctant, for example, to expose a human being to a possibly fatal germ disease, then we shall be obliged to rely, either upon the second-best version of Difference known as Concomitant Variations to be discussed in the next chapter, or upon negative Agreement, examining more and more instances of the effect to see whether we can find one in which the alleged cause is absent. Obviously the two methods are not antagonistic but complementary. Both should be employed to the fullest extent wherever the nature of the subject matter permits them to be effective.

8. Difficulties in Eliminating by Mill's Methods

Throughout our discussion of the methods, it has been assumed that we have been dealing with an hypothesis under ideal conditions from the point of view of proof. Yet, even where the causes and effects are all on one level, and easily isolable within closed systems, the task of applying the canons can be an extremely difficult one. With each departure from the optimum conditions, the essential preliminary judgments of relevance become more dubious, troubles of all sorts increase, and our alleged proofs become less and less impressive.

For one thing, the temper of the whole enterprise is negative rather than positive. We are far safer in inferring the absence of causal conditions than their presence. We seem to be obliged to find out what causes are, chiefly by demonstrating what they probably are not. Those factors which survive our attempts to eliminate them may be said to possess the minimum qualifications as causes of effects. We shall have occasion, in the following section and in Chapter 12, to inquire whether, in our endeavors to eliminate, we are working against a genuinely unlimited variety in the nature of things, or whether we are justified in assuming that it is limited.

Certainly if the methods of elimination are to be used with any ease and success, we must be able to isolate, in the maze of processes going on about us, all the relevant, independent, single variables that we hope to link up in pairs as causes and effects. Some of the interacting processes which we wish to analyze are of such a nature that isolation is hard to manage, with the result that Mill's methods do not satisfactorily apply. Among these obstacles are:

(1) *Reciprocity of causes and effects.* When two processes go on at the same time, rather than in succession, they may turn out to be related reciprocally — each being both the cause and the effect of the other. An example of this is the seal-oil lamp of the Eskimo, which consists of a wick in a stone trough containing seal blubber. The burning wick melts the blubber; and the melting enables the wick to burn. Reciprocal causes and effects complicate the argument over mass education as the best means of enriching an underdeveloped country. Are the rich countries wealthy because they are literate, or are they literate because they are wealthy? Or both?

(2) *Possibility of a hidden third factor.* Another danger, when two processes are coextensive rather than successive, is that their invariable association may be taken for a cause-effect relationship when actually both are effects of a hidden third cause. We might discover, for instance, that scrambled teletype reception was invariably associated with displays of the aurora borealis, or northern lights, and conclude by the Method of Agreement that the aurora was the cause of the scrambling; when in fact both the aurora and the scrambling are effects of a third process: electrical disturbances on the sun's surface known as sun-spot storms.

(3) *Counteracting causes.* Mill's methods are stated in terms of actual events; but it is a mistake to limit our analysis of possible causes to changes that have already taken place, ignoring our knowledge of tendencies to change which may be temporarily held in abeyance by "counteracting causes." That is, a man who had never seen dynamite explode would be foolish to toss it around like a two-year-old just because he had never actually experienced its explosive potentialities. Causes are invariable and indispensable antecedents of effects *in the absence of factors which prevent their operation.* Pulling the trigger of a loaded revolver is no less the usual cause of an explosion because

sometimes a safety catch prevents it; nor is a lethal dose of poison unrelated to death because it does not prove fatal in the presence of an antidote. Human flight is an achievement in counteracting gravity. The latter is just as essential to the phenomenon of flight, as we know it, as the whirling of the plane's propellor. To take away the counteracting impediment, in some instances, is to release the actual cause; but the Method of Difference is likely to center our attention upon what apparently made the difference — the absence of the counteracting cause, rather than upon the presence of the cause that had, up to that moment, been inoperative because it had been counteracted.

(4) *Catalytic causes.* A somewhat similar error occurs when a catalyst is taken for a full-fledged cause. As every student of chemistry knows, there are not only conditions which obstruct reactions, but those which forward them. Faraday, for example, found that the combination of hydrogen and oxygen was inhibited by the presence of even minute quantities of carbon monoxide, carbon disulphide, sulphuretted hydrogen, and hydrochloric acid; but that, in the presence of a clean platinum plate, totally unaffected by the process, it was accelerated to the point of explosion. Such substances, whose presence is necessary to the production of the effect, but which take no active part in it, are known in chemistry as *catalysts* or "looseners." Various metaphors have been used to describe their accelerating function, such as "spark plugs" and "lubricants," but C. N. Hinshelwood prefers to liken them to "by-pass roads with easier gradients." Where such catalytic causes are present, it is obvious that, although they cannot be eliminated without modifying the effect, they do not stand upon the same plane as the operative causes which they serve only to liberate or assist.

(5) *Composition of causes.* Two or more causal factors may be separable, and no one of them alone sufficient for the production of the effect, yet when they are combined in a certain way, the effect may appear. Charcoal, saltpeter, and sulphur taken singly and exposed to a spark yield no explosion; but grind them up in certain proportions, add a spark, and the mixture called gunpowder explodes. A loose or broken wire will keep a radio from functioning, but one could hardly say that a whole or connected wire was the cause of proper reception. A plant cannot grow without such essentials as food, light, heat, each one of which is an indispensable condition of its growth, as can be shown by the Method of Difference. Yet no one of them alone is a sufficient cause of growth. Failure to realize that a cause may be a nexus or complex arranged in a more or less definite pattern often leads to pointless controversies among those who insist upon emphasizing only one of the several factors. In the treatment of wounds, it is necessary to take three sorts of measures: the surgical asepsis which excludes organisms from the wound as far as possible, the antisepsis which kills any which may have entered, and the internal resistance of the body's cells to infection. Yet a partisan of any one of the three methods is likely to give the impression that it alone was responsible for the patient's recovery.

But Composition of Causes, as this difficulty is known, does not prevent Mill's methods of elimination from isolating the set of causes which must co-operate. It should, however, put us on our guard once more against the supposition that whatever can be isolated is therefore a single element incapable of further analysis into many factors which may have varying shares in the production of the effect. Since the whole tenor of the methods is to find out, if possible, what more and more carefully refined variables can accomplish singly, composite causes are frequently overlooked.

(6) *Plurality of causes, or lumping of effects.* Can the same effect have more than one cause or "assemblage of conditions"? Mill believed that it could; and supposed that elimination by the Method of Agreement was thereby fatally impeded. "Many causes," he wrote, "may produce mechanical motion; many causes may produce some kinds of sensations; many causes may produce death. A given effect may really be produced by a certain cause, and yet be perfectly capable of being produced without it."[6] If this were strictly true, the Method of Difference would also be useless, since the assumption that a specific effect can have but one cause is the very backbone of elimination.

It will be found on closer examination, however, that most of the common examples of Plurality of Causes are merely instances of disproportionate refinement in our analysis of causes as compared with effects. We tend, for convenience' sake, to group such effects as automobile accidents, college failures, and persons in normal health under single labels which conceal their innumerable individual differences. Each effect should, strictly speaking, stand by itself as a particular change with its single or composite cause. It is just our penchant for causal generalization which makes us lump similar effects together under some such abstraction as suicide or bankruptcy. Then we proceed to seek a single cause for our lumped effects, and we discover an apparent plurality of causes. If we carried our analysis of the effects to the same pitch of refinement as that of the causes, the difficulty would disappear. What the cause is, of a carefully analyzed effect, may be extremely hard to discover, but not because that specific effect may have a number of specific causes which are genuinely alternative. The history of science, however, is dotted with misleading experiments, a large number of which have been assembled by Professor Wilder D. Bancroft of Cornell University; and there is every reason for caution in accepting the results of any known method of proof, no matter what the reputation of the experimenter.[7]

9. Agreement and Difference in the Social Studies

When we leave the sphere of gross physical "closed" systems with independent single variables, we find that each of the six difficulties in using Mill's methods of elimination increases tremendously. If we can grasp the fundamental reasons why that is so, we shall be well on our way to an understanding of the obstacles to the use of laboratory experiment in the social studies. To find out what is relevant is largely a matter of getting rid of the

---

[6] John Stuart Mill, *op. cit.*, p. 505.

[7] Wilder D. Bancroft, "The Misleading Experiment," *The Rice Institute Pamphlet*, vol. XV (1928), pp. 224–85.

irrelevant. Success in the latter enterprise hinges upon a delicate balancing, in our world, of partial order or uniformity, on the one hand, and partial diversity on the other. Large-scale physical phenomena are just uniform enough, *and* just diverse enough, to enable us to get down to a few manageable, stable factors which we can isolate one by one. Where that is possible, the methods of elimination serve us well.

In a wholly chaotic or completely disorderly world, there would be no point in trying to eliminate; and in a wholly orderly world, of which we knew the formula in advance, there would be no need to — we should simply proceed to deduce the answers to all our questions. Any problem-situation in the realm of human behavior is one which, compared to the billiard ball example, is chaotic and disorderly. But it is not *wholly* so. There are, apparently, some limits to the diversity. Yet we must expect elimination to work badly wherever the diversity is great, as compared to the amount of the uniformity or order; and wherever the order itself becomes complex, displaying an excess of internal variety.

DIVERSITY OF INSTANCES — INDIVIDUAL DIFFERENCES

The sciences of man abound in individual differences. Each organism, even on the biological level, differs slightly from every other organism; and on the levels of consciousness and culture, the differences quickly multiply into the millions and billions. If no two snowflake crystals are exactly alike, although all are hexagonal, how much greater are the differences in entities as complex as men! It is conceivable that we might arrive at a level where no two individuals were alike in *any* single respect. If that were true of human beings, no hypothesis connecting them could ever be tested by the methods of elimination, since both Agreement and Difference call for at least two instances which are alike in at least one respect. As Mill remarked, in all inductive reasoning we assume "that there are such things in nature as parallel cases."

The remark is frequently made that each historical event is unique, that nothing *just* like it ever happened before. But we do not say: "Nothing *anything* like it ever happened before." Even the most extraordinary happenings have some characteristics in common with other events. If that were not so, we should be powerless, not only to test any hypothesis about such an event, but also to use any intelligible language to describe it. By claiming that an event of human history is "unique," we are simply calling attention to the extreme diversity in the combination of important characteristics on that level as compared with less complex levels. Each movement of a billiard ball is also "unique," in that it happens in exactly that manner only once; but any two of its movements have far more characteristics in common than any two occasions on which a man tips his hat in public.

As long as we can use concepts and language successfully, we can be sure that there is enough order in the universe to warrant our attempts to use elimination. J. M. Keynes has suggested that what we assume is a Principle of Limited Independent Variety, namely, "That the amount of variety in the universe is limited in such a way that there is no one object so complex that its qualities fall into an infinite number of independent groups."[8] Whatever we can select and identify in experience is not equally associated with everything else. There are some "things" which hold together — that is, recur in experience; and some generalizations of the type of "laws." Every attempt to discover stabilities, as Professor C. I. Lewis points out, not only does not fail, but such a universal failure is inconceivable, since all our concept-making is directed toward ordering what is presented, and not even a demon of disorder could keep us from some degree of success in eliminating some aspects of what was presented, and using others. The actual successes which we have achieved by using such assumptions as "things exist," and "laws of some kind hold," thus making elimination worth attempting, are more impressive than any formulation which philosophers have been able to give to the notion of limited independent variety.

The presence of great diversity on the levels which are most important for the social studies would seem to favor the use of the Method of Agreement, which starts with many differing instances of the effect. But the canon of the method, stated positively, calls for a multiplicity of instances of a relatively uniform effect differing in all respects *save one*. What we are obliged to seek in a high degree of uniformity on the effect side accompanied by great diversity is the possible causal circumstances combined with a *single* isolable uniformity. Now it is the easiest thing in the world to collect diverse instances of such effects in human behavior as tooth decay or fear of the dark or belief in palmistry or business failure or what you will. But it is not nearly so easy to show that diversity in the surrounding circumstances is not actually accompanied by a corresponding but unnoticed diversity in the effect, such as concealing under the same label "tooth decay," instances of tooth-decay-from-too-much-sugar, tooth-decay-from-too-little-calcium, and tooth-decay-from-bacterial-infection. These subvarieties may, from the point of view of causal explanation, be different effects. Social studies investigators are notoriously prone to indulge in this kind of lumping of effects, grouping together many sorts of suicides or military campaigns or revolutions as the "same effect," and then wondering why they are plagued by an apparent plurality of causes. A sociological study of suicides in France needed nine categories of "methods employed" and six of "probable causes," but only one for the effect, suicide.[9] Care should be taken to lavish an equal amount of analytical attention upon both ends of the causal process, upon effects as well as causes, even though the result will be to diminish the effective scope of the Method of Agreement. For we shall no longer be permitted to treat all suicides as instances of a single effect having multiple causes, or all lawbreakers as numbers to be treated by the wholesale.

In regard to single likenesses amid great diversity, it is evident that Nature runs to patterns, or related likenesses in clusters, rather than to isolated identities. This is especially true of such complex organisms as human beings living together socially. When they are at all alike, they are usually similar in *several*

[8] *A Treatise on Probability* (London, 1921), p. 258.
[9] Walter A. Lunden, "Suicides in France, 1910–1943," *American Journal of Sociology*, vol. LII (January, 1947), pp. 321–34.

relevant respects at once; and any one of the several may be causally related to the effect. That is why clear instances of positive Agreement are so rare as to make the use of that method for proof unimportant in practice.

The Method of Difference makes almost equally impossible demands upon the nature of things. If taken literally, it calls for two instances identical in all respects save one, accompanied by a parallel uniformity in the effect. But we cannot swear that any two instances are exactly alike without examining all the possibly relevant circumstances, which is impossible; while to declare arbitrarily that they are "enough" alike to justify the use of the method begs the whole question of relevance. It appears once again that Nature, when it runs to uniformity, seldom happens to achieve utter likeness in ninety-nine out of a hundred respects, any more than it reaches diversity in just ninety-nine out of a hundred. Her averages are just close enough to that figure at times to make elimination tempting without the promise of conclusiveness.

Probably the optimum material available in the social studies for the application of the Method of Difference consists of instances of uni-ovular multiple births, or so-called "identical twins." These are two or more individuals originating in the same fertilized ovum, with exactly the same hereditary factors operative and "as much alike as the two sides of the same person."[10] Fraternal twins, on the other hand, develop from simultaneously fertilized ova. If we wish to find out by elimination the parts played by heredity and environment respectively, we have only to establish four comparable sets of twins: (1) identical twins with same environment from birth; (2) identical twins with entirely different environments, separated at birth; (3) fraternal twins with same environment from birth; and (4) fraternal twins with entirely different environments, separated at birth. It would probably be too much to hope to find a single pair of parents obliging enough to furnish the ultimate in comparability by producing samples of all four sets in quick succession and of exactly the same sex distribution throughout!

It is hard enough to find pairs of identical twins which have been sufficiently separated in infancy, but University of Chicago scientists managed to round up nineteen sets. They found that "in all the mental traits tested, the separated identical twins differed more than do those brought up together." But "this comparison was not very satisfactory, because in some cases the separated twins were brought up in homes which were very much alike, were given about the same kind and amount of education, and had lived subsequently under the same general conditions." The difficulty in applying the Method of Difference is apparent: About all that can be concluded from the study of one-egg as compared with two-egg twins, according to Professor L. C. Dunn, is that "Physical traits in general show high concordance in one-egg twins, in reaction to mental measurements one-egg twins also show greater resemblance than two-egg twins, although the effects of education are clearly in evidence." The environmental factors show up with even more prominence in emotional tests.

[10] Frank N. Freeman, "Heredity and Environment in the Light of the Study of Twins," *Scientific Monthly*, vol. XLIV (January, 1937), pp. 13–19. See also cited article by L. C. Dunn in *Race and Science*, pp. 276–77.

DIVERSITY WITHIN SYSTEMS — INTERNAL COMPLEXITY

The usefulness of Agreement and Difference also depends upon our ability to isolate the single likeness or difference which we desire to test. We may succeed in closing off a system, but how shall we manage to focus our attention upon the single independent variable in which we are interested? On the billiard table, the ballistics expert would have little difficulty in so doing. But if we shift to a comparatively simple physical-chemical system like Professor L. J. Henderson's illustration of a tightly stoppered thermos bottle containing ice, whiskey, and soda-water, the task becomes harder. The reason is not that the system cannot be closed off or isolated from the rest of the universe, but rather because it is internally complicated by the fact that a change in any one of the variables is accompanied by changes in all the rest. The chemical components of the mixture are in three physical phases: a solid, or water in the form of ice; a liquid mixture; and a gaseous mixture. Now, if we increase the physical pressure factor by driving the stopper more deeply into the bottle, there will be a movement from the gas phase to the liquid phase, accompanied by a change of temperature that will alter the density of the solid phase. "Thus all the factors that characterize this system are seen to be mutually dependent."[11]

If, in such a system, a change in pressure resulted in a change in temperature, then that change in temperature would bring about a secondary change in pressure, and so on in an infinite succession of approximations to a condition of equilibrium. But such a description, of a chain of single cause-and-effect changes, is not an adequate account of what actually occurs. The "linear" eliminatory technique of isolating single factors breaks down in practice, and has to be replaced by some method of analysis which can deal with the simultaneous variations of mutually dependent variables. It is hardly necessary to add that all organisms, and, even more, all societies of organisms, are systems of mutually dependent variables. This accounts for the limited value, in the social studies, of Mill's methods of elimination as proof. It also illuminates many of the difficulties in using them which have already been pointed out, such as reciprocity and composition of causes.

Clearly Mill's methods represent an oversimplification of the problem of proving causal hypotheses. In the words of Professor Hyman Levy, Mill's view "suggests that the universe in all its manifestations acts not merely as a large machine but as a mass of self-contained small ones." The methods of elimination presuppose that the workings of these "small ones" can be analyzed into isolated and independent variables which can be wholly absent in some of the instances. They deal in blacks and whites, in gross qualitative characteristics or "differences in kind," and not in fine quantitative shadings or "differences in degree." Where a factor cannot be entirely eliminated, as in the example of the moon and the tides, or a person and his heredity, they cannot function negatively, which is their principal use, except by "thinking things away" in the imagination. The latter expedient often leads to unbridled speculation of the "ifs-of-history" type.

[11] Lawrence J. Henderson, *Pareto's General Sociology* (Cambridge, 1935), chap. III.

Yet, just because the methods of elimination are effective in establishing high probabilities only in a few types of closed systems, most of them on the large-scale physical level, it would be a great mistake to suppose that they are therefore useless in the social studies. By restricting our attention to a single phase of a complex social process, it is often possible to treat single variables as if they could be isolated, and to glean significant results, provided that we recognize how little we have accomplished in the way of proof. The positive uses of the methods direct our observations toward factors which *may* be causes and effects, at least in the sense that they have not yet been eliminated, and have so far fulfilled the minimum requirements. As for the negative uses, we assume in practice that every factor which can be eliminated brings us a step closer to the one or more which cannot be, even though we are unable to prove that the world is not infinitely various, and even though it is probable that we habitually underestimate the number of possible alternatives which need to be eliminated in order to make our hypothesis highly probable.

It is sometimes said that a theory can be instantly killed by a single fact. If that means that an hypothesis can no longer be maintained as originally stated if it is negated by one contradictory instance, the statement is true enough. But the metaphor is too violent for what generally occurs. Most elimination is not as drastic as it sounds. The disconfirmation of a hypothesis does not show that it is all wrong, but merely that there is something wrong enough about it to prevent its being confirmed. Few hypotheses in the history of science have been totally discarded. Many of them have been taken apart and reconstructed until scarcely recognizable, but some of their former features have usually been retained. If a theory is killed by elimination, it usually comes to life again with great promptness in an incarnation that bears some resemblance to its former self.

The greatest practical obstacle to the use of eliminatory methods in the social studies consists in the refusal of public opinion in most countries and communities to countenance either experiments that may harm human beings (and possibly animals) or those which involve the omission to use measures which might help them. Once the public is convinced that a certain drug is beneficial, it becomes impossible to test it by setting up a control group of ailing persons to whom the drug is denied. The same principle controls the conduct of experiments in education. Suppose that it was proposed to test the value of some allegedly superior method of teaching in a high school. No parent would want his child to be a member of the group that was to be denied the supposed benefit of the new discovery. But, unless a control group of students whose ability was equal to that of the test group was included, there would be no way of proving that the new method was superior to the old. One can hardly eliminate factors which one is not allowed to isolate and test.

FOR CLASS DISCUSSION

A. In the testing of hypotheses lies the prime difference between the investigator and the theorist. The one seeks diligently for the facts which may
overthrow his tentative theory, the other closes his eyes to these and searches
only for those which will sustain it. — G. K. Gilbert   (1)

B. A more real danger, because most people do not know that it exists, is the
belief that a working hypothesis must be right if it describes the facts accurately. One is safe only if one knows that no other hypothesis will
describe the facts equally well. — Wilder D. Bancroft

C. No two instances of a phenomenon are ever exactly the same in all respects,
and no series of observations by the aid of the most exact instruments ever
yield precisely identical readings. The most we can say is that there are
many events so similar as to provoke no difficulty in identifying them by
the same terms, and that observations of their relationship often yield
results agreeing so closely that we feel the differences may well be ascribed
to defects in our instruments or a varying personal equation in the observer. — Edwin A. Burtt

D. Experiments are designed to test the fit of the axiomatic model at new
sample points. If they fail, the model is rejected; but their success, even
when it is as spectacular as the discovery of Neptune, can never make the
model probable in itself. It can, in fact, only make it more probable than
another specified model . . . it can give reasons for preferring one model
to another. — J. Bronowski

E. Macaulay's comments on Baconian method have been summarized thus:
The man who infers that mince pies have disagreed with him because he
was ill when he ate them, well when he ate them not, most ill when he
ate most, and least ill when he ate least, has employed unconsciously but
sufficiently all the tables of the Novum Organum.   (3)
                                                    — R. F. Piper and P. W. Ward

F. If so little can be done by the experimental method to determine the conditions of an effect of many combined causes, in the case of medical
science; still less is this method applicable to a class of phenomena more
complicated than even those of physiology, the phenomena of politics and
history. There, Plurality of Causes exists in almost boundless excess, and
effects are, for the most part, inextricably interwoven with one another.
                                                    — John Stuart Mill   (9)

G. The inhabitants of our planet have always, for the most part, lived in the
hope that they were becoming better men; but few of them have ever
stopped to think of the dislocation which would be caused if their hopes
suddenly began to be realized. The rapid demoralization of the police force
and a crippling blow to the manufacturers of handcuffs, would be among
the more obvious consequences of a sharp rise in our moral standards.
Criminal lawyers and fingerprint experts would be on the streets, people
who had installed burglar alarms would write indignant letters to the press,
and the breeders of bloodhounds would be thrown into uncertainty and
despair. — London Times

EXERCISES IN MILL'S METHODS OF ELIMINATION

Directions:
(1) What is the phenomenon (or phenomena) to be accounted for? On what level is it?
(2) What hypothesis (or hypotheses) is being tested?
(3) Is the preliminary analysis of relevant factors complete and satisfactory?
(4) What method or methods are used? Positive or negative use? Explain, using symbols.
(5) How probable is the conclusion reached, if any? On what grounds?

1. Reports of wholesale runs in nylon stockings poured in on the nylon division of E. I. du Pont de Nemours Company from Washington, New York, Chicago, Minneapolis, Nashville, Jacksonville and even from a ship at sea. The office girls who suffered the excessive number of runs in their hosiery noticed that they occurred out of doors, and that those who did not go out for lunch escaped the blight. Mr. W. E. Mann, technical engineer for the Du Pont firm, explained that on some occasions soot particles containing sulphur dioxide and trioxide combine in the air to form sulphuric acid which can destroy any sheer stocking, not only nylons. Such particles also damage threads in other kinds of clothing, but such damage passes unnoticed, whereas one thread in a stocking may cause a run.

2. Late in the summer of 1933, the sudden deaths of eight prominent leaders in the United States lumber industry, occurring as far apart as New York City and Oregon, led to the suspicion that they might have a common cause. On investigation, it was found that each of the eight had succumbed to amoebic dysentery. It was further established that all eight had attended a convention of lumber dealers in Chicago a month earlier, and had lived at the same hotel. All had used the hotel's water supply, which was found to have been contaminated by the backing-up of sewage containing dysentery germs.

3. Eleven cases of keratitis, a common form of blindness resulting from the flooding of the cornea of the eye by a superfluous number of blood vessels, have so far been studied by doctors of the University of Georgia Medical School. In each case the diet of the patient was found to have been deficient in riboflavin, a member of the vitamin B group, contained in liver, milk, eggs, vegetables, and yeast. Normal sight was restored in all eleven cases by a diet rich in riboflavin, the lack of which is believed to be the cause of keratitis.

4. It had long been supposed that in order to maintain human intelligence unimpaired, the whole of one's brain was needed. But a psychologist doubted that human intelligence depends upon the possession of all of the parts of the brain. He found that there were four cases of brain surgery known, in which certain parts had been removed, the patients had recovered, and in which the intelligence tests had been given both before and after the operations. The results of the tests showed that in each of the four cases, the patient after the operation made just as good a score as before (and in one case, better).

The psychologist concluded that the possession of the brain parts in question was not causally related to the maintenance of intelligence.

5. Agricultural experts G. E. P. Smith and L. J. Booker of the University of Arizona were puzzled by the discrepancies encountered in forecasting the amount of water which winter snows would supply to farm crops in irrigation states. Snow surveys in the surrounding mountains did not furnish an accurate indication of the amount of water actually received. They suspected that the loss was due to sublimation, or direct evaporation into the air. To prove that this took place, they devised two sets of pans, one in which, when filled, no evaporation into the air could take place, and the other left open to the air with false bottoms which permitted the melting snow to run down in such a manner that it did not evaporate any more than the water which is normally absorbed by the ground. When a pan was filled, it was weighed, and then it was weighed again twenty-four hours later. The first set of pans weighed substantially the same at the beginning and the end of the twenty-four-hour period; while the loss of weight in the second set, sometimes at the rate of five inches of water per month, showed how much water had disappeared by sublimation.

6. Investigators of the navigational abilities of migrating birds framed the hypothesis of an internal "clock" which enables birds to guide themselves by the position of the sun. They tested the hypothesis by assuming that the birds' clock was running on local time, and "reset" the clock by shifting the light-dark cycle to which the creatures were exposed. They predicted that subsequently the birds would take off in a "wrong" angle to the sun; and this proved to be the case. The angle was dependent upon the amount and direction of the resetting.

7. A three-year experiment by the Rockefeller Foundation to cut down infant mortality in two Egyptian villages showed, first of all, that providing clean water and modern sewage disposal, without fly control, had almost no effect. Once the fly population was virtually annihilated by gammexane and chlordane, the infant mortality dropped from between 275 to 325 per thousand live births to 100. One year later the flies, having developed immunity to the insecticides, were back again, and the infant death rate was also the same as before.

8. Dr. H. V. Allington of Berkeley, California, treated two comparable groups of patients who had warts. In both groups he made injections intended to make the warts disappear; but one group received distilled water only, and the other were given shots of a medicine supposed to be effective. In both groups there was about the same fairly good rate of cure. He concluded that a large factor in the disappearance was psychological: they were cured simply by being looked at and treated in some fashion or other.

9. Drs. Peter V. Karpovich and Creighton J. Hale of Springfield College (Mass.) reported to the annual meeting of the Federation of American Societies for Experimental Biology that they had speed-tested three athletes on a "bicycle ergometer" to find out whether their performances were bettered or not by a five-minute preliminary warm-up. Their speed both with and without the warm-up was exactly the same in twenty-four trials each. They then tried with seven athletes three different types of "warm-up" before run-

ning 400 yards each outdoors: (1) preliminary exercise; (2) "deep" massage; and (3) light digital massage. Again the results were the same, with or without the warm-up. They concluded that such warm-ups before athletic contests were a waste of time and energy.

10. From Brisbane, Australia, comes the report of identical twins, Lin and Lee Mills, separated at an orphanage at the age of eight, who met again thirty years later, each 5 feet, 6 inches, each wearing an open-neck shirt and smoking the same brand of tobacco. Comparing tastes after their long separation, they found that they both intensely dislike marmalade, are fond of horses, drink moderately and smoke heavily. Neither has ever had a serious illness; both have lost the same teeth and have had the same front teeth filled.

11. In an experiment reported to the American Institute of Biological Sciences, a psychological test was given to forty-five pairs of identical twins and also to thirty-seven pairs of like-sexed fraternal twins. The identical twins scored alike so many times that it was held that only heredity could account for the findings. This was true of tests of use of the hands, skill with words, analytical thinking and such personality quirks as stubbornness. The fraternal twins almost universally differed in their scores on the same tests.

12. Dentists in Idaho towns were struck by the number of mottled teeth found among their patients, but noticed that such teeth had less than the average number of cavities. Further research disclosed that the drinking water of the localities had a high natural fluorine content, and the caries-resistant teeth contained more fluorine than ordinary teeth. This led to one of the greatest mass experiments in medical history, during which 2,139 children in Newburgh, N.Y., where the water supply had one part fluorine for every million parts of water, were carefully checked against 2,255 children in Kingston, where no fluorine was present in the water. The cities are comparable in size, thirty-five miles apart; and the experiment lasted from 1945 to 1955. It was found that the number of missing, decayed, or repaired teeth was from 40 to 68 per cent lower in fluoridated Newburgh than in non-fluoridated Kingston, depending upon the age group. The younger a child is when he begins drinking fluoridated water, the fewer the cavities. The New York State Health Commissioner concluded that the experiment "presents irrefutable evidence of the safety and effectiveness of the fluoridation of drinking water."

⚜ 11 ⚜

TESTING THE HYPOTHESIS:
Concomitant Variations, Measurement, and Statistics

1. Variations in Degree

JOHN STUART MILL thought that he had found a partial remedy for some of the obvious weaknesses of Agreement and Difference in what he called the Method of Concomitant Variations. He realized that, in testing many hypotheses, we are not dealing with the comparatively simple issue of the qualitative presence or absence of a supposed cause or effect under optimum conditions. We can speak of the presence or absence of ice in a jar of water, or of liquid condensing from steam. But all things do not behave like water at certain points on the scale of temperature, where it undergoes identifiable phase-changes of qualities from solid to liquid to gas.

Most of the changes in which we are interested, especially where human beings are concerned, are not these "either-or" changes in kind, but less drastic alterations in degree. But, just because we are frequently unable to vary a factor to the extent of its complete absence, the slogan of the Method of Difference, "Vary one thing at a time," does not need to be discarded. We may, instead, vary the *amount* or *quantity* of the factor which we suspect to be the cause, *CH;* and then see whether or not it is accompanied or followed by any corresponding variation in the amount of the effect, *E*. Or we may measure a variation in *E*, and then look around for a corresponding variation in some *CH*. Such joint variations are said to be "concomitant" or "accompanying" or "running along with."

Mill's statement of the canon of Concomitant Variations is:

> *Whatever phenomenon varies in any manner whenever another phenomenon varies in some particular manner, is either a cause or an effect of that phenomenon, or is connected with it through some fact of causation.*

On its face, this would be an absurdity if taken literally and applied at random to observed variations: the fluctuations of the sales of wastebaskets in Liverpool *might* exactly parallel the measles rate among the children of Topeka, Kansas. But if we remember that Mill was thinking of isolated and controlled situations under optimum conditions, the canon becomes much less nonsensical. If, in such a setting, we keep all other factors constant in amount, and

260

repeatedly vary the quantity of a single chosen factor, with accompanying variations in the effect, it is probable that the two are causally related.

A Detroit engineer, for example, was studying the cooling rate of the cylinders of airplane engines, supposing that thin films of enamel would act as insulators and decrease the cooling rate. Instead, he found that the more thin coats he added, the more the cooling rate seemed to increase. One coat raised it 13 per cent, two coats, 20 per cent, three coats, 23 per cent, and four coats, 24 per cent. He concluded that the thin coats of enamel acted, not as simple insulators, but as the reverse. In terms of our symbols, with the figures in parentheses indicating the amounts or quantities involved:

$abc(0)CH_1$....(100%) $Exyz$ (No coat, reg. cooling rate)
$abc(1)CH_1$....(113%) $Exyz$ (1 coat, 13% increase in cooling rate)
$abc(2)CH_1$....(120%) $Exyz$ (2 coats, 20% increase in cooling rate)
$abc(3)CH_1$....(123%) $Exyz$ (3 coats, 23% increase in cooling rate)
$abc(4)CH_1$....(124%) $Exyz$ (4 coats, 24% increase in cooling rate)

The abc and xyz factors, remaining unchanged in quantity, indicate the assumption that all the other relevant conditions of the engine stay the same throughout the experiment, although that state of affairs is improbable.

Note the importance of the two bases from which the changes are calculated. In this particular instance, the causal side of the process happens to start with "no enamel," adding the roughly equal amounts of the successive thin films in units of one; while on the effect side there is, at the start, a known rate of cooling reckoned as 100 per cent, and increased by percentages of the original amount. Concomitant variations do not have to be uniform in amount — that is to say, the observed variations in the amount of E do not have to correspond directly in quantity to those in the supposed causal factor CH. An addition of one unit of CH does not have to lead to an addition (or subtraction) of exactly one unit of E.

It is only the *direction* of the concomitant variations which needs to be uniform and roughly proportional throughout. It does not matter whether the two changes (in CH and in E) are directly or inversely proportional, as, for example, the decreasing of the amount of pain by an increase in the dosage of drugs. If the CH factor increases, all that is required is that E shall either increase or decrease with it (or after it) in some proportionate way; and the same if CH decreases. But if CH increases only, then E cannot *both* increase and decrease concomitantly, and the result still be held to fit the canon of the method.

Another point is illustrated by the airplane engine example, namely, the method covers only the scope embraced by the observed instances. It is always dangerous to extrapolate beyond the examined cases. A sharp watch has to be kept for what the philosopher Hegel called the "dialectical points" in processes of change. They are the points of "the passage of quantity into quality," where a difference in kind suddenly emerges from a difference in degree.[1] If the Detroit engineer had assumed that the addition of a fifth and a sixth thin coat of enamel would still further increase the cooling rate, it is highly probable

---

[1] For many examples, see chap. X, "The Passing of Quantity into Quality," in Hyman Levy, *Modern Science* (New York, 1939).

that he would have been mistaken. At the point where the coats get thick enough to act as an insulator, a dialectical point of phase-change is encountered. From that point on, each additional coat of enamel *reduces* rather than increases the cooling rate. That fact in no way disproves the former causal hypothesis that a few thin coats of enamel increase the cooling rate. But it does show the grave danger of extending the method from examined changes to those members of a series that have not yet been observed.

2. Concomitant Variations as a Method of Elimination

Assuming the optimum conditions for the proof of a cause-and-effect relationship — a closed system with independent single variables — the Method of Concomitant Variations greatly resembles a modified Method of Difference. It seems at first sight like an application of the Method of Difference to more than two instances, with all the relevant conditions kept exactly the same except one only, and with small quantitative variations in that one factor, accompanied by concomitant variations in the effect. It is not a matter of the total qualitative presence or absence of CH, but rather of a variation in the amount of CH from an arbitrarily selected base quantity, accompanied (or not accompanied) by a related variation in the quantity of E from its similarly chosen base.

This method of procedure, as we should expect, has many of the same strong and weak points which have already been noted in the Method of Difference. Its requirements, however, are considerably harder to fulfill. We must not only have included in our original analysis all of the elements which are relevant to any change in the effect; we must also see to it that none of them, save only the one which we are testing, varies *in amount* in all of the instances considered; and furthermore, that those instances are sufficient in number to constitute an inclusive series of changes without running into a change of quality, or phase. Only when all of those conditions have been met are we entitled to use Concomitant Variations as a method of elimination — that is, negatively.

NEGATIVE USE

Let us suppose that, keeping all other relevant factors the same in quantity, we make a difference in the quantity of a single, independent variable CH_1, and find that it *does* make a difference in the quantity of E, and that a further difference in CH_1 makes a further proportional difference in E in the same direction, and so on. The result is positive with regard to CH_1; but what about all the other relevant factors which remained the same in amount while E changed? Our reasoning with respect to them is similar to the first negative use of the Method of Difference. Using the airplane engine example, let a, b, and c represent the volume, the weight, and the thickness of the metal composing the cylinder walls, none of which varied in quantity during the experiment, although there was an observed variation in the amount of E. Are we not entitled to conclude that a, b, and c are *not* causally related to E? *That is not the cause of a phenomenon which remains constant in amount when the phenomenon varies in amount.*

On the other hand, what if making a quantitative difference in CH_1 does *not* make any corresponding quantitative difference in E? Then we shall be in a situation analogous to the second negative use of the Method of Difference. Changes in the quantity of CH_1 (the number of thin coats of enamel) would have no effect whatever of any proportional sort upon the quantity of E, the basic cooling rate. Represented symbolically, the situation would be:

Base quantities: $abc(0)CH_1$.... $(100\%) Exyz$ (No coat, reg. cooling rate)
First addition: $abc(1)CH_1$.... $(100\%) Exyz$ (1 coat, reg. cooling rate)
Second addition: $abc(2)CH_1$.... $(100\%) Exyz$ (2 coats, reg. cooling rate)
         and so on.

CH_1 would then be eliminated as the cause of E, since its changes of quantity had no effect upon the amount of the latter, by the rule: *That is not the cause of a phenomenon which varies in amount when the phenomenon remains constant.* It should be noted that the same rule eliminated CH_1 as the cause of x, y, and z (which might represent the color, sound, and smell of the running engine), since they, like E, the cooling rate, remain constant while CH_1 varies in amount.

Both of the above applications of the Method of Concomitant Variations as a means of elimination face all of the obstacles encountered by the Method of Difference, and more besides. It is hard enough to procure *two* identical instances of a process, but Concomitant Variations ordinarily requires three or more. If CH and E change in amount simultaneously, we must consider the possibility of Reciprocity of Causes; while if a change in the quantity of E follows a change in CH after an interval of time has elapsed, it is hard to be sure that "all else has remained exactly the same," especially when minute quantities are involved. There is, too, always the possibility of Composition of Causes: an increase in one factor by itself might not be sufficient, but, if accompanied by an increase in another, it might increase the amount of the effect. Counteracting Causes may also damage the proof, as when increasing the amount of the dose of a poison causes it to act as an emetic, and so to have a disproportionately small effect.

The logical value of Concomitant Variations as a method of elimination is, therefore, considerably less than that of Agreement and Difference in their negative uses, although it would seem to make possible finer and finer discriminations in barring out factors which show no alteration when the amount of the supposed cause or effect does. This is because the conditions required for elimination by Concomitant Variations — namely, the proof that certain factors do *not* vary in a sufficiently large number of cases where a single factor *does* vary proportionately with another single factor — are extremely hard to satisfy. What we usually find is a quantitative change in one variable accompanied by slight quantitative changes in a number of other variables, no one of which, by the rules, can be eliminated as a possible cause of the change in the effect. Even if a certain factor remains constant in quantity, it may yet be a merely catalytic cause, whose presence is indispensable to the rate of the effect, in spite of the fact that the canon of the method would rule it out.

Nevertheless, the psychological value or convincingness of Concomitant Variations in influencing our common-sense judgments is great, and out of all proportion to its logical force as proof of a causal hypothesis. Nature abounds in joint variations; and our environment is full of apparatus for measuring quantitative changes with great exactitude on many different levels: thermometers, barometers, lie-detectors, index numbers, and public opinion polls. We have developed mathematical instruments of precision for setting up normal curves of performance in all sorts of contexts, and for detecting slight discrepancies in such curves. While we may be skeptical about the positive implications of some of these numerous covariations, most of us are nevertheless easily convinced that whatever does *not* vary concomitantly with something else may be dismissed from consideration in determining its cause.

There is something very striking about a predicted variation which turns out as forecast, such as: "Eat more spinach, and you can do more work," "Increase your advertising with us, and your sales will increase proportionately," or, "Repeal of prohibition will ruin the candy business." Those are strong arguments *if* the facts bear them out. But they are even more deadly boomerangs if making the specified quantitative difference in the supposed cause fails to make any difference in the result. One soon stops taking the medicine which seems to have no effect whatever. A negative verdict seems decisive; where a positive outcome might be open to serious doubt. The patient who feels better is never sure that it was the amount of the medicine that was the cause.

3. Positive Use of Concomitant Variations

Let us now assume that we are fortunate enough to find an instance of the application of the method which yields a positive result under optimum conditions. That means that we shall have succeeded in isolating a closed system in which we are able to keep all the factors quantitatively constant except one. When that factor is varied in quantity, we find that another circumstance varies in quantity in a proportionate manner. The canon tells us that the two are causally related in some manner. But which one is the cause, and which the effect? The canon does not inform us. That depends upon the wisdom of our preliminary analysis in stating our hypothesis, together with further tests to establish which factor hinges upon which.

Ordinarily we have little difficulty in settling the question, since we find that the covariation works only in one direction. If we have observed that a change in the amount of factor *a* is accompanied by a change in the amount of factor *x*, we have only to devise an experiment in which we begin by changing the amount of factor *x*, and then see whether factor *a* changes in amount also. The more we expose our skins to the sun, the darker they become. But by exposing darkened skins, we do not expect to produce increased amounts of sunshine. The trouble comes when we encounter such a Reciprocity of Causes as that exemplified by Boyle's Law concerning the volume and pressure of gases. If we keep the temperature in a gas chamber constant, then a change in the volume will be accompanied by an inverse change in the amount of the pressure with a slight correction. Halving the volume at a constant temperature roughly doubles the amount of the pressure; while doubling the volume halves the pressure. If, on the other hand, we keep the chamber's volume constant, and change the temperature, the pressure will vary in an approximately direct ratio. Which of these changes we shall choose to regard as cause, and which as effect, will depend on the points at which we choose to initiate and terminate the experiment. Since the co-variations happen simultaneously, or nearly so, we cannot truly analyze the whole group of processes into antecedents and consequents.

There is also the question of the time element in Concomitant Variations. Strictly speaking, concomitance does not admit of succession in time. Cause and effect vary together, or at the *same* time. Yet such a definition deprives us of "before and after" as a test of cause and effect, leaving only the test of dependency by reversing the factors (such as *a* and *x* above), which is not always practicable. Many of the effects in which we are interested occur long after their causes, such as the consequences of fertilizers for crops, diets for human health, drills for learning languages, and free education in advancing political intelligence. If a rise in the price of hides is followed several months later by a comparable rise in the price of shoes, all other factors remaining approximately the same, we do not think it unreasonable to speak of the two variations as concomitant. But it would be manifestly absurd to attribute an increase in a cotton crop to fertilizer which had been added to the soil ten years previously. Unless we are dealing with such enormously long-range processes as ice ages, soil changes, or alleged "race memories," we had better be on our guard against stretching concomitance to cover too broad a range of time.

THE MATHEMATICAL NOTION OF FUNCTION

Positive concomitance derives much of its convincingness from a loose association with the mathematical conception of function. In mathematics, we say that one magnitude is a function of another if for every value of the former there is a corresponding value of the latter. A simple example would be the ages of two brothers, John and James. If we knew that John was five years older than James, for every age of either of them, there would be a corresponding age of the other. The age of either would be a *function* of the age of the other, calculable by adding or subtracting five years; but the age of neither would be a *cause* of the age of the other. Whichever one we choose as the basis of our calculation (let us say the age of James, who is 20), is known as the *independent variable*; while that of John (20 plus 5, or 25) is the *dependent variable*.

In such an example, or in the similar statement that the circumference of a circle is a function of its radius (or *vice versa*), we must be careful to restrict the meaning of dependence to its mathematical significance: dependence in calculation. The trouble comes when we encounter examples of magnitudes which depend upon other magnitudes in a somewhat more complex sense. When will our friends, who have one hundred miles to cover, arrive to visit us? That will depend upon their average rate of speed, of which, together with their time of departure, their time of arrival will be a function. At twenty-five miles an hour, it will take them four hours; at fifty miles an hour, only two hours. But the rate also *explains* in a sense the hour of their arrival, as well as enabling us to calculate it. "It took us four hours," they might explain, "because we drove only twenty-five miles an hour."

One of the earliest of the mathematical discoveries made by the ancient Greeks was the closely guarded Pythagorean secret of the functional relationship of the pitch of a stringed instrument to the length of the plucked string. This line of thinking, followed through the centuries by a brilliant succession of mathematical geniuses, resulted in the firm expectation that eventually all the so-called "laws of Nature" could be stated in functional equations. When the most dazzling successes in this direction were achieved in the fields of astronomy and mechanics, the belief became prevalent that the mathematico-mechanical pattern was applicable to everything, since ultimately all things were composed of the same measurable components: solid molecules or atoms. Any special case of the relationship of two variable magnitudes became simply an instance of the invariable mathematical laws of mechanics. The result was the apparent absorption of cause and effect into the broader conception of the universal laws of matter in motion in space and time.

Yet any student who has reached as simple a formula in his elementary physics or chemistry textbook as that of Boyle's Law already mentioned will recall that it applies exactly only to an "ideal gas," and not, without correction, to real gases. In other words, the statement of a functional relaitonship in mathematical terms, such as the familiar equation which states that the volume of a gas is equal to its temperature divided by the applied pressure multiplied by the constant coefficient of proportionality of that particular gas: $v = k\ t/p$ is only a definition of its dependent variable, the volume. It remains to be seen whether the definition of volume stated in the equation is borne out by operations of measurement which we can perform on actual gases. To have any hope of success, these operations must be performed in a laboratory under highly simplified conditions, with impurities excluded, all the variables rigidly controlled, and so on. When such conditions are established, it so happens that our measurements come very close to fitting the mathematical formula. But there is always the possibility that they are defective, and that more precise figures may upset the applicability (but not, of course, the mathematical validity) of the formula. The history of science is dotted with such overthrows of simple mathematical "laws."

To discover a relationship between two variables which is statable in terms of mathematical functionality is thus no guarantee that the formula will fit our world exactly, much less that it will apply indefinitely, no matter how much the quantities are varied. According to the Law of Charles, the volume of an ideal gas under constant pressure (or the pressure that it exerts at constant volume) is directly proportional to the absolute temperature. Since for each centigrade degree of temperature which the ideal gas drops at constant pressure, it loses 1/273 of its volume, at — 273° C., the ideal gas would have zero volume. But this has not been observed to happen, not only because absolute zero has never been achieved, but because a phase-change occurs before it is reached. If we relax our control of the variables, as we do when we explore the earth's atmosphere by means of balloons, we shall find that the pressure-temperature curve drops smoothly enough as the altitude rises to 40,000 feet, where the barometer stands at about 5 inches, and the thermometer at — 67° F. Yet, beyond that point, although the pressure continues to drop (to about 3.1 inches at 65,000 feet), the temperature remains constant at — 67° F.

When the rate at which some of the changes are made is considered, still further complications arise. The quick-freezing process for the preservation of foods is a good example of rapid passage through a series of phase-changes which, if passed through slowly, would terminate in strikingly different results. In dealing with living things, the time element in such formulas is of great importance. The qualitative effect of a sudden outgo or intake of oxygen or water or food may be very different from that of the same quantitative change at a slower tempo.

All such considerations merely emphasize the fact that the evidential foundation of whatever assurance we possess that mathematical functions hold true of the physical world is not mathematical, but observational and operational. The most reliable form of observation, the approximate coincidence judgment, is subject to error. At its best it is only approximate. Yet so fruitful has the notion of mathematical functionality been, especially as a tool of analysis for the discovery of interdependent relationships, that it stands today as the ideal scientific instrument. Every branch of human knowledge strives to attain "exactness," or mathematical form, even though its functional equations may be prematurely formulated. For outward mathematical appearance is almost universally regarded as the sure sign of scientific maturity.

4. Fallacies of Positive Concomitant Variations

In addition to the normal overeagerness of the would-be scientist to "read in" causal dependence wherever he sees a glimmer of mathematical functionality, there are several other common fallacies which lurk beneath the surface of what appear to be instances of the positive use of Concomitant Variations. One of them corresponds to the "possibility of a hidden third factor" already mentioned in connection with the Method of Difference. When we find that two quantities vary proportionately, how do we know that they are not, both of them, causally dependent upon a change in some third quantity which we have not taken into consideration? In a controlled situation, we can try varying each one separately, in order to see whether or not the other one also varies. If a change in the quantity of neither brings about a quantitative change in the other, then we shall have eliminated both as causes by a negative use of the method.

But what if we are unable to control our two concomitantly changing variables? Then the method not only does not tell us which is cause and which is effect; it also fails to indicate whether both changes are (or are not) the effects of a hidden third factor which is their common cause. In the example already cited, of the scrambled teletype reception occurring at the same time as a display of the aurora borealis, we might eliminate the scrambling as the cause of the aurora by disarranging some of the messages ourselves, and finding that it has no corresponding effect upon the illumination of the heavens. But we cannot, unfortunately, control the amount of the aurora in order to test its effect upon the scrambling. So we may easily fall into the error of regarding the illumination as the cause of the scrambling, when a more searching analysis would reveal that *both* aurora *and* scrambling were concomitant effects of electronic storms on the sun's surface known as sunspots.

The hidden-third-factor fallacy is especially dangerous in the social studies wherever a single broad influence has been felt over a long period of time, and so has become merged in the background of the taken-for-granted. From the days of Columbus until well into the twentieth century, for example, American business men, in making their calculations, could assume a steadily expanding demand for goods from an increasing population. That state of affairs had many effects upon the price and uses of labor and land, as well as upon the habits, attitudes, and expectations of individuals. Many of the effects were carelessly attributed to other, more immediate, and more spectacular causes. No doubt many men sincerely thought that they were getting rich, and would continue indefinitely to go on getting richer, solely because of their own ingenuity, industry, and thrift; when actually, in many instances, they were merely riding the crest of a double wave of immigration and a high birthrate. It was not until both of the latter factors changed in direction that they realized that some of the things which they had regarded as causes of effects were actually, to a large extent, other effects of more remote causes.

The notion of gigantic fundamental cycles in our universe, whether of sunspots or cosmic-ray storms or whatever, which would account for the lesser "tides in the affairs of men" and of animals, is a perpetually attractive one. There is something very alluring to the orderly mind in the prospect of bringing together rainfall cycles, fever charts, stock market ups-and-downs, grouse, goose, coyote, and rabbit abundance-curves, and so on, in a single rhythm which would account for all of them. Economic analysts have been busy ever since W. S. Jevons, in 1878, called attention to the remarkable correspondence between the sunspot cycle, which he calculated at ten and three-quarters years, and the ten-to-eleven-year business cycle. Numerous attempts have been made to connect sun-spot variations and market movements by way of the amounts of ultraviolet in the sun's rays, which affect the vitamin content of plants, which in turn modify the action of endocrine glands, and thus determine human moods of optimism and pessimism. Cyclones on the sun, weather tides, biological rhythms, emotional surges, political movements — who knows but what they are all one tide, the charting of which would yield an unrivaled harvest of long-range predictions? Yet little genuine progress has been made in demonstrating the truly fundamental nature of any "curve of curves" that has so far been advanced. What we seem to find is not one grand cycle upon which all lesser cycles can be shown to depend, but an interlacing web of causal relationships in which some of the changes are taking place in relative independence of one another.

Perhaps the most dangerous of all the fallacies of the positive use of the method is that of Coincidental Concomitance. This is committed whenever two changes which are only accidentally related are represented as causally linked. There are some curves of quantitative change which "fit" one another with amazing precision, and yet which almost certainly have no significant causal connection with each other. Professor Morris R. Cohen cites the unpublished study by Dr. George Marshall of the Brookings Institution, which shows that variations in the membership of the International Association of Machinists from 1912 to 1920 correlate almost perfectly (+.86) with the death rate of the state of Hyderabad, India, from 1911 to 1919.[2] It is said that the unprecedented increase in college enrollments from 1920 to 1931 closely parallels the rise in inmates of institutions for the insane during the same period; and that there has been, at times, a close correspondence between the average salary of Presbyterian ministers in Massachusetts and the price of rum in Havana, Cuba.

No matter how strongly we may hold the view that all living things are interdependent, it strains our credulity to believe that such covariations are any more than coincidental. A minute study of thousands or millions of curves of quantitative change would doubtless reveal a large number of amazingly close correspondences, very few of which would indicate direct causal connections. Where we cannot control either of the factors concerned, we must look beyond the fact of positive concomitance to some reason to suppose that a direct or indirect causal connection does exist. Mere surface unlikelihood is no proof that it does not exist; nor is exact concomitance alone any proof that it does.

As in using the methods of Agreement and Difference, attention must be paid, in interpreting instances of Concomitant Variations, to the diversity of systems, and especially of levels (see above, Chapter 10, Section 9). The social studies are full of situations in which there are relevant variables on different levels: physical, biological, psychological, and social-cultural. Some of these variables, notably on the so-called "lower" levels, can be controlled and varied one at a time. But we have no assurance that "all else" has necessarily remained the same on all the other levels, just because we have not attempted to make any other change. Many ambitious research projects have come to grief because the cause-and-effect relationship between the variables has been greatly oversimplified. Changes in working conditions, for example, are not directly linked to changes in output, but through the "meanings" they have for the human beings involved — a complex matter of past conditioning and present and future social situations. It is always fatal to try to deal with a human situation in non-human terms.

Concomitant Variations remains an excellent preliminary tool of research for disentangling causal factors. An English newspaper, for example, noting

---

[2] Morris R. Cohen, *Reason and Nature* (New York, 1931), p. 92. See below, Section 10.

that Germany's share in Nobel prizes in science, "which used to be 40 per cent," had slumped in 1960 to 6 per cent, while in the same period the American share rose from 4 per cent to 49 per cent, commented: "It is curious how parallel these figures are." Whenever we find two sets of quantities varying together over a considerable period of time, we may suspect a possible causal relationship worth investigating. Positive concomitance does not of itself establish any such causal relationship, nor does it cope with the question of a hidden third factor. There must be additional evidence in the form of some intelligible reason why the two concomitant processes should vary together, plus a series of resolute attempts to eliminate the one which is believed to be the cause.

5. The Method of Residues

The fifth and last of Mill's methods he calls the Method of Residues, of which the canon is:

> Subduct from any phenomenon such part as is known by previous inductions to be the effect of certain antecedents, and the residue of the phenomenon is the effect of the remaining antecedents.

Mill seems to think that Residues is an extension of the Method of Difference, and that it deals with inductive proof. But it is only too plainly in the nature of a conclusion drawn from previous eliminations — that is, a deduction based upon two closed lists of factors, all but one of each of which has been eliminated.

To use a somewhat artificial illustration, if five small boys, A, B, C, D, and E, were caught breaking windows under such circumstances that it was known that each boy could not have broken more than one window, then the boy E could be proved to be the cause of breaking the window Z, if only windows V, W, X, Y, and Z were broken, and it had already been shown that

A broke window V,
B broke window W,
C broke window X,
D broke window Y,

leaving E as the breaker of window Z. Note, however, that the deduction would fail to hold if any sixth factor F could have been the cause of the breaking of Z; or if any one of the boys could have broken more than one window.

The Method of Residues is therefore little more than a restatement of the final stage of elimination. Given a strictly limited number of independently acting causes which have already been linked to distinguishable effects, but with one effect and one possible cause left over, then these two remaining elements must be held to be causally connected. That is just the sort of simple deductive arithmetic which we use when we compute our expenses after traveling. If we recall that we spent money only for carfare, hotel, and the theater; if our total expense was $30; and if we know that carfare cost $12 and the hotel $10; then the cause of the expenditure of the remaining $8 must have been the theater. But there was that book which we purchased for $3, and forgot to include. The danger of Residues is incomplete elimination, the forgotten factor which is carelessly overlooked.

Astronomers have used the Method of Residues with brilliant success, notably in the famous discovery of the planet Neptune by noting discrepancies in the path of the planet Uranus which remained after the gravitational influence of the sun and all other relevant heavenly bodies had been computed. The forces which remained to be accounted for were assigned to the as yet undiscovered planet, whose size and approximate position were then calculated. Telescopes were trained on the spot where deduction showed that it ought to be; and there it was! The method has also been helpful in biology, where it has been used in checking off the functions of the different organs in animals until only a few remain. Glands which seem to have no ascertainable function are then paired off hypothetically with known functions which have no identifiable organ, sometimes with illuminating results. The use of Residues in cost accounting is obvious: profits are remainders when costs have been subtracted. But it does not follow that the cause of a profit is what is left over when you take away all the causes of the costs. Subtraction is a very dangerous procedure wherever the quantity from which one subtracts is the resultant of many factors which are not paired off independently of one another.

6. Measurement

In using the Method of Concomitant Variations we take for granted the desirability of expressing the qualities which we find to vary proportionately by means of numerical symbols. An observer could, of course, reach a fairly reliable conclusion without them, merely noting the fact that as he flew higher and higher in an airplane, for instance, both the oxygen content of the air and the temperature decreased. Such a judgment, however, would be sadly lacking in precision, and liable to distortion by all manner of subjective influences. The observer would be much happier if he were able to state that the oxygen content of the air drops 50 per cent at an altitude of 20,000 feet above sea level, where the temperature reaches −12° F. What he has done is to substitute numbers or quantities (50 per cent, 20,000, and −12) for three crude qualities: thinness of the atmosphere, height above the earth, and coldness, or absence of heat.

This systematic assignment of numerical symbols to qualities in the world about us is the process known as *quantification* or *measurement*. It can be carried out in many different ways, from the simple counting of objects to the subtle complexities of index numbers. It is the language of modern science. The scientist is always uneasy when he cannot talk in figures. One of the articles of faith of nineteenth-century science was an "unlimited precision at the heart of things," a faith that seems to be warranted when we read of measuring devices which discriminate to a fifty-billionth of an inch, or which detect the amount of light thrown on the palm of a man's hand by a single candle one mile away. Only in our day has a suspicion of an "inherent fuzziness" in Nature become widespread, and measurement come to be regarded as one of the storm centers of the controversy over the limitations of scientific method. On the one hand, there are those who still agree with the saying attributed to Nicholas of Cusa in the fifteenth century: "Knowledge is always measurement"; while on the other, there are those who blame most of the ills of humanity upon modern man's allegedly exclusive preoccupation with the measurable.

So loud have been the complaints against overemphasis upon measurement that it is hardly necessary to laud its merits in an age which is often characterized as measurement-mad. Few people need any longer to be convinced by argument that a measure which purports to tell "just how much" is far superior to a vague qualitative impression. So closely are measurement and scientific proof identified in the public mind that the young man in the cigarette advertisement who volunteers the dubious information about "28 per cent less nicotine" is rewarded by the smiling reply of the young lady: "I like knowing scientific facts about my cigarette." Any kind of alleged yardstick or "meter" commands initial respect. Yet the low repute of statistical proofs in debate ("You can prove anything by figures") should remind us that it is far easier to go through the motions of measurement, or to cite its supposed results, than it is to understand exactly what a set of figures signifies. The trouble lies in failing to grasp the fundamentals of the differing varieties of measurement, and to recognize the ways in which they are frequently confused. He who understands the various relationships of quantity to quality is well on his way to the mastery of what statistics mean. It can be safely said that the crux of most of the problems of scientific method in the social studies lies in this vicinity.

OF ADDITIVE OR EXTENSIVE QUALITIES

Let us begin with the simplest use of numbers to answer the questions "How many?" and "How much?" Suppose that two groups of children are playing on separate playgrounds, and from cursory observations, we gather the qualitative impressions that there are more children on playground A than on playground B; but that those on playground B are heavier, in the aggregate, than those on playground A. Such vague impressions would remain open to doubt until we could find some way of making them more precise. One way to confirm (or invalidate) our first impression concerning the comparative size of the two groups would be to arrange them in parallel lines; and then to establish a one-to-one correspondence between pairs of children (one from each line), until one or the other group gave out. This could be done without assigning numbers to either group. But a much more economical method would be to *count* the children at each playground, and then compare the numerical results, such as: 24 children on playground A, and 16 on playground B.

One great advantage of counting as against lining up is the substitution of mental for physical operations. By manipulating the numbers 24 and 16 "in our heads," we learn that there are 8 more children on A than on B; and that if 4 children on A could be induced to transfer to B, then the numbers on each playground would be the same, or 20. Thanks to counting, in other words, we have been able to bring into play that branch of mathematics known as arithmetic, adding and subtracting mental concepts instead of lining up and comparing groups of children; but with results which can be verified by such physical operations, if desired.

We are able to carry out the attaching of numbers because our subject matter, children, is composed of distinguishable units which retain their separateness from one another. Children are distinct from rag dolls, scarecrows, statues, and chimpanzees. But they are not so easily distinguishable from youths or young adults. If, on each playground, there were fourteen- or fifteen-year-olds who did not fit our classification of "children," then we should find it hard to determine the number of children there. Once we have fixed upon the specifications of our unit to be counted, however, the operation of counting yields a very valuable property of the group, its number, which is wholly independent of the order of the counting. The children may shift their positions relative to one another again and again, but if we can enumerate all of them without duplication, the numerical result will always come out the same.

When we come to compare the total weights of the children at the two playgrounds, the problem becomes more complicated. We might go back to lining up and comparing, in the hope of showing that each child from B is heavier than his or her opposite number from A. But that method does not take care of the eight extra A children. Or we might build a huge balance, or scale, big enough to accommodate all the children of each playground on its two weighing platforms, and then see which side outweighed the other. We might try to count by "hefting" each child and putting down a number, but that would be both laborious and inaccurate. What we do, instead, is to fix upon a unit like the pound or kilogram or stone. Then each child can be weighed in pounds by the operation of balancing, and the numerical totals added. If the 24 A children weighed 1800 pounds, and the 16 B children 1280 pounds, we might suppose ourselves entitled to conclude that each A child weighed 75 pounds, and each B child 80 pounds, which they do "on the average." But if we went on to assume that a shift of four of the A children to playground B would subtract exactly 300 pounds from the total weight of A and add it to that of B, so that the latter, now 1580 pounds, would exceed that of A, reduced to 1500 pounds, we should probably find ourselves in error. Children can be weighed in pounds, and the numbers can be manipulated. But it does not follow that you can do everything with the separate pounds of child weight that you can do with the numbers which represent them, and still have live children.

So far we have been dealing with what scientists call a *fundamental* scale of measurement, rather than a *derived* scale, such as that of the density of the bodies of the children, which would have to be determined by taking the ratio of two fundamental scales, their weight and their volume. Or if we wanted to measure their abilities to run a hundred yards, we should have to measure both distance and time.

Even our attempts to use numbers to stand for qualities on a fundamental scale have revealed several pitfalls. Our first undertaking, the enumeration of the children on the two playgrounds, we may call Direct Counting, which can be reduced to approximate coincidence observations. Naturally it is greatly facilitated by the invention of a number system; but even savages can perform the basic operation of tallying by means of their fingers, or piles of stones, or notches on a stick. Yet this simplest sort of counting cannot be carried on unless (1) we know in advance what is to be counted; (2) the group to be counted is finite, can be bounded or marked off; and (3) the group is composed of discrete and similar elements or units which are separable from one another and identifiable by independent observers. We should hardly tell a person to go to playground A and just count. "Count what?" he would inquire. It would be equally nonsensical to say: "Go outside and count children." In practice, we have to mark off a limited area, such as "the children on this playground." To count the number of flies on an unscreened porch would be extremely difficult; screening would make it much easier. The number of drops of water in a tumbler cannot be counted directly while they remain in the tumbler, since they are not discrete units. Before they were separated for counting by means of a dropper, "a drop of water" would have to be defined.

Wherever the above three conditions obtain of a group of anything, however, we can assign a number to each member of the group. When that is done for the mere purpose of identification, such as automobile license numbers, telephone numbers, catalogue numbers, and similar "tags," counting is not usually involved. Such numbers are classificatory devices of the index variety, which are not intended to convey anything about the qualities of the objects to which they are attached. That low numbers of automobiles should convey intimations of "influence" to traffic officers is a perversion of the original intent of the numbering system, which was quick identification without regard to standing in the community. Expressed in another fashion, the average automobile license number of any given group in the community ought to be a matter of chance, entirely without significance.

But there are some states in which automobile license numbers are still given out on the strictly serial, first-come-first-served basis. In those states, the latest number issued at any given moment also serves to count the number of cars registered to that date. Where the three conditions prevail, and where we begin our enumeration of the discrete, similar units of a finite group with the number 1, proceeding in serial order, we can not only assign numbers by Direct Counting; we can also safely manipulate the resulting whole numbers by addition and subtraction without misrepresenting our subject matter. Whatever we can do with the integers mentally, we can also find to be true of the objects physically. Qualities which satisfy these conditions are called *additive* or extensive. There must always be some physical operation by which the quantities of the quality measured can be shown to independent observers to stand in strictly additive relationships. It must always be possible, ultimately, to make the arithmetic visible in terms of some sort of tallying or measurement.

OF NON-ADDITIVE OR INTENSIVE QUALITIES

To return to the playground illustration, let us further suppose that we wish to compare, not only the numbers and weights of the children, but also their intelligence and dispositions. We might have the impression that "the children of playground B are twice as intelligent as those of playground A," or, "that the children of playground A are three times as cheerful as those of playground B"; but how could those qualities be translated into quantities? At once we encounter a serious difficulty, for we are now dealing with qualities which are *non-additive* or intensive.

The trouble is not with our judgment that there is a greater-and-lesser relationship to be measured. It is true that individuals would differ in the orders in which they would rate particular children for intelligence or cheerfulness; but no one would be likely to question that there were individual differences in those qualities. We could probably get a jury to arrange a given group of children in order from the most intelligent to the least intelligent (as the jury defined the quality), or from most cheerful to least cheerful. We could then go further, and assign to each child a number according to his standing in the quality being measured. But such numbers would indicate only the child's *position in a series with respect to the single quality* — the lower his number, the higher his position relative to the rest of those being measured. We cannot for one moment assume that the steps between the numbers are the same as those between the children with respect to the qualities. The number 1 child on playground A might be much more intelligent than the number 2 child, yet the latter might be only slightly more intelligent than the number 3 child. Nor are we entitled to assume that the numbers indicate the child's possession of any specifiable amount or quantity of the quality that is being measured. Still less can we legitimately suppose that adding or subtracting the position-numbers has any exact meaning whatever.

Our environment abounds in qualities which can be arranged in a continuous series by imperceptible degrees: oceans by smoothness, razor blades by sharpness, pencils by hardness, hands by cleanliness, paints by durability, foods by appetizingness, drunks by intoxicatedness, teachers by interestingness, and so on. An ordinal scale for the measurement of one of these intensive qualities is usually made by placing at each end the extreme degrees of it which are known or commonly encountered. Sometimes, as in the Beaufort international scale of wind force, a beginning is made at the lower end, complete calm, which is designated as zero. Sir Francis Beaufort of the British Navy then assigned the numbers 1, 2, and 3 to what sailors called a Light Breeze, numbers 4 and 5 to a Moderate Wind, 6 and 7 to a Strong Wind, 8, 9, and 10 to a Gale, 11 to a Storm, and 12 to a Hurricane. Note that the Beaufort Scale was designed to measure wind force as experienced by sailors, before there was an exact science of meteorology. In 1906 it was translated into extensive units: knots per hour as measured by an anemometer. Some scales begin at the other end, such as the scale of hardness based on the diamond as the hardest substance ordinarily encountered, which is given a rating of 10. Anything which it can abrade, but which cannot abrade it, is ranked below it on the scale, such as steel, which stands at 6½.

Now the temptation is strong to infer that diamonds "possess" ten units of something called hardness, of which steel has only six and one-half; or that if we could somehow add three and one-half units of it to steel, the latter would be as hard as a diamond. The presence of numbered differences may incline the unwary to the belief that the numbers of the scale must represent amounts of qualities in the same manner as yards and pounds and acres. But that is decidedly not the case. We cannot even say that the difference in hardness between diamonds and steel, or three and one-half, is the same as the difference between steel and some other substance which stands at a point three and one-half numbers lower on the same scale.

One trouble is that there are some scales measuring intensive qualities which permit operations for determining equal distances along the measuring device, such as the Fahrenheit and Centigrade thermometers, which are called *interval scales*. We can carry out operations which will correspond to differences in degrees of temperature, but we cannot give any meaning to ratios, such as the claim that 90° F. is twice as hot as 45° F., or that two beakers of water each at 45° F., would measure 90° F. if they were poured together in a single vessel.

Intensive qualities which are arranged on an ordinal scale do not commonly permit the difference between any two points on the scale to be exhibited as a separate intensive magnitude. Hence the addition and subtraction of the numbers assigned to the magnitudes have no precise meaning for the qualities, as they do in dealing with extensive qualities. One can only say that there is more or less of the quality than in the preceding or following instance on the scale. One cannot say how much.[3]

But in spite of the fact that almost everyone recognizes, when it is pointed out to him, the stupidity of statements that one race is twice as criminal as another, that one city is four times as religious as another, or that one girl is ten times as beautiful as another, many users of statistics still persist in making the equally foolish assumption that four children receiving grades of 40, 60, 80, and 100 on an examination are separated from each other by equal increments of twenty units of something; and that the child rating 80 is twice as far from zero in that subject as the one who got only 40. Differences in rank on a scale of intensive quality are not quantities or even units of anything, in spite of the fact that they may have numbers assigned to them. Between mediocrities, the differences may be microscopic; while between the dolt and the genius they may be of astronomical proportions. Does this mean that there is no point in arranging instances of intensive qualities in order, and in comparing relative positions in the different orders? Not at all. Such in-

---

[3] For an amusing satire based on the notion of measuring "prestige" in quantitative terms, see the chapter "The American Sociometric Peerage" in Mark Epernay (pseud.), *The McLandress Dimension* (Boston, 1963), pp. 33–55.

formation may be highly useful for a number of purposes. What has to be remembered, however, is that if numbers are used, they must not be treated as numbers usually are, namely, as manipulable representatives of unit-quantities.

7. Statistics

The methods of measurement applied to the component units of large groups are said to be statistical. The word "statistics," which has, incidentally, no such singular in good use as "statistic," comes from various expressions dealing with affairs of state, but it has long since ceased to be restricted to "political arithmetic." Today the term is applied to all the numerical techniques which deal with the members of large groups (and also to the data themselves), whether the latter are electrons or star-clusters or genes or bond-yields. It cannot be too often pointed out that methods designed for the handling of great numbers of cases will seldom work when applied to small numbers, and *vice versa*.

On the one hand, statistics is patently a branch of applied mathematics; while on the other, it is an economical means of estimating and interpreting the significance of large masses of data. It is not enough to stress just one of these aspects at the expense of the other. Mathematical manipulation is especially prone to outrun observation and inference. Mere arithmetical precision may be left meaningless for want of proper interpretation. The statistician must always keep an eye on his material as well as on his technique; for inattention to either may vitiate his final results. Naturally his conclusions can be no better than their original sources; for he is engaged in that risky business — abstracting from abstractions.

One of the paradoxes of the present state of affairs in the social studies is the high importance attached to statistics as a method of investigation as contrasted with its low prestige as a method of proof. On all hands, the student finds himself assured that statistics is the prime language of social science, the one tool-subject upon which the latter depends. He may even be told that it is as important for him to gain a mastery of statistical methods as it once was for a person to learn how to read and write. At the same time he will hear such gibes as: "You can prove anything by statistics"; "Figures don't lie, but liars do figure!" and "There are liars, black liars, and statisticians." Small wonder if he is at a loss to understand how any subject can be held simultaneously in such high and such low esteem. One reason is undoubtedly that figures are quoted and requoted, once they have attained currency, without being verified. Everyone "knows" that "more Americans go to symphony concerts than to ball games." But do they? Total attendance figures do not tell you whether the same "fans" of both attractions go again and again, or whether the crowds are made up of different people each time? The expert manipulation of abstract numerical quantities is no guarantee of anyone's comprehension of what they are supposed to represent. Floods of figures carry with them no assurance of an advance in understanding. There is a gap between the qualities and the quantities which must never be forgotten if we are to talk sense and statistics in the same breath. Since elementary statistical manuals are easily available, no attempt will be made in this section to outline any more of the fundamental numerical attributes of groups than will be found necessary to understand logical strengths and weaknesses. Statistics are also utilized for the purpose of predicting or estimating the probable or approximate status of the individual as a member of a group. Those aspects — statistical regularity, sampling, and probability — will be discussed in Chapter 12.

8. Measures of Central Tendency

In the playground example used above, numbers were employed to make a comparison of the two groups of children with respect to the quality of weight. Merely to add up the total weights and compare them was not sufficiently informative, for we should expect the poundage of twenty-four children to exceed that of sixteen. What we wanted was two numerical symbols which should be typical or representative, respectively, of the central tendency of each of the two groups with respect to weight. The procedure we adopted was the common, everyday method of "striking an average," or *arithmetic mean*, by dividing the total weights of each group by the number of children in it. One trouble with that method is that the result may be some such fraction as 72¼ pounds, which may not be the actual weight of any child in the group. But there are other possible measures. We might have lined the children up in order of weight, and then picked the *median* or midmost child in the line (splitting the difference between the midmost two, if the group was composed of an even number). Or we might have grouped the children's weights by intervals of five or ten pounds, and then selected the *mode*, or the interval containing the largest number of children. Each of these so-called "measures of central tendency" — the mean, the median, and the mode — has its special advantages and disadvantages for portraying the typical or "normal" representative of what is called a *distribution*, namely, a set of comparable numbers such as the weights of the children. When such numbers are arranged in order of magnitude, they are called a *frequency distribution*; and when they are grouped by smaller classes, the latter are called *class intervals*. The right-hand columns labeled "Frequency" in the tables display the playground distributions in class intervals of ten pounds each.

THE ARITHMETIC MEAN

Commonly known as "the average" of any set of figures, although there are many other varieties of averages, the arithmetic mean is by all odds the easiest measure of central tendency to understand, and usually one of the easiest to compute. It has the advantage of including all of the items of a distribution; but it may not, as we have seen, correspond with any actual item, since it is a computed figure which characterizes the whole group rather than any individual in it. It is the center of gravity or point of balance of a distribution. Its greatest disadvantage is the way in which it is distorted by extreme cases. For

Illustrations of Frequency Distributions, I–II

Purpose: To compare by measures of central tendency the weights of children on two playgrounds.

	I			II	
	PLAYGROUND A (24 children)			PLAYGROUND B (16 children)	
Child	*Weight*	*Frequency*	*Child*	*Weight*	*Frequency*
A1	95	} 90–99—2	B1	136	Over 100—1
A2	90		B2	97	
A3	85		B3	97	90–99—4 _ _ MODE
A4	84		B4	94	
A5	84	} 80–89—6	B5	92	
A6	82		B6	81	80–89—2
A7	81		B7	80	
A8	80		B8	79	_ _ _ _ _ _ _ _ _ MEAN
A9	79		B9	79	_ _ _ _ _ _ _ _ _ MEDIAN
A10	78		B10	78	70–79—3
A11	76		B11	69	
A12	75	_ _ _ _ _ _ _ MEAN	B12	68	60–69—3
A13	74	_ _ _ _ _ _ _ MEDIAN	B13	66	
A14	74	70–79—9 _ _ MODE	B14	59	50–59—2
A15	72		B15	58	
A16	71		B16	47	40–49—1
A17	70				
A18	68				
A19	67				
A20	65				
A21	64	60–69—7			
A22	63				
A23	62				
A24	61				

24)1800 lbs. (75 lbs. = Arithmetic mean.   16)1280 lbs. (80 lbs. = Arithmetic mean.

The median weight lies between child A12 and child A13 = 74.5 lbs.

The mode lies in the interval 70–79, which contains the most items, 9.

The median weight lies between child B8 and child B9 = 79 lbs.

The mode lies in the interval 90–99, which contains the most items, 4.

example, 500 is the average of 499 and 501, but it is also the average of 1 and 999. If a group of ten hoboes were trying to determine their average net assets, and a billionaire should suddenly join them, the average would go sky-high without making ten of the eleven individuals a cent richer. In the tables, the average weight of the children on playground B, which is 80 pounds, would drop 4 pounds if child B1, who weighs 136 pounds, was disregarded; while it would rise 6 pounds if child B16, who weighs only 47 pounds, was left out of consideration. In the figures for playground A, where the weights of the heaviest and lightest children differ by only 34 pounds instead of 89 pounds, the omission of child A1 would lower the mean by only 1 pound; while disregarding child A24 would raise it by only about .6 pound. As the number of items increases, the distorting effect of extreme instances decreases. Note that the arithmetic mean by itself never gives us any information about the degree of dispersion or "scatter" of the data from which it has been computed.

One of the advantages of the arithmetic mean — namely, that it can itself be averaged with other averages — disappears when the groups do not happen to be of the same size. Let us suppose that we wished to find the average weight of all forty children on the two playgrounds A and B. It would not do to add the two group averages of 75 pounds and 80 pounds and divide by 2, because the answer: 77½ pounds is composed of one-half which is derived from twenty-four items, while the other rests on only sixteen. In such cases we remedy the difficulty by *weighting* the average, multiplying, 75 pounds × 24 = 1800 pounds, and 80 pounds × 16 = 1280 pounds for a total of 3080/40 pounds = 77 pounds. No one can attend school for very long without becoming acquainted with the weighted arithmetic mean, since the grades received in quizzes, examinations, and term-papers are not regarded as of equal importance in computing the total grade. Hence they must be weighted before being averaged. It is also probable that most students realize that the weights assigned are a matter of the teacher's judgment, and are not to be justified by pointing to the accuracy of the mathematical computations. Weighted means are essential in making up an *index number*, which compresses many averages of varying importance in a single composite measure. It would be folly to construct a cost-of-living index in which food and music lessons were of equal importance, or to represent business activity by averaging steel and cough-drop production on a fifty-fifty basis. The weighting of index-number components has to be kept abreast of the times or else it may become misleading.

But whether the arithmetic mean is weighted down or not, its calculation is always a one-way process: you cannot work backwards from the mean to its components. Any mean may represent an infinite number of possible combinations of numbers, and it may be produced at will from any given assemblage of quantities by the single addition of one other quantity (plus or minus). That indicates the possibility of an infinite number of interpretations of any particular mean. A factory owner who paid himself $102,000 and his 100 workmen $1000 apiece in one year, but who paid himself and his workmen $2000 apiece the next year, could report the same average payment for the two years, namely, $2000. Yet the economic situation of everyone concerned would be vastly different in the two years. Arithmetic means are, therefore, dangerously open to misconstruction unless it is known that they represent distributions which have no extreme cases and are grouped symmetrically around their central tendencies. But that is exactly what the arithmetic mean itself does *not* inform us. Consequently, it needs to be supplemented by other measures of central tendency, as well as by those of dispersion.

THE MEDIAN

Fastening upon the midmost item in any frequency distribution is one way of insuring that its central tendency will be represented by one of its actual members. The median is strictly a measure of position. It is that item in a series arranged in order of magnitude on each side of which an equal number of items is located. If there are an even number of items in the distribution, the median is usually computed by splitting the difference (finding the arithmetic mean) between the two midmost items. If the items are grouped, and the middle one by counting lies, for example, one-fourth of the way from the bottom of interval 70–79, the median would be located at 72.5, since the items in the group are assumed to be distributed uniformly throughout the interval, although that is seldom actually the case.

The median has the great advantage, as compared with the arithmetic mean, of being unaffected by extreme instances. If a group of five doctors and five lawyers were comparing their gross incomes, it might be that the physicians would report some such figures as $6,200, $7,600, $8,200, $9,800 and $12,200; of which the arithmetic mean would be $8,800. Let us further suppose that the five lawyers reported incomes of $5,100, $5,400, $6,000, $14,200 and $17,300 respectively. Their arithmetic mean would be $9,600. The medians, however, would be $8,800 for the doctors and $6,000 for the lawyers. Yet the fact is that every one of the physicians received more than three-fifths of the lawyers, even though the doctors "averaged" $1,200 a year less than the attorneys. The median does not misrepresent the situation to the extent that the mean does.

Since the median is a positional measure, it is especially useful in the social studies where so many of the qualities measured are intensive, and can therefore be compared only in terms of more and less. The median can be determined, even though the items in a series cannot be quantitatively expressed. But it is of little value where a distribution is badly "skewed" by the presence of the bulk of the items at the top or bottom; or divided between the two; or where a single off-center interval predominates. If over one-half of the students in a class received zero in a test, the median would be zero, but that would give little indication of what was accomplished by those who passed. If one-half of the class got 30, and the other half 90, the median would be 60, and meaningless. The median must never be averaged with other medians, or manipulated algebraically. It works best where the data are closely grouped about the center of a distribution, but in just those instances it corresponds most closely with the mean.

THE MODE

The mode is the value on any scale which occurs most frequently. Like the median, it is unaffected by extreme cases. In the playground example, there are more playground A children in the 70–79-pound interval than in any other, which makes it the commonest or modal weight of that distribution. On playground B, the 90–99-pound interval includes four children, and is the mode, but only by a narrow margin over the 60–69- and 70–79-pound intervals, each of which contains three children. That state of affairs shows the restricted value of the mode as a measure of central tendency where no one value or group predominates. If the weights of playground A were not grouped, then there would be two modes, one at 84 pounds (two instances) and one at 74 pounds (two instances); but both would be insignificant. Distributions with two modes are called bimodal, and, when plotted, yield a curve with two humps. This is usually taken as an indication that the data are not homogeneous, and really belong in two separate distributions. The mode has little value unless the total number of items is large, and unless there is a considerable concentration of them at not more than two or three points at most. Like the median, it is not susceptible to averaging.

Yet the mode may be extremely important to a person who is stocking a store with commonly used and standardized articles, such as shoes, hats, shirts, nails, window screens, or rugs. It would help such a merchant little to know the mean or the median of the foot sizes of his customers. He wants to know which sizes are most in demand. As Bowley remarks: "Even the favorite coin in a church collection may show the spirit of the congregation better than the arithmetic average of their contributions." On the other hand, to be told that "the typical American college professor teaches English," on the ground that there are slightly more teachers of English than of any other one college subject, conveys little meaning.

All three measures of central tendency — mean, median, and mode — aim to supply a single number which will sum up and characterize a whole distribution. They are most effective when the latter is "normal" — that is, when the items cluster closely and symmetrically about a central value. But that is just when mean, median, and mode are identical, or nearly so. In other words, they are most accurate as measures when there is very little point in distinguishing them. No one of the three measures has much significance if the number of items in a distribution is small (less than twenty or thirty, for example), or if they are freakishly deployed (in the sense of mostly concentrated at one end while the rest are spread over the whole scale). When such distributions are encountered, it is foolish to try to "average" them at all. It is better to exhibit the whole table of figures. But the greatest weakness of all the measures of central tendency is their failure to convey any indication of the degree of scatter or variation. That supplementary task calls for another set of measures, those of dispersion.

9. Measures of Dispersion

THE RANGE

The number of values on the scale between the maximum and the minimum items in a distribution is known as its *range*. In a new locality, one frequently inquires: How hot does it get around here in summer? and how cold in winter? For what extreme range of temperatures, in other words, should one be prepared? Stock-market quotations in terms of high and low prices for the year are examples of useful ranges. In the playground example, the range of weights on playground A is $95 - 61 = 34$; while that of playground B is $136 - 47 = 89$, or almost three times as great. It is apparent that the range is a measure of "lateral width," which is dependent upon but two values, the highest and the lowest. The disregarding of child B1, for example, would reduce the range of playground B from 89 to 50. A business firm might truthfully say to a man considering employment that its employees were paid from \$50 to \$1000 per week, but if only one man received the higher figure, and the others from \$50 to \$60, the impression conveyed would be decidedly misleading. So, while easily calculated, the range remains crude, erratic, and violently distorted by extreme cases.

THE MEAN DEVIATION

If five men were shooting at a target in competition, they might award the palm to the one who made the largest number of bull's-eyes; or they might, if few bull's-eyes were made, decide to give it to the man whose misses averaged the least. They would then add the distances of the misses from the bull's-eye in inches, and divide by the number of shots, with the low man winning. Something of the same kind is done in computing the average or *mean deviation* of a distribution from a chosen measure of central tendency. The bull's-eye in this instance has to be selected arbitrarily, and is, unless otherwise stated, the arithmetic mean, although the median is sometimes chosen.

In Table III, for example, will be found the grades of ten students in Section I of a certain course. When added and divided by the number of students, the arithmetic mean turns out to be 80. The grade of student I1, which is 90, deviates from the mean by 10 percentage points; while that of student I10, which is 68, deviates by 12 points. One is a plus deviation (above the mean), and the other a minus deviation (below the mean); but in averaging the deviations the algebraic signs are disregarded. The deviations are listed in column x; and, when added and divided by the number of items (10 in this instance) by the formula $MD = \Sigma x/N$, they yield the mean deviation, or (in this case) 6. The meaning of that figure is simply that the grades of the students in Section I, on the average, deviate 6 percentage points on either side of the mean. If you knew only two things about the grades in Section I — namely, that the mean was 80 and the mean deviation was 6 — you would expect a majority of the grades to lie between 74 (or 6 points below the mean) and 86 (or 6 points above it). This happens to be true of 60 per cent of the grades. Similarly, in Section II (Table IV), the mean is 68, but the deviations are much greater — that is, the items are less concentrated about the mean; so that the mean deviation is 18, or three times as great as that of Section I.

One other measure is sometimes used as a check upon the relative sizes of the mean deviation and the mean from which it is computed. This is called the *coefficient of dispersion*. If we were dealing with artillery fire in thousands of yards, deviations of a few feet would be trivial; but if we were shooting a rifle at a one-foot target fifty yards away, errors of the same size

Illustrations of Frequency Distributions, III–IV

Purpose: To compare by measures of dispersion (in addition to measures of central tendency) the grades of students in two sections of a course. Total numbers smaller than warranted, to simplify computation.

	III				IV		
	SECTION I				SECTION II		
Stu-dent	Grade	Deviations		Stu-dent	Grade	Deviations	
		x	x^2			x	x^2
I1	90	10	100	II1	98	30	900
I2	88	8	64	II2	87	19	361
I3	88	8	64	II3	84	16	256
I4	83	3	9	II4	75	7	49
I5	81	1	1	II5	73	5	25
I6	77	3	9	II6	72	4	16
I7	76	4	16	II7	51	17	289
I8	75	5	25	II8	42	26	676
I9	74	6	36	II9	30	38	1444
I10	68	12	144				

SECTION I: $10\overline{)800}(80$ $10\overline{)60}(6$ $10\overline{)468}(46.8$

Mean — Mean dev. — of which sq. root is $6.8 + = \sigma$ Standard deviation

Range 22

Median 79

SECTION II: $9\overline{)612}(68$ $9\overline{)162}(18$ $9\overline{)4016}(446.2$

Mean dev. — of which sq. root is $21.1 + = \sigma$ Standard deviation

Range 68

Median 73

Coefficient of dispersion

Mean   Mean dev.

$80\overline{)\ 6.00}(.075$

Coefficient of dispersion

Mean   Mean dev.

$68\overline{)18.0}(.26+$

would be magnified in importance. By dividing the mean deviation by the mean from which it has been reckoned, a coefficient is found which gives an idea of the relative proportions of the two. That of Section II will be seen to be substantially larger than that of Section I.

THE STANDARD DEVIATION

Where it is desired to emphasize the extreme deviations, all the x's are squared, added, divided by the number of items, and the square root extracted, by the formula:

$$\sigma = \sqrt{\frac{\Sigma\, x^2}{N}}$$

The result is called the *standard deviation,* or root-mean-square deviation, or sigma (σ). It is by far the most frequently used measure of dispersion, because of the fact that it is less influenced than the others by fluctuations in sampling. If a distribution is "normal," and a distance of one sigma is laid off on either side of the mean, it will be found to contain 68.26 per cent of the items; (see Figure 22 in Chapter 12) and the mean deviation will be equal to .7979 σ. In Tables III-IV, however, since neither distribution follows the normal curve, the above percentages do not hold. It will be seen that squaring the deviations (in the column marked x^2) both eliminates the signs, and also amounts to a process analogous to weighting, which makes the sigmas larger than the mean deviations, especially in Section II. Sigma gains much of its importance from its usefulness in computing coefficients of correlation.

THE PROBABLE ERROR

Another measure of dispersion, the usefulness of which is restricted to normal distributions, is the *Probable Error*, unfortunately named because it is neither an error nor probable in the usual senses of those terms. "Error" in statistics has the technical meaning of deviation. The *P.E.* is the amount of deviation which is exceeded by half of the items of a distribution, measured from the arithmetic mean. The probability that a given item will deviate from the mean by an amount greater than the *P.E.* is exactly one-half. In a normal distribution, the *P.E.* is the same as the quartile deviation, and has a constant relationship to sigma, such that $P.E. = 0.6745\ \sigma$. The *P.E.* is of considerable importance as an index of the magnitude of deviations in sampling.

Roughly speaking, then, we may say that in normal distributions and those which are nearly normal, a distance of 1 *P.E.* on either side of the mean will embrace one-half of the items, while a distance of 1 σ in each direction will take in two-thirds of them. The mean deviation comes between the two, since it includes about 55 per cent of the items under the above conditions. All of the measures of dispersion, however, agree in having little meaning except in terms of the measures of central tendency (usually the means) from which they are reckoned. The formulas of variations in ounces in the growth of human babies would look ridiculous if applied in pounds to baby elephants, and *vice versa*. One must always keep in mind both of the "dimensions" of a given distribution, its center and its scatter, either by the use of the coefficient of dispersion, or of Pearson's *coefficient of variation*, known as V, which is equal to sigma divided by the arithmetic mean.

10. Correlation

Having discovered some of the main statistical characteristics of distributions, we are now in a much better position than formerly to compare any two sets of figures which we find to be comparable. We may take, for example, such paired data as the two sets of grades received by the members of a single high school class in mathematics and music, and examine their respective means, medians, modes, ranges, mean deviations, and standard deviations.

But all those measures of central tendency and of dispersion would tell us very little about the way the individuals varied in their performances in the two subjects. The two distributions might resemble one another strongly, and yet the individuals who were tops in mathematics might be at the bottom in music. If we wanted to find out how ability in mathematics was related to ability in music in the same individual, or *vice versa*, the group figures would be of little assistance.

To make a start toward answering such questions by means of a single measure, we should probably make use of a subtler statistical device called the *coefficient of correlation*, or *r*. Correlation is used loosely in common speech to indicate any concomitance or covariation. To say that there is a "close correlation" between profits and accurate accounting means merely that the two are believed to be intimately connected. But in statistics the term is reserved for a mathematical process which yields a symbol of the interrelationship of the spreads of the individual members belonging to two or more distributions about their respective means. This number may range from + 1.00, perfect positive correlation, through 0.00, or no correlation, to − 1.00, or perfect negative correlation. It is hard for many persons to realize that *r*, which is usually some such intermediate figure as − .57 or + .31, is not a fraction or a percentage of anything, but a "pure number without physical dimensions," as Dr. R. A. Fisher calls it, symbolizing a very complex network of relationships.

To return to the grades of the class in mathematics and music, it is apparent that if it consisted of five pupils (for the sake of brevity in explanation), and if they ranked in either of the following two orders, there would be a perfect correlation between their reports in the two subjects.

We see at once that when there is a perfect positive correlation or a perfect negative correlation, we can tell from the position of a given pupil's grade in mathematics *with respect to the mean in mathematics* that the same pupil's grade in music will be above (or below) the mean in music, and *vice versa*. But when the correlation is 0.00, as it is in III, we cannot, from a knowledge of a pupil's grade in one subject with respect to its mean, tell anything whatever about the probable location of his grade in the other subject with respect to its mean. When a correlation is positive, but less than perfect — that is, between 0.00 and + 1.00, it indicates a tendency, greater or less according to its size, for measures above the mean in one series to be above the mean in the other. When it is negative, but less than perfect — that is, between 0.00 and − 1.00, it indicates a similar tendency for measures above the mean in one series to be *below* the mean in the other.

The examples given involve too few cases to have any significance. When enough instances are available, the coefficient of correlation serves as a fairly precise measure of the association of the items in the two distributions relative to their respective means. It shows how one group of instances concentrate and scatter about one mean, as related to the way in which they concentrate and scatter about another. The units compared do not have to be the same in nature or in size; and the means from which they are com-

Distributions for Correlation

I.		Grade in Mathematics	Grade in Music
	Pupil A	90	95
	Pupil B	80	85
	Pupil C	70 Mean	75 Mean
	Pupil D	60	65
	Pupil E	50	55

II.		Grade in Mathematics	Grade in Music
	Pupil A	90	55
	Pupil B	80	65
	Pupil C	70 Mean	75 Mean
	Pupil D	60	85
	Pupil E	50	95

In I, the perfect correlation is positive, while in II it is negative. In the following example, III, however, it is zero.

III.		Grade in Mathematics	Grade in Music
	Pupil A	90	65
	Pupil B	80	95
	Pupil C	70 Mean	75 Mean
	Pupil D	60	55
	Pupil E	50	85[4]

puted do not have to be identical, although it is an advantage to state them numerically in figures of comparable magnitudes.[5]

What makes a correlation high or low depends upon the subject matter. It may be said that in psychological and educational subjects a correlation below .30 (either plus or minus) is regarded as *low*, from .30 to .60, marked but *moderate;* over .60 *high*. But if individual predictions are desired, a correlation of .80 or .85 is desirable. All authorities agree that a correlation of .90 is a great deal more than twice as significant as one of .45, and that, as one's experience with the use of *r* increases in a given field, one's judgments of its significance tend to become much more reliable.

[4] Note that if the grades were laid off on a rectangle divided into quadrants by the two means, with the mathematics grades figured horizontally from the lower left-hand corner, and those in music vertically, distribution I would yield a straight line running from the lower left quadrant to the upper right; II, from upper left to lower right; while III would scatter the items, one in each quadrant.

[5] Attention is called to the *method of least squares* by which the straight line best fitting a set of data may be found.

FALLACIES IN INTERPRETING CORRELATIONS

Correlation, being a complex form of concomitant variation in which the cancelling-out of chance variations is substituted for control in a closed system, is subject to all the fallacies of interpretation already discussed in Section 4. Correlations may be merely coincidental, they may conceal a hidden third cause, and they may be falsely supposed to indicate which factor is cause and which is effect. The telephone numbers of fifty people chosen at random *might* correlate closely with the automobile license numbers of the same persons. A college instructor who amused himself by working out the correlations, in successive years, of the sizes of the shoes worn by students in his classes and the positions of their seats relative to the front of the room, obtained fairly high positive r's in some years, with low or equally high negative ones in others. It has been shown to be possible, mathematically, to produce a substantial r when none is present, or to exaggerate one which is, merely by a faulty arrangement of the statistical material. The probability that any given correlation is the result of chance depends somewhat upon the size of the group. In agricultural statistics, tables of the reliability of r for groups of different sizes have been worked out by Henry A. Wallace and George W. Snedecor.[6] A correlation does not indicate which of the factors correlated is cause and which is effect. As for a hidden third factor, one may very well be obscured by the two which are correlated. There is said to be a positive correlation between the amount of soft drinks, consumed by children in summer and certain children's diseases; but the drinks do not cause the diseases, nor the diseases the consuming of the drinks. It is more likely that the hot weather is to be held accountable for both.

In short, the chief danger of misinterpreting correlations is the almost irresistible tendency to read into them more significance than they will sustain. The principal safeguard against this peril is the use of commonsense in pairing off the data to be correlated. Once this has been done, one must be careful not to assume that a correlation holds beyond the cases which have been included in its calculation, unless upon a fairly secure basis of sampling (See Chapter 12, Section 2). In ordinary weather, the amounts of rainfall and of the hay crop correlate closely, but a summer of complete drought or violent floods would upset the calculated relationship. A high school class might show a high positive r between their grades in drawing and Latin; yet it might be most unsafe to generalize for all such classes, even in the same school, since the class in question might happen to be composed of individuals unusually gifted in those two respects. Time upsets many correlations, such as those which politicians sometimes count on between racial origins and party preferences. Old correlations should always be distrusted, since new and dynamic elements are constantly entering and altering the variables in complex situations. That is particularly true of multiple correlations, by which the variation in one factor is associated with variations in all of the other factors combined.

The chief value of correlations is not for the purpose of proof, except where

[6] *Correlation and Machine Calculation* (Iowa State College, 1931).

they buttress (or weaken) other and stronger evidence; but in the exploratory stages of inquiry where experiment is impossible. In the days when the mechanism of human inheritance was much less understood than it is now, it was generally doubted that it resembled the process revealed by the results of animal breeding. Since experiments in human breeding were frowned upon, an impasse seemed to have been reached. But biometrical studies of humans revealed correlations which made the close resemblance of their heredity to that of other organisms indubitable. In the words of M. J. Moroney, "at no point are statistical methods more of a sausage machine than in correlation analysis. The problem of interpretation is always very much more difficult to deal with than the statistical manipulations. . . . The man who plays carelessly with sharp tools is asking to be cut."[7] As J. M. Keynes remarks, "sensible investigators only employ r to test or confirm conclusions at which they have arrived on other grounds."

11. Ratios and Percentages

A large part of the statistical material which we encounter in our daily lives is in the form of ratios and percentages. Sometimes we read a report that "only 5 out of 1005 heads of white families have been found to be free of physical defects"; but we find such miscellaneous ratios difficult to retain. They are more likely to be remembered if translated into such statements as, "1 in 201 heads of families, etc.," or, "Less than half of one per cent. . . ." The reason is obvious: numbers "stick" better in our memories if they are in tens or hundreds. One hundred has long been the primary instrument of statistical comparison; children learn it in their earliest years at school; and it is so widely understood that it is in constant use in headlines and advertisements: "79 Per Cent of Public School Teachers Are Women," or, "25 Per Cent Reduction in Prices."

Yet there is hardly a department of statistics that is more prolific of fallacies than that of ratios and percentages. The principal trouble lies in the acceptance of the ratio without a clear understanding of the *base figure* or *base* to which it refers. People get percentages fixed in their minds, but do not stop to think what they are percentages *of*. During the depression, there were many reductions of salaries and wages by various percentages, such as 10 and 20 per cent. Later some of these cuts were said to have been "restored" by raising the lowered compensation by similar percentages. But a cut from $100 per week to $80 is a 20 per cent decrease, while a raise of 20 per cent of $80 is only $16, bringing the "restored" compensation to $96, not $100. A similar error may be committed by adding percentage declines by years. A college might lose 25 per cent of its enrollment for five years in a row, an apparent (and impossible) loss of 125 per cent, and yet have 30 per cent of its original number left. That is because the losses would be successively one-quarter of 100 per cent, of 75 per cent, of 57 per cent, and of 40 per cent of

[7] M. J. Moroney, *Facts from Figures*, 3rd ed. (Hammondsworth, England, 1956), p. 303.

the number at the start. The same college, supposing that it had declined from 1000 to 300 students, might even claim (mistakenly) to have decreased 233 per cent, on the ground that the 700 students lost constituted 233 per cent of its *present* enrollment, when, of course, its loss is 70 per cent. In comparing percentages of things like speed records or sales records, it must be remembered that such figures become harder to change by large percentages as performances improve. Between 1492 and 1819, the speed record by ship across the Atlantic was reduced by 62 per cent (from 69 days to 26 days); in the following twenty, by 40 per cent (to 9 days); but since 1879, when it was 7½ days, the record has been reduced by steadily declining percentages to its present 4½ days.

Conversely, when one begins with sufficiently small figures, enormous percentages can easily be produced. A small factory owner who lost $2150.60 on one year's business, and made a profit of $1800 the next year, was accused of "boosting his profits 72,000 per cent." Percentages should never be applied to very small numbers, as in the famous legend about the Turkish population of a small New England city which was officially reported to be "300 per cent criminal." It consisted of one Turk who had been arrested three times. Much care must be taken to distinguish "per cent of" and "per cent greater than." To say that a city's population in 1960 was 90 per cent *of* what it was in 1950 is one thing; to say that it was 90 per cent *greater* in 1960 *than* in 1950 is to say that the 1960 total was 190 per cent *of* the 1950 total. Often the base from which a percentage is computed is slurred over, as in the advertisement reading: "Most girls marry in their early twenties, 65 per cent before they are twenty-five." This does not mean that at the age of twenty-five, only 35 per cent of all girls are left unmarried; for the figures are "based on 60,000 marriages," and show merely that, *of those who marry*, according to this sample, 65 per cent do so before the age of twenty-five. The dangers of averaging percentages without weighting them with regard to what they are percentages *of*, have already been pointed out in Section 8.

It is difficult to lay down rules about ratios other than percentages, since there are so many different types of them, each with its own characteristic conventions and fallacies: per-capita ratios, birth- and death-rates, batting averages, accident rates, operating rates, agricultural ratios, and so on. Per-capita ratios are especially useful in comparing things like money in circulation, costs of government, and consumption of food. A per-capita figure tends to bring home to the individual his imaginary "share" in an immense and otherwise meaningless total. But there is always the danger that per-capita ratios will lead people to think of costs as individually unitary, so that with one hundred fewer children to be educated (at $500 per capita), the apparent saving $50,000 should at once be lopped off the educational budget.

Birth- and death-rates are notoriously deceptive unless corrected for place of residence as well as place of birth or death. In the period from 1924 to 1934, for example, the Census Bureau figures for the birth- and death-rates per thousand of population in Boston and Cambridge, and in the two suburbs Belmont and Wellesley, were as follows:

	Birth-Rate	Death-Rate
Boston	20.2	14.5
Cambridge	19.3	11.8
Belmont	1.7	5.9
Wellesley	1.2	5.6
Whole United States	17.1	11.0

From the crude figures, one would certainly gain the impression that Bostonians were twelve times as prolific as their neighbors in Belmont, while Cantabrigians had sixteen times as many children as the residents of Wellesley. Life would also seem to be about three times as perilous in the large cities as in the towns. The truth of the matter is, of course, that Belmont and Wellesley had no large hospitals, while Boston and Cambridge were plentifully supplied.

The National Safety Council gave the passenger death rates per 100,000,000 passenger miles traveled in 1961 as 2.2 for passenger automobiles and taxis, 1.1 for passenger automobiles on turnpikes, 0.15 for buses, 0.10 for railroad trains, and 0.38 for domestic scheduled air transport planes. But the total passenger miles traveled varied from 1,400,000,000,000 for passenger automobiles and taxis, to a mere 30,290,000,000 for railroad trains. By states, the figures for deaths per 100,000,000 automobile vehicle-miles in the various states during the same year 1961 reached a maximum of 9.4 in Nevada and a minimum of 2.1 in Rhode Island, but neither state can be described as typical of nation-wide traffic conditions. The Council also informs us that in 1961 there was a motor vehicle accident death every 14 minutes in the United States, as against a non-motor-vehicle accident death every 32 minutes, but in the absence of any exposure figures, the rates are meaningless. American coal mines have fewer accidents per worker per year than British coal mines, but this is due in part to the increased exposure of the British miners in hours worked per week.

Crime ratios, in addition to being plagued by definition troubles, are even trickier. In 1890, for example, the census authorities announced that there were 1768 prisoners in jail per million of the foreign-born population, and only 898 per million of the native-born, giving the impression that the foreign-born were about twice as "criminal" as the native-born. But it was pointed out that any population composed of immigrants has a high proportion of adult males, who, in any group, form the largest share of those who are likely to be imprisoned. When the ratios were revised on the basis of male white prisoners per million males of voting age, the figures became:

Native-born whites of native parentage: 3395 per million
Foreign-born whites of foreign parentage: 3270 per million
Native-born whites of foreign parentage: 5886 per million

One difficulty with ratios covering a large territory is that they are likely to conceal smaller differences, such as the figures for density of population in the Western hemisphere as compared with the Eastern. The same is true of national divorce and suicide rates, which misrepresent some of the component regions. To be significant, a ratio should rest upon a homogeneity of material; a county which included a city of 25,000 people and an army camp of 25,000 soldiers would have combined birth, marriage, and death rates which would represent neither the camp nor the city. During 1953–54, for example, the Mississippi state expenditure per pupil in elementary and secondary schools was $70.66, but the figure for white pupils was $98.15 and for Negro pupils was $43.17. Unfortunately the ratio itself does not tell us whether the data upon which it is based are homogeneous or not. Yet it would be a mistake to convey the impression that all ratios are deceptive, for some are very enlightening.

12. Questions to Ask Oneself about Statistics

Each variety of statistics has its own logical pitfalls, but there are a number of questions which it is useful to ask about any figures which are offered as evidence in proving or disproving an hypothesis.

(1) *What are their sources?* Is anyone trying to "prove something" by their use? Are all the figures on one side of the argument? Were they gathered especially, or merely in the course of daily routine? Just how much has bias, conscious or unconscious, affected their worth?

(2) *Are the quantities used representative of the qualities under discussion?* Are additive and non-additive qualities kept distinct? Are the units well chosen with respect to the material? Clearly defined? Stable enough to be comparable?

(3) *Are the data sufficient in volume to support the conclusions drawn from them?* Enough instances? Covering enough time? From a sufficient number of sufficiently independent observers? If samples, are they representative? (See below, Chapter 12.)

(4) *Has a definite effort been made to discover and present data which might overthrow the conclusions reached?*

(5) *Have any of the following common fallacies in making inferences from the data been committed?*

(a) Forgetting that statistics are abstract, and that they therefore omit many qualities which are not selected for attention.

(b) Comparing data out of their contexts, when the latter, if included, would vitiate the comparisons.

(c) Assuming falsely that all other variables except those measured and compared remain constant.

(d) Extrapolating on the assumption that no new factor has entered or no old one has changed in importance.

(e) Mistaking coincidental variations for causal dependencies.

(f) Claiming greater precision in the conclusions than is warranted by the nature of the materials and units used.

(g) Supposing that group data justify predictions about individual cases, other than probability judgments.

(h) Supposing that figures about masses of individuals convey information concerning the interrelations of the individuals in groups.

FOR CLASS DISCUSSION

A. The discovery by Halley that comets were periodic and were not necessarily connected with the death of princes had an incalculable effect on the history of superstition. — *Herbert Dingle*   (1-4)
B. Perhaps the greatest achievement of modern science is its ever increasing capacity to measure. Matters that were formerly entirely outside man's ken are now measured with superhuman mechanical accuracy.   (6)
— *Lynn Thorndike*

Numerical precision is the soul of science. — *Sir John Herschel*
C. Nothing computed from a series of measurements can be more accurate than the original measures themselves. — *Charles W. Odell*
D. Nature does not work with fractions. She makes a whole leaf, a whole calf, a whole man. — *Waldemar Kaempffert*
E. . . . the weight of taxes must be calculated, not by what is taken, but by what is left. — *Ralph Waldo Emerson*
F. Statistical thinking will one day be as necessary for efficient citizenship as the ability to read and write. — *H. G. Wells*
G. Statistics is a tool, an implement used in the making of data, and, like the razor, is a good tool if made of good steel and well honed. The razor does not give the shave; the result is dependent on the skill and care of the hand that guides it . . . also, a deviation of even one inch may mean cutting one's throat. — *John Candler Cobb*   (7)
H. Wherever the statistical method definitely gains the ascendancy, the number of students of a high intellectual level who are attracted to sociology tends to fall off considerably. — *Florian Znaniecki*

EXERCISES IN CONCOMITANT VARIATIONS

Directions:
(1) What are the phenomena which are alleged to vary concomitantly? On what levels are they?
(2) What are the bases from which the variations are measured, and in what quantitative units, if any, are they expressed?
(3) Is the use of the method positive or negative?
(4) How probable do you regard the conclusion drawn, if any, and why?

1. U.S. Department of Agriculture investigators found that tree growth depends upon the length of the day: short days induce dormancy; long days

prolong tree growth. By planting similar trees in places with eight hours of natural light, and in other places with as much as sixteen hours (natural and artificial), it was found that some varieties of trees grew continuously in the longer hours. Most trees will stop growing in four weeks if limited to eight hours of light per day.

2. Drs. Taniyama and Miyasaki of the Saniku Maternity Hospital in Tokyo, Japan, noticed that the average daily birth-rate at their hospital was 4.8, but "when a prolonged low pressure area hits Japan, the rate jumps to ten births a day." They claimed that they could predict the beginning of birth pains in expectant mothers by measuring the speed of low pressure areas approaching Japan.

3. Dr. L. Bradley Pett, nutrition expert of the Canadian Department of National Health and Welfare, reported in 1953 that increasing the amount of milk given to 150 children at a boarding school in Ottawa from 8 to 24 ounces a day decreased the number of colds, of enlarged and infected tonsils, and increased their weights, gave them greater liveliness, better work in school, and more energy. The 150 children all had various vitamin deficiencies before the experiment was undertaken.

4. Under the heading "Embezzlement Rises 400% in Ten Years," the New York *Times* in 1955 printed the information that it was "dishonesty claims" upon capital-stock insurance companies made by employers and paid between 1944 and 1954 which had increased 400 per cent, but that "probably not more than 20 to 25 per cent of embezzlements involve bonded employees." An insurance official, Mr. James M. Henderson, said: "Our worry is continuing inflation. The more active businesses become, the greater opportunities there are for stealing. . . . Assets have grown faster than company protection facilities."

5. Using the 1929 general wholesale commodity price-level in the United States as 100, the drop by the end of 1930 reached 83, in 1931 it was down to 72, and at the close of 1932 it fell to 65. During the same period, the price of steel rails remained at $43 per ton until October, 1932, when it dropped to $40 per ton; and the price of sulphur stayed at $18 per ton throughout the entire period.

6. Just after the end of World War II, two American dental scientists at the University of Illinois, Drs. Isaac Schoor and Maury Massler, reported on dental examinations of 3,905 Italian schoolchildren in four cities where the wartime diets had been predominantly carbohydrates such as spaghetti, macaroni and bread, with very small amounts of sugar. They found that the Italian children had only one-half to one-seventh the amount of tooth decay compared to American children of the same ages. They concluded that children can eat freely of starchy foods and yet remain relatively free of tooth decay, provided the intake of refined carbohydrates such as sugar is kept low.

7. Among a number of experiments concerning factors influencing worker output in Western Electric's Hawthorn plant near Chicago, was one designed to discover the relationship between the quantity of illumination and the efficiency of workers. The workers were divided into two groups, a control group which worked under constant normal illumination, while a test group

had its lighting stepped up from 24 to 46 and then to 70 foot-candles. The rise in output of both groups was roughly the same. Then the test group's illumination was cut to 10 and then to 3 foot-candles, with the output in both groups continuing to rise by about the same amount. Not until the test group's lighting reached .06 of a foot-candle, or about the equivalent of ordinary moonlight, did their output begin to decrease. In two other experiments, the test group were led to believe that the illumination was being increased, although no change in intensity was made, and the same for a supposed decrease. No appreciable change in output resulted in either case. The investigators concluded that psychological morale factors not directly connected with illumination must have kept the output high, although the illumination varied.

EXERCISES IN MEASUREMENT

What point about measurement does each example raise? Are the qualities in question additive or non-additive? Point out any fallacies in the reasoning.

1. For many years, all measures of length in the United States have been based on the lines crossing a platinum-iridium bar imported from Paris in 1890 and checked in 1926 and again in 1956 against the international standard bar, which is 39.37 inches long at the temperature of melting ice. Scientists measuring in millionths of centimeters, however, found a cadmium ray much more accurate; and more recently a light green ray emitted by the transmutation of gold into mercury has been found to be ten times more accurate than the cadmium ray. Its accuracy is to within one billionth of a centimeter.

2. A Chicago chemist-editor, Edward L. Gordy, protested in 1948 that a U.S. Air Force announcement of the speed of an F-86-A fighter plane over a 3-kilometer (9,842.4-foot) course as 670.981 miles an hour was much too refined (to three decimal places) to be accurate. The time was measured by an electronic trip device and a high-speed camera which took 500 pictures per second. But Mr. Gordy pointed out that a plane traveling 670.981 miles an hour would travel 9,841.055 feet in 10 seconds, whereas a second plane going one one-thousandth of a second faster would reach 9,841.069 feet, finishing .014 of one foot, or less than one-fifth of an inch ahead of the first plane. But a camera taking 500 pictures a second would only measure the progress of the two planes in successive jumps of about one foot (actually .9841 of a foot) for each picture. To justify the three decimal places in the speed record, it would need to go 67 times as fast.

3. General Electric Company engineers developed a system of measuring roughness and smoothness by a series of 10 metal blocks representing 25 surfaces and 10 different degrees of roughness from four millionths of an inch, each block being about twice as rough as the one before. To measure any object for roughness, one rubs a finger or scrapes a fingernail across it and then across the various blocks to find the one which corresponds most closely. The result is then checked by an electronic device which "feels" each surface. Ordinary windowpane glass was found to deviate from "perfect smoothness"

by only 4 ten-millionths of an inch, or 7,500 times less than the thickness of an ordinary sheet of paper; satin measured 120 millionths of an inch deviation, or 300 times rougher than glass; a female hand of the "dishpan" variety, 60 millionths, or twice as smooth as satin.

4. Dating of fossil remains has been made fairly accurate by the C^{14} technique: the measurement of the radioactive isotope of carbon of atomic mass 14. As soon as a plant or animal dies, it ceases to exchange radioactive carbon with the atmosphere, so that it loses the element at a known rate of about one-half in every 57 centuries. This technique enables us to measure the elapsed time since the death of living material to within a hundred years in some cases. But its use is limited to the last 30,000 years, because by that time the radioactivity drops below a measurable level.

5. On the basis of some 40,000 statues of her in France alone, Jeanne d'Arc stands as the world's greatest heroine, outranking all others by tons and tons of bronze and marble. — Neal O'Hara

6. In a novel by Lion Feuchtwanger, The Jew of Rome, the author says of a character: "He wondered whether it mattered seriously if a man were to transgress 181 instead of 178 of the 365 prohibitions in the Law so ingeniously excogitated by the learned doctors, and which of these prohibitions had most weight and by how many ounces they outweighed the others?"

7. After a six-months' investigation, a committee of the Board of Higher Education of New York City reported that "formal examinations of any type" were impracticable for determining relative merit in selecting or promoting teachers at the college level. The report said that "formal examinations can be expected to test only a small part of the qualifications which college teachers should have. They cannot reveal ability to stimulate enthusiasm for scholarship . . . nor can they uncover or measure the qualities of mind, character, and personality essential to good college teaching."

EXERCISES IN STATISTICS

Directions: Where relevant, ask the questions listed above in Section 12.

1. It is a fact that an automobile driver averaging forty miles an hour on a ten-hour trip, drives almost thirty-five of the four hundred miles with his eyes shut. This is true because the average person blinks his eyes twenty-five times a minute, and the blink lasts for an average of one-fifth of a second.

2. Dr. Roger J. Williams, professor of chemistry at the University of Texas, argued in the *Journal of the A.A.A.S.* that very few human beings can be shown to be "normal." Suppose you measure a group of them and declare the 50 per cent who come the closest to measuring the same are "normal." Then repeat successively five times with five other measures, and you will find that only 0.03 per cent of the original group remains. If you measure the group 100 times for 100 different characteristics, only 0.0059 per cent of the original members will remain. Dr. Williams based his theory on seven chemical measurements of fats found in the blood plasma of 65 men at different

ages. For any one measurement, 33 of them could be regarded as the middle or "normal" group. But when he tried to establish a normal group for two measurements, the number dropped to 21 out of 65; for three, to 14; for four, to 10; for five, to 8; for six, to 3; and for seven, to 2.

3. If the population reporting income in the U.S. in 1950 were divided in fifths, the top fifth would be found to have received 47 per cent of the nation's income, the second fifth, 24 per cent, the third fifth, 17 per cent, the fourth fifth, 9 per cent, and the last fifth, 3 per cent. But the Census Bureau pointed out that this is income before taxes, which are high in the upper brackets, and it does not include non-money income, which is plentiful in the farm states. The greatest inequalities (as between highest and lowest fifths) occurred in Missouri, New York, and Texas.

4. In 1946 there were 27 divorces recorded for every 100 marriages which took place in the United States; and from this figure came the often-repeated statement: "One in every four marriages today is ending in divorce." It would be just as sensible, says Dr. Samuel C. Newman of the U.S. Public Health Service, to say that, because there were about 3 million births and 1.5 million deaths in that year, to say: "One of every two people born this year died."

5. In 1920, mothers who had been foreign-born had about 150 children per year for every 100 born to native-born Americans; but in 1940 they had only about 99 children to every 101 born to native parents. During the 20 years, the native-born birth rate declined by about one-sixth, while that of the foreign-born dropped by two-fifths. One explanation: the foreign-born mothers were largely residents of cities, where the birth rates tend to be low, while the native-born were spread over both rural and urban localities.

6. The U.S. Public Roads Commission and the National Safety Council made a joint study of 9,000 automobile accidents on 4,000 miles of highways of different types in ten States with these results: When a cross road carried more than 10 per cent of the total traffic of the highway it crosses, the accident rate of 3.7 for each 10,000,000 vehicles per year rises to 13.1 or even more if the intersection handles as many as 10,000 vehicles per day. On two-lane roads carrying more than 9,000 vehicles per day, the accident rate decreases because of slowing down by congestion. Three-lane highways have an accident rate about three times higher than four-lane highways. Four-lane divided highways probably carry a large volume of traffic more safely than four-lane undivided highways.

7. The impression is sometimes conveyed that the small stockholder is taking over control of American business because his numbers have grown over 100 per cent since 1953. It is said for example that the average stockholder in General Motors owns only 270 shares. But the average is made up, among others, of Alfred P. Sloan and his foundation's 686,152 shares (value $52 million); John L. Pratt's 644,276 shares (value $48 million) and the 1,826,421 shares (worth $138 million) given by Charles S. Mott to a foundation bearing his name, leaving him personally with only 103,421 shares (value: $8 million). The average stockholder in Woolworth's has 107 shares;

yet Allen P. Kirby is reputed to hold 356,485 shares (worth about $25 million). A study of "Characteristics of Stock Ownership" made by Jean Crockett and Irwin Friend for a Ford Foundation project estimates that persons with incomes over $100,000 (less than one-tenth of one per cent of the taxpaying population) own 19.5 per cent of all the stock in the country; while those in the $25,000-and-over income brackets possess 48 per cent of all owned shares.

8. 1929 is generally regarded as the worst year for losses of capital in the stock market, but this is a false impression, said Winthrop Parkhurst in the New York *Times* in 1946. It is true that the *Times Index* went from a peak of 311.90 on September 10, 1929, to a low of 164.43 on November 13, a drop of 147.47 points in two months. But it "is the percentage decline that counted then, and counts now." In 1929 the index declined 47.2 per cent; but in 1930 it dropped 44.9 per cent; and in 1931 it was much greater, 60.9 per cent. Even in 1932, it was 58 per cent, or about one and one-quarter times the 1929 tumble. At the top in 1929, a capital fund of $100,000 invested dropped to $52,800 in that year; a similar amount invested in 1932 would have finished that year at $42,000. Percentage losses of 48.4 per cent in 1916–17, of 41.4 per cent in 1919–21, and 43.9 per cent in 1939–42 attracted far less attention than the 1929 debacle.

9. The then-chairman of the Atomic Energy Commission, Dr. Lewis L. Strauss, gave currency in 1955 to the charge that "more than half (53 per cent) of our high schools do not teach physics at all . . . half do not teach chemistry either." It turned out to be based on a sample of 715 out of the more than 24,000 U.S. high schools, or 3.09 per cent, in 1947–48, disregarding the alternation of courses in the smaller schools, which often give physics one year and chemistry the next. In a given year, these schools were counted as not offering one of the two subjects. A study by the Office of Education in 1956 showed that only 23 per cent of all U.S. high schools offer neither physics nor chemistry, and these are the small schools enrolling about 6 per cent of all high school students.

10. An article in *Collier's*, November 11, 1955, entitled "Bay City Beats the Teaching Shortage," on the almost miraculous benefits conferred by the employment of teacher-aides, said that Bay City teachers, after teacher-aides were employed, were able to spend 80 per cent more time in personal counseling for students. It turned out later that this actually amounted to four minutes a day.

11. Dr. Harvey C. Lehman of Ohio University made a study of the ages of leaders in the 100 years from 1846 to 1946, using medians for his comparisons: Congressmen from 35–39 to 55–59; Senators from 45–49 to 60–64; Supreme Court (at appointment): 48 to 56; Cabinet members, 46 to 60; diplomats, 42 to 60; Protestant bishops, 56 to 60; Generals, 48 to 58; Admirals, 36 to 59. One theory holds that the U.S. was a "younger country" 100 years ago; another that it has become less venturesome and more complacent.

≱ 12 ≰

TESTING THE HYPOTHESIS:
Prediction, Sampling, and Probability

1. Using the Group to Predict Individual Instances

STATISTICS MAY SERVE ANOTHER PURPOSE besides furnishing shorthand knowledge about the qualities of groups as groups, thus aiding in the proof or disproof of hypotheses about them. Figures about large numbers of instances may also afford us help in predicting the probable fate of individuals by virtue of their known membership in groups with definite numerical characteristics. "Our salesmen average two hundred dollars per week," runs the alluring advertisement; "why not enroll in our training course today?" The individual is continually wondering "what his chances are" if he does this or that; and statistics are supposed to furnish the odds in favor or against, especially where the factors which are operating in each direction cannot be disentangled by any other form of analysis.

If it is known that a young person smokes twenty or more cigarettes a day regularly, what can be predicted about his life expectancy as compared with that of a non-smoker? Can it be said, for example, that "if the national habits continue in the road they are going, one million children now in school will die of lung cancer?"[1] Such questions plunge one into the bitter and continuing debate between medical authorities and the $7–8 billion American tobacco industry. It got under way in Europe as early as the 1930's, and spread to this country, largely through the persistent efforts of Dr. Alton H. Ochsner of New Orleans, shortly after World War II. What is undisputed is that there has been, during the last four decades, a concomitant increase in two things: the consumption of cigarettes and the deaths from lung cancer. From an average of 1,365 cigarettes per adult smoked in 1930 (less than 50 per adult in 1900), the figures rose to 4,005 in 1962. Approximately 70 per cent of the adult male population now smoke; and 523 billion cigarettes were consumed in 1963. The use of other forms of tobacco has declined during the same period; and there has been no such extraordinary increase in any other variety of cancer. It is abundantly apparent that there is an "association" between cigarettes and lung cancer; but that is not enough to prove "causal connection" between the two.

[1] Ruth and Edward Baker *et al*; *The Consumers Union Report on Smoking and the Public Interest*, (New York, 1963), and Maurine Neuberger, *Smoke Screen: Tobacco and the Public Interest* (New York, 1963).

In 1954 the American Cancer Society published a study of 181,756 men smokers and non-smokers which strongly indicated a death rate among smokers that was 75 per cent higher than that among non-smokers. This conclusion was attacked by the tobacco industry on the ground that other possible causal factors had not been eliminated. To meet this criticism, Dr. E. Cuyler Hammond of the Society conducted a massive inquiry with the aid of a computer, involving in all 1,270,474 adult men and women smokers and non-smokers in 1,121 counties in the United States between October 1, 1959, and September 30, 1962. This "prospective" study was conducted by means of a detailed questionnaire concerning all the suspected factors affecting the death rate. The core of his logical argument was the pairing-off (by the Method of Difference) of 36,975 adult males, virtually identical in fourteen other relevant respects, but differing in that one man of each pair smoked 20 or more cigarettes a day regularly, and the other did not. Dr. Hammond sought thereby to eliminate the factors of race, height, native or foreign birth, rural or urban residence, urban exposure to fumes, etc., religion, education, marital status, use of alcohol, normal sleep, nervous tension, use of tranquilizers, health when studied, family cancer history, and family heart history.

He found that the number of deaths of men in the group studied during the two-year period was 1,385 for the smokers and 662 for the non-smokers, or more than twice as many for all the age groups and for all the causes of death. Of the smokers, 110 died of lung cancer, as against 12 of the non-smokers; while coronary heart disease claimed 654 victims among the smokers and 304 among the non-smokers. Thousands of the men were paired in respect to other possible cause-of-death factors, but in no instance did any of the suspected causes produce a decisive difference between the smokers and non-smokers. Dr. Hammond's conclusions were further buttressed by evidence that the death rate increased with the number of cigarettes smoked each day, and with the degree to which the smoke was inhaled. They were also greater for those who started smoking early in life; and they decreased for those smokers who lessened their consumption or gave up the habit.

These findings along with thirty-five other similar investigations were carefully reviewed over a period of fourteen months by ten scientists comprising the Surgeon General's Advisory Committee on Smoking and Health, who filed a 150,000-word report in January, 1964.[2] In addition, they surveyed the animal experiments and clinical and autopsy studies bearing upon the crucial question of "causation." The Committee reached the unanimous and unequivocal conclusion that the smoking of cigarettes is causally related to lung cancer in men to an extent outweighing all other factors. They found it a significant element in the causation of other diseases as well, although it "is not clear that the association of smoking with heart attacks has causal significance." There is no denying that other factors, such as urban air pollution, are significant, but in comparison with smoking they are minor. To consume cigarettes regularly, then, is, beyond any reasonable doubt, to run the risk of decreasing a person's life expectancy.

A team of British cancer-research specialists computed the life-expectancy

[2] *Smoking and Health* (Washington, D.C., Government Printing Office, 1964).

figures for the 658,000 Britons who were 15 years of age in 1963, and concluded that the loss in life-expectancy for the average smoker (20 cigarettes a day for men, 10 for women) would be 13.4 years for a man and 14.8 years for a woman. They found that the chances that an average smoker would die prematurely from a cause associated with smoking were 1 in 4.5 for men and 1 in 17.5 for women; and that roughly 10 per cent of the 15-year-olds would eventually die from causes associated with smoking: 56,106 men and 9,208 women.

In 1954 the tobacco industry established a Research Committee to investigate the possibly harmful effects of smoking, and it has since expended over $7,000,000 with allegedly negative results. Huge economic interests are at stake: the incomes of the 750,000 tobacco farmers; the annual cigarette advertising budget of over $200,000,000; and the taxes paid by the industry each year, said to be equal to the cost of the whole space program. The case against cigarettes is portrayed by the industry as the invention of fanatical crusaders or "merely statistical" in nature. It may all be due, some say, to coincidence: "the men predestined to an early death might also be those constitutionally inclined to smoke." But the almost universal industry defense is the assertion that none of the proofs offered is "conclusive." Much is made of the fact that the exact substance in cigarette smoke that causes the alleged damage to health has not yet been identified, although the Surgeon General's Committee pointed to the "total tar content" and seven polycyclic hydrocarbons as likely candidates. Thus an industry spokesman can keep on denying specific proof that "there are any harmful agents in tobacco," despite the Committee's warning that it is more prudent to think so rather "than to suspend judgment until no uncertainty remains."

No one on either side of the controversy doubts that further research is needed, since both tobacco smoke and the health of a given individual are extremely complex matters. To establish by experiment an overwhelmingly convincing link between smoking and lung cancer would require, as the retired Dean of Yale University Medical School has pointed out, the control of several thousand human beings. "You would have to take them in the early stages of their lives," he says, "lock them up and control every bit of their behavior for twenty years," after which half of them would be given cigarettes to smoke, and half not.[3] Anything short of such a rigidly controlled inquiry can be attacked as "statistical" and "inconclusive;" but that should not be interpreted as giving the tobacco industry a clean bill of health.

Meanwhile doubts are freely expressed that the present massive preponderance of evidence against the cigarette will have much effect upon the individual smoker or prospective smoker. For what the young person wants to know about smoking and health is told to him in terms of his membership in a statistical group (the smokers or the non-smokers) and its probable effect upon his life expectancy. This is stated in a table constructed by selecting an ideally typical group of 100,000 individuals and totalling the number of years lived until the last survivor dies. The average length of life for the group be-

[3] Dr. Stanhope Bayne-Jones interviewed by Stuart H. Loory. *New York Herald-Tribune*, January 13, 1964.

comes his life expectancy in a comparable group, it being assumed that advances in medical science, diet, and other factors are always slightly improving his chances of survival. At any age reached, his life expectancy can be recomputed on the basis of the total years lived beyond that age by persons in a comparable past grouping. A vast system of insurance and annuity payments has been constructed by actuaries using extremely refined mathematical methods of calculating the odds which have prevailed for various occupations and age groups. Nothing, however, assures the individual that he will prove to be typical of his own group, or that his contemporaries will behave, in respect to survival, like a similar aggregation in the past.

2. Sampling

To examine all instances of a phenomenon, such as "all the men who have served as Chief Justice of the United States," is to make a *perfect induction*. But frequently we should like to make an inductive generalization without examining all the cases. We may do this by the process known as *sampling*, or the selection of one or more instances as representative of many unexamined instances. The problem is to determine when we have chosen a *fair sample*, namely — when the examined instances are truly representative of both the examined and the unexamined? If we could answer that question, we should be well on our way to understanding the problem of evidence for and against hypotheses which reach into the future, and which are believed to furnish reliable bases for predictions about individuals or groups.

There is no one answer that will fit all conceivable operations of sampling. But the central principle is clear: when the material of the field to be sampled is known to be *homogeneous* throughout, a single sample will suffice. As the heterogeneity increases, the size of the sample, if it is to be representative, must increase. Suppose we wish to determine whether the water in a small pond near the seashore is salt or fresh. If the pond was not connected with any other body of water, it would presumably be the same throughout; and one cupful would be characteristic of the whole as far as the quality of saltness-freshness is concerned. But if we wanted to determine, by a process of sampling, the temperature or the bacterial content of the pond, a single sample, especially if the contours of the shore and bottom were irregular, would hardly suffice. In those respects, pond water is not completely homogeneous. In summer, surface water is warmer than depth water; and water filled with vegetation is higher in bacterial content than water lacking in vegetation. So, in order to be sure of not misrepresenting the total situation with respect to those qualities, we should be obliged to take a sample from each main area or region of the somewhat heterogeneous whole.

The same principle would apply in determining what brands of soft drinks were most popular in a college of two thousand students. How many of the students would need to be chosen at random for interviews in order to be sure of a representative sample? Would 10 or 20 or 100 or 200 be needed? The answer would depend upon our knowledge of the homogeneity of the student body with respect to their soft drink imbibing habits. Suppose the college was situated in a location where nearly all the soft drinks were bought at a single store, which for some reason refused to handle more than two or three brands. A small sample would be likely to indicate how the student preferences were divided among the small number of alternatives, although there is always the chance that such a small group chosen at random will be highly untypical. But if the college was located where a large number of stores provided many brands, all well advertised, a much larger sample would be needed.

What if we do not know whether the material with which we are dealing is homogeneous or heterogeneous? We might undertake a survey at a college without any knowledge of its surrounding circumstances. If we began with a small sample at random, and then gradually increased its size, the very process of sampling itself would reveal the nature of the material. If, as we enlarged the sample by successive increments, the proportions of the brands chosen remained virtually unchanged, we could be fairly sure that the material was relatively homogeneous, and we should soon recognize the futility of any further sampling. When enlarging the sample makes no alteration in the result one way or the other, it is a waste of time and energy to go on sampling, the primary purpose of which is economy in just those things. But if the successive enlargements of the sample kept on altering our notion of its general complexion, we should have to continue with our sampling until the changes slowed down or ceased. If they went on indefinitely, we should be obliged to abandon the short cut of sampling entirely, and carry out a complete enumeration.

The likelihood that a given sample is typical of the whole collection of which it purports to be a sample is known technically as its *reliability*. As the size of the sample increases, its reliability, or probability of being typical, tends to increase, but there is no guarantee that this holds true of any given step. It can be shown that the continued random sampling of any finite collection with determinate characteristics is inherently self-corrective.[4] If we had an opaque bottle containing one hundred colored beans, and shook out a group of ten of them, recorded the colors, and replaced them, we might get an entirely false idea of the actual distribution of the colors. But if we continued shaking out samples of ten, more of them would approximate the true proportion than not, and our total sample would steadily increase in reliability. If we knew in advance that the bottle contained only black beans and white beans, it would not take us long to gain a fairly accurate idea of the proportions of each. If we knew that it contained black, white, red, and blue beans, we should expect the task of sampling by tens to take longer; whereas if the bottle were filled with beans of fifty colors, no amount of sampling by tens would enlighten us very much.

Thus, it appears that a rough knowledge of the character of the heterogeneity with which we are dealing is the key to estimating the size and character of the sample which will be most reliable — that is, will be most likely

---

[4] Demonstrated for an urn containing four black balls and two white balls in Cohen and Nagel, *op. cit.*, pp. 284–86.

to be representative of it; and that such knowledge may be gained in the process of going ahead with the sampling. When the material is known in advance to be homogeneous, there is no point in increasing the size of the sample. When it is not known whether the material is homogeneous or heterogeneous, that issue may sometimes be decided in the course of the sampling process. When it is known that the material is heterogeneous, and the general nature of the heterogeneity is known also, a fairly sound judgment concerning the size of an adequate sample may be made in advance. Where it is known that a comparatively small number of factors enter into the making of the heterogeneity, the size of an adequate sample may be greatly reduced by the device of the *stratified sample*, or *cross section*. If it were known in advance, for example, that students bought only two different brands of soft drinks, and that cost was the only factor which affected any student's choice, then the task of obtaining a representative sample would be much simplified, since one would merely have to classify the student body on the basis of amount of spending money: those having plenty, a moderate amount, a little, very little, etc., and then assign correct percentage quotas from the different groups, to be filled by individuals chosen at random from among those groups. But if one could not classify in advance, then the procedure would have to be a random sampling up to the point where the classes began to appear in the returns.

STRATIFIED SAMPLING: POLLS AND RATINGS

The old-fashioned straw vote taken in advance of an election has become an industry through the development of the public opinion poll. It is based upon the discovery that it is not size which is paramount in sampling mass opinions, but correct judgment of the nature of the heterogeneity of the population being sampled. In a straw vote, a comparatively small number of prospective voters are questioned impartially by neutral or "non-loaded" questions prior to the election; and the distribution of their replies regarding their intentions is taken as an indication of the way the larger group will vote. One cannot be sure, of course, that the persons queried will vote in the election at all, or that they will vote according to their annnounced preferences at the time when they happen to be interviewed. Pre-election samples have another peculiarity: to be of any practical value as predictions, they must be extremely accurate, since democratic elections may be decided by margins as small as a single vote. Merchandising surveys, from which the Gallup and other surveys grew, do not have to be nearly so precise. A manufacturer of washing machines who arranges for a poll of housewives on the question: "What make of washing machine would you buy if you could afford one?" will not quibble over the difference between a favorable figure of 45 per cent and one of 50 per cent. But a political poll in a close election becomes almost useless for purposes of prediction when its figures fluctuate around 50 per cent to each candidate, with a margin of error of at least two percentage points each way.

Yet, in spite of all such obstacles, and dozens of others besides, astonishingly accurate results have been achieved, and from almost incredibly small samples. Many of the best predictions have been based on as few as ten to thirty straw votes per one thousand votes actually cast in the election. The Gallup poll and its imitators have attempted with substantial success to "duplicate in microcosm" the opinions of the nation's millions of adults on the basis of personal interviews with from 3,000 to 5,000 carefully chosen individuals. They have been greatly assisted by the prevalence of the two-party political system offering normally only two alternatives.

The open secret of the successful cross section is accurate balancing of the weights of the "segments" or factors believed to be about to be influential in determining the result. In an American election, these are such voter characteristics as sex, age, geographical region, size of community, economic status, and political party. In some elections, racial and religious backgrounds loom large, depending upon the candidates.

The great bane of all cross-section formulas is the delusion that one which works once or twice is therefore final and sovereign for all varieties of problems. A few successes may lead a polling organization to "freeze" its pet sample, which is the quickest way to transform success into failure. The poll proprietors who have not only maintained but improved their reputations for accuracy have been quick, on the other hand, to adapt their methods to changes in political and social conditions.

What brought the *Literary Digest* to ruin in 1936 was a failure to realize that their previously reliable sampling technique had been extremely biased in favor of the higher-income groups. Their purely mathematical error, in disastrously predicting a Landon victory over Franklin D. Roosevelt in 1936, was only about 1 per cent, but they erred in loading their sample, which was top-heavy with magazine and telephone subscribers, by close to 20 per cent.

Another method of sampling is by the *cluster* or selected group: the members of an organization, or a neighborhood or city block that is supposed in some way to be typical of other areas. But the method will not work unless the chosen cluster or clusters are each of them stratified samples, that is, are heterogeneous enough to represent the larger group. In political forecasting, the cluster method is exemplified by the supposedly typical, barometer, or "swing" area. A single election district is pinpointed, which "always (or nearly always) goes the way the election goes," and it is used as a sample. Computers have been brought into the process by feeding into them the pertinent information concerning past returns in such districts, on the basis of which early voting may, by comparison, indicate how the election is going. In the 1960 presidential election, however, this method produced predictions of a Kennedy landslide which were not borne out by the later returns.

A common use of the stratified sample which stirred up so much controversy that it was investigated by Congress in 1963 is the television rating service furnished to advertisers and networks by about a dozen different market-research companies, using varied techniques. Some of them rely on random telephone inquiries about what program is being viewed; others ask selected viewers to keep diaries of their television hours; and still others send out interviewers with "roster-recall" lists of past programs about which householders are queried.

The largest poller in the field, A. C. Nielsen Company of Chicago, constructs a scale model of the national viewing audience composed of 1,150 homes scattered throughout the country with the exception of the sparsely inhabited Mountain States. In each chosen dwelling, at a cost of about $600, the company installs an Audimeter which keeps a record of the times the set is turned on and the channel tuned in. It does not tell whether anyone is seeing or hearing the program, or whether they liked it. Every two weeks the householder removes the tape to be mailed in, and is rewarded by a cash payment from the machine. Allowance has to be made for the failure of about 15 per cent of the homes to report, and a small percentage of machines out of order. The most faithful viewers and reporters (the retired and the young) tend to be over-represented, while the busy people (professionals and the like) are often under-represented in the sample. In spite of these and other defects in the method of sampling, a single point in the Nielsen ratings is said to be regarded by advertisers as "five times as important as 50,000 letters received by the network."

It should be noted that sampling works best when the alternatives are few, both in politics and in advertising. The daily television audience in America is said to number 100,000,000 persons, but they are concentrated in the "prime time" periods of evenings in fall and winter. About 60 per cent of the time sold is bought by just five mass-audience industries: toiletries, drugs, tobacco, detergents, and food. By keeping down the number of "leading brands" in each field, the samples needed to predict trends can be kept small.

Most of our attempts to predict the future courses of groups or of their individual members are much more complicated than the examples drawn from political polling or market research. Sampling is inherently self-corrective only when the collection being sampled is finite and has determinate characteristics. In dealing with natural objects, and especially with classes some of whose members are instances in the future, we can seldom be sure that our collection is a finite one which offers no possibility of inadvertently counting its members more than once. To take a time-honored example, suppose that a man in a field is sampling crows to see whether all of them are black. If ten separate crows come flying across the field, and all are black, is he not in the same position as the shaker of the bottle from which ten black beans have successively emerged? When a bean comes out of the bottle, however, it is retained and kept in sight; but it is much more difficult to be sure that an observer has not seen one of the same crows for a second or even a third time. The difficulty increases as the number of crows observed reaches a hundred or a thousand. We may increase the number of our samples to the utmost limit of our ability, and we shall still be very far from exhausting the number of crows in the world, to say nothing of all past crows, and all the crows which may exist in the future. And every one of the unobserved crows, for all we know on the basis of sampling, *may* be white! Any such probability as

$$\frac{10{,}000 \text{ crows observed,}}{N \text{ crows unobserved}}$$

which we may hope to establish by sampling, still remains so small as to be mathematically negligible.

Yet this situation does not prevent us from sampling all sorts of things, including crows, with a good deal of success in practice. The theoretical problem is to set up some principle which will give us assurance of a finite collection of which we are to do our sampling, or of the exhaustiveness of our finite ordering of what we are trying to know. It is not a question of guaranteeing success every time we sample, but of giving us an intelligible reason for our actual degree of success. We cannot prove in advance that Nature will turn out to be less than infinitely complex; but we are at liberty to postulate J. M. Keynes's Principle of Limited Independent Variety already mentioned in Chapter 10. When it is applied to the future, it amounts to a substitute for the less satisfactory Principle of the Uniformity of Nature. It might be stated as the assumption of a high degree of orderly resemblance between the future and the past, especially with respect to observed frequencies of association, without prescribing just what form the resemblance shall take. While there is an immense variety of facts in our world, the variety of *independent* facts is restricted by some degree of grouping in the qualities of things, and is therefore less than the total variety. There is enough uniformity, in other words, to sustain us in postulating some "invariable" connections on the basis of our knowledge of homogeneity and heterogeneity. We are obliged to take a leap in the dark in every inductive inference, but that does not mean a leap into chaos . Presumably our chances of a correct guess about the heterogeneity with which we are dealing will be improved as we gather more evidence possessing a greater and greater variety. Another limiting principle, as far as our knowledge-getting is concerned, has been suggested by Professor C. I. Lewis from the point of view of our repertory of ordering concepts and our use of them to single out stable elements and patterns in the worst imaginable chaos. By what he calls the "Principle of Statistical Accumulation," he shows how the man who takes account of his past, conceptualizes it, and keeps on revising his judgments to the best of his ability, will always be better off than the man who does not do so. Ordering by mental selection and abstraction pays *something* in the long run, no matter how great the apparent variety of our experiences.[5]

Whichever clue we may prefer to the fact that induction, although sometimes it errs grievously, works well a good deal of the time, we are still in the position of a person sampling huge collections without much advance knowledge of their heterogeneities, or even any assurance that they are finite. We have found out by sampling that, in some of our approaches to segments of the universe, it works well in terms of successful predictions to frame our hypo-

[5] C. I. Lewis, *Mind and the World-Order* (New York, 1929), pp. 386–91.

thesis *as if* we were dealing with finite collections having only a few decisive factors, all equi-probable. So we frame our theories in those fields on the beans-in-the-bottle model, and scrutinize the results. If they yield a long series of successful predictions, we take it that we have hit upon the right method for obtaining fair samples of those particular materials. But we may still be wholly in the dark about the factors which form the pattern, much as a political adviser might advise a candidate: "Make speeches on the following sides of the following issues and you'll be elected, although I can't tell you why." Still less should we be warranted in assuming that our limited successes prove that the whole world will be amenable to the same method of sampling. Just how we shall have to proceed in order to establish statistical generalizations in the social studies, for example, is something which we shall have to learn by actual repeated samplings of our material.

3. *Statistical Regularity*

One evening the New York *Post* carried the startling headline: THESE TWO ACCIDENTS WILL HAPPEN TONIGHT — MAN AND CHILD TO DIE IN CITY. It went on to say that it was "reasonably safe" to predict that a man about fifty-five years old, a resident of New York, would be fatally injured driving home from work that evening, and a child of five would run into the path of a passing automobile. "The daily death toll now is 2.4 persons. Only two may die today, but three should die tomorrow. The average is almost constant over a period of years." The same might be said of ships completely wrecked, letters misaddressed, false alarms of fire turned in, rubbers forgotten on trains, or burglaries committed. Get enough instances of any sort of behavior, and the numbers per substantial period of time are likely to be astonishingly uniform, in spite of short-term perturbations. What happens when the period of time considered is not long enough to establish a trend is shown in the table of snowfall in New York City from 1927 to 1933. Judging by the first three years, the amount remains about constant at the 13- to 14-inch mark; but within the next four years New York experienced both the lightest and the heaviest snowfalls in 13 and 29 years respectively.

What makes the statistical regularity of long-run human conduct so striking is the fact that it shows itself in acts which are not the simple outcomes of a few mechanical forces, like the movements of spun coins, but in masses of close decisions of a very complex sort. Consider, for example, the table of Female Suicides in New York City: over a stretch of seven years, the annual total varies only from 161 to 185. Even more remarkable is the way in which each of the various methods of self-destruction attracts what appears to be a fixed number of devotees for each twelve months, never once changing their relative positions. The only strange break in the whole table is the fifty-five deaths by poison in 1922, which may have been a "wave" of some sort brought on by a few spectacular cases. Note that the figures for the other methods remained constant, so that the high total for the year was apparently due to the increase in that one column alone.

Illustrations of Statistical Regularity

FEMALE SUICIDES IN NEW YORK CITY

Year	Gas	Poison	Hanging	Shooting	Trains	Total (incl. misc. methods)
1918	118	27	19	7	5	176
1919	104	27	13	12	5	161
1920	103	25	25	13	2	168
1921	102	32	15	11	6	166
1922	101	55	18	8	3	185
1923	116	40	12	7	2	177
1924	109	41	10	8	3	171

SNOWFALL IN NEW YORK CITY — U.S. WEATHER BUREAU

Year	Total in inches
1927–28	14.3
1928–29	13.3
1929–30	13.5
1930–31	9.7
1931–32	5.1*
1932–33	24.0
1933–34	52.5†

* Lowest since 1918–19.
† Highest since 1904–05.

SHIPS COMPLETELY WRECKED U.S. MERCHANT MARINE

Year	Number	
1913	274	
1914	293	
1915	289	
1916	317	
1917	324 ⎱ War	
1918	380 ⎰ years	
1919	303	
1920	285	
1921	222	Depression
1922	277	
1923	275	

DOMESTIC ANIMALS ON U.S. FARMS (THOUSANDS) U.S. DEPT. OF AGRICULTURE

Year	Cattle	Dairy Cows	Sheep	Swine	Chickens	Turkeys
1951	82,083	29,722	30,635	62,852	442,657	5,091
1953	94,241	24,094	31,661	54,284	429,731	5,305
1957	94,502	22,816	30,840	51,703	390,137	5,799
1959	93,322	20,132	32,605	58,045	387,002	6,105
1960	96,236	19,257	33,170	58,026	369,484	5,633
1962	99,500	19,215	31,446	56,962	365,447	5,352

Yet when one considers the network of intricately woven causes on a number of levels which bring a woman to the point of self-destruction, nothing seems more unlikely than the notion that just a few simple factors are working in a small variety of combinations. When we come to pick out single factors, such as health, religion, sex, family status, money, and so on, we discover that, no matter which one is selected for testing, it can always be pointed out that in other cases it has been present and has *not* resulted in suicide, or has *not* been present when suicide has resulted. Once the dread decision to take one's life has been made, what could be more subject to permutations and combinations of moods, memories, hints, and ingenuities than the choice of the method? Yet the same amazingly constant totals keep staring one in the face year after year; and lead some people to adopt the fatalistic attitude that

"about so many women *must* commit suicide in New York City every year."
    But we have seen too many constant ratios overthrown by campaigns of prevention which have somehow managed to reach the decisive influences. It used to be thought, in 1900, that 202 of each 100,000 of the population *had* to die of tuberculosis, but by 1938 that number had been reduced to 49. It is a mistake to suppose that statistical regularity must be a matter of the combined action of a vast number of equally important "atomistic" causes, each one of which makes only a minute contribution to the final result. Of course any event has an infinite number of causal antecedents. But, as we saw in Chapter 9, most of them come to focus, especially in a world populated by organisms, in crucial and decisive changes which deserve the rank of primary causes. We are obliged by economy of thinking to concentrate our attention upon the events which make the significant differences, disregarding the influence of vast numbers of minor antecedents as negligible in comparison with a few crucial happenings. If we could not do this with some success, experiment by the use of the Method of Difference would be hopeless, since it assumes that the hypothesis that a change in *one* supposed causal factor will alter the effect is worth testing. If events came about through the accretion of thousands of equally trivial causes, it would be impossible to omit one at a time and observe any appreciable difference in the result. It has also already been pointed out, however, that our habitual tendency to seize upon key causes of the spectacular variety does lead to a slighting of the cumulative influence of minor factors, as when we blame an assault upon a single provocation that was really only the last in a long series of pinpricks. Statistics may help to counteract this urge to find an individual scapegoat by calling attention to the health (or lack of it) of the social organism as a whole.
    The discovery of statistical regularity where none had been suspected is a strong hint of the limitation of independent variety in that sector of the universe. Masses of quantitative data act as magnifiers of hidden uniformities. The reason why we have so much difficulty in acquiring a knowledge of the causes which might enable us to reduce the female suicide rate in New York City is not necessarily because female suicides are brought about by thousands of small variables in purely chance combinations yielding constant ratios, but because we are not yet ingenious enough to locate, frame hypotheses about, and test the main types of the many crucial, complex, dynamic, and interacting causes which are continually in operation within and upon the members of a changing social order.

REGULARITY AND IRREGULARITY SUGGEST HYPOTHESES

    As an example of the way in which statistical regularity can lead to the making of hypotheses about the reasons for it, the classic work of the abbot Johann Gregor Mendel (1822–64) may be cited. When breeding the culinary pea, Mendel noticed that hybrids of purebred parents with differing characters (such as color of the seed) reproduced the latter in their offspring in definite numerical proportions. When yellow-seeded sweet peas, for example, were crossed with green-seeded ones, the first filial (F_2) generation all had yellow seeds, the yellowness being dominant over the green, which was recessive. When the F_1 generation self-fertilized, the results in the F_2 generation were, in 8123 cases: yellow 75.05 per cent, green 24.95 per cent, or a ratio of very close to 3 to 1. Six of Mendel's successors ran the total number of instances up to 203,500, of which 75.08 per cent were yellow, and 24.92 per cent were green.[6]

Having determined the numerical constancy of the results, Mendel proceeded to frame an hypothesis which would account for them in the form of a "something" in the parents which would act according to the principles of mathematical probability and yield three yellows to one green in the F_2 generation. Briefly, he supposed that hybrid parents produced in equal quantities just two kinds of pollen (sperms) and two kinds of egg cells. When yellow pollen joins with yellow eggs, which is one-fourth of the time, since it is assumed that all chances are equi-probable, yellow results. When both pollen and eggs are green, green results. Since each of the "pure" colors comprises 25 per cent of the cases, that leaves 50 per cent to be produced by the two mixed combinations: yellow pollen-green eggs, and green pollen-yellow eggs, both of which turn out yellow, because yellow is dominant over green whenever a mixture occurs. The results, in other words, seem to be almost exactly, in the long run, what they would be *if* the genes, or determiners, were behaving like beans from a bottle or coins being tossed. Notice that until Mendel framed an hypothesis in terms of understandable factors which might be capable of behaving in such a manner, the mere statement of the odds of three to one on yellow in the F_2 generation told us little.

Statistical regularity also works in the other direction, for when an expected constancy does *not* behave or continue to behave in a near-mathematical manner, we look for some disturbing factor. It is well known, for example, that the proportion of boys to girls born over great areas for long periods is not 1 to 1, as a theory of "pure chance" would lead us to expect, but about 1.06 to 1. This slight irregularity has led to prolonged investigations of the determiners of sex in human beings, which have altered many of the earlier theories. If all the winners in a nation-wide lottery in which it was known that tickets were held in every city, town, and village were found to live in a single county, the cry of fraud would be raised immediately. There is nothing theoretically impossible about such an outcome, but it departs so violently from the anticipated pattern that it is hard to believe that no extraneous influence has been at work. When we are confronted by a numerically regular distribution of any sort, we may try to figure out the character of the distributing mechanism from its presumable results, just as a farmer judges another farmer's sowing by the patterns of the sprouts. Where he sees straight lines, he infers machine-sowing; and where we observe consistency, we look about for processes which might have produced it.

Much of the reasoning in the social studies consists of an application of

---

[6] A more recent example is the proportion of 2377 normals (74.91 per cent) to 796 dwarfs (25.09 per cent) in Coral Gem peppers found by Ernest E. Dale, "Inheritance of Dwarf in Capsicum," *Papers of the Michigan Academy of Science, Arts, and Letters*, vol. XIII (1930).

the Method of Concomitant Variations from the side of a supposed effect, using as a base some curve or tendency which is believed to be stable enough to sustain an inquiry, if not a conclusion. In the tables, there are several examples of temporary departure from the statistically regular. The rise in the suicide rate in New York State from 1929 to 1933, followed by a return to normal, is marked enough and steady enough to call for the hypothesis of a broad and continuing "outside" influence, which is found in the economic depression of those years. The increase (1917–18) and the decrease (1921) in the number of ships completely wrecked, although the figures would be somewhat reduced if they were stated in terms of ratios to the total number of United States ships in operation, are attributable to the war and the decline in foreign trade respectively.

The fluctuations in such large totals as those involved in the table regarding Domestic Animals on U.S. Farms give clues to changes in farm life, dietary and other habits. Any sharp change in the prevailing trends should prompt us to look for some new factor. Market and other analysts look for "a kink in the curve," not merely a rise or fall which is carried on indefinitely, since the latter might be due merely to the strengthening or weakening of factors already at work. It is evident from the Domestic Animals table that the number of cattle, dairy cows, and chickens kept on U.S. farms declined steadily and steeply from 1951 through 1962. Meanwhile the number of sheep remained surprisingly constant; while the total for swine fell, rose, and fell again; and that for turkeys rose to a peak in 1959, and then came back to its 1953 figure.

4. Kinds of Probability

Few words are more dangerously ambiguous than "probable." In modern physics and the social studies it has various technical interpretations which are centers of violent controversy, and even in ordinary speech it has many shades of meaning which are not easy to keep distinct. Consider the following examples:

Rain by seven o'clock tonight is probable.

That is probably his sister.

It is probable that the portrait is by Rembrandt.

He will probably outlive his life expectancy by ten years.

Unless this law is passed, 1250 miners will probably die next year.

If we have a large number of electrons able to move freely, the probability of finding one of them is equal all over space.

A .340 hitter will probably get at least one hit per game.

The probability of getting an ace from a well-shuffled pack of normal cards in one draw is 1/13.

It is probable that the Book of Genesis had more than one author.

The most probable value of the probable error of that kind of distribution is 3.2.

Probably his theory of probability would not be acceptable to most logicians.

It is easy to get lost in a jungle of misunderstandings unless one holds fast to a few guiding distinctions. First of all, it will be noticed that "probable" in all of the above contexts refers to some proposition which is regarded as less than certain, but for which there appears to be some evidence. If a thing were known to be one hundred per cent certain, there would be no talk about its probability; and if nothing whatever were known about it, the same rule would hold. Probability, then, falls short of certainty or conviction or full belief on the one hand; and yet it implies *some* grounding or basis in some sort of evidence, even though the latter may not be consciously definable, on the other. Whenever something is said to be probable, we understand that the person speaking intends to convey two impressions: (1) he is not sure of it; and (2) he has some reason for believing that it may be so. There is an expectation regarding some future event, plus the notion that it is an intelligent expectation, such as would be entertained by "an intelligent person reasoning about the facts of the case."

A probability assertion, then, gets its meaning from the system of knowledge upon which it rests. "Relative to complete ignorance, probability has no meaning" at all, as Professor Cohen points out. Furthermore, nothing is just probable in itself. If you say, "Peace is probable"; the sentence has no meaning until you specify when, where, and in what context. That is why the same proposition can have different probabilities in the minds of different people, depending upon their respective systems of knowledge concerning it. Let us suppose that four persons, A, B, C, and D, sit down to play bridge. A hand is dealt, and each of the four is asked this question: Do you think that the dealer, A, has a good hand? Suppose further that A knows nothing about the mathematical probabilities of the distribution of good hands in bridge, and has not looked at his hand. He may say, "This is my lucky night. I'll bet I have a wonderful hand." But this probability judgment of his will be a mere expression of subjective expectancy based on a vague hunch for which he can present no evidence. Suppose that B, his partner, knows the mathematical probabilities, but has not looked at any of the hands. His guess will be based on a fraction of which the numerator is the number of ways good hands can occur, and the denominator is the number of ways they can occur and fail to occur. The third player, C, knows nothing of the mathematics of bridge, but has looked at his hand. His judgment is likely to be a little better than A's, since it will be based on his knowledge of what cards are left to be divided among A, B, and D, plus his vague ideas, gathered from past bridge sessions, of "the chances" of good hands in general. The last player, D, knows the mathematics and has looked at his hand. He will be in position to do a somewhat better job of calculation than B, for he knows what cards remain to be distributed among A, B, and C. All four estimates relate to the same situation, and yet they are likely to differ, because they are based on four different systems of knowledge about it; and there is no point in debating their relative merits until one knows what evidence has gone into the making of each of them. In practice, it is always assumed that a probability judgment is based on *all* the relevant knowledge its maker possesses; but different people possess different amounts, and may differ in their judgments of relevance. To bet on a sure thing is to take advantage of a superior system of knowledge: the probability that a given horse will win a race that has been "fixed" in advance is not the same for the general public and for those on the inside.

Three meanings of probability are already apparent in these examples, although their boundary lines are not clear-cut. First comes *qualitative expectancy,* the subjective state of mind of one who makes a rough estimate, often on the basis of nothing more substantial than a subconscious hunch of some sort. People have, for example, all kinds of strange premonitions about what is going to happen, often on the basis of unnoticed stimuli which do not enter into consciousness. These beliefs are of varying degrees of strength, and seldom have any specifiable foundations except those which may have been improvised later to support them. If those who hold them were asked to state the exact odds each way, they would consider such a request ridiculous, since the systems of knowledge on which the judgments rest do not afford a basis for numerical calculations. Many such expectancies are as flimsy as that of the chicken which has been fed every morning for years, until one day it gets the axe instead. Routine without understanding breeds thousands of expectations; but if they are not reasonable expectations — that is, if they have no grounds which are clearly apprehended — great shocks are always possible in the form of sudden upsets.

There is another quite different type of qualitative or non-numerically expressible expectancy which has to do with the recognition of likenesses and differences in patterns of faces, signatures, paintings, and even crimes. The art critic who declares, on the basis of prolonged study, that "this painting is probably a Titian," may base his judgment on many subtle qualitative resemblances, hard to put into words, and impossible to state in figures. Such evidence may nevertheless supply a solid foundation for his probability judgment. The judge who comes to the conclusion that a witness is probably withholding some of the truth may have equally substantial, and intangible, grounds for his belief. The detective who says, "This job looks like the work of the X-gang," may be using an analogy which will bring excellent results, and yet may find difficulty in putting it down on paper. Most of our qualitative expectancies, however, lack any such supporting systems of knowledge, and are often little more than rank conjectures.

The second type of estimate makes use of *empirical probability,* which is based upon past performances. This we have already encountered in the life-expectancy examples. As it applies to the future, it is a combination of the relative frequencies known to prevail in large classes in the past, plus the assumption that the same frequencies, on the whole, will continue in the future. It differs from the mere qualitative expectancies which are also, in many instances, based on past happenings, in that it is capable of expression in statistical form, such as mortality tables and ratios of college graduates whose names are in *Who's Who.* When a ballplayer who is hitting over .333 for the season comes to bat, we say that "the chances are" one in three that he will get a hit. But he may thereupon strike out four or five times in a row, and end his day with an average of only .328. Empirical probability never includes present or future instances, except by assumptions that they will resemble the observed past occurrences upon which the empirical judgment rests. The latter are treated as a fair sample of what the future will bring, but that does not prove that they will turn out to be so. Consequently, all empirical probabilities in numerical form are only approximate, being subject to constant revision in the light of new items which may be added to our samples as time goes on. Unless the numbers of instances are large enough to eliminate chance variations, empirical probabilities are likely to have little significance. In the period from 1620 to 1937, New England had but one severe hurricane, yet it experienced two more within the next six years (in 1938 and 1944).

We have already seen how, in the example of Mendel's discovery of the principles of heredity, an empirical probability based on a large sample which displayed the approximate proportions of three to one led to the hypothesis of an "ideal" mathematical relationship at work in the intermingling of the genes. That introduces the third type of probability, the mathematical, which is so distinct that it deserves treatment by itself.

5. Mathematical Probability

The subject of probability has been almost equally the product of two human interests: statistics and gaming. The former has provided mountains of material for empirical probability judgments; the latter has led to the development of a complicated deductive theory or calculus which is a branch of modern mathematics. The two traditions have interacted fruitfully, but the very fruitfulness of the interplay has brought about no little confusion concerning their relationship to one another.

A good way to grasp the nature of mathematical probability is to recall the characteristics of a game of chance, or a game of skill constructed on a chance basis, such as those played with cards or dice. In theory, the game operates strictly within certain completely calculable limits, since the pack is limited to fifty-two cards of four recognized suits, with no wild "ace of hippogriffs" included, as in one of Heywood Broun's stories. It is also assumed that nothing extraneous will enter to make any one of the possibilities any more likely to occur than any other. If that did happen, it would "spoil the game." Suppose that a person had practiced until he could control his arm and finger muscles in such a manner that he could turn up any face of a die at will; we should refuse to let him play. Loaded dice and marked cards ruin a game, even if all the players know that they are in use, because they make it extremely difficult to determine the revised basis for the calculation of the chances. It is of the essence of a game of chance that no one participant shall have any more knowledge than another of the specific causes of the tiny variations which bring about the results, upon which he could base a superior probability judgment.

Mathematical probability might better be called mathematical possibility-ratio, since it applies only where two "ideal" conditions are assumed to prevail: (1) all the relevant possibilities are known and stated, and (2) all are equi-probable. The second requirement, that the events must be "equally likely" to occur, sounds straightforward enough, yet conceals within itself a number of difficulties. For if we know nothing about the factors affecting the events, then, as far as *we* are concerned, they are "equi-probable." Some thinkers therefore hold that events cannot be declared to be equally likely unless we know all the factors impinging upon them, and know that they are equal. Only if we have carefully weighed and examined a coin should we say that, if tossed impartially, it is equally likely to show a head or a tail.

Under such circumstances, necessary deductive inferences in advance about what is formally probable can be drawn from the premises if the latter are fully defined. All we need to compute any mathematical probability is a finite set of equi-probable alternatives which exhaust the possibilities. The number of these alternatives forms the denominator of a fraction, of which the numerator is the number of "favorable" alternatives according to the terms of our problem. If we want to know the mathematical probability of getting a head on one throw of an ideally "true" coin, the number alternatives is two, and the number of favorable alternatives is one, so the answer is 1/2. The same for any given face on a single die, such as a three, is 1/6; and for any given card in a normal pack, such as the ten of hearts, is 1/52. The formula is always $f/f + u$, when f equals the favorable alternatives, and u equals the unfavorable, all being equi-probable and collectively exhaustive.

All the formulas of mathematical probability are "ideal" in the sense that their symbols refer to the imagined actions of perfect coins, dice, cards, or whatever, which function impartially in a sort of super-vacuum where all deflecting influences are excluded. They can, as we shall see presently, no more be overthrown by the failure of an actual coin to behave that way than Euclidean geometry can be discredited by the failure of surveyors to lay out a perfect square one mile on each side. Mathematical probability, like formal logic, is primarily a matter of careful definition of the premises followed by valid reasoning. First we must decide whether the events whose mathematical probability we are discussing are *independent, disjunctive,* or *complementary.*

Independent events. Two or more events are independent if occurrence of one is not affected by the occurrence or non-occurrence of the others. Examples: the simultaneous tossing of two coins, or two successive tosses of the same coin.

Disjunctive events. Two or more events are disjunctive if the occurrence of one of them affects the occurrence or non-occurrence of the others so that if one occurs, the other cannot. Examples: either heads or tails on a single toss of one coin; or a single face on one die, which excludes all the other faces.

Complementary events. Each of any pair of completely disjunctive events is said to be the complementary of the other. The sum of the probabilities of any pair of complementary events is one, or certainty, provided one or the other must occur. Examples: heads or tails on one toss of a coin; getting or not getting a six on one throw of a die.

Once we have determined the proper classification of our events, it remains only to apply the proper theorem; and the rest is arithmetic.

THE PRODUCT THEOREM

To find the mathematical probability of the joint occurrence of independent events, compute the individual m.p.'s and *multiply*. Example: What is the m.p. of getting two heads on two successive tosses of a fair coin? The m.p. of the first toss is 1/2, and that of the second toss is the same: $1/2 \times 1/2 = 1/4$. Proof: There are four equi-probable possibilities, HH, TH, HT, and TT, only one of which gives the desired two heads. There is a special case of the product theorem which deserves attention, namely, the m.p. of a joint occurrence of two independent events when one of them has already occurred. Let it be supposed that a bag contains three red and two white beans, and it is desired to find the m.p. of getting two red beans on the first two drawings if the first bean drawn is *not* replaced. The m.p. of the first red bean is 3/5, and that of the second is 2/4, since there is no probability of two reds whatever unless the first one is red, and if it was, then four beans, two of which are red, remain. Multiplying, the probability of the joint occurrence in succession, taking account of the first event's happening having affected the odds on the second is $3/5 \times 2/4 = 3/10$.

THE ADDITION THEOREM

To find the m.p. of the joint occurrence of disjunctive events, compute their independent m.p.'s, and then *add*. Example: What is the m.p. of getting *either* two heads *or* two tails in two tosses of a single coin? The m.p. of a head on the first and second tosses is $1/2 \times 1/2 = 1/4$, and that of a tail on both is also 1/4, or a total of 1/2. Proof: There are four possibilities as before: HH, TH, HT, and TT, only two of which give the required two heads or two tails.

There are a number of special cases which arise under the addition theorem because of the fact that all m.p.'s are expressed as fractions which cannot exceed 1, or certainty. No wholly satisfactory way can be found to express some of these probabilities, but that is the fault of the number system. Example: What is the m.p. of getting *at least* one head on three tosses of a single coin? If you add, the result: $1/2 + 1/2 + 1/2 = 1\text{-}1/2$, being more than certainty, is absurd, since we know that it is perfectly possible to toss a coin three times and not get a single head. But to do that, we must get three successive tails, the m.p. of which is $1/2 \times 1/2 \times 1/2 = 1/8$. This turns out to be the complementary of at least one head in three tosses; so, since the sum of complementaries is 1, we may subtract: $1 - 1/8 = 7/8$. Proof: In three tosses there are eight equi-probable combinations, only one of which fails to give at least one head, viz, HHH, HHT, HTH, THH, TTH, THT, HTT, and TTT.

A somewhat more complicated example: What is the m.p. of drawing *at least* one red bean in one draw each from two bags, the first containing six red and two blue beans, and the second containing five reds and four blues? If the addition theorem were used, then the m.p. from the first bag is 3/4, and from the second is 5/9, which would make 47/36ths, or more than certainty.

It is necessary, therefore, to treat the m.p. of the event which would prevent the one in question, namely, the drawing of a blue bean from both bags, as its complementary, thus, $1/4 \times 4/9 = 1/9$, which subtracted from 1, gives the answer, 8/9.

6. Mathematical and Empirical Probabilities Compared

Much confusion has been produced by the so-called "tests" of mathematical probability, to see whether or not it predicts in detail the behavior of actual coins or cards or dice, which no one should ever have expected it to do. In the field of coin-tossing, where the m.p. of a head on each toss is 1/2, these are some of the results:

		M.p.	Actual
Buffon	4040 tosses	2020 heads 2020 tails	2048 heads 1992 tails
De Morgan (pupil of)	4092 tosses	2046 heads 2046 tails	2048 heads 2044 tails
Jevons	20,480 tosses (2048 of each of 10 coins)	10,240 heads 10,240 tails	10,353 heads 10,127 tails
P. R. Hill	100,000 drawings of 1 penny from a can containing 100 pennies dated 1919 matched with 100 pennies dated 1920	50,000 (1919) 50,000 (1920)	49,855 (1919) 50,145 (1920)

Before concluding that mathematical probability "does not apply to our world," it would be advisable to remind ourselves what m.p. expresses, namely, a ratio among limited possibilities which are equi-probable by definition. The possibilities are what they are stated by definition to be, and certain formal ratios of probability prevail among them. By definition, no "ideal" coin can come to rest on its edge; therefore, there are only two possibilities: a head or a tail. If any actual coin has ever or can ever balance on its edge, then there are not two, but three empirical possibilities. Thus, we are never entitled to condemn the formulas of mathematical probability on the ground that "things do not work that way in practice." Granting the correctness of our arithmetic, our conclusion should always be the other way around: we should conclude that our coin or dice or pack of cards falls short of ideal equi-probability. It is equally absurd, as John Dewey has pointed out, to suppose that if even a million tosses produced exactly 500,000 heads and 500,000 tails, that would "verify" the theoretical m.p., because there would be no justification for stopping the series short of the next toss, which would be bound to upset the "verification."[7]

If, without examining the coin, one started a series of bets with an unknown stranger on the likelihood of heads or tails on a coin flipped by him, the m.p. of a head on each toss, taken by itself, is exactly 1/2, even though the first

[7] John Dewey, *op. cit.*, p. 477.

ten tosses resulted in tails. The question is, Under those circumstances how long would one continue the game without demanding to see the coin? An even knottier problem is posed by the sale of a gambling device that is represented to the buyer as an approximate instrument of mathematical probability — that is, so constructed that it will, in the long run, turn up the same proportions of reds and blacks. Suppose that in actual operation the device produced 700 blacks and 300 reds on the first 1000 turns. Is the machinery out of order? Is the buyer entitled to recover what he has paid? Or is it just an empirical run of luck, perfectly possible on the mathematical basis, since there is nothing in the possibilities to prevent 1000 successive reds (or 1000 blacks, or *any* combination of the two colors which adds up to 1000).

The mistaking of mathematical probability for a statement about actual cards or coins is responsible for the famous *gambler's fallacy*, or the doctrine of "the maturity of chances." According to this reasoning, in the long run, equi-probable possibilities "even up" or reach an "equilibrium," by a "law of averages" which influences the individual cases. If there is a "deficit" of 100 heads in tossing a coin 1000 times, then the likelihood of heads at the start of the second 1000 tosses becomes more than 1/2. But this implies what Bertrand, the French mathematician, denied, that coins have consciences, and memories of how they have fallen. All we can say is that in the long run (and no one can say what its exact length must be), the *proportion* of equi-probable outcomes tends to be approximately equal *if* somewhere near ideal conditions are maintained. That tells us nothing about the next toss, which is independent of all past and future tosses, and has an m.p. of exactly ½, no matter what happens before or afterward. One of the strangest things about gamblers is their ability to produce logical doctrines to justify almost any system they happen to be using, since some schools of roulette players advise betting on the numbers which have occurred frequently, instead of infrequently; and all gamblers, when and if they set up in business for themselves, count on neither the maturity nor the immaturity of chances, but rely instead upon the uniform long-run operation of a small percentage in their favor.

Another fallacy closely connected with mathematical probability concerns the occurrence of extremely improbable events, when rarity is confused with a small m.p. ratio. The card player who picks up a hand containing thirteen cards of one suit considers it a rare one, which it is, since only four out of the 635,013,559,600 possible combinations of cards in bridge permit it. Yet, from the point of view of mathematical probability, *any* specified combination of thirteen individual cards is just as rare in the sense of unlikely to occur, and is just as "hard to predict" as any other, as you will find out if you write out a prescription for a hand in advance, and then try to deal it to yourself honestly. The extremely improbable, in this sense of prediction from the mathematical possibilities, happens all the time with every hand that is dealt.

The incessant occurrence of the extremely improbable (in the above sense of difficult to predict successfully) should warn us to expect extraordinary coincidences, and should protect us against the absurd notion that "only the probable happens." That there should be occasional striking coincidences in their due proportion is one of the best proofs that we are living in a universe which is somewhat orderly; and yet, ironically enough, they are often adduced as evidence of cosmic caprice and disorder. In a series of indefinite length, such as "all the fair coins which have been and are being tossed," some long runs of heads and tails should be expected, although no one can tell *when* they are likely to occur. If they never occurred, we should probably doubt the orderliness of the physics of coin-tossing. One of the reasons why large odds against a person seldom discourage gamblers is that they concentrate their attention upon the fact that *someone wins*, even though the initial odds against that someone may have been tremendous — in some French lotteries, as high as 22 billions to 1.

Mathematical probability gives us no help in determining what events are so very improbable as to be "out of the question" in the world of experience. In an article in the *New Yorker* of February 3, 1940, which has become a classic, Russell Maloney had a great deal of fun with the idea that "if six chimpanzees were set to work pounding six typewriters at random, they would, in a million years, write all the books in the British Museum . . . along with a mountain of gibberish, of course," by supposing that six actual chimpanzees started in by writing correctly a dozen or so large volumes "without spoiling a single sheet of paper." Given the twenty-six letters of the alphabet, and enough time, mathematical probability can set no limit on the patterns which might be formed. Yet many of the operations of chance which have been performed with a fair approach to equi-probability, such as coin-tossing and die-throwing, seem to stay within empirical limits.

THEORY OF GAMES

In 1927 Professor John von Neumann and E. Borel formulated independently the mathematical theory of games, which has proved a fruitful application of mathematical probability to economics and military operations. Game theory deals with the interactions or "strategies" of individuals or groups in making optimum moves against one another on the basis of incomplete information.

The simplest games are of the zero-sum variety, such as matching coins, where one player wins all and the other loses all. Von Neumann propounded for such games a "min-max" theorem to the effect that a player can mix his moves so as to guarantee that he will not win or lose more than a quantity y, known as the "value" of the game. This mixture can be announced frankly without giving his opponent any advantage.

In non-zero-sum games, where there are three or more players, and where the advantage of one player does not cause a loss to another, no such simple theorem applies. Attempts have been made, however, to extend game theory to poker and blackjack, and even to football and baseball, usually by greatly oversimplifying the alternatives.

THE BINOMIAL THEOREM AND THE NORMAL CURVE

One of the most useful devices in modern statistics, the so-called *normal curve of error*, or simply the *normal curve*, is approached as a limit by simple coin-tossing. If two coins are tossed simultaneously, or one is tossed twice in succession, the possibilities are

$$2H, 0T \qquad 1H, 1T \qquad 0H, 2T$$
$$1 \qquad\qquad 2 \qquad\qquad 1$$

which may be expressed as the expansion of the binomial $(\frac{1}{2}H + \frac{1}{2}T)^2 = \frac{1}{4}H^2 + \frac{1}{2}HT + \frac{1}{4}T^2$. When three coins are tossed, the possibilities are

$$3H, \qquad 2H, 1T \qquad 1H, 2T \qquad 3T$$
$$1 \qquad\quad 3 \qquad\qquad 3 \qquad\quad 1$$

which will be seen to be $(\frac{1}{2}H + \frac{1}{2}T)^3$ expanded to $\frac{1}{8}H^3 + \frac{3}{8}H^2 T + \frac{3}{8}HT^2 + \frac{1}{8}T^3$. The exponent of the binomial in each instance is the number of coins tossed. When ten coins are tossed, the distribution becomes

$$\frac{1}{1024} H^{10} + \frac{10}{1024} H^9T + \frac{45}{1024} H^8T^2 + \frac{120}{1024} H^7T^3 + \frac{210}{1024} H^6T^4 + \frac{252}{1024} H^5T^5 +$$

$$\frac{210}{1024} H^4T^6 + \frac{120}{1024} H^3T^7 + \frac{45}{1024} H^2T^8 + \frac{10}{1024} HT^9 + \frac{1}{1024} T^{10},$$

as shown in Figure 21. If one determines the m.p. of any event, symbolized by p, and the m.p. of its sole exclusive alternative, symbolized by q, then the m.p. of a complex event with n components may be calculated by selecting the proper term in the expansion of the binomial $(p + q)^n$. For N trials of n coins, it becomes: $N(p + q)^n$.

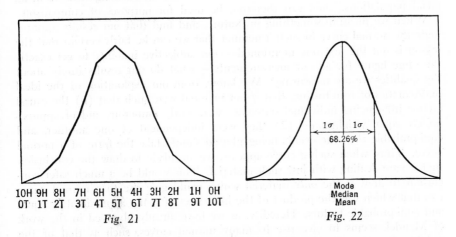

10H 9H 8H 7H 6H 5H 4H 3H 2H 1H 0H
0T 1T 2T 3T 4T 5T 6T 7T 8T 9T 10T

Fig. 21

Mode
Median
Mean

Fig. 22

As n increases, the symmetrical distribution (Figure 21) approaches more and more closely the smooth, bell-shaped *normal curve of error* (Figure 22), in which mode, median, and mean are identical, and the two segments measuring 1σ in distance on each side of the mean include 68.26 per cent of the cases. It is sometimes referred to as De Moivre's curve, in honor of its discoverer, Abraham de Moivre, a Protestant who was driven from France by the revocation of the Edict of Nantes in 1685, and who achieved membership in the Royal Society at the age of thirty. The normal curve is approximated empirically by two kinds of distributions. The first consists of the many measurements by different observers of some quantity that is difficult to measure, such as the mass of the moon, which is an important constant in astronomical calculations. Many equally competent astronomers differ slightly in their measurements: in 1900, for example, A. B. Hinks, an English astronomer, determined the moon's mass to be such that it would have to be multiplied by 81.53 to be equal to that of the earth. In 1930, Dr. N. E. Wagman announced a figure of 81.28; and in 1938 Dr. H. R. Morgan of the United States Naval Observatory found it to be 81.26, subject to an error of around .11. If a large number of such estimates were plotted on a frequency table, their subjective variations (reflecting the personal equations of the observers and their methods) would be likely to cluster around the average in a normal curve.

The second type of distribution is obtained whenever we measure a large number of examples of organisms or parts of organisms, such as the lengths of all the leaves on a single tree, the size of the shells of many snails of a single variety, the heights of a regiment of soldiers (not especially selected for height), or the grades of thousands of students on a test composed of several hundred items. In all these distributions, a few cases will be found at both extremes, with more and more as we approach "mediocrity" (the mean), thus forming the normal curve, or, as it is sometimes called in this connection, "the biological line." We are told, for example, that in studies of racial characteristics, "Experience has shown that the Normal Curve is the typical form of distribution in the case of all metrical characters of racial significance in all racial populations," and can therefore be used for purposes of comparison.[8]

When we measure something in Nature, and find that our results approximate the normal curve in such a manner that we can be fairly certain that the reason is not the first one mentioned — our subjective inability to get exactly the same figure for all our measurements — what do our results imply about the qualities we are measuring? We know, from our exploration of the ideal mathematics of coin-tossing, that *if* our material were such that (1) the causal factors influencing individual outcomes were fairly numerous and of approximately equal weight; and (2) they were independent of one another, and equi-probable *then* the events being plotted should take the form of a normal curve. Thus, when such a curve appears, we are likely to draw the conclusion that we are dealing with just such material. This would be a much safer conclusion to draw if the *only* material which could give rise to a normal curve was that which was the product of the influences of many approximately equal and equi-probable factors. Heredity, as we have already observed in the work of Mendel, seems to give rise to many normal curves, such as that of the weight of newborn babies; but what about environment? There is some evidence that it may also produce effects which fall in normal curves, such as the amount of slowing down by motorists at an unguarded street crossing. When the grades of a class in algebra follow the normal curve, is it because native intelligence is hereditary, or because algebra teaching produces "random" effects?

[8] L. C. Dunn in article cited, *Race and Science*, pp. 320–28.

If used with discretion, the normal curve can be a powerful instrument of analysis in the social studies, particularly where it is "skewed" by extraneous factors. Income and other "success" curves depart markedly from the normal curve, which is often believed to hold for innate mental capacity. This would be a clear indication of the intrusion of such factors as property rights and social status. On the basis of a normal distribution of hereditary intelligence in the population, college students would be drawn from all the social strata, instead of unevenly from a few privileged groups.

The weak spots in most of our efforts to read back a simple form of order from the occurrence of normal curves in Nature are the assumptions of independence and equi-probability. It does little good to assume that the weather which affects crops, for instance, is a compound of wholly independent factors which are equi-probable; or that the weather is one independent factor which is somehow shuffled together with other independent equi-probable factors in the making of the crop. Most of our first observations of the world about us do not take the form of the normal curve. For one thing, they are too few in number, forming too small a sample. Often there simply are not enough instances to enable us to establish a curve except indirectly. The social studies are constantly faced with "too few cases" in a period of time short enough to insure stability. Not even the huge populations of the twentieth century furnish numbers large enough to compare in statistical uniformity with the swarms of molecules in the kinetic theory of gases, the members of the super-galaxies in the heavens, or the countless clouds of electrons in subatomic physics.

7. The Probability of Generalizations

We have seen how hopeless it is to expect to test an hypothesis relating to an individual instance by means of statistical evidence. The latter can afford no proof by complete elimination, since by definition a statistical generalization holds only for a certain proportion of the cases it covers, and one never knows in advance exactly where an individual instance belongs. But what about the generalizations themselves? Is there any meaning to be found in the conception of the generalization, hypothesis, or theory having a greater or lesser probability? As more evidence, and particularly as more evidence of a certain weight or quality, comes in, we certainly suppose that our theories come to have an increased or a decreased probability.

Let us set up the hypothetical generalization that "All Negroes are right-handed," and, to restrict it to its simplest and most manageable form, let us confine it to "All the Negroes riding on this bus, five in number, are right-handed." We shall assume (1) that there are just two possibilities — a Negro may be either right-handed or left-handed, and not ambidextrous; and (2) that we have no reason to believe that either independent possibility is any more probable than the other. Applying the formula of mathematical probability, the m.p. that all five are right-handed (on the above conditions) is $1/2 \times 1/2 \times 1/2 \times 1/2 \times 1/2 = 1/32$. We inquire of the first one, and find that he is right-handed. Immediately the probability that our *generalization* is true rises above 0. Mathematically it becomes $1 \times 1/2 \times 1/2 \times 1/2 \times 1/2 = 1/16$. *But that does not, on our assumption of independence, increase the probability that the next Negro will be right-handed one iota.* It is still 1/2. We may continue, discovering that the second, and third, and fourth Negroes are right-handed; whereupon the m.p. that our hypothesis will hold of all five cases reaches 1/2. But the fifth Negro may be left-handed, whereupon its m.p. becomes 0.

There is a paradox here which easily deceives the unwary. Every time we discover a fact implied by an hypothesis of ours, that discovery increases the probability of the hypothesis; and yet it does not increase the probability that the hypothesis will hold in any unexamined instance one particle. We are always, in situations where all factors are assumed to be equi-probable, at the mercy of the next unexamined case, like the gambler who has won nineteen times in a row, and would like to make it twenty. If the fifth Negro is left-handed, our hypothesis is worthless unless it is revised to read: "All Negroes are right-handed to the average proportion of 80 per cent," which makes our bus inquiry a problem in sampling — that is, in homogeneity or heterogeneity.

But to return to our original hypothesis to the effect that "All Negroes are right-handed." Our collection has ceased to be a finite number; and the problem resembles the question whether "all crows are black." To make any headway, we must, as we saw in Section 2 above, invoke some form of postulated limitation of variety, probably in the shape of abandoning independence for an interlocking of the qualities of things. As we add positive instances (observations of additional Negroes who are right-handed), the probability of the hypothesis could therefore be said to increase, subject always to demolition by a single negative instance (a left-handed Negro). What we lack is any intelligible notion of the connection between being a Negro and being right-handed which would transform our descriptive hypothesis into an explanatory one.

Some few of our generalizations rest upon mere numbers of observed instances because we have no inkling of any better foundation for them. But the evidence for most theories has weight which does not come merely from the number of positive instances, but from their variety as well. Suppose that we have two theories, X and Y, for which there are no negative instances. There are two hundred positive instances of X, which have been found in only one field of inquiry; while there are only one hundred positive instances of Y, which have turned up in five different fields of inquiry. The probability of Y would be regarded as greater than that of X, because of a greater risk, successfully survived, of finding negative instances. Where the finding of a positive instance was unexpected on the basis of all other theories and established knowledge, but was predicted by theory Y, that single instance might have a greater evidential weight than all two hundred items in favor of X.

It is also apparent that we attach greater weight to the evidence for theories which predict outcomes with a high degree of precision, although that may depend upon the skill of the verifier. A more important source of increased weight is the buttressing of one theory by the positive instances for another theory which is systematically connected with it. The hypothesis of a common origins of two racial stocks would be increased in probability by finding many instances, in a variety of quarters, of common blood-transfusion-group characteristics; and also of similar cranial-index measurements. Each kind of evidence would increase the weight of the other, if both kinds could be woven into a larger theoretical nexus or system, the science of anthropology. In a sense, each bit of evidence for any scientific theory increases the probability of all other scientific theories, for it is the method of science which is thereby shown to be more and more likely to lead to reliable knowledge. This mutual buttressing of a common method by its results, and of our confidence in the probable results by the method used in seeking them, is characteristic of the entire quest for knowledge. Thanks to the haphazard growth of some sciences and the nature of particular subject matters, some types of theory have much wider ranges of application than others, and some enjoy closer and more systematic relationships with other theories. These circumstances may give them a higher standing in terms of "probable confirmation to date." But all scientific theories have a share in the steadily increasing probability that science as a method is the best available source of reliable knowledge.[9] The danger lies in concluding that science is therefore entitled to be as dogmatic as the theologies which for centuries opposed it.

FOR CLASS DISCUSSION

A. A sample may be adequate in size, yet be faithless because it is not representative; or, again it may be representative so far as it goes, but unreliable because it is not adequate in size. — *Claude E. Robinson*   (2)

B. Universes are not as plentiful as blackberries. — *C. S. Peirce*

C. The constants of natural science, resulting from a single constant causal combination (like the determination of the position of a star, or the co-efficient of expansion of a metal) and statistical constants, resulting from a multiplicity of causal combinations of very different sorts (like the count of the number of suicides in a month, or of pedestrians who pass a certain street corner in a day) are constant from different causes and with entirely different significance for the knowledge of causal relations.   (3)
                                                                    — *Hermann Ebbinghaus*

D. The true logic for this world is the calculus of Probabilities, which takes account of the magnitude of the probability which is, or ought to be, in a reasonable man's mind. — *J. Clerk Maxwell*   (4)

   Probability is the very guide of life. — *Bishop Joseph Butler*

E. If we pass to the details (of crime in France in 1833) we find a regularity not less appalling. Thus we count about 100 to 150 annually sentenced to death, 280 sentenced to penal servitude, 1220 to solitary confinement, etc.; so that this sort of budget for the scaffold, the chain gangs and the

[9] For a discussion of Reichenbach's views, set forth in his *Experience and Prediction* (Chicago, 1938), see Ernest Nagel, *Principles of the Theory of Probability*, vol. I, no. 6 of the *International Encyclopaedia of Unified Science* (Chicago, 1939), pp. 62–77.

prisons is paid by the French nation with a greater regularity no doubt than the financial budget. — *Jacques Quételet*

F. The normal curve is the history of the Average Man — the visualization of what he is likely to do in a given set of circumstances. Thanks to the curve the Average Man has become a despot who rules us with an iron hand. He dictates when an eighteen-hour train shall start for Chicago, when strawberries shall be exposed for sale, when flannel trousers shall be worn in Toledo. . . . — New York *Times*

G. I have never found anyone who could tell me what the law of averages is.
                                                    — *Dr. Irving Langmuir*

H. We cannot say that the generality of inductions are probably true, but only that in the long run they approximate truth. We only know that by accepting inductive conclusions in the long run our errors balance each other.
                                                    — *C. S. Peirce* (7)

EXERCISES IN SAMPLING AND PREDICTION

In each of the following instances, make a critical estimate of the method of sampling used for the announced purpose, and of any predictions based upon its use.

1. Dr. Robert Seashore of Northwestern University stated in 1938 that the average college student has a recognition vocabulary of 176,000 words, instead of the 15,000 words which are often credited to the "average intelligent adult." He arrived at the figure by taking the third word from the top of the first column of each even-numbered page in a standard dictionary, and then dividing the words into two groups: commonly used and rarely used. Giving the two groups to his undergraduate and graduate classes to define, he determined that the average student recognition vocabulary was 62,000 basic words and 114,000 derived words.

2. The representatives of the freezer-food plan industry protested in 1952 the publishing of an article entitled "Home Freezers Don't Slash Living Costs, U.S. Economists Find," emanating from the Department of Agriculture. They claimed that the article was based upon a survey made in 1948–49, before the freezer-food cooperative plans reached their full development and efficiency, and that it included only eleven families located in Arizona, "no one of which was participating in a freezer-food plan or any other method of planned purchasing."

3. P. C. Mahalanobis, an Indian statistician, demonstrated that considerable intermixture, strictly forbidden by law, occurred among Bengalese castes during the past two thousand years. He arrived at the conclusion by a statistical analysis of the physical measurements of living inhabitants of villages in Bengal. There were no written records available.

4. Much confusion has been created in assessing the accuracy of political polls by interchanging the terms "per cents" and "percentage points." Thus if it is predicted that candidate X will get 54 per cent of the vote, the poll expects

that he will actually get between 52 and 56 per cent. In the famous Truman-Dewey presidential contest in 1948, however, the three principal polls gave Truman 42.3 per cent of the vote, but he received slightly over 50 per cent, an error of 7.7 percentage points, but of 18.2 per cent. Similarly the polls forecast a 3 per cent vote for Thurmond, when he received only 2 per cent, "an error of one percentage point," but of 33⅓ per cent.

5. A method of predicting the votes of members of Congress was devised by two Washington psychologists, Drs. Dean R. Brimhall and Arthur S. Otis, who tabulated the votes cast by 512 Congressmen over a five-year period and rated each vote on a scale of seven points from liberal to conservative. They found that there were 46 chances in 100 that a given Congressman's rating would not change at all from one year to the next; 83 chances in 100 that it will not vary by more than 1 point from year to year; and 95 chances in 100 that it will not change more than two points on their scale. In 83 per cent of all votes cast, there was either no change in the Congressman's attitude or a change of not more than one point.

6. In 1953 Dr. Alfred C. Kinsey and his associates at Indiana University published *Sexual Behavior in the Human Female*, based upon extensive interviews with 5,940 female volunteers, of whom 1,840 were college students from 16–20, 2,480 women who had been married, and 649 women of 26 years and over who had never married. Of the sample, 58 per cent were single, when only about 20 per cent of the female population over 14 were single; 90 per cent were urban, when only 64 per cent of the population in 1950 were urban; and over half had had some college education. Dr. Kinsey himself pointed out that his conclusions were "least likely to be applicable" to age groups over 50; persons with no more than grammar school education; the previously married; all Catholics; devoutly Jewish groups; laboring groups; rural people; persons born before 1900; and to the Southeastern quarter of the United States, the Pacific Northwest, and the high plains and Rocky Mountain areas. He defended the use of volunteers rather than random sampling on the ground that the latter sort of interviewing would have led to too large a percentage of refusals to discuss intimate personal matters.

EXAMPLES OF STATISTICAL REGULARITY

1. The tendency of the weather in almost any part of the United States to remain as it is at any given time is so great that a forecaster who predicted "No change" every day would be right about 66 per cent of the time, and in certain "settled" periods of the year he would be right about 75 per cent of the time. The claimed average of correct predictions for the Weather Bureau throughout the country is said to be 88 per cent.

The best professional handicapper of horse races has never been able, as a matter of record, to pick enough winners in advance so that a person who bet an identical amount on all his choices would show a profit at the end of a racing year. The highest average known is under 40 per cent correct, and some of the pickers hold their jobs with averages as low as 23 per cent. In 1937, only about 35 per cent of all favorites won, and a bettor on all of them would still be a loser by 15 to 20 per cent.

2. According to a century-old tradition, the departure of the swallows of the ancient mission of San Juan Capistrano, California, happens each year on Saint John's Day, October 23. In 1939, however, they departed on August 11; and in 1940, they disappeared on July 16.

3. The Stanford-Lane hospital in San Francisco reported that on two days in one week, nineteen babies were born; all girls; and that on two days in the following week twenty-two babies were born, all boys.

4. In demanding a cleanup of conditions in the welfare institutions of Bristol County, Massachusetts, a Boston newspaper pointed out that the tuberculosis hospital had 111 employees for a capacity of 60 beds, and that its annual cost of operation, $156,000 a year, or $2600 per bed, was way out of line with comparable hospitals elsewhere. Why, it asked, "should the cost per capita of food for the New Bedford house of correction be more than double the corresponding outlay at the Charlestown state prison?"

5. Harry Bitman, Denver tailor, offered the prize of a suit of clothes to anyone who could pick all ten winners of college football games on a list prepared each week. For five weeks no one was able to win a suit, but Bitman happily paid off one suit to the person who came the closest to picking ten teams. Then in one week, nine persons were winners. And in the week following, no less than 412 contestants turned in perfect scores, costing Bitman an estimated $22,248 in suits. There was not a single upset in the list of ten games, "a thing that couldn't happen again in a lifetime."

EXERCISES IN PROBABILITY

Distinguish the kinds of probability in the following examples, and estimate the reliability of predictions based upon them.

1. If you are elected Vice-President of the United States, you have a better than one-in-four chance of becoming President, because ten of the thirty-seven Vice-Presidents so far have become President.

3. Reports to the National Office of Vital Statistics indicate that an average of 370 persons a year are killed by lightning in the United States, so that the odds against such a fate are 375,000 to 1. A Metropolitan Life Insurance study of such deaths in 1941–45 showed that one-third occurred while persons were standing under trees. Nine-tenths of the deaths occur in rural regions; and there are five times as many among males than among females. In the years 1940–44 the state of Rhode Island did not have a single death from lightning. It is not true that "lightning never strikes twice in the same place." On a beach near New York City three persons were killed by lightning in two successive years at the same spot and within one day of the same day of the same month.

5. In December, 1948, Mrs. Herbert Boettcher of Waterloo, Iowa, was called

on the telephone to answer a quiz question on the American Broadcasting Company's "Ladies Be Seated" program, and won $2,000 in household equipment for correctly identifying the tower of Pisa. She had been selected by one of four members of the studio audience picking a telephone book out of a group of 230 books, while a second person chose the page, a third the column, and a fourth the line. One week later, by the same complicated process, she was called again, and asked that someone else be given the chance to win. A statistician representing the sponsor calculated the odds against the second call at something over one trillion to one.

4. United States Golf Association statisticians collected figures on the frequency of holes-in-one, and concluded that at least 3,000 Americans make authenticated aces in a given year. Both the Association and the British *Golfer's Handbook* place the odds against success in a year's play or continuous series of practice shots at between 1,500 and 2,000 to 1. On any one effort, the odds are closer to 10,000 to 1. In the nine years during which the New York *World-Telegram* conducted a hole-in-one tournament, 4,360 players, making 5 shots apiece, scored 4 successes in 21,800 attempts. Another similar contest produced 4 holes-in-one in 41,525 attempts. Are the odds against, therefore, 7,266 to 1, or 10,381 to 1? A single golfer, Michael Buchka, a pro at Webster, Massachusetts, made 3,333 attempts on a 135-yard hole in twelve hours without sinking a single shot, although he hit the pin six times.

5. According to Hellin's law of multiple-birth expectancies, which is the standard commonly used by the medical profession, triplets may be expected once in 64,000 births; quadruplets once in 510,000 births, and quintuplets once in 40,000,000 births. Yet in a single week of September, 1963, two sets of quintuplets were born, in Venezuela and South Dakota; and also two sets of quadruplets, in Iran and Mississippi. The odds against the successful prediction of any such constellation of joint occurrences run into the trillions.

6. Two French mathematicians, André Chéron and Emile Borel, calculated the mathematical probabilities involved in the card game of bridge, and found that 8,006 hands out of 100,000 should contain exactly one heart, so that allowing 100 deals a day at intervals of 5 minutes, a player may expect to hold one heart about 8 times a day. In 100 days of such play, there should be not more than four occasions on which both the player and his partner held only one heart. The dealer in bridge, after the cards have been shuffled, can make 5×10^{28} distinct deals, or a number of 20 digits. If all the adult inhabitants of the earth played bridge at 300 million tables playing 100 hands a day, it would take 5×10^{15} years (50,000 milliards of centuries) to deal that number of hands. Cheron and Borel identify 39 distinct types of bridge hands, of which the 4-4-3-2 is the most common with a probability of 21.55 per cent. The hand which contains exactly 5 cards of one suit and not more than 5 of any other has a probability of 44.34 per cent. If 6 cards are specified instead of 5, the probability is 16.55 per cent. In about thirty years of play at 100 deals a day, a player may expect to hold one or two hands with 9 or 10 cards of one suit. The probability of holding no card above a 9 is 0.0547, or about 5 of such hands in 3 months of play.

7. An almost perfect game for gambling-house purposes, from the mathematical point of view, is solitaire or Canfield, invented by the gambler Richard Canfield of Saratoga Springs, New York. The prospective player buys the pack of 52 cards from the house for $50, and receives $5 for every card which he gets out after going through the undealt cards only once. If he gets all 52 cards out, he receives $260 for a profit of $210. For the house to break even, the average player must make a score of less than 10 cards. A retired engineer in New York City who has played and recorded over 64,000 hands, shuffling each time by three different methods, and using his maximum skill, has a grand average of almost exactly 9 cards, or a consistent "house" profit of $5 per deal. In each sequence of 1000 hands, his average has never gone above 9.6 or below 8.5 cards. It is most unlikely that Mr. Canfield computed the mathematical probabilities in devising the game. No doubt he discovered the empirical average of 9 cards, and thus fixed the price at 10 cards (or $50), which was sure to yield him a profit in the long run.

8. It is said that in 1813 a Mr. Ogden posted a wager of one thousand pounds to one (roughly $5000 to $5) in a St. Petersburg gambling club that seven could not be thrown with fair dice ten successive times. An individual one evening made nine sevens in a row, using a different pair of dice on each throw to eliminate the possibility of loading. Before the tenth throw, Mr. Ogden offered to settle for 470 pounds (a much better offer than the odds warranted). But his offer was refused, and the tenth throw was a nine. The odds against ten successive sevens are 10,077,696 to 1.

9. Examples of empirical approximations to the normal curve:

(a) Lengths of ears of corn grown from seeds taken from ears ten inches in length, Illinois Agricultural Experiment Station

2	2	3	9	8	12	19	32	40	67	63	38	21	8	2	1
less than 5 inches	5	5.5	6	6.5	7	7.5	8	8.5	9	9.5	10	10.5	11	11.5	12

(b) Heights of Scottish soldiers aged nineteen years in millimeters, J. F. Tocher, *Anthropometric Observations* (Edinburgh, 1924), vol. III, p. 159.

3	21	99	190	250	193	84	16	4
1495	1545	1595	1645	1695	1745	1795	1845	1895

❧ 13 ❧

SCIENCE AND THE SOCIAL STUDIES

1. The Prestige of Physical Science

THE GREATER PART OF OUR ATTENTION has been focused upon the physical sciences in the belief, well stated by Professor Ernest Nagel, that "they are the most reliable instruments men have thus far devised for ascertaining matters of fact, but that withal the conclusions reached by them are only probable because they rest upon evidence which is formally incomplete." That view in no way precludes the existence of other ways of knowing which may also be fruitful, but it gives the premier place to what is commonly known as scientific method in the strict sense of the term. Whether we like it or not, more differing human beings have been able to stabilize their judgments about different kinds of knowledge-claims by means of what we have called the mechanical pattern than by any other method of knowing. That does not imply that they have unanimously agreed to accept final verdicts which are unalterable, but that they have adopted a common means of reaching, testing, and revising their conclusions which produces a progressive consensus of opinion. A common astronomy guides the ships of all countries, a common aerodynamics sustains their planes, a common chemistry makes possible the fashioning of both shattering bombs and healing drugs.

This state of affairs, the result of centuries of unwearying endeavor by thousands of the forgotten men of the laboratories, has given to physical science a prestige which has often proved a handicap and an embarrassment, since it as led to a dogmatism in the name of science which is the antithesis of the scientific spirit. Everyone wants a share of the authority that goes with the claim that "Science says" this or that. Science has thus acquired hosts of camp followers who take advantage of the general public's inability to distinguish between those who are entitled to speak in its name, and those who are not. Scientific "proofs" are invoked to promote toothpastes, cigarettes, vitamins, and miracle-working strains of yeast.

All this commercial charlatanry in the name of science is made possible by the fact that faint copies or feeble imitations of scientific method have been utilized in so many new fields of endeavor, all going under the name of science. Research laboratories have been mistakenly sold to the public as "houses of magic" spewing forth salable technological wonders in an endless stream. On the other hand, ever since the atomic bomb and sputnik, a new tendency to enhance the importance of science has arisen in the form of blame for all the woes of the contemporary age. If anything has gone wrong with modernity,

331

according to this school of thought, it is the scientist who is to blame. Irrational fear of science takes the place of irrational worship of science.

Even after all this over-praising, over-exploiting, and over-damning of science has been considered, however, the person who is interested in the achievement of reliable knowledge is obliged to return again and again to the physical sciences and their indubitable accomplishments. If there is any possibility whatever that their method of approach in solving their problems could be extended to the tangled web of human social relationships, that possibility ought not to remain unexplored. We must be deterred neither by the false hopes of those who have expected an immediate utopia through a "social physics," nor by the exaggerated fears of those vested obscurantists who harp on the limits of science out of fear that their sacred absurdities will be exposed.

2. *Essentials of Scientific Method in the Physical Sciences*

What is the secret of this hard-earned and well-merited prestige of science in the strict sense? We do not refer to science as just any broadly self-critical attempt to establish knowledge-claims by publicly testable evidence, for that is virtually equivalent to the quest for reliable knowledge, but to sciences on the mechanical pattern (although not necessarily the mechanical model in the narrow sense), such as physics, chemistry, and astronomy. Our aim is not to insist that nothing else deserves the prestige label of science; but rather to discover approximately to what extent the methods of these sciences, which vary in detail but have very nearly the same criteria of validity, can be extended to the subject matters of other fields of inquiry. Our estimate of the situation will necessarily take the form of a condensed recapitulation of much that has already been surveyed.

(1) *The method of physical science is neither theory-less observation nor observation-less theorizing.* It is neither crude empiricism nor crude rationalism, neither pure induction nor pure deduction, but a balanced combination of the two in which each cross-fertilizes the other. Ordinarily, observation in a problematic situation gives rise to an imagined hypothesis, which is elaborated deductively and tested by more observation.

(2) *On its empirical side, physical science rests solidly on approximate coincidence observations of selected aspects of changing natural processes, which can be duplicated, checked, and made progressively more precise by competent normal observers.* A science, however, is not composed of isolated facts or random collections of items, no matter how meticulously observed. Selection, analysis, symbolization, and that form of abstraction known as *measurement* enter into most observation from the start; and all of them require directing criteria of relevance or interestingness. Individual "personal equations," biases, and illusions are eliminated as far as possible by laboratory safeguards and the systematic cancelling-out of deviations.

(3) *On its rational or theoretical side, physical science formulates its im-*

agined hypotheses in such a way as to guide inquiry by furnishing the necessary criteria of relevance; and in the form of generalizations concerning the relationship of two or more variables in such a way that the deductive implications can be tested by observation. Having formulated its central concepts and frames of reference, it does this ordinarily by constructing "ideal cases" in terms of quantitative numerical symbols which are abstracted from classified concrete situations (and sometimes from other mathematical symbols) in order to predict other concrete situations with a fair degree of approximation. It can often quantify and predict successfully without full knowledge of "that which" is being measured, such as electricity.

(4) *Physical science aims at the progressive unification of its generalizations* (in practice, statistical laws stating the functional relations of selected qualities of groups of facts) *in systems consisting of the fewest possible explanatory principles, yet possessing the widest possible scope, depth, and fertility.* An hypothesis should no more be viewed in isolation than a fact. This interconnection of laws is what enables one science to buttress the probabilities established by a neighboring science, and to be reinforced in turn. It is the whole interdependent structure of the physical sciences that surpasses all other bodies of knowledge in flux-borne solidity.

(5) *Physical science on the mechanical pattern tests its elaborated hypotheses, where possible, by experiment.* This involves the setting-up of an approximation of the ideal mathematical or physical model in the form of an artificially closed-off system or "container," in which single independent variables can be successively subjected to attempts to eliminate them. That hypothesis which cannot be eliminated by the most strenuous and ingenious efforts may, within a margin of error, be accepted as compatible with the examined evidence, pending severer tests to show that it is the *only* one, and *systematically the simplest* one, which fits all the relevant facts. This implies the incessant retesting of all hypotheses in the light of new facts as fast as they can be brought to light.

(6) *As the result of the discovery of limiting circumstances through testing, physical science modifies, purifies, and enlarges its hypotheses.* New empirical material stimulates developments in mathematics and logic; and such developments extend the range of their applications in the laboratory.

The impression should not be conveyed that the foregoing generalizations constitute a complete and universal methodology of physical science. For nothing is more marked than the tendency of scientists to specialize in minute subdivisions of their subject matters. Each investigator, in the exploration of his specialty, "follows the lay of the land" with scant respect for the imaginary restraints of any general code. Often it takes years for the specialized methodologies either to transform, or to become assimilated to, the broader traditional pattern. This means that there will always be sciences that are in the early stages of development, and lacking in some of the characteristics of the more exact disciplines.

3. *Physical Science and Social Science*

Throughout this book, attention has been called to the great good fortune of the physical scientists in the relative simplicity of their subject matters, at least as far as what we have called the gross physical level is concerned. This is not to minimize in any way the ingenuity of those pioneer astronomers, physicists, and chemists who seized so swiftly upon the basic variables of their domains. But, once the latter were guessed at, the progress of physical science was almost stupefyingly swift. Compared with other inquirers, the physical scientists appear like motorized divisions sweeping rapidly forward over smooth terrain by the use of perfected methods of attack, while far off on the flanks green and untried regiments of social science struggle slowly and painfully to advance a few yards through swamps and jungles where none of the orthodox maneuvers seem to work.

That the less successful disciplines should try to imitate the spectacularly triumphant ones was only to be expected, especially since it could so easily be shown that there are some aspects of human nature to which the methods of physical science genuinely apply. The human body has a number of machine-like or automaton characteristics which can effectively be analyzed in terms of matter in motion in space and time; and the seventeenth-century social physicists exploited them to the full. Society, they believed, could be regarded as a sort of astronomical system whose members were subjected to attraction and repulsion in "social space" and even in "moral time." There was much talk of social molecules, social atoms, social statics, social dynamics, and social equilibria. Everything was resolved into quantity and universal mechanical laws, culminating, for the character of any human individual, as Edward L. Thorndike has expressed it, "in one great equation — John Smith, equaling so many units of this, plus so many units of that, and so on."

Now the trouble with all such efforts, valuable as some of them have been in their criticisms of earlier theories and in their scientific by-products, has been that they are built upon necessary but not sufficient conditions for the explanation of human conduct. One cannot get more out of abstractions than one puts into them. The main predictive abstractions of physical science are on the gross physical level. But that does not mean that they will necessarily prove adequate for the prediction of phenomena on the higher levels. It is no answer to this to say that a rock, a rose, and a man are equally composed of electrons, and that therefore the laws of electrons are the laws of rocks, roses, and men. Components are not the only things that matter — how the components are put together is what counts in predicting how a rock, a rose, or a man will behave. As the complexity of arrangement of the components increases, new concepts may be essential in spite of the value of parsimony as a general rule.

Naturally the old abstractions go on being useful for certain aspects of behavior: human bodies fall from airplanes at just the same rate as equally heavy bombs or sandbags. That means that we do not need a special science to take care of the way a parachutist leaves a plane, since we already have a law of falling bodies which covers such events. But the law of falling bodies does not tell us what he is thinking at five thousand feet, or when he will pull the rip-cord of his parachute. A transport officer who is in charge of loading a vessel with soldiers would do well to take exact account of their physical characteristic of weight in planning their quarters on board the ship. A failure to make the correct calculations might seriously disturb the ship's center of gravity and consequent seaworthiness. But no amount of figuring of weights could tell him whether to put soldiers and marines on the same deck, or whether the machine gunners or the medical detachment should be closest to the gangway. For those are matters of qualities with which physical abstractions simply do not effectively deal. That is why "reduction-to" is ultimately unsuccessful, in spite of the fact that the lower levels admittedly underlie and limit the activities of the higher.

Even if the verbal reduction of the higher to the lower should appear to succeed, there would still be distinctions on the lower level which would be unaccounted for. If people are said to "gravitate" to large cities "in direct ratio of the mass and in inverse ratio of the distance," as Henry C. Carey once declared, there is still a considerable difference between the gravitational attraction of the sun for our earth and that of Los Angeles for the residents of Iowa. The physical law of gravitation simply does not enable us to predict the growth of cities, or the "attraction" of the sexes for one another. Not even as loose analogies are such mechanical concepts socially enlightening.

PARETO'S SOCIAL MECHANICS

The most ambitious modern attempt to interpret society in terms of the mechanical pattern is that of Vilfredo Pareto in his four-volume *Trattato di sociologia generale* (1915–16), translated into English under the title of *The Mind and Society* in 1935.[1] An Italian mathematical economist with violent political prejudices and other temperamental disqualifications, Pareto compiled about one million words in 2612 badly organized paragraphs which he imagined comprised a "first approximation" to a mathematical formulation of all the forces operating in human society in terms of a Gibbsian system of multiple variables in a state of mutual dependence and equilibrium. The forces, according to Pareto, give rise to overt conduct which is either *logical* (the use of means appropriate to immediate and obvious ends), or *non-logical* (all other conduct, and the great bulk of all human activities). Behind non-logical conduct are two main groups of tendencies which are to be observed and quantified: the inner organizing drives or sentiments which Pareto calls *residues*, and their rationalizations (intended to make the non-logical acts appear logical) called *derivations*. The objective outcomes of our actions and our subjective versions of them seldom correspond, although we do our best to convince ourselves that they do.

But this very discovery of man's pervasive tendencies to deceive himself and others by putting up a brave front of rationality ruins Pareto's original intention to lay bare, with perfect objectivity, the conditioning forces of social

[1] Reviewed by the present author: "Pareto and the Philosophers," *Journal of Philosophy*, vol. XXXII, pp. 505–15.

equilibria, since he crams his four volumes with surface *manifestations* of the residues — the psychologically subjective forces which he has already proclaimed to be largely overlaid with the camouflage of the derivations. Since the same residue may appear in many disguises, or derivations, which interact with the residues they temporarily conceal, it is hard to see how either can be reliably identified in terms of the other, much less disentangled and quantified. Thus, Pareto himself is "in the position of a man who, something of a truth-distorter himself, wants to state the truth about lying on the basis of lies about lies.[2] His gigantic attempt to force the abstractions of a backward psychology into the antiquated framework of nineteenth-century mechanics does not succeed in unifying the physical and the social sciences, or in demonstrating that there are no important differences between the two.

On the contrary, Pareto starts out with the successful methods of mechanical physics adapted to "ideal" mathematical economics, hoping to write an immense series of equations to express the whole of human social behavior. His methods were originally developed to deal with gross physical happenings from the outside; but he attempts to make them work in a field where we observe from the outside with a good deal of help (and interference) from the inside. Pareto, however, sees only the interference, and savagely attacks philosophers, psychologists, and sociologists for their sins of lack of objectivity due to the deflection of their observations and measurements by their subjective wishes and emotions. Because of this, he will welcome openly none of the help which might come from observations on non-physical levels. He commits the fatal error of the extreme behaviorist, the mistake of supposing that the only way to get reliable knowledge about human conduct is to cut off all the light upon it which comes from the inside.

Then, having renounced all "unscientific" subjectivity, he promptly readmits it in the form of his own unconscious prejudices and preferences, to which he is amazingly blind. For what he finds in the way of "uniformities" is dictated to a far greater degree than he realizes by what he is looking for, especially after the closing of his chosen list of residues and derivations. Many critics have pointed out that his particular selections of facts confirm his beliefs about human nature, but that a different selector might bring to light a very different set of uniformities. Even had his oversimplification of psychology been sounder and less handicapped by unconscious bias, it is doubtful whether the smallest Gibbsian sociological system could be set up mathematically without an expenditure of labor that would be out of all proportion to the possible gains in enlightenment. In spite of all his clamor about immaculate quantitativism, Pareto himself expresses only a few economic "interests" in numerical form.

4. Differences in Subject Matter

It is apparent that the direct, all-out attempt to apply the methods of physical science to human social behavior has yielded only a meager harvest of

[2] *Ibid.*, p. 512.

reliable knowledge. This failure has given rise to two schools of thought among those who are genuinely desirous of seeing the social studies become as trust-worthy as possible. One school clings to the view that the setback is only temporary, that the objective of bringing human conduct into the scheme of universal sciences is a sound one, and needs only to be pursued with unrelenting vigor. It finds its spokesman in Professor Read Bain: "The only certainties transcending common sense in sociology or in any other science are statistical in nature. The degree to which such methodology can be applied to social data will determine whether sociology is to become a natural science or remain forever a bastard discipline sired and dammed by common sense and normative knowledge; whether it is to be a natural science or a hodgepodge of pretentious words, random observations, speculations, opinions, pious hopes and fears, attitudes, wishes, sophistical logic, and literary purple patches. Should the sociologist be a Zola or a Quételet?"[3]

This position allows of no compromise, no possible synthesis of Zola *and* Quételet. If only certain corners of human conduct can be fruitfully subjected to the methods of physical science, then so much the worse for all the rest. "No quantification, no science." By which is meant no ordinary degree of quantification if the label of science is to be affixed. Nevertheless there are other investigators, no less anxious for reliability in knowledge, whom this doctrine leaves unimpressed. They are not professional edifiers; but they realize that "while music may be explained through certain underlying laws of physics . . . the power of music upon the individual and the group, and the aptitudes and genius of the musician are on a different plane and are of a different sort . . . beauty, style, aspiration, appetites and behavior are not measured by the simple rules of digestion and assimilation. . . ." They protest against the dogma that "because we have not been able to cope with the variables and complexity of human phenomena through the usual methods, there may not be, therefore, a science of human relations."

As between these two extreme views, any decision would seem to hinge upon the nature of the obstacles which are encountered when an effort is made to apply physical science methods (or an approximation thereto) to the materials of the social studies. It may be that such methods will fruitfully apply wherever there is enough stability in the subject matter to support them. But the social studies have peculiarities in that respect, some of which have already been mentioned in the discussion of levels in Chapters 6 and 9. Among them are:

(1) *Multiplicity of alternative levels of observation and explanation,* already noted in Chapter 6, Section 6. It may be argued that this is no final barrier to "one big equation," if the higher levels can be shown to depend upon the lower, which may be deemed to be basic. That the lower levels should constitute limiting conditions for the activities of the higher, however, does not mean that the latter, and especially their values, can be reduced to the lower, predicted by them, or fully explained by them.

(2) *Multiplicity and complexity of the interdependent variables on the multiple levels.* That the greater complexity of the   phenomena exists, no one

[3] Read Bain, "Measurement in Sociology," *American Journal of Sociology,* vol. XL, p. 486.

would deny. Social-cultural phenomena are more complex than those of the psychological level; psychological are more complex than biological; and so on. But the same line of argument brought forward against the multiplicity of levels can also be used to suggest that if we could only uncover the *basic* variables, the difficulties would disappear. Perhaps some future generation of men will look back upon our era as one of good scientific intentions, but of stupid blindness to the fundamental social concepts. But about all we can say in reply is that surely many candidates for the position of basic variables have been tried and found wanting; and that it does not look, at present, as if there were single concepts which would do for the social studies what mass or energy have done for physics.

(3) *Volatility, intangibility, and inaccessibility of the material to be observed.* It can hardly be denied that some of the pivotal factors in human conduct may be extremely evanescent in character, such as the mood of a ruler or the rage of a criminal. Mere brevity in time, however, might conceivably be overcome by the increasing delicacy of instruments. After all, a mood is no shorter than the bursting soap-bubbles which are now so beautifully photographed. Intangibility, moreover, should be no obstacle to anyone who finds it easy to believe in such useful but intangible fictions as the atoms and electrons of physics; and it might be overcome by methods that are similarly indirect. What complicates things in the social studies is the fact that evanescence and intangibility are combined with inaccessibility to public observation; since whims and fancies are matters of inner consciousness not easily brought into the open. The usual answer is that we study animals by their overt acts, without bothering about their possible "states of mind." Why not do the same with human beings? Yet there is something missing in the most conscientious behavioristic account of a human activity. We may record the stimulus and the response, but our correlations between the two will remain merely "zoological information" (as some of Dr. Kinsey's results were called) unless we get some help from within, from the persons who are doing the responding.

The difficulty is that exactly the same physical stimulus may call forth widely differing sorts of responses; and the same responses may be evoked by varying physical stimuli. If we do not consult the person who is reacting, we are forced to describe the stimulus as it appears *to us,* and not necessarily as it appears *to him.* If we insist upon selecting as the units of stimulus and response what we as scientific observers suppose the person being studied is responding to (because that is what we ourselves would respond to in his place), we may make all manner of false inferences. A missionary in the South Seas once denounced a native dance as the height of obscenity, only to discover that it was a harmless oyster-gathering festival. "Scientific" analysts of exotic religious ceremonies have been guilty of similar howlers. A man who entered a grocery store just in time to see a clerk take five dollars out of the cash register and hand it to a friend of his might well hasten to call the police. But if, two minutes before, the friend had bought a five-dollar article and handed the clerk ten dollars, the latter's whole activity would appear in a totally different light. The situation in the social studies is partly defined by the inner consciousness of the persons involved; and no amount of indirect methods of inferring the nature of that consciousness from overt acts furnishes a solid basis for judgments concerning the full significance of what is going on.

(4) *The observer in the social studies is a part of what he is observing in a peculiar sense.* It is not merely that he uses his body and sense organs as instruments of knowing, for that is true of physics as well. It is rather that, as Professor G. H. Sabine puts it, "in social studies the relation between an observer and his subject matter is very like the relation between a man and his acquaintances. The behavior which he observes and describes has as its frame of reference the common meanings of the actors — their purposes, valuations, and customs; and this body of meanings, if not shared by the observer, must at least be apprehended by him and accepted as an adequate ground for the action. . . . His theory of it must at least be faithful to the action as it is for the actors, because that is precisely the datum which the theory must explain." This shows why successful observation in the social studies depends so much upon conditions internal to the observer: "it is the body of his own experiences which enables him to enter into and comprehend the experience of others."[4] The ultimate units in the physical sciences are abstractions which are dissected out by the intellect and manipulated; but the ultimate units of social relationships are minds and personalities which can be known with immensely greater intimacy, and which are only feebly represented by the physical types of scientific abstractions. Reliable knowledge in the social studies requires a degree of sympathetic insight, as well as the objectivity of the laboratory; and the two do not easily combine.

(5) *Social studies form a part of their own subject matter, and are involved in the continuous reconstruction of human ends.* It is a commonplace that the development of the science of chemistry does not have very much effect upon the chemical elements, which remain pretty much as they are, regardless of men's knowledge or ignorance of them; but an economic or political theory may interact with practice in such a way as to render itself more applicable, or even to make itself obsolete. Social studies are themselves phases of the social evolution which they investigate. They are at one and the same time a revelation of and a part of the processes of human readjustment. You cannot permanently insulate knowledge from society, or society from knowledge, and keep both alive. There is an "indissoluble union" between social science and social growth. This state of affairs introduces some peculiar difficulties in the testing of social studies hypotheses, since their applicability will vary with the social tendencies prevailing at the times and places of the tests. The orthodox "laws" of prices in terms of the gold standard cease to be applicable in an era of "managed currencies." In an ideally defined economic order they remain entirely valid, but the empirical conditions of their application have ceased to exist. This would be true in the physical science of meteorology if there should be a sudden change in the earth's atmosphere. But major changes in the earth's atmosphere are not brought about by the propagation of theories of meteorology. Yet the time of a country's abandonment of gold for a man-

---

[4] George H. Sabine, "Logic and Social Studies," *Philosophical Review*, vol. XLVIII, p. 168.

aged currency may very well be effected by the spread of sentiment for the latter in theory form.

It is hard to be sure, then, that in choosing one's fields of inquiry, to say nothing of concepts and frames of reference in the social studies, there is not a large element of what one wishes to be so. This suspicion generates opposition, on the part of other interested parties, of a type that physical science nowadays seldom has to face. An honest statement of medical fact about the identity of white and Negro blood for purposes of transfusion may raise a storm of denunciation in Congress among the champions of white supremacy. Yet to confuse the reliability of a proposition with the reasons why people come to accept or reject it, as in the extreme forms of what is called the "sociology of knowledge," is a fatal error.

5. Obstacles to the Development of Social Science

If we now array the broad essentials of scientific method in the physical sciences in the face of the differences discovered to exist in social studies subject matter, we should be able to gain a comprehension of the principal obstacles to the development of disciplines which deserve the name of social sciences. It is no longer a question of the direct application of physical science methods to social material; nor is it an effort to find reasons for not making the attempt to make the social studies as scientific as possible.

After all, the physical sciences have constantly invented new methods to deal with new sorts of data, as in astrophysics and biochemistry. The biochemists, for example, did not conclude, because the methods used in the analysis of simple inorganic compounds would not work in dealing with complex organic substances, that therefore no adequate methods were possible, so that there could be no respectable science of the chemistry of living beings. On the contrary, they went ahead to invent new methods as well as new techniques for the understanding of organic part-whole relationships. In the same manner, those who aim to be social scientists are entitled to invent their own ways of mastering their materials, and to challenge the skeptic to doubt the reliability of their results.

The obstacles which they encounter consist largely of the resistances of social studies materials to their efforts to make explanatory hypotheses "stick." These may be given condensed expression in the form of allegations that:

(1) *Agreement on basic concepts is impossible.* That it has been attained in any field, few social scientists would allege. Long lists of alternative conceptual schemes are a common feature of social studies literature. Grandiose attempts to map these alternatives in logical compartments are also plentiful. Yet a book of definitions remarks that "any logical organization of the sociological subject matter is likely to depart somewhat far from present and familiar practice . . ." which has evolved historically "without design, through the activity of individuals following specialized research and teaching interests." Interests in turn are influenced to varying degrees by what the various investigators would like to see come true. The closer they are to the immediate social

problems, the harder it is for them to avoid bias in their choices of conceptual alternatives and frames of reference. Once chosen and popularized, conceptual schemes such as the Christian, the Marxist, or the Freudian, may have a powerfully pervasive influence upon the course of social development.

The usual answer is that it is the business of social science to develop, as soon as possible, basic concepts which are *wert-frei*, that is, value-free or ethically neutral. But in dealing with value-drenched materials in a live social setting, ethical neutrality is itself a valuational and socially influential position to adopt. That does not mean that it may not be a highly desirable attitude in certain contexts; in fact, the achievement of a high degree of disinterestedness in courts and universities is one of man's proudest and most difficult accomplishments. It does mean that the attainment of a consensus of acceptance with regard to basic concepts in the social studies is made extraordinarily difficult by the fact that it may virtually involve the choice of what sort of social future one deems desirable. Not only may wars be fought over the question of whose dictionary is to prevail, but they are also continually being waged to determine whether the prevailing "climate of opinion" shall be scientific or theological or military or nihilistic.

To set up the world-wide acceptance of a uniform code of basic social concepts as an end in itself certainly smacks of totalitarianism and dictatorship. Yet the alternative need not be a wholly chaotic pluralism. The social scientist can always point to the somewhat similar situation in physical science in the sixteenth and seventeenth centuries, when large numbers of allegedly basic concepts were in competition for the favor of the early modern scientists. One after another, those ideas which did not fruitfully organize experience fell by the wayside and were forgotten, in spite of the unlimited enthusiasms of those who admired them. Use is a ruthless weeder-out of such impotent forms, although their disappearance from the fields of human relationships may be much slower because of the persistence of ancient and beloved habits of thought. As the social studies are cultivated, to the extent that concepts prove illuminating, they can be expected to gain in favor, and gradually to shake down into general patterns which are bound to continue to change, and which may always be far from universal acceptance. One thing is sure — sciences do not achieve genuine maturity in their basic concepts by first straining after formal or theoretical consistency without regard to the sweat and toil of actual use. Neither do they reach it by dogged and unreflective trial and error. The pathway to conceptual clarity and organization (that is something more than a pleasant fantasy) is the one long ago pointed out by Socrates: the incessant dialectical effort to re-examine ideas in the light of their meanings in practice.

(2) *Measurement of the basic variables cannot be sufficiently precise.* One of the characteristics of a mature science is the precision of its measurements. Physicists spend long months of research in attempts to refine their figures for the speed of light or of sound, for each advance in precision brings with it possibilities of new discriminations of differences, and hence of new discoveries. By contrast, the most definite statements concerning human conduct seem vague and imprecise.

It should be made clear at once that the issue is not simply one of the lack, in social science, of such *direct* measurements as counting and weighing, since many of the measurements of the so-called exact sciences are exceedingly indirect and inferential. But the latter terminate in some sort of approximate coincidence observations upon which the inferences can be shown to rest. The trouble with many of the indirect measurements of social science, such as opinion surveys which seek to probe public sentiment with regard to issues concealed within the questions, lies elsewhere. It is not that they are indirect, but that they follow devious inferential pathways, only to terminate in shaky outer "observations" of inner states of mind. It is not enough to proclaim that the social studies are not sufficiently quantified, and therefore cannot be scientific; for, as Michael and Adler observe, "wherever measurement is impossible, precise observation is impossible . . . if the observation of social phenomena cannot be metrical, neither can it be sufficiently accurate to be worth anything for scientific use."[5] The issue, in other words, is primarily one of accuracy of observation relative to the problem in hand; and secondarily one of valid inferences. There is no universal standard of precision of the data — to how many decimal places it is worth while to carry the calculations must always be decided in the light of the problem in hand.

Warnings have already been posted against being deceived by the sort of pseudo precision of measurement which goes beyond the accuracy inherent in the original observations. "Data that are themselves unreliable or non-objective are not made a whit more reliable through the use of statistical methods . . . therein lies the chief danger of the statistical approach to sociology."[6] A study of "Factors in the Distribution of Success in Marriage," points out "the interesting relationship between difference in age between husband and wife and marital satisfaction. . . . Where the wife was older than the husband, the difference was considered negative. A free hand curve of the type $(x - h)^2 = - 2p(y - k)$ gives a correlation index of $+ .60$ with an error of .06, indicating that such a parabola fits the data rather well. For men, the axes of the parabola must be rotated toward the left through an angle of about 10°. In terms of the data themselves, these facts indicate that the women were satisfied with their husbands when their husbands were from zero to five years older than they, and that their satisfaction tended to diminish at about an equal rate when this difference increased, regardless of whether it was they or their husbands who were the older. The men tended to be most satisfied with their wives when they were from zero to ten years older than their wives, but their dissatisfaction with their wives tended to increase more rapidly when their wives were older than they, than when they were older than their wives."[7] Now in spite of the admission that these conclusions are "quite tentative," and that "the extreme complexity of the interrelationships of the variables involved in marriage cannot be overemphasized"; the

[5] Jerome Michael and M. J. Adler, *Crime, Law and Social Science* (New York, 1933), p. 74.

[6] Dorothy S. Thomas, "Statistics in Social Research," *American Journal of Sociology,* vol. XXXV, p. 13.

[7] Jessie Bernard, "Factors in the Distribution of Success in Marriage," *American Journal of Sociology,* vol. XL, pp. 49–60.

spuriousness of the exactitude of the mathematical operations in terms of the material measured is apparent. Aside from the question of what constitutes "success" or "satisfaction" in marriage (is it the state of mind of one of the married pair, or of both, or of their neighbors, or of a jury of experts?), the figures are based on a sample of only 252 married individuals representing 146 marriages in St. Louis, Seattle, and Los Angeles, most of them highly educated persons in comfortable economic circumstances, whose "success in marriage" had been rated on a scale of 100 by means of a test.

It is only necessary to recall the discussion of the measurement of extensive and intensive magnitudes by numbers in Chapter 11, Section 6, to see where many of the difficulties in quantifying in the social studies lie. Success in marriage is an intensive quality which admits of degrees, but not of separable units; and age, as related to it, is by no means a strictly extensive quality, in spite of calendars and clocks, since age in personal relationships has a good deal of the "old-as-you-feel" quality about it. Moreover, judgments about success in marriage are notoriously variable from person to person and even from day to day. There simply is not enough stability in the data to support the mathematical structure; but unfortunately that does not prevent a high degree of refinement in the mathematics from concealing the crudity and shoddiness of its foundations.

The social studies have an even more troublesome problem of quantification than the mere mathematical mingling of extensive and intensive qualities, for they are constantly called upon to compare two or more sets of intensive qualities which have been ranked on different bases. If a study were to be made of success in marriage as related to success in business, for example, or success in marriage as related to the ability to solve detective mysteries, a super-scale of comparison of the two scales of intensity would seem to be required. Now, in spite of the declaration of such a logician as Professor William E. Johnson that "it is impossible to compare two kinds of intensive magnitudes such as the brightness of a light sensation with the loudness of a sound sensation," the social scientist is constantly attempting to do something of the sort through the measurement of choices actually made between values varying both in degree and kind of intensity. Professor Johnson suggests that two different kinds of intensity may be said to differ in *distensive* magnitude according to the number of relations involved, but that is a highly formal distinction. Professor Ralph Barton Perry speaks of the summation of qualitatively unique values through the concept of the "inclusiveness" of interests producing a non-spatial "overlapping," as when "an act which is virtuous and priceless, as well as beautiful," is adjudged "better than an act which is merely beautiful."[8] But when we come to attach relative weights to the wants, needs, and desires of all sorts of valuers, past, present, and future, there is an arbitrariness that is difficult to overcome by averaging the "best-informed opinion" of the people whose judgment we approve.

Social studies material, then, possesses qualities with three kinds of magnitude which may be said to be measurable in some sense: extensive, intensive, and distensive. But to only one of the three, the extensive, is it safe to apply

[8] Ralph Barton Perry, *General Theory of Value* (New York, 1926), p. 647.

numbers with any confidence that they can be manipulated and the results correspond in amount to the qualities. Intensive and distensive qualities may be compared only in degree. Furthermore, when one tries to measure human desires and preferences, some of them, such as the realization of a life ambition, or the loss of sight or hearing, turn out to be "infinites" located beyond the extreme end of the person's scale of value-comparison. The attempt to measure these boundless desires or immeasurable aversions in terms of money brings answers of "no sum sufficient." The whole business of scaling wants, rests on the possibly baseless assumptions that the same individual will rate desired things in the same order under different conditions, or that other individuals can be counted on either to agree with him, or to disagree. To find out whether Mr. and Mrs. Blank's success in marriage over a twenty-year period should be rated as greater or smaller than their standing in the community would be a complex undertaking; but to determine whether they should be rated higher or lower than Mr. and Mrs. Dash in either or both respects would be an even tougher job. Yet rough attempts to measure some human preferences do "work," and should be refined, extended, and safeguarded. It may well be that there is a fairly wide zone of those "small and dubious differences in preference" distributed in normal curves, where it does no harm to use the crude money yardstick of "which would you rather have for your dollar?" — always remembering that allowances must be made for a wide margin of error in the form of personal equations.

(3) *Controlled experiment is seldom possible.* There can be no doubt that the citadel of physical science is the laboratory from which come forth the greater part of its discoveries and clinching proofs. The heart of the experimental process is the control of all relevant conditions, whereby Nature is made to repeat herself in certain specific ways under close observation, and to answer leading questions (hypotheses) which have been carefully prepared to be addressed to her. The experimenter uses knowledge which has already been gained to say to Nature, "If you have not been deceiving me you must behave in such-and-such a manner." To speak of a controlled experiment is really to be guilty of a redundancy, since there is little point in speaking of experiment where control is lacking.

The purpose of rigid control is to make possible what Ernst Cassirer calls a "pure phenomenon," free from all "accidental" and irrelevant circumstances; or, as John Dewey expresses it, to "prepare" or "reconstruct" the material so that it can figure as evidence for or against the hypothesis. The control need not literally be in the hands of the one who performs the experiment, so long as he is fully aware of exactly which variable is being altered, and which ones are supposedly remaining the same throughout the experiment. Now it is a commonplace that in the social studies it is extremely difficult, first of all, to close off an isolated system without changing its character in certain ways that are hard to define, and yet which may make the isolated system quite unrepresentative of the same class of systems when not closed off for purposes of experiment. An example would be a single class in a school which received differential treatment in a single respect, such as instruction by television, with the result that its "marked-out" character might account for its differences in performance, which might be mistakenly attributed to the value of the television technique rather than to the general stimulus-to-good-work of the special privilege granted. There is also the matter of human learning which goes on during an experiment: a person who was serving as the victim of a surprise electric shock in a laboratory could not be used over and over again as if the surprise had exactly the same psychological quality on each successive occasion. In addition, there is the high probability that a change in one human variable will bring about slight changes in other associated variables. Few variables in the social studies, in other words, are genuinely independent.

These strictures are not intended to demonstrate the futility of attempting experimental proof in the social studies, but to indicate how great is the undertaking and how little has yet been done. Relationships among measured but experimentally uncontrolled factors have been established in increasing quantities; but they must be regarded as exploratory and descriptive rather than matters of scientific explanation or proof. Yet there is a vast amount of what goes by the name of social experiment which is constantly going on as laws are passed, rules are enforced, and other social changes made. Our cities and states, we are told, are great laboratories in which experiments are constantly being conducted, from which we could profit if we could only discern them. Americans are reputed to be great pragmatists who are constantly trying out new schemes. But trying out new devices is not the same as conducting a scientific social experiment. John Dewey pointed out that we do not often formulate experimental alternatives and discriminate the consequences of social policies. The result is hasty improvisation of isolated remedies, success or failure as a "gross whole," and then more improvisation.

None of our college presidents can afford not to be conducting "a pioneer educational experiment" on his campus. Such programs are announced with great fanfare as experimental, but their sponsors seldom make clear just what they are alternatives to, or what their success or failure (if reported at all) will prove. Still less frequently is there any time set for a period of fair trial, or any provision for the impartial reviewing of the results. This is especially true of plans which are discarded, and from which a great deal might be learned, as for instance the "noble experiment" of prohibition.

One thing that is often forgotten in discussing experimentalism in human affairs is the paradox of flexibility versus rigidity implied in the free experimental attitude. To set up controlled laboratory conditions in human affairs requires an extreme degree of interference with the personal liberties of individuals. In order to measure with precision a man's use of energy from food, for example, the subject must live in a glass cage under the most minutely regulated conditions of temperature, humidity, pressure, and so on. To study a whole group in such a manner as to exclude the influences of other groups requires a degree of isolation even greater than that of a penal institution. Literally to keep all but one variable constant, in other words, means a freezing of normal activity which mutilates social intercourse. It is only when the individual is sacrificed, or sacrifices himself, that very much is genuinely learned about human beings by experiment. Distinguished services to medical research have been made by conscientious objectors and prison inmates who have submitted to dangerous tests of drugs and medical techniques. It takes a high degree of social discipline for a town or city, in time of peace, to offer itself for the conducting of a meaningful experiment, such as fluoridation of its water supply, a drastic change of diet, police or fire protection, working hours, or means of transportation.

It is obvious that there are certain kinds of social experiments that our civilization simply will not allow to be tried: such as shock tests on children, abolition of policing, or an hour of silence during prime broadcasting time. If a probable cure of a disease causing an epidemic were discovered, it would be impossible, because heartless, to set up a control group who were to be deprived of the probable cure.[9] It is only in times of major social crisis: a war, a strike, or a depression, that far-reaching changes occur that would never be contemplated in ordinary times. It would seem, then, that they offer ideal opportunities for controlled experiments. In normal times, the person who maintained that a city could get along with one-third fewer streetlights, or one-fourth fewer firemen, would probably never be able to see his proposal tried. Comes a depression, and off go some of the lights. But the results are not always easy to interpret. In the dark days of 1932–33, a Middle Western city could keep on only one-half of its streetlights, and decided to turn off all the lights on two out of four of its main parallel traffic arteries, leaving on all the lights on the other two. The outcome was that during the first month of the semi-black-out, the number of accidents on the two lighted streets went up, while there were fewer accidents on the two unlighted ones. The explanation was easy: most of the traffic took to the lighted streets.

Social experimentation, then, has become associated in the public mind with crisis government, dictation, and the totalitarian state, since it is in the latter that we find the maximum control, in theory and in practice, of its members, and therefore the maximum liberty to conduct any experiments it pleases. In a totalitarian order, "everything which is not forbidden is compulsory." No act, no matter how minute, can be sure of escaping governmental regulation from above. Yet the totalitarian spirit is wholly foreign to social experiment in the sense of the free exploration of all possible alternatives. Dictatorial "experiment" is for one of two purposes: to "prove" what is already laid down as dogma (which is mere rationalizing of the national orthodoxy), or to find a cleverer means of reaching the dictated ends. The free experimentalist, on the other hand, tries alternatives in the hope of finding something genuinely new and better than what is; and in a spirit of willingness to abide by the results of the experiment, whatever its effect upon his hitherto-cherished ideas.

To experiment in this liberal sense, men's minds must be plastic and adaptable enough to pioneer along untrodden pathways. Yet to carry experiments to the point of proof, rigid scientific conditions must be established. Those who

---

[9] For an overdramatized instance, see the West Indian epidemic episode in Sinclair Lewis's novel *Arrowsmith* (New York, 1925). Occasionally a metropolis is involuntarily subjected to a large-scale "difference" in its habits, such as the 114-day newspaper strike in New York City in December–March, 1962–63, resulting in, among other things, a loss of 400,000 circulation by the city's newspapers.

have reason to fear that an experiment may succeed, and thereby damage some vested interest, will oppose it on that ground. Others may object to compelling the trial by the whole of society of a theory which only a bare majority believes to be worth trying. That may lead to a sabotaging of the experiment which may mean that it will "fail" without ever really having had a fair trial. The problem of democratic experimentation thus becomes one of educating the public to a willingness to discipline itself to the extent of setting up the conditions for the discovery and proof of the value of new ideas. This does not mean a reckless "try-anything-once" attitude. On the contrary, it places a heavy responsibility upon democratic leadership to point out what experiments are worth trying, and to win enough initial support to insure that they get a fair chance to succeed or fail. Governments need planning boards to suggest new experiments, but they could also find plenty of worse ways of spending money than by the establishment of an office to check upon past experiments, and to record what has been learned, without fear or favor, in exact and readable form.

(4) *The scarcity of laws in the sense of invariant "timeless" relations observed to hold (within a relatively narrow margin of approximation) of collections of abstracted data.* This is but a restatement of the low predictability which prevails in the social studies, due to the lack of the kinds of reversible uniformities which are so plentiful in the physical sciences, and the difficulties of exact measurement. As sciences on the mechanical pattern become more mature, their laws tend to take the form of functional equations expressing the relationships between numbers which have been obtained by various complicated operations ("pointer-readings") usually involving instruments. Such generalizations are presumed, not always justifiably, to hold with a high degree of probability wherever the conditions are substantially duplicated. Classical mechanics taught that, under more and more ideal conditions of observation, we might approach closer and closer to the rational demonstrations of the "ideal cases" of the textbooks; but modern quantum mechanics with its Principle of Uncertainty has rudely upset any such confidence. It seems that we are further from a firm grasp upon what is going on behind the scenes of Nature than we supposed, and that we are constantly mistaking our mental models of natural relationships, which serve us as ordering devices, for something deeper and more fundamental that eludes us. It does little good, however, to wrangle over the degree to which the discovered uniformities of physical science can be distinguished from man's physical and mental apparatus for establishing and understanding them. The important thing is that, in those departments of knowledge, the same patterns of a fairly small number of variables frequently repeat themselves, and are found to exhibit the same functional relationships, thus yielding a high degree of predictability.

Even in the more "scientific" of the social studies, a very different state of affairs prevails. Here we find ourselves on the many levels of an apparently "newer," less settled, sphere, where most of the uniformities in which we are interested are not "timeless" or reversible. When we attempt to set up such laws, as in the demand-curves of mathematical economics, we find that we are dealing with high abstractions or "ideal cases" that are seldom closely approximated in practice. We are obliged to postulate, in place of actual human beings, a hypothetical constant called *economic man,* whose conduct is determined by very few variables, such as demand and price under conditions of "free competition." Now it is often argued that the ideal cases of mathematical economics are no more abstract than those of mathematical mechanics. But the contrast in terms of predictability is immense. The reason for the low predictability in economics is not that its formulas are abstract, but that its technique of abstraction takes the form of a staggering reduction in the number of the variables. *Homo oeconomicus* acts from a few simple motives; the behavior of actual man is highly complex. In physics, the complexity is overcome by the discovery of a few *basic* variables; why has not economics done the same? Simply because, up to the present, no satisfactory proof has been brought forward that human economic conduct is fully predictable in terms of a small number of variables.

The lack of universally accepted basic concepts in such fields as psychology, upon which many of the social studies must build, accounts for the fact that most of the so-called "laws" of social science are merely abstracted similarities of behavior which show a tendency to conserve or repeat themselves, such as the laws of phonetics or of women's fashions; or else descriptive statistical generalizations about group conduct, such as "Divorces increase in times of prosperity," which are scientifically unsatisfactory, since they lack explanatory significance. We may be able to predict successfully that women's skirts will be longer next year, or that divorces will go up five per cent if the national income increases by ten per cent; but in the absence of any theoretical explanation of the interrelationships of the variables involved, we shall have gained little in the way of organized knowledge.

6. Behavioral Sciences

It has become fashionable to classify the sciences as physical, biological, and behavioral, according to their concern with inanimate objects, living things and human beings. As already indicated, the three areas overlap: whatever is behavioral in the human sense is also biological and physical in part, and the biological partakes of the physical. But there is little profit in a reductionism which seeks to bring biology and behavior under purely physical laws. Neither should one make the mistake of identifying the behavioral with John B. Watson's psychological theory called Behaviorism.

What distinguishes a behavioral science is that it seeks to explain the conduct of an organism in the whole of its environment, which is viewed as a field embracing both internal and external factors. Following the lead of John Dewey and A. F. Bentley, we may give the name of "transaction" to what happens when human behaving occurs. Behavioral science seeks to frame hypotheses which, in the words of Rollo Handy and Paul W. Kurtz, can be *"experimentally confirmed by reference to publicly observable changes in behavior."*[10]

[10] Rollo Handy and Paul W. Kurtz, "A Current Appraisal of the Behavioral Sciences," supplement to *The American Behavioral Scientist,* vol. VII, No. 1 (September,

On first sight, the behavioral sciences as above characterized present a panorama of a dozen or more approaches to the one subject: man. The result has been a profusion of terminologies, theories, and specialized methods of approach. Is there any thread that can lead us through the labyrinth of these sciences-in-embryo, sciences-in-babyhood, and sciences-in-adolescence?

One possibility is to arrange the behavioral sciences according to their successes in adapting the mechanical physical science pattern to their subject matters, and those which are obliged to adhere to what we have called the historical pattern. Among the first belong economics, some parts of psychology, and fewer parts of sociology. Among the second group, besides history itself, are law, political science, education, and anthropology.

Under the general title of "systems sciences," and sometimes "cybernetics," there has been a multiplication of attempts to formalize human and animal behavior, including decision theory, management theory, automata theory, operations research, general systems theory and the theory of games already mentioned. All these subjects are concerned with quantifying the complexities of rapidly changing systems, and especially with those which, like the human being, apparently regulate themselves. By the omissions which they make in abstracting the quantifiable aspects of behavior, they give the impression, both of treating human beings as robots, and of swallowing up the individual in the maw of statistics. Hence the charges that these alleged sciences promote "a Gallup-poll mentality which exalts quantity at the expense of quality," and that they portray individuals as pawns to be manipulated by "human engineers." When a man finds himself figuring only as a string of digits in a computer, he begins to wonder about the boasted "dignity of the individual." Can the social studies reap the genuine advantages of scientific method without dehumanizing themselves in the process? It is upon our answers to such questions that the cultural climate of coming generations will depend.

FOR CLASS DISCUSSION

A. The essence of science, the *understanding* as distinct from the mere photographic reception of concrete phenomena, is theory, and the essence of theory is analytical abstraction. Whatever its dangers, there is no other way. — *Talcott Parsons*   (1)
Science is madness if good sense does not cure it. — *Spanish Proverb*
The vast development of science has thrown us out of balance. Science has overshadowed other components which are indispensable to the harmony of life. This balance must be re-established. — *Walter Gropius*
B. A method is a dangerous thing unless its underlying philosophy is understood, and none is more dangerous than the statistical. . . . Overattention

---

1963), p. 6 (italics theirs). Their survey comprises sixteen chapters, divided into "The Older Fields: Anthropology, Sociology, History, Economics, Political Science, Jurisprudence, Psychology and Education;" and "The Newer Fields: Information Theory, Cybernetics, Linguistics, Sign-Behavior, Game Theory, Decision-making Theory, Value Inquiry, and General Systems Theory."

to technique may actually blind one to the dangers. . . . In the long run it is clear thinking, experienced feeling, and a patient poise, not automatic systems and methods, that wins the strongholds of science.

— E. B. Wilson

C. The scientific man has above all things to aim at self-elimination in his judgments, to provide an argument which is as true for each individual mind as for his own. — Karl Pearson

D. We thus stand before the fact that many, and among them the most important, laws of nature are asserted and hold of conditions, which in reality in general are never found. — Wilhelm Ostwald   (2)

E. We want regularity and we have devised (in physics) methods of obtaining it. But the regularity is purchased at the price of depriving normal uncontrolled experience of its complexity and individuality. — George Boas

F. The proper study of mankind is man, says man. — James Thurber

G. The social sciences, like the natural sciences, proceed upon the one great premise that the intricate flux of events can in some way be explained. . . .

— Allyn A. Young

H. The fundamental difference between the investigations of external nature and of human affairs lies in the character of the facts to be observed.

— James Bryce (4-5)

I. It is still true that the natural scientist seeks the enduring laws afforded by most of his subject matter, while the social scientist must seek truths which may become obsolete while he is finding them. — Richard T. Ely

J. No science tells us what to do with the knowledge that constitutes the science. — George A. Lundberg

K. Only when economists can persuade governments to use their coercive power in experiments with their peoples' economic actions in the interest of discovering truth, can economics become an exact science.   (6)

— Dixon Ryan Fox

L. Undoubtedly a large part of our trouble (in social psychology) has been an overrapid development of research techniques which can be applied to the surface aspects of almost any social response and are reasonably sure to give a publishable numerical answer to almost any casual question. . . . Woe to that science whose methods are developed in advance of its problems, so that the experimenter can see only those phases of a problem for which a method is already at hand. — Gardner Murphy

M. The prophet and the poet may regenerate the world without the economist, but the economist cannot regenerate it without them.

— Philip H. Wicksteed

14

THE HISTORICAL PATTERN:
Formulating and Testing the Hypothesis

1. The Two Approaches

THE QUEST FOR RELIABLE KNOWLEDGE is a search for stable order in a changing world. Broadly speaking, we have discovered just one plan by which that objective can demonstrably be achieved — that is, by observation — analysis — hypothesis — elaboration — observation leading to a consensus of opinion. But there is more than one possible pattern which the general method may assume, as already suggested in Chapter 9, Section 4, depending upon the kind of order in which we are interested. It would indeed be surprising if a world so many-faceted as ours revealed only one kind of uniformity which had to be approached from a single point of view. The same subject matter can figure in many sciences and many histories and many arts. A small globule of lead may be described mathematically, physically, chemically, geologically, and so on; but it may also be authenticated as the bullet which killed Lincoln in 1865; and it may even figure in a story or a poem or a painting relating to that period.

So far we have been occupied mainly with the first of these modes of knowing — the strictly scientific treatment of any subject matter on what we have called the *mechanical pattern*. The latter may be envisaged as a sort of horizontal cross-sectioning or abstract "freezing" of Nature in order to reveal the relatively "timeless" structures of things. It does not attempt to investigate all the qualities of its material, but only those which give promise of proving useful from its limited point of view. Its ideal is an hypothesis in the form of a perfect case, which may then be approximated in an artificially isolated laboratory experiment by any competent observer anywhere. Its essential method is analytical. It consists in setting up strictly comparable and measurable likenesses and differences among abstractions from groups of instances, which have been selected and classified with a view to exhibiting functional or causal relationships. Once the abstract terms of his hypothesis have been framed, the scientist cares nothing about the times and places of the individual occurrences. When decisive differences can be publicly approximated by repeated tests in such a way as to eliminate all other imagined possibilities, a high probability that the hypothesis is an inductive "law" may be said to have been established, subject to correction by further observation and further theorizing. It will be expected to hold for all "like" instances within a very wide area of space and time, perhaps for the whole known spatio-temporal universe.

351

It is knowledge-claims thus evidenced which have won continuing assent concerning their reliability from more different sorts of knowers than any other variety. One result of their unparalleled success in securing common agreement has been a sharp depreciation in the prestige of all other procedures for the testing of knowledge. In the eyes of many, reason has come to be identified with scientific method in the sense of this formal, mathematical ideal and its exclusively laboratory types of safeguards. Such persons envisage the completion of the task of knowledge as being achieved on the day when some scientist "ties up the last variable," and every last scientific proposition has been given public demonstration. They point with emphasis to the fact that when the safeguards of the laboratory are relaxed, even to the slightest degree, one can no longer speak of proof in the scientific-mechanical sense. Open the gates one tiny crack for a single instant — unpredictable error slips in, and proof leaks out. The burden of proof that proof is possible by any other method is squarely on the shoulders of anyone who would venture to champion such a view.

Yet it is apparent that there are immense areas of knowledge-claims which cannot be tested by the mechanical pattern or any of its modifications, and yet which are constantly rated by conscientious judges of knowledge in terms of their reliability. Among them are all the humanistic studies, most of the social studies, and most of the evidence in courts of law. We say, for example, that it is highly probable that George Washington was our first President, that John Wilkes Booth was killed, that the French Revolution was hastened by the American, and that Mr. X was at fault in a collision of automobiles. These are examples of "vertical" or historical hypotheses connecting individual instances arranged in space and especially in time. Every history is a history *of* something; and when we trace the history of anything: a log of wood, the Roosevelt family, Eureka Hook and Ladder Company Number 7, the Byzantine Empire, or the theory of isotopes, we follow our interest in the subject along some of the latter's particular space-and-time relationships to whatever is contiguous to it in some respect. Usually we find ourselves enmeshed in larger and larger configurations of occurrences, since there is no limit to what *might* be found relevant to any particular history. No more than sciences are histories mutually exclusive — a single happening, just as it can enter into innumerable scientific hypotheses, can also be involved in an infinite number of histories.

There are, then, two distinguishable but related and overlapping ways of approaching our world and exercising our knowing powers upon it. Both of them use the imagination checked by observation in order to achieve a better understanding and control of the raw material of experience. Both are limited by a particular interest in manipulating what they choose to examine. But where the strictly scientific mind seeks knowledge through the kind of analysis which leads to generalizations correlating the various common qualities of things with no specific temporal or individual reference, the historically minded knower looks for a different sort of order of connection among unique, individual, non-repeatable wholes. All his work is essentially "biographical," although that does not mean that he deals only with single persons, for he may try to write the history of a whole nation, or even of mankind. But his subject is always some specifically existing or previously existent network of interlinked events, and not the disconnected but "typical" occurrences which the scientist attempts to sum up in his equations.

Although no one of his events can be repeated in its original fullness, the historian occasionally finds that certain types recur, which leads him to suspect that a process is at work. When that happens, the material can be turned over to the scientist to become the subject matter of the scientific type of generalization. The stuff of life possesses both kinds of characteristics: those attributable to the repeatable processes; and to the non-repeatable configurations which the interacting processes kaleidoscopically manifest. Whether a given inquirer will try to unravel the first or the second will depend upon what kind of understanding or control he seeks. The two approaches, except in their extreme and dogmatic forms, are not antagonistic, but supplementary, as indicated in the causal analyses of Chapter 9. Few sciences are so "pure" nowadays that they are not infected with history to some extent; and there is hardly an historical subject which does not boast that it is in some degree "scientific." Written history, as we shall see, has aspects which deserve the name of science, but it is not science on the mechanical pattern. The social studies occupy an intermediate position, and therefore blend both the mechanical and the historical patterns in ways that outrage the partisans of each of them. To the very limited extent that their subject matter consists of invariant processes and structures which can be analyzed and isolated, the social studies can become social sciences. But, for the most part, as explained in the previous chapter, they deal with things which have not yet been ironed into manageable variables, so that their approach must be largely historical. It is for that reason that we shall attempt to see what the "pure" historian, as distinguished from his opposite number the "pure" scientist, is trying to do, and how it may be possible to test the reliability of his knowledge-claims.

2. Historical Hypotheses

What, exactly, is the difference between the mechanical and the historical patternings of things? Both, we assume, deal mainly with events going on outside the knower and "given" to him as something factual and coercive, although not, of course, in finished form. Things happen in the order in which they happen — it is not within the power of the historian to place the discovery of gold in California before the battle of the Alamo, although he may inadvertently do so, and the error may be propagated in a hundred textbooks. Both science (here used as a synonym for the mechanical pattern) and history have this unbudgeable substratum of the given in common; and must ultimately take account of it. History, like science, has a whole host of auxiliary techniques for determining, by inferences resting upon approximate coincidence observations, what is known to have occurred, and in what order. If this compilation of correct annals were the whole task of history, it would be a mere science of the particular, directing its attention to establishing the authenticity and temporal location of isolated instances. But it is more than that, as we shall presently see.

Both history and science proceed by the use of hypotheses which are self-limited and selective: no scientist tackles the science of everything, and no historian writes the history of everything. Both kinds of hypotheses, the historical as well as the scientific, go beyond the immediately visible evidence in the making of their imaginative conjectures. The scientist's hypothesis is governed by his problem and by what he believes to be relevant to its solution; and so is the historian's. Both men must be steeped in the lore of their particular fields, if they are to divine the hidden interconnections of things. Both employ multiple hypotheses in the endeavor to exhaust the relevant possibilities, and then eliminate, although the historian is seldom able to do the latter with the scientist's finality. The historian is also less likely to record those theories which he has considered and rejected, for fear of distracting the reader's attention from his accepted view. Like the scientist, he assumes a high degree of uniformity in his material. Physical Nature and human nature, he supposes, have remained pretty much the same throughout the ages — a postulate which can lead to dubious conclusions when extrapolation on the basis of the present is used to explain the past.[1] Neither is the difference to be found in the observational stages of the thinking. The same falling apple which is supposed to have started the mind of a Newton on the trail of his laws of gravitation might have set an historian to wondering about the date upon which apple trees were first introduced into England. The initially observed facts of science differ from those of historical inquiry only in the extent to which the former are points of departure quickly abandoned as soon as their qualities are classified into general types. Where the scientist is always trying to get away from individual instances, the historian is ever seeking to come closer to them. An historical fact is something to be cherished, and adorned with ever richer meanings; a scientific fact is something to be stripped and conceptualized for the purposes of generalization.

As for the final stage of a complete act of thought — the producing of the empirical evidence for or against the elaborated hypothesis — the historian, like the scientist, must offer present evidence, even though it refers to a past which has largely disappeared. The knowledge-claims of an historian have reference to events which have happened; but his evidence is always in the form of vestiges which have survived into the present, or may yet be unearthed. The historian never observes the past which preceded his own lifetime directly; and he is never able to recover more than a fraction of it. Even if he sticks to what he has personally observed, his present memory has selected and reworked only certain of the aspects of his experiences which impressed him at the time, for reasons which he may never have known, or has perhaps forgotten. He may be obliged, therefore, to reconstruct a man or a nation or an era from a

[1] Cf. J. A. Froude's remark in connection with his studies of the English monasteries, that the "true motive," when he was able to discover it, was "almost invariably of a kind which no modern experience could have suggested." *Short Studies on Great Subjects*, World Classics ed., p. 286.

single relic or document, filling in enormous gaps by an audacious act of the hypothetical imagination. If he is aided by the accounts of others, he must first assure himself or their authenticity by reference to present evidence. It does no good to produce a dog-eared diary with the inscription: "This is really my diary. (Signed) A. Lincoln." The past cannot guarantee its own genuineness; only present evidence can determine that. Not even a newsreel of a past event *is* assuredly one view of what actually happened. There is always the possibility that the film was faked. The proof either way is a present proof, and not a past one.

DESCRIPTIVE HISTORICAL HYPOTHESES

It has already been pointed out that there is an elementary type of historical inquiry which is close to that of science in that it is preoccupied with "establishing the fact that such-and-such occurred." It is the sort of fact-finding in which the knower's selective purpose, the material, and the conventional frames of reference are in control, and for which the questions of meaning and value are relatively unimportant. An hypothesis of that simple order would take the form: Let it be supposed that a particular event happened at the following time and place . . . e.g., that the Thirty Years' War began in Prague on May 23, 1618. It hardly needs pointing out that even an historical fact of this rudimentary sort is a highly complex concatenation of innumerable circumstances, and not a cold, hard entity which can be added to other similar entities. As Professor Carl L. Becker pointed out in his address entitled "What Are Historical Facts?" before the American Historical Association in 1926: "A thousand and one lesser 'facts' went to make up the one simple fact that Caesar crossed the Rubicon; and if we had someone, say James Joyce, to know and relate all these facts, it would no doubt require a book of 794 pages (i.e. *Ulysses*) to present the one fact that Caesar crossed the Rubicon."[2]

As historian Allan Nevins remarks: "The beginning of wisdom in history is doubt." To test our May 23, 1618, hypothesis there is no need of inquiring into the causes of the war, or its results. The evidence for and against it hinges upon the existing records of the relationship between the accepted calendar and the series of incidents which historians have agreed to define as the Thirty Years' War, as well as the common notion of what it means for a war to begin. Our inescapable center of reference is the present. We do not expect to decide the matter by hunting for a diary in which someone made the entry: "Prague, May 23, 1618. The Thirty Years' War began here this afternoon." The people who were alive on that date had no idea that the war would last thirty years or would receive its name from that circumstance.

Plainly the establishment of a fact of this kind would be an affair of existing documentary sources to be tested by the canons of historical criticism. The latter are ordinarily divided into the tests of *external* criticism, which reveal frauds and forgeries by the minute examination and comparison of paper, ink,

2 Quoted in Harry Elmer Barnes, A *History of Historical Writing* (Norman, Okla., 1937), pp. 267–68. See also Chapters III–VIII in Louis Gottschalk, *Understanding History* (New York, 1950).

wrappings, seals, chirography, abbreviations, and forms of protocol with other already standard (i.e., accepted) samples of similar material; and those of *internal* criticism, which do the same by meticulous attention to matters of style, emendations, anachronisms, and textual inconsistencies in general. This is the familiar province of critical historical scholarship, which has been developed through the centuries by the labors of uncounted generations of specialists in such arts as paleography, epigraphy, diplomatics, sigillography, numismatics, and heraldry.[3] The tests used by all of these branches of criticism rest upon known or supposed uniformities of human behavior with respect to relatively homogeneous materials — how paper was made at the time, how scribes worked, how kings signed their decrees, and so on. The individual peculiarities of the practices of European chanceries in the mediaeval and modern periods are now so well classified that experts have little difficulty in dating diplomatic documents within a small margin of error. The "trial" of an alleged relic or manuscript for genuineness corresponds in outline to that of a criminal court. Some scholar who believes in its authenticity acts as its champion; others take the part of devil's advocates; and the world of scholarship is in the jury box. Many of the same rules of evidence prevail — the hypothesis of genuineness is opposed by the hypothesis of fraud; possible motives on both sides are examined; witnesses are heard and evaluated; independent corroboration from many different sources weighs heavily; and a verdict in terms of probability buttressed by other probabilities is reached.

But the bare facts of history piled up in a heap by uninspired collectors are indeed dry bones. The least exacting part of the historian's task is this necessary assembling and authenticating of his source material, what Professor A. M. Schlesinger calls "the microscopic examination of myriad data." When that "anatomical" phase of his labors is complete, there is another harder assignment awaiting him, and upon another plane of effort. It is to determine the meaning and value of the evidence before him — to frame explanatory as well as descriptive hypotheses about the events "as they occurred."

EXPLANATORY HISTORICAL HYPOTHESES

Suppose that he asks himself: How did it happen that the Thirty Years' War broke out in Prague on May 23, 1618? What were its causes, immediate and remote? This assumes that he desires an *understanding* of that particular turn of events in terms of its causal antecedents. Such an explanatory hypothesis might take the form: Let it be supposed that the inciting cause of the Thirty Years' War was the Defenestration of Prague on that date. This goes beyond the fact that the war began at a certain time and place, to assert a hypothetical causal relationship between two highly complex configurations in a state of change. It says virtually: If you want to understand the outbreak of the Thirty Years' War, consider the theory that the Defenestration *meant* war. But why did it mean war? To understand that, one would have to examine the evidence in the form of its bearings, or relations to still other complex configurations:

[3] See John M. Vincent, *Historical Research* (New York, 1911), and Allen Johnson, *The Historian and Historical Evidence* (New York, 1926).

the state of unrest in Bohemia, the intricate theologico-political maneuvers of Protestants and Catholics, linked in turn to the Reformation and the previous dynastic wars. A merely external or behavioristic account would reveal that two of Emperor Matthias's Regents, Slawata and Martinitz, and his private secretary Fabricius, were thrown out of the window of the chancery of the Hradschin, some fifty or sixty feet into the castle-ditch below, by a Protestant deputation which had come to present a petition. But there is no historical "law" which states that throwing imperial regents from windows starts wars. People have been thrown from windows without starting wars; and wars have been started without throwing anyone from a window. About the only help we can get from any general rule of behavior is that "wars have often been started by acts of violence to persons in authority." This particular instance is not only unique in its details; it is probably the only one of its kind in history.

Now it would be idle to talk of testing an historical explanatory hypothesis of this sort until a person had attempted imaginatively to enter into the situation to which it refers. We cannot experiment by bringing back the original actors and re-enacting the scene in all its pristine richness. Much less can we arrange to have it done twice over — once with the Defenestration, and once without, to see whether or not, in the absence of the famous incident, war would have broken out? Historians sometimes resort to this hypothetical "thinking away" or "thinking in" of supposedly critical factors in the effort to apply the Method of Difference;[4] but the results have seldom earned any great measure of acceptance by other historians — the variables are much too numerous and interwoven. Certainly it would do no good to wait for history to repeat itself.

The alternative is to resurrect the situation in its concrete fullness, which requires a vast amount of collecting of reliable information, but also a great deal more than that. The full meaning of an historical explanation which relates to human conduct can only be grasped and tested by one who is capable of putting himself in the places of each of the participants and of those who recorded the event. To get under the skins of both the departed actors and their scribes requires a kind of capacity for personal acquaintanceship through the sympathetic imagination which is quite different from the impersonal abstracting of the scientist. The proof of this is the complete dissatisfaction which we feel when another person writes an external and uncomprehending historical account of something with which we are acquainted at first-hand. We object that "it was not really that way at all — he has utterly failed to grasp what it felt like to be alive in 1941," and so on. Unlike the scientist, who picks out qualities common to classes of things, usually on a single level, for the abstract terms of his hypotheses; the historian must seek a "synthesis of reconstitution," the recovery of the living fullness of the complex events which form the terms of his conjectural interpretations. Some of the obstacles

4 A book called *If: or History Rewritten*, by Philip Guedalla and other historians (New York, 1931), has been made of such attempts, with chapters entitled "If Booth Had Missed," "If Drouet's Cart Had Stuck," "If Louis XVI Had Had an Atom of Firmness," etc.

to accomplishing this are only too apparent in Case IV of the Introduction, where neither the happenings at Ford's Theater nor their meanings and values are easily agreed upon.

THE RÔLE OF GENERALIZATIONS

Nevertheless, it may be objected that the historian, like everyone else in search of reliable knowledge, and even more than most inquirers, is obliged to get most of his data from the past in the form of words; that words are themselves abstract generalizations; and that historical knowledge is therefore only a crude and inexact imitation of the sciences. But this overlooks the way in which general expressions function in historical narrative. There is a difference between their use in what Ernst Cassirer calls "living speech" in direct connection with the proper names of individuals, and their sophisticated entrance as highly abstract symbols into the hypotheses of mechanical science. To refer once more to the Defenestration of Prague and its putative connection with the outbreak of the Thirty Years' War, let us suppose that an historian has satisfied himself of the genuineness of documents which describe the state of public opinion in Prague on that day as "blazingly indignant," the attitude of the Regents as "insolent," and the response of Thurn and his Protestant associates as the "hurling of violent invectives." These are word-symbols of psychological attitudes and psycho-physiological activities which might be used abstractly in a textbook of psychology without reference to any individual person. But, as used in history, they do not exclude the individuals of whom they are predicated; on the contrary, the function of the general symbols is precisely to heighten our concrete impression of the specific anger, insolence, and invective-hurling of these particular individuals at that definite time and place. For it is just that, plus our own inner knowledge of how we and others react under similar circumstances, which enables us to understand the outbreak of a particular war. The words "indignation," "insolent," and "violent invective" are not sterilized into innocuousness as they would be in a scientific treatise (see above, Chapter 7, Section 2). Instead, they act as aids in the effort to recover the full emotional impact of the original encounter in the Hradschin "just as it occurred."

History as narrated deals in proper names, and attaches class-concepts to them (except when the historian tries to turn sociologist and proclaim broad historical "laws") for the purpose of enhancing their vivid determinateness, not for diminishing it. That is why the practicing historian must be both something of a scientist in the testing of his data, and an artist in interpreting them. He is at his best when he uses the art of narrative in such a way as to evoke from his audience the same sympathetic appreciation which he has brought to his material. By his own stirring reliving of past episodes with the added wisdom of the present, he may enable others to relive them also, at least to the extent of their resources in experience and imagination. Thus he enlarges both their concrete experience by this vicarious living of other lives, and their arsenal of understanding of all kinds of experiences. That is why the framing of the highest type of explanatory historical hypothesis, in a work which attempts to sum up the spirit of an age, is an exercise of the art of synthesis that can only be judged by standards which are literary and philosophical as well as narrowly scientific.

3. The Testing of Historical Hypotheses

If what we have been saying is correct, then a small mind cannot write an adequate history of a great event. Great events call not only for great-minded historians, but for great-minded readers to appreciate their works. Scientific exactitude of the minute sort is highly desirable in the preliminary stages of research, but no amount of it can take the place of breadth and balance of vision in organizing the material, its subtle meanings and its subtler values, into a living, breathing work of art. No man can write a lasting history of a period in which he is not at home, or of personalities whose intricacies of motive are beyond his comprehension. The man who can re-create Hannibal, as Sydney Smith remarked, is he who sees with the brilliancy of Hannibal's single eye. As Rear Admiral Samuel Eliot Morison wrote of his predecessors as biographers of Columbus, they give us the Genoese navigator only "to the water's edge." A salt-water sailor with an erudite command of the documents and a vibrant literary style can do much better, as his *Admiral of the Ocean Sea* so amply proves.

But if the finest variety of historiography requires a sympathetic and convincing reliving of the past, a number of awkward questions about testing its reliability soon arise. Does not that state of affairs disqualify a mind which has been formed in the social and intellectual climate of the present? We seem to be caught in a dilemma, one horn of which is the fact that the most reliable history of the seventeenth century can only be written in the twentieth by a seventeenth-century scribe who has lived on for three hundred years unscathed by any of the spiritual changes in the interim. The other horn is constituted by the reflection that, to be useful for twentieth-century readers, and to be read by them, a history of the seventeenth century would have to be written from the twentieth-century, and not the seventeenth-century, point of view. The generations are forever at odds over two sets of standards: one based upon faithfulness to the actual temper of a bygone age, and the other yielding to Professor Carl L. Becker's conclusion that "every generation must inevitably play on the dead whatever tricks it finds necessary for its own peace of mind."[5]

But one does not have to consider the differences between generations in order to find examples of variations in the judgments of historians. If the reliability in which we are interested is that of historical interpretation, not of the mere admissibility of evidence; and if interpretation is in part at least a matter of individual insight into meaning and value, what check have we upon all manner of outrageous perversions and distortions of the data, made even worse by the rhetorical attractiveness with which they are presented? Histories are written by fallible men, and not by omniscient machines which turn out

[5] Carl L. Becker, *Everyman His Own Historian* (New York, 1935), p. 253.

conclusions "untouched by human hands." "No important history," says Allan Nevins, "has yet appeared which did not reveal some bias," and contends that "while the historian should avoid bias in the sense of prejudice, he should court it in the sense of honest conviction."[6] To be read, history must be written with fire and force, which means that it will have an unmistakable "point of view," not chosen in anticipation of the outcome of the research, but springing from it as it progresses. Timidity disguised as impartiality has ruined far more histories than the robust advocacy of positive interpretations. The sparks of truth may fly when reasoned convictions clash, but never from the jostlings of prejudices or from the inertia of the perpetually suspended judgment.

HISTORICAL RELATIVISM AND THE SOCIOLOGY OF KNOWLEDGE

What seems to one historian a principle appears to another as only a prejudice, in Professor Nevins's phrase. With all the sincerity in the world, says the relativist, each writer becomes the unconscious victim of his cultural background and prejudices: local, national, racial, economic, political, and religious. Personality, temperament, and early upbringing are writ large on the pages of all our history books. Sometimes, of course, the bias is far from unconscious. It may even be paraded, in the attempt to give the timid reader those "stupidities with which he is familiar," and which Anatole France declared most men preferred to any new idea that might take them by surprise.

This charge of bias is an ancient one, and by no means easy to refute in any given case. Denials of bias on the part of the person accused are thrown out of court as biased in favor of denying bias. Since many of our prejudices are unconscious, no one is ordinarily allowed to pass upon his own impartiality. Judges are in an especially difficult position regarding bias. In federal courts, and in some state jurisdictions, a judge is prohibited by statute from ruling on his own bias as affecting his qualification for sitting in a particular case. According to common law, however, a judge can rule on his own bias or prejudice, and this interpretation still holds in Massachusetts, and in some other states. This point was given world-wide publicity because it became an important issue in the Sacco-Vanzetti case, where the trial judge was allowed to rule that the defendants had received a fair trial at his hands. In some instances, the person accused of bias may protest that he is impartial because the conclusion he has reached not only yields him no profit, but is actually harmful to his interests. "I must be telling the truth, because it is costing me something!" This test is frequently utilized in courts of law, where an unwilling witness is sometimes regarded as *per se* trustworthy if he testifies against his friends. Yet a strict application of the principle to the writing of history would mean that no one could write anything that he wanted to believe, for no author could be trusted unless he stood to lose something by his statements. History would then become one long saga of misanthropy. Historians could hardly escape the charge of bias by confining their writings to matters in which they had no conceivable interest whatever; for that contradicts the

[6] Allan Nevins, *The Gateway to History*, revised edition (Chicago, Ill., 1963), pp. 54, 58.

requirement that they must become sympathetically *en rapport* with their materials.

There seems to be no avoiding the conclusion that all historians are biased; and so are all who try to judge whether or not their volumes contain reliable knowledge. Does this compel us to accept the cynic's version of history as a *mensonge convenu* — "a lie agreed upon" — and the criticism of history as nothing but the scrutiny of the way in which the sordid agreement is reached? Is one man's version of the past just as good, or just as bad, as another's? Because no one of us is wholly disinterested, does that mean that there can be no degrees of "interestedness"? A closer examination of the actual uses of historical relativism should help us to answer those questions. For the modern relativists have repeatedly used their doctrine for the purpose of overthrowing ("debunking") the supposedly absolute position of the other man, but not of their own. As against the prudes and the censors, Freud called attention to the unsuspected influences of sex in its many disguises which accounted for their hatred of it. As against the capitalists, Marx pointed to the inescapable bias of one's position in the class struggle. As against everybody but himself, Pareto hammered away at the pathetic refusal of human minds to admit their own irrationalities. But as soon as everyone learned the trick, it was turned against the debunkers. The enemies of Freud submitted Freud to Freudian analysis; Marx was placed by the anti-Marxists under the Marxist microscope; and Pareto was obliged to suffer the indignity of a Paretian dissection. When everyone was able to expose the biases of everyone else, the result was a sort of intellectual nudism, a universal flaunting of the sudden distrust of any conceivable sort of clothes.

Universal skepticism never prevails very widely or for any great length of time. Man is obliged to act; and action calls for discrimination among his beliefs. The striking thing about bias is that, although it is universal, so is the belief that it can be detected. Complete trust in human disinterestedness is a position that is impossible to maintain for long; but so is complete distrust. Those who come to distrust both overconfidence and underconfidence in knowledge are faced with the problem of formulating relativism in terms that avoid both absolutism and complete skepticism. One variety of historical relativism, which its principal champion, Karl Mannheim,[7] prefers to call "relationism," has become known as the *sociology of knowledge*. As a technique of research concerning the ways in which men of various cultures and centuries come to acquire their beliefs and the criteria by which they test them, the sociology of knowledge gives signs of usefulness. But Mannheim and his followers claim much more for it than that, denying that the meaning and validity of an historical thesis can be judged apart from the social conditions from which it emerges. He stretches the Marxist term *ideology* to cover all existentially determined thinking, and concludes that it comprises all thought, since all men's minds are moulded by the social groups of which, in some particular historical period, they are members. But he confuses the harmony of a given thought and its historical setting (which accounts for its effective-

[7] Works in English: *Ideology and Utopia* (New York, 1936), and *Man and Society in an Age of Reconstruction* (New York, 1940).

ness in its day and age) with its logical status in other and wider contexts. Such a view is inadequate for the complete understanding of pure science, or of formal logic, or of many varieties of contemplative thought.

Thought has many partial determiners: its social-historical origin, "race," climate, diet, language, and so on. But it also has tests which seem to have little to do with any of these. The whole world saw the absurdity of the Nazi doctrine of truth as determined by the strictly "Aryan" origin of the one who uttered it. Class, as used by Mannheim, is somewhat better than "race"; but any of the variables already mentioned, and many others, might have been chosen instead. What criterion of objective validity we shall choose to regard as "functionally absolute" depends upon a multitude of factors, no one of which is entitled to claim a permanent position of priority.

4. "Pure" History and Its Criteria

There are two bases for the judging of written histories that are particularly difficult to disentangle. For histories are written from many different motives; and motives tend to have an effect upon the reliability of the product, even though the two cannot be uniformly correlated. Some highly accurate accounts have occasionally been written by biased reporters; and some avowedly disinterested narrators have sometimes gone wide of the mark at which they have aimed. But generally, where there is the pressure of a present problem, we look for signs of "coloring the account," and, as Lord Acton said, "The most respectable of these influences is the most dangerous." Suppose, for example, that it has been found politically desirable to promote military co-operation between countries A and B by informing the peoples of the two countries about each other's history. A historian from each country is appointed to write the respective books. Each would undoubtedly select, from "the total welter of past happenings," those items for emphasis which he believes will inspire kindly feelings toward his own country in the other nation's populace. Unquestionably the merit of the work of each would be judged by its immediate success in promoting military co-operation. Ten years later the book might be forgotten or even suppressed, not because anything in it was factually incorrect or even exaggerated, but because the need which brought it forth had disappeared.

But to go to the other extreme, there are some histories which are written out of an intellectual curiosity about the past which is just as "pure" as that of the research scientist. They may have no visible connection with any contemporary problem or any that is foreseeable in the future. They are individual searches for answers to purely *historical* questions: How did that alleged event happen to occur, if it did? Where did this curious object come from, and how did it get here? How did men long ago come to set such a value on that strange idea? Such interests have their locus in the present, it is true; and, when satisfied, will presumably yield a value in the future. But they need not serve in any way in the solution of any present non-historical problem. Yet they may give rise to better histories than those which are produced on order.

Suppose, for instance, that two other representatives of countries A and B, equal in imagination and research skill to the first two, set to work independently on histories of their respective countries with just such interests in view — not even thinking of publication, perhaps, but solely of settling questions about their native countries which had been bothering them intellectually. Surely it is arguable that the histories which they would produce might be far more faithful portraits than those which were painted for a crisis-purpose.

It is important to see just what is at stake in this comparison. What is *not* intended is the implication that "pure" history is a neutral mosaic of facts without meanings recorded in a sort of intellectual vacuum. That would not be history of any kind, but a mere aggregation of inert items. History that is to amount to anything must grapple with meanings and values. It must do something with its material if the latter is to receive the breath of life. Now meanings, as was pointed out in Chapter 4, Section 8, attach to things which we propose to do something about. They are tentative "leadings" whose following may result in success or failure. That thing is meaning*less* to us which gives us no lead, which utterly baffles all our purposes, so that we can do nothing about it. Meanings, then, are hypothetical estimates which do or do not justify themselves. Some are limited to a single context; others are useful in innumerable ways.

The same thing may have one meaning for a past generation, and another for ours, because it serves the two generations differently. There are many objects and ideas, such as powder horns and infant damnation, which meant a great deal to our forefathers, but which no longer "have any meaning" for us, except the historical meaning which they had for our forbears. There are other meanings which have remained fairly stable for centuries, because they relate to perennial human purposes. Now it is the special undertaking of the historian to appreciate and to convey to his present and future audience what things meant to the peoples of the past in the latter's own perspectives, as far as he is able to recapture their experiences. If he does that well, there is a sense in which that particular part of his task will not have to be done over. Minor corrections and additions will continue to be made; but what has happened, has happened; and what it meant to the participants (as distinct from what it *might* have meant to them, or to us), it meant to them.

But it would be absurd to infer that the past must continue forever to have just those same past meanings for us with our different purposes, or that the historian's task is to discover the one fixed and final meaning of each of his facts. As Professor Lamprecht has pointed out, "there is not a standard meaning in any part of history . . . that requires all historians to treat it in an identical fashion . . . though many meanings may be clear, genuine, and important."[8] What, then, is to prevent the historian from imposing upon the facts and their past meanings any present or future meaning that he chooses? Or even from filling in gaps by manufacturing a meaning or two? Can he not arbitrarily set up, for example, the Second Coming of Christ, or the triumph of the proletarian revolution, or the world rule of the Third Internationale as his

[8] Sterling P. Lamprecht, "Historiography of Philosophy," *Journal of Philosophy*, vol. XXXVI (1939), p. 455.

focal point, and give to all past events their meanings in terms of their alleged relationships to the one "far-off, divine event toward which Creation moves"? The answer is that he can; and that millions of men are accustomed to having their historical problems solved for them by just such dogmatic philosophies of history. Otherwise, as such absolutists are in the habit of saying: "Human life would be meaningless."

But absolutism does not produce reliable history, since none of the terminal situations which would give definitive meaning to the whole of history have come in sight, nor is any final dénouement easily conceivable in an evolving world. Men have their purposes; but, as the late Dean Woodbridge argued so cogently in his *The Purpose of History*, history is pluralistic; Nature plays no favorites; and the whole idea of histories is "just the denial of absolute considerations."[9] Are we then wholly at liberty to assign to historical events any tentative meanings which may serve our own personal interests? Beyond the substratum of coercive fact, and the primary relationships of processes about which there can be little dispute, apparently we are, unless we are restrained from within. In the endless realms of secondary meanings and values, there is not very much in the nature of most happenings which can prevent us from making erroneous interpretations if we are bent upon doing so. That is why the great danger in the use of the historical pattern is irrationalism — the denial of the potency of systematic general concepts, and the confining of one's standards to "whatever happens as it happens." Where the users of the mechanical pattern tend to err in the direction of overemphasis upon the importance of the general, those who see the world in terms of the historical pattern are likely to overdo the particular. The historian, only a little less than the journalist, is continually tempted to play up the extraordinary and exciting, and to let the dull and the ordinary go. That is why it is so essential to make use of both patterns in the quest for reliable knowledge in the social studies.

Of one thing we can be sure, and that is that small-minded special pleading has never produced great histories. Biased accounts which are unusually clever or charming in a literary way sometimes attain popularity, but eventually they lose their holds, no matter how well they may have served a cause or built up a patriotic consciousness. Even a glance at some of the histories which have won enduring fame, such as the works of Thucydides, Gibbon, Mommsen, Grote, Guizot, Prescott, and Parkman, reveals that their authors, whatever their biases or private convictions, were guided by a determination to promote the fullest possible understanding of what had happened in the tangled affairs of men. Their accounts are not great because they are regarded as final; for there is not one of them which has not been superseded in some respects by more recent studies. Understanding is an endless undertaking; so all histories which aim at it must be constantly rewritten as human purposes and situations change. A pre-atomic age history of international relations is now out of date, because our minds are full of problems to which its interpretations have little relevance.

As time goes on, each history feeds on those which have preceded it, and ought to take advantage of each added bit of hindsight to enlarge the scope

[9] F. J. E. Woodbridge, *The Purpose of History* (New York, 1916), p. 52.

and depth of our comprehension of events. The yardstick by which these major historical hypotheses are measured is therefore a progressive ideal. It is no less, we venture to assert, than the ever-growing self-enlightenment of mankind — of all mankind — concerning its own authentic past with an eye to "living rationally in the light of what is possible" in a more knowledgeable future. That is a goal which recedes as it seems to be approached, an aim that transcends all petty purposes and transient programs of reform — that man should come to know himself as he was and as he is and as he may be.

It is for these reasons that the ultimate test of a large-scale history is philosophical, for it takes no less than a philosophy to supply the scale upon which major historical hypotheses are to be adjudged. Every history that interprets the past in terms of the future is a wager about the way events are actually linked together, and about the intellectual climate of the ages to come. For the test of any hypothesis is its capacity to furnish the most comprehensive account of all the facts that it purports to cover, in a way that is intelligible to those who are judging it. If a history is permeated with meanings and values derived from an optimistic philosophy of progress, for example, and humanity "goes pessimistic," that particular history will probably be relegated to oblivion, at least until there is a shift in the direction of optimism. The same, of course, would be true of a pessimistic history in an age of predominant optimism. The obvious formula would seem to be a history that was both optimistic and pessimistic, all things to all readers. It would resemble the book written by the hack who had been told that the best-selling books were those about Lincoln, about doctors, about dogs, and about psychiatrists, and so produced *Lincoln's Doctor's Dog's Psychiatrist*, which was not a best seller.

Because the final tests of histories are philosophical, it does not follow that every history must aim directly at encompassing the total task of all history. There will naturally be a division of labor among historians: some will attempt grandiose panoramas of world history; others will stick to limited areas or cultures; and still others will cultivate minute corners of the total plot. But essentially the same tests may be applied: has the historian selected and recreated, from the totality of life "as lived," those aspects which will best assist his contemporaries and posterity to live the life of the mature intelligence? Individuals will continue to differ, of course, about the exact nature of that "life of reason" in the partly stable, partly fluctuating world in which we find ourselves. In a word, they will have different philosophies. But there is only one central point on which they need to agree in order to make possible the writing and reading and judging of histories — that is, that it is better for man to know himself completely than not. The ancient motto which comes down to us from the Wise Men of Greece, "Know thyself," is still the last word in the testing of our explanatory historical theories.

If this hypothesis about historical hypotheses is a tenable one, then the one essential qualification of the historian is the spirit of critical inquiry, the determination to find the answers to the most searching questions that he knows (or can learn) how to ask. And there is also, as Professor Nevins adds, "but one golden rule in reading history: it should be read by the blazing illumination of a thoroughly aroused intellectual curiosity." These qualities may be found mixed with lesser motives; but to the extent to which an historian lets his main objective become cluttered up with such minor considerations as the relevance of past events to contemporary problems, he is likely to write poor history, although it may be excellent propaganda. As Professor Arthur O. Lovejoy points out, "His task is to become acquainted, as thoroughly and as objectively as he can, with both the variables and the constants in human thought and feeling and action; and he is less likely to accomplish it if he limits his interests to that which bears only upon those variables which differentiate the present from the past."[10] If that is the historian's job, then obviously he has a great deal to learn from psychology and all the other sciences which deal with the biological and social nature of man.

5. Historical "Laws" and the Philosophy of History

Henry Adams wrote of the fascination felt by "four out of five of the serious students of history" of his day, that of standing "on the brink of a great generalization that would reduce history under a law as clear as the laws which govern the material world . . ."; or the hope that "in the thickset forests of history, one corner turned, one faint trail struck would bring him on the highroad of science."[11] Having portrayed a segment of the story of mankind, the historian senses the fact that "particulars carry generalities within them," as von Ranke said, and he is strongly tempted to indulge in what is called the *philosophy of history*, which has resulted in a great variety of alleged master formulas. Some of them have been catastrophic, like that of Saint Augustine and his doctrine of the struggle of the Two Cities; others have been dominated by some linear concept of evolutionary progress, such as Herbert Spencer's (largely developed by John Fiske) and H. G. Wells's; while still others have been rhythmical or cyclical, such as those of Hegel, Marx, Spengler, and Pareto. Then there have been the more specialized formulas of the "great man" influence (Carlyle); the physical environment (Buckle); the Three Stages (theological, metaphysical, positive) of Auguste Comte; and the innumerable minor interpretations of history in terms of almost every conceivable notion from lice and hay to sex and kismet.[12]

What is notable about all these attempts to establish laws running through the continuities of human history is that their concepts, if broad enough to serve in the framing of generalizations, find too few exemplifications to support any. Let us say that an historian has studied a number of nationalities or religions or revolutions, and wishes to ascertain the "laws" of the rise of new nationalities, or of the decline of religions, or of the course of revolutions. He begins to collect his individual instances in their historical fullness in order to make comparisons and discern patterns which may be found to be common

---

[10] Arthur O. Lovejoy, "Present Standpoints and Past History," *Journal of Philosophy*, vol. XXVI (1939), p. 484.

[11] Henry Adams, *Degradation of the Democratic Dogma* (New York, 1920), p. 127.

[12] Dr. T. R. Glover has even suggested that a great deal of history might be explained by "man's dislike for getting wet."

to all of them. But how many new nationalities have arisen in history under anywhere near comparable conditions? And how many religions have declined, or revolutions run their courses? The study of comparative social morphology so assiduously cultivated by Spengler and others always suffers from "too few cases" imperfectly isolated.

It is here that the historian makes contact with the sociologist, who is trying to conceptualize some of the same material in terms of cultures or institutions or classes. We have already noted some of the latter's difficulties in doing this: the alternatives are endless; the variables are of differing kinds of stability (rational and irrational, for example); the instances are too few on the grand scale and too many in detail; so that no one theory seems to have any chance of furnishing the master key by a convincing elimination of all its rivals. Sociology, in other words, is primarily committed to the scientific pattern of seeking constants through analysis; while history can never abandon its primary fidelity to the individual configuration. For, as soon as the historian starts to generalize about his material, he, like the scientist, finds that he must pick a few supposedly constant qualities, and then abstract from his differing instances. The Peloponnesian War and the Hussite War and the Spanish-American War must all become examples of the term "war" in general, thereby losing their specific individual characteristics in the process. But it is just the unique qualities of a war which give it historical causal significance. Take them away, and it loses all its historical vitality. Moreover, such generalizing will work best where men are most backward, inert, routined in all respects, and least creatively concerned with the remolding of their destinies. And even in those cultures, the "law" which the historian may be able to establish will turn out at best to be little more than a tendency.

Such considerations need not bar the historian from paying the closest attention to whatever the sociologist (or anyone else) can furnish in the way of general "laws" supported by evidence; or the sociologist from seeking a vast amount of his material in histories. It should merely place both guilds on their guard against confusing the two enterprises in terms of logical structure and methods of proof. For the sociologist will ultimately strive to establish his hypotheses in terms of their universality in the scientific sense; while the historian will go on studying "biographies," and will seek the vindication of his theories in another quarter. There are dangers, too, in the so-called "cultural approach" to history through the science of anthropology,[13] since it uses the forms of primitive societies as a means of detachment from "the frame of reference of Western culture." There is undoubtedly some profit to be gained from seeing café society through eyes accustomed to dissecting the tribal practices of the Melanesians. But there is no guarantee that the rigid patterns which prevail in the earlier and simpler cultures will serve for the understanding of a complex industrial city. Little will be gained by forcing the unstable and pluralistic coexistences of a highly diffuse society into the rigid monism of a "cultural whole."

This brings us to a final question about the testing of what we have called major historical explanatory hypotheses. To the extent that they are broad and

13 Caroline F. Ware, ed., *The Cultural Approach to History* (New York, 1941).

philosophical in scope, such tentative conjectures about the long-run trend of things cannot be submitted to the snap judgment of a short-run test. A theory which is stated in terms of the progressive rise or fall of civilizations and cultures is not to be credited or discredited by the ordeals of a single man or a single generation. When H. G. Wells declares that history is a race between civilization and catastrophe, who is to decide when the finish line has been reached? And until it has been reached, how is the winner to be determined? Neither a philosophy nor a philosophy of history can be shown to be adequate in any final sense on the basis of its sufficiency in a restricted context. For there is always the element of its acceptance making it come true — "it would work if everyone could be induced to believe it would work" — to be considered. As for disproving a philosophy by its failure in a particular case, it is always easy to explain away a discrepancy between a very general theory and the specific facts which it is supposed to illuminate. Thus, there is bound to be a large ingredient of faith in our acceptance of any major historical explanatory hypothesis, which accounts for the survival of so many mythological philosophies of history long after they have lost all standing with the sophisticated. They thrive on the lack of "disproof positive," and the perennial resurgence of human hope.

The aim of the historian should be to supply his fellows with the kind of reliable knowledge which concerns (in the concluding phrase of one of Santayana's noble odes):

> " . . . in all things mortal, only
> What is eternal."

But the eternal with which the historian should concern himself is not that which is merely out of time, or lacking in any specific temporal reference. That is the largely negative eternality of the scientific abstraction. The eternal of the historian is rather the immortally relevant in time, the unique individual so grasped that it is a complete and everlastingly appealing synthesis of fact, meaning, and value. The artist seeks something of the same goal in the wider range of all imaginable possibilities. The historian must stick to those possibilities which have been realized, with their overtones of what may yet come to pass. He has the disadvantage of having to be faithful to what has actually occurred; but he has also the great advantage of the teller of the true story over the mere fabulist, or spinner of tales. For he can always add the words, "And this is no lie." His theories about man, when confirmed, always rest upon and remold the immortal historic past, which is man's best guarantee of an understood future.

6. Summary

The historical pattern, when applied to any variety of subject matter, may take the form of hypotheses which call for testing on three distinguishable but overlapping planes. They concern man's efforts to achieve:

(1) *The establishing of the record of past occurrences in their actual order in time and space.* These are the descriptive hypotheses employed in the fact-finding, fact-attesting phases of inquiry usually called historical research. The

methods of testing are semi-scientific, and yield their verdicts in terms of a complex system of probabilities. Even a detailed record of this sort is always far from complete.

(2) *The establishing of the meanings and values of past occurrences for the people of their historical periods.* These are explanatory hypotheses in terms of bygone ages, which may be tested only by those whose historical imagination combined with (1) above enables them partially to relive the meanings and values in question — that is, to share what were the living purposes, meanings, and values of those now dead. One of the assumptions of the criteria used is the precarious one that we can use our own psychology as the measure of the motives of earlier men and women. To the extent that psychology becomes a science — that is, increases in analytical and theoretical power — we shall undoubtedly be increasingly able to understand what data we are able to recover from the past. Conclusions on this plane of inquiry are only probable, and are always liable to be upset by the coming to light of new evidence.

(3) *The establishing of tentative meanings and values of past occurrences, as established in (1) and (2), for ourselves and future mankind.* These are explanatory hypotheses which venture to suggest that selected past occurrences made highly probable by previous tests have certain meanings and values for universal human self-enlightenment. When advanced on a broad philosophic scale, their "proof" may take centuries; but theories of lesser scope, such as those economic-social hypotheses which throw light on the future of a given society, may be "verified" on a smaller scale, subject always to correction when more returns come in. We learn little from history just because it seldom repeats itself.

FOR CLASS DISCUSSION

A. Comments on history:

(1) Not to know what happened before one was born is always to be a child. — *Cicero*

(2) The first quality of an historian is to be true and impartial; the next, to be interesting. — *David Hume*

(3) History, at least in its state of ideal perfection, is a compound of poetry and philosophy. — *T. B. Macaulay*

(4) Historians relate, not so much what is done, as what they would have believed. — *Benjamin Franklin*

(5) History is bunk. — Ascribed to *Henry Ford,* 1915

(6) History is all party pamphlets. — *Ralph Waldo Emerson*

(7) The histories of mankind that we possess are histories only of the higher classes. — *T. R. Malthus*

(8) I don't believe the truth will ever be known, and I have a great contempt for history. — *General G. G. Meade,* 1871

(9) An account, mostly false, of events unimportant, which are brought about by rulers mostly knaves, and soldiers mostly fools.
— *Ambrose Bierce*

(10) History can be well written only in a free country. — *Voltaire*

(11) History is a child's box of letters. You can spell with them any word you will. — *J. A. Froude* (2)

B. There is not to be found in all history any miracle attested by a sufficient number of men, of such unquestioned good sense, education, and learning, as to secure us against all delusion in themselves; of such undoubted integrity, as to place them beyond all suspicion of any design to deceive others; of such credit and reputation in the eyes of mankind, as to have a great deal to lose in case of their being detected in any falsehood; and in the same time, attesting facts, performed in such a public manner, and in so celebrated a part of the world, as to render the detection unavoidable.

— *David Hume*

C. Years of analysis are required for one day of synthesis.

— *Fustel de Coulanges*

D. The sort of omniscience which complete historical science would achieve would merely furnish materials for intelligence: it would be inferior to intelligence itself. . . . The profit of studying history lies in something else than a dead knowledge of what happens to have happened.

— *George Santayana*

E. "You are first a Christian; I am first a historian. There is a gulf between us." — *Leopold von Ranke* to a correspondent (3)

F. Most of what is taught in history books is merely the enforced propaganda line of a succession of victorious parties which have eliminated their rivals. — *Hugh Ross Williamson*

G. The function of historical imagination is to penetrate the minds, the strange and complicated minds, sometimes even the barbarous, repellent minds, of remote centuries, in order not merely to retrace the routine of human behavior, the old ruts and tracks of past events, but to understand the springs and compulsions, the dilemmas and predicaments, the genius and folly of the human decisions that made that behavior. (4)

— *Hugh Trevor-Roper*

H. Knowing what was to happen after the events which they are chronicling, historians nearly always make it seem too inevitable. They make us feel that anybody with any sense ought to have been able to foresee it. They lead us to forget how heavily the path ahead is obscured by fog, how infinite are the number of directions which the course of events may take.

— *Frederick Lewis Allen*

I. The historian is caught in a dilemma of his own making. If he wishes to make his work vital to the society which supports him, he must take up again his ancient role of poet-interpreter, with all its lurking subjective dangers. The other horn is to continue his slavish acceptance of the false analogy he has made between man and matter. . . . History must be very much more than a science. — *Lesley Byrd Simpson*

J. The villains which disturb the sleep of today's historians are, first, the typewriter and the multigraph, and second, the telephone and the radio. The former two have packed millions upon millions of filing cases with tons of records of no value whatever. The latter two, in devilish contradiction, have prevented the recording of conversations upon which the true interpretation of history depends. — *Henry F. Pringle*

K. When a man understands the art of seeing, he can trace the spirit of an age and the features of a king even in the knocker on a door.   (5)
— *Victor Hugo*

L. As a nation, we do not need more histories, but more thoughtful ones.
— *Thomas C. Cochran*

EXERCISES IN HISTORY

In the following examples, identify the kind or kinds of hypotheses used, and criticize the evidence offered in proof of them.

1. The German historian Giesebrecht pointed out that certain chronicles of the eleventh century drew their information from a common source which was no longer available. So sure was he of their dependence upon this early chronicle, which he named *Annales Altahenses*, that he constructed the missing manuscript from these later derivatives. Some twenty-six years later the missing chronicle was found, and it confirmed these shrewd conjectures in every important particular. — Allen Johnson, *op. cit.*, p. 17.

2. A persistent attempt has been made to find historical evidence of landings by Norsemen somewhere on the Atlantic coast of North America around 1000 A.D. from Greenland on their way to a place called Vinland. Dr. Johannes Brondsted, Director of the Danish National Museum at Copenhagen, made an exhaustive study of all the tangible evidence which has been offered as proof of the presence of Vikings anywhere between Labrador and Florida, as follows: (1) the Beardmore Find, consisting of three iron objects, including a broken sword, dating from the Viking age, but probably imported from Scandinavia and not buried in a mount of earth near Beardmore, Ontario, as claimed; (2) the famous Newport Tower in Touro Park, Newport, Rhode Island, shown by its architecture to have originated at a later period; (3) the so-called Kensington Rune Stone, found in 1898 by Olof Ohman, a farmer of Kensington, Minnesota, and dated 1362, which, although vigorously championed by Mr. Hjalmar Holand in a number of books, "fails to tell us," says Dr. Bronsted, "anything positive for or against" its authenticity, which is doubted by expert philologists who have studied its language. Dr. Bronsted concludes that all the evidence so far offered proves nothing.

3. Mabillon in his *Iter italicum* (1724) tells of a church in Spain which petitioned Pope Urban VIII for a grant of indulgences at the feast of Saint Viar, whose body it claimed to possess, buried beneath a slab of stone. The only evidence of any such saint was the "S VIAR" on this stone, which was shown to form the remains of an old Roman inscription ending "PRAEFECTUS VIARUM."

4. Lord Acton, lecturing on "The Study of History" at Cambridge in 1895, named the American Revolution as a subject whose main aspects were so thoroughly understood that the work on it need never be done over again. Yet in the years since this pronouncement more progress has been made in

arriving at the truth of that episode than in all the years before . . . chiefly from a re-examination of evidence that was old and familiar. — Arthur M. Schlesinger, Sr.

5. "Hilaire Belloc, in his life of Marie Antoinette, is certain that the friendship of the beautiful Queen for Comte de Fersen never passed platonic bounds, for Mr. Belloc had a Catholic's conception of what his heroine must never allow herself to do. Stefan Zweig, however, in his biography of the queen, is certain that she and De Fersen loved one another with romantic unconstraint; for Herr Zweig's code expected that of a woman in Marie Antoinette's position. The fact is that no evidence exists for a positive statement." — Allan Nevins in *The Gateway to History*, rev. ed., p. 194.

6. Dr. James H. Gaul of the Peabody Museum of Harvard University in the Boston *Evening Transcript* in 1940: "A hundred years ago there was a battle at Abbéville near Amiens which had an effect on world history more profound, possibly, than the holocaust consuming that otherwise placid area today. It was a battle over fossil man and flint implements. The protagonist, Boucher de Perthes, attempted to prove the existence of antediluvial man, the presence of humanity before the Biblical flood. He lost his battle, but the bulge he made in the buttressed fundamentalism of the nineteenth century opened the way for Darwin's revolutionary theory of evolution."

7. To illustrate the dangers of false inferences from archaeological remains, Professor Alfred M. Tozzer of Harvard in an address before the Massachusetts Historical Society pointed out that, one thousand years after Harvard's tercentenary celebration in 1936, all that remained might well be a few bronze medals and two stone monuments, one a gift from China and the other from Japan. If archaeology were alone to be depended upon, some rising young student of 2936 might write a dissertation on the strong Mongolian influence at the university in 1936.

8. In a French best-selling book entitled *Le Matin des Magiciens* by Louis Pauwels and Jacques Bergier, the authors describe in detail the success of an alleged experiment in communicating from land to the U.S. atomic submarine *Nautilus* by means of extrasensory perception on July 25, 1959, while it was commanded by Captain William R. Anderson. *This Week* magazine found out that on the date in question the *Nautilus* was "high and dry in dock at Portsmouth, N. H.," being overhauled; and that Captain Anderson had been succeeded by another officer. The authors said that they had not done anything to verify "the reports" on which their book was based.

15

COMBINED USE OF THE MECHANICAL AND HISTORICAL PATTERNS:
Law and Government

1. The Character of Social Problems

MANKIND IN THE TWENTIETH CENTURY has developed at least two corps of specialists who are permitted the almost unbridled indulgence of their curiosity in seeking and testing knowledge: the pure scientists and what we have called the pure research historians. Each guild has surrounded itself with the elaborate technical apparatus of the sophisticated inquirer. The scientists have their isolated laboratories, and the historians their libraries and museums. Long training in the techniques of investigation is necessary before one can feel at home in either type of setting, or can understand the learned jargon that is spoken here. The layman feels almost as incompetent to judge the validity of the latest hypothesis about the Minoan civilization of ancient Crete as he is to pass upon the most recent developments in quantum physics. The tempo of the scholar-scientist is by preference a leisurely one; for, as Professor Lynd remarks, "the precise penetration of the unknown seems too grand an enterprise to be hurried . . . " when "ultimate relevance" is its only criterion of worth. And so that slow accumulation of knowledge which Justice Frankfurter has called its "production" contrasts sharply with its "distribution," or final incorporation in the minds and habits of the public at large.

In time of war or social revolution, however, even the physical scientist discovers how it feels to have a pressing practical problem thrust upon his attention, accompanied by a demand for an immediate "answer." He finds out, in other words, what it is like to be a social scientist. For the latter is never wholly shielded from external pressures. The social studies are organized articulations of the very things which they investigate, and so they are legitimate objects of those struggles for power which are continually going on. Their teachers are constantly being tempted to take refuge in the pure learning which relates to some remote historical period whose emotional volcanos have long since become extinct. But for the social studies to become irrelevant to their foundations, and not worth fighting about in any society would be for them to invite eventual death by progressive anaemia.

As far as reliable knowledge is concerned, the immediate issues of man's social life for a long time to come are going to be decided, in the main, neither by the aid of the certified results of the laboratory nor the attested conclusions of the pure historian. The makers of decisions are seldom permitted to develop the specialist's nice feeling for the boundaries of a particular subject matter (and hence the limits of its particular methods of proof). Social problems have a way of ignoring the carefully discriminated boundary lines of such disciplines as history, economics, government, sociology, or philosophy. Taxes must be raised, or automobile accidents reduced, or schools consolidated, or prisoners kept busy. Each one of these difficulties overflows the confines of any single branch of learning. Taxes may be "primarily" an economic problem, yet who would say that they were not often more than fifty per cent political? Little can be done about lowering the automobile death rate without an extremely complex and co-operative attack from literally dozens of points of view: by the automobile industry — its designers, engineers, advertising copywriters, and service men; by the government — its legislators, administrators, judges, juries, and police; and by miscellaneous agencies of public education too numerous to mention.

This means that for the ordinary consumer of produced and distributed knowledge, the stringent tests of the pure scientist or historian will seem remote indeed. Like the delicate instruments of the operating room, they will appear to be wholly unsuitable for everyday use. He will not demand proof in the sense of the precise establishment of a high degree of probability for a single case or type of cases. Instead, he will consider himself lucky if he is able to improve upon common sense by gathering, from all kinds of sources, evidence sufficient in quality and amount to warrant the action which must be taken. Where the homogeneity of the material permits, he will use the scientific pattern; but where individuality is important, the historical. That policy of judicious eclecticism will annoy purists in both branches of learning, to whom the social studies will appear hybrid monstrosities entirely lacking in proper reverence for methodological standards.

Since the lore of human behavior is endless, this chapter will deal with only one example of the combined use of the two patterns to attain knowledge that is more or less reliable: proof as it is established in Anglo-American courts of law. In surveying the subject, technicalities will be avoided except where they are necessary in order to clarify the problems involved and the nature of the ways in which men have invented for the purpose of solving them. The chapter should serve as a sample of the way in which common sense can be refined in both directions at once, the mechanical and the historical, in such a way as to assure us of a degree of reliability, even though it falls far short of that afforded by either method in its purer forms.

2. The Aim of Law Courts

The place where most individuals come into direct contact with the formal process of proving something is in a court of law. One who enters a courtroom (few go through life without doing so) and alleges something, must be prepared to "prove his case." A guild numbering thousands of members has grown up to administer justice by a ritual which sometimes seems to have little to do with the end in view. Efforts to define that end have been numerous, but not conspicuously successful. Let us be content at this point merely to observe that the law deals with *the specific determination of allowable conduct exclusively by government.* The need from which it arose and by which it is sustained is obvious — for a peaceful settlement of human conflicts of interest. Its essence is contention brought to a non-violent, although it may be a coercive, conclusion.

But courts do not exist to pass upon abstract principles. One does not call a session of a court, for example, to pass upon the constitutionality of a law. There must always be a specific case or cause before the court to be tried, such as the Schechter "sick chicken" case in May, 1935, in the trying of which, on appeal, the constitutional basis of the NRA was destroyed *in view of that particular past injury.* A law might be passed at any time which was obnoxious to a person, or even to a large group in the community, but the courts could do nothing about it until there was a "test case," some alleged damage or threat of damage which could be brought to the court's attention. Anything which a human being does *may* become a legal matter, provided it brings him into some kind of serious conflict with one or more of his fellow men.

The meaning of this in terms of methods of proof should at once be clear: all legal inquiry is essentially historical, in that it is always eventually reducible to a concrete past instance — the cause at issue; and yet it is always the application of a general principle, since no law can be written in terms of an individual case. Like the historian, the trier of a case selects and to a certain extent reconstructs events which are of interest to him at the time. No more than the historian can he restore the entire living complex of experience which occurred some days or weeks or months before. Since cases are presented by opposing sides, two competing selections and interpretations of the facts will be placed together before the court, from which judge or jury must somehow piece together their own selected picture of the actual relationship of the litigants. The experience which is before them is "dead experience," and there is little in any rule of law to tell them how far they should go in their attempt to revivify it in order to recover "what actually occurred." So far, then, the problem of proof in court seems to be a matter of the use of the historical pattern with respect to human disputes.

3. Judicial Impartiality

But courts differ from the seminars of historians, in that governments appoint presiding officers with wide powers known as judges, whose special duty it is to conduct the process of trial in accordance with certain established rules. The judge is there, ideally, in order to "see that justice is done" according to the laws of his particular jurisdiction. He is not simply a referee keeping the bout of wrangling lawyers in hand, or just an umpire reconciling the contending parties. He must, on the one hand, supervise the findings of the relevant facts of the case; and on the other, he must bring to bear the existing laws (including a vast amount of precedent and custom) with a view to promoting the welfare of the entire public. This latter task calls for the weighing of the conflicting interests in scales that have already been approved. That is what gives meaning to the famous dictum about a government "of laws, not of men," namely, that the men who make the decisions are restrained by laws laid down in advance and known (presumably) to all who may be affected by them. To aid him in the preliminary chore of ascertaining the facts, the judge ordinarily has the assistance of a jury of twelve (or less) untrained citizens of average intelligence acting as a sample of the public in whose behalf the trial is being held. The jury, as James Gould Cozzens says in his novel *The Just and the Unjust*, "is like a cylinder-head gasket. Between two things that don't give any, you have to have something that does give a little, something to seal the law to the facts." The procedure is not that of the scientific laboratory, but of a traditional kind of somewhat clumsy social engineering carried on by a few highly trained legal experts and a small number of relatively disinterested laymen.

In the performance of his duties, every judge is called upon to realize an extremely high ideal of impartiality and objectivity. It has seldom been more forcefully stated than by the Court in the *People ex. rel. Union Bag & Paper Corporation vs. Gilbert*, 143 Misc. New York 287 (1932):

> Courts should scrupulously maintain unsullied their dignity and integrity. Every litigant is entitled to nothing less than the cold neutrality of an impartial judge who must possess the disinterestedness of a total stranger to the interests of the parties involved in the litigation. . . . In the administration of justice it is not only requisite that a judge should be honest, unbiased, impartial and disinterested in fact, but equally essential that all doubt or suspicion to the contrary should be jealously guarded against and eliminated. Not only is it the duty of a judge to render a righteous judgment, but it is of transcendent importance to the litigants and the public generally that there should not be the slightest suspicion as to his fairness and integrity. Caesar demanded that his wife should not only be virtuous but beyond suspicion. The people should not exact less from the judiciary, the most powerful branch of our government.

Aside from the question of how many frail human beings succeed in realizing this austere ideal, it might be questioned whether the "cold neutrality" of a "total stranger" has enough sympathetic understanding in it to qualify anyone to act as judge. The best judge, like the best historian, is one who is able, at one and the same time, to enter fully into the experiences of all those concerned, and yet to keep his own subjective preferences rigidly under control. None of us wishes to be judged by a man from Mars. The ideal judge in a labor dispute would not be a man to whom the experiences of employing, of being employed, and of being unemployed were all equally foreign, but a person who understood the joys and sorrows and aspirations of both parties in the larger setting of the public welfare, and who both knew and discounted whatever leanings he might have in one direction or the other. A number of books have been written to show that many who wear the judicial halo fall far short of that ideal;[1] and Lincoln quoted Jefferson with approval on July 17, 1858, at Springfield, Illinois, "I am too familiar with the history of judicial proceedings to regard them with superstitious reverence. Judges are but men, and in all ages have shown a fair share of frailty." Or, as Colonel Robert G. Ingersoll pungently expressed the same idea in Washington in 1883: "We must remember, too, that we have to make judges out of men, and that by being made judges their prejudices are not diminished and their intelligence is not increased."

4. Kinds of Actions and Degrees of Proof

Actions which are of sufficient moment to be brought to trial are classified broadly as either *criminal* or *civil*. A civil action is one in which there is a dispute to be decided, but no allegation of corrupt or evil intent on either side. A bull might escape from a field and harm crops, or a truck might collide with another in such a way as to inflict damages the amount of which could not be decided out of court. A civil suit would then be brought, and the amount of the damages judicially determined. But if a farmer charged his neighbor with deliberate intent or criminal negligence in the escape of a bull or a collision, before punishment of any sort could be inflicted there would have to be an indictment and trial in a criminal court.

Corresponding to the two sorts of actions are two main degrees of required proof. In civil suits, all that is necessary to establish is a fair *preponderance of the evidence:* it must merely be shown that the probabilities arrayed on one side are greater in weight than those arrayed on the other. It is easy to see why this is so, because the main interest of the public in a civil case is that it should be settled expeditiously, so that the potential threat to the public peace will be removed. It is more important to reach some decision than it is to reach a perfectly just decision, since presumably the stake involved is too small to warrant a completely exhaustive inquiry. Criminal actions, however, require for conviction what is called proof *beyond a reasonable doubt* in the minds of all twelve members of a jury. This does not mean proof beyond all doubt whatever, but it calls for what is sometimes described as "hanging proof," the attainment of that degree of probability which comes so close to certainty that, under the circumstances, no reasonable person would vote to acquit. The evidence must be inconsistent with the defendant's innocence and consistent with his guilt to the point where one would have no hesitation in acting oneself "in any matter of like importance" (*Holt vs. U.S.*, 218 U.S. 245). Lord Hardwicke may have been correct in saying that "the law aims at certainty"; but it does not profess to arrive there, even when it condemns a person to death.

[1] Louis P. Goldberg and Eleanore Levinson, *Lawless Judges* (New York, 1935); and the chapter "Judges Are Corrupt" in Percival E. Jackson, *Look at the Law* (New York, 1940). See also Joseph Borkin, *The Corrupt Judge* (New York, 1963).

5. Rules of Evidence

Cases are no longer decided by the supposedly infallible discovery of secret marks, ordeals, or the casting of dice, but on the basis of *evidence* submitted by the prosecution or defense, and admitted by the presiding judge. Evidence is anything which is put forward as a means of determining a fact; but there is no fixed rule from which a judge can deduce how relevant an item must be in order for it to be legally competent, or admissible. Everything admitted as legal evidence, however, must be openly sharable by all the parties to the trial. A judge's personal knowledge as a private citizen is not evidence, and as a judge he must ignore what he knows as an individual observer. Evidence must be presented without exciting prejudice by references to extraneous matters, thereby causing a mistrial. Prosecutors, said the United States Supreme Court in *Berger vs. United States*, 295 U.S. 78, 84, have as much the duty "to refrain from improper methods calculated to produce wrongful conviction as to use every legitimate means to bring about a just one." Almost every layman who has examined the rules of evidence with any care is amazed at the lengths to which they go in confining witnesses to a bare "recitation of the facts" in order to avoid the slightest illegitimate influence upon the minds of untutored jurymen. As William Seagle remarks, "The common law has a vast system of rules, the purpose of which is to exclude from presentation to the jury evidence conceded to be logically probative, but which might be misleading to a jury of simple laymen, who, unlike trained judges, cannot be trusted to disregard evidence of doubtful value or to forget anything they have once been allowed to hear."[2]

It is of course the duty of a lawyer to take advantage of every legal technicality which may favor his case. But this, according to Dean Roscoe Pound, has given rise to "the sporting theory of justice" and an "exaggerated contentious procedure" in "the modern American race to beat the law." As a consequence, says Dr. Sheldon Glueck, the chief qualification of the American lawyer "is an ability to keep constantly alert to discover open or rusty joints in the armor of justice."

Trials would be interminable if everyone in a court knew only what had been offered and admitted in evidence. If would be absurd to have to call in witnesses to swear to the fact that there are seven days in a week, or that hot air has a tendency to rise. Three devices have been invented for expediting the work of courts by means of agreements in advance which reduce the scope of the controversy. They are: *judicial notice, presumptions,* and *admissions.* A judge may take judicial notice, thereby accepting as a fact without evidence, of anything which is so universally believed as to constitute common knowledge beyond dispute, such as the geography of the locality, the ordinary properties of matter, the officers of the government, the conventions of weights and measures, and the main outlines of historical events. "Nothing in the realm of law," says Professor William P. Richardson, "is more elastic than the doc-

[2] William Seagle, *The Quest for Law* (New York, 1941), p. 175. See also Harold J. Berman, *The Nature and Functions of Law: An Introduction for Students of the Arts and Sciences* (Brooklyn, N.Y., 1958).

trine of judicial notice."[3] Yet the line has been drawn to exclude facts merely on the strength of their appearance in dictionaries or books of reference, as well as such matters as the length of time needed to repair an automobile, or the location of a town in another state.

Presumptions are inferences which the court is compelled by law to make from certain facts, once they are established by evidence. A few of them, such as the presumption that a child under seven years of age cannot commit a crime, are conclusive. But most presumptions are temporary and rebuttable — that is, they may be overcome by evidence, such as the presumption of innocence until proved guilty, the presumption of sanity, and that of death after seven years' absence without word.[4] Admissions consist of facts which are brought out and conceded by both sides in open court. Note that all three of these devices are ways of saving time by setting up a non-controversial background of a common world, against which the conflicting versions of the disputed facts may be debated. This "freezing" of much of the setting by agreement has something of the air of the "other things being equal" of the laboratory experiment. It enables the jury to concentrate its attention upon the main business in hand, just as an experimenter pays attention only to his apparatus. But of course it does not guarantee the ultimate reliability of what has been unanimously conceded. All of those present at the trial of Joan of Arc made plenty of assumptions which we should consider contrary to fact.

The chief remaining rules of evidence have to do with the exclusion of *hearsay* and *opinion*, and the safeguarding of confidential relationships deemed useful to society. The hearsay rule, to which there are numerous exceptions, is to insure that no testimony about what someone else said shall be presented without the opportunity for cross-examination of the person quoted. The no-opinion rule is needed to restrain ordinary witnesses from going beyond the necessary inferences involved in testimony about facts to indulging in gratuitous conjectures. It does not apply to admittedly expert witnesses, whose opinions are based upon technical knowledge not available to the ordinary juryman, such as the interpretation of an X-ray plate (see below, Section 7). *Privileged communications* are those between attorney and client, clergyman and penitent, physician and patient, husband and wife, whose secrecy does less harm in the long run to the administration of justice than its violation would presumably do to the interests of society. Whether a journalist can protect his sources of information against all comers remains uncertain.

6. Kinds of Evidence

The burden of proof in court rests upon the one who makes an allegation. In civil cases, it is usually upon the plaintiff; and if, at the end of the trial, the evidence is equal in weight on both sides, the verdict automatically goes against the party bearing the burden of proof. In criminal cases, the burden of proof

[3] William P. Richardson, *The Law of Evidence,* 5th ed. (New York, 1936), p. 23.
[4] Some abuses of presumptions, especially those of universal knowledge of the law, and of criminal intent from an act, are attacked by P. E. Jackson, *op. cit.,* pp. 126–51.

is always on the prosecution, irrespective of the nature of the defense. The task of the prosecution is to sustain the hypothesis of guilt advanced in the indictment, by showing, if possible, that every other reasonable hypothesis can be eliminated. No one could be convicted of homicide if it could be shown that the facts of the case were consistent with suicide, for obviously the failure to exclude the suicide hypothesis would leave in the minds of the jury the basis of a reasonable doubt. Every scrap of evidence which is presented and believed must be consistent with the guilt hypothesis, and at least some of the evidence must be inconsistent with every other reasonable theory which would result in acquittal, if a conviction is to be secured.

In considering all legal hypotheses, evidence is not to be viewed in isolation, but as pointing in the direction of guilt or innocence. This is the important principle of the *convergence of evidence*, adapted from scientific proof, by which many isolated items may cross-buttress one another in a firm logical structure of proof, although no one of them by itself would furnish any great degree of probative force. As the New Jersey Court of Errors and Appeals said in upholding the conviction of Bruno Richard Hauptmann for the kidnap-murder of the Lindbergh baby, "it was the evidence pointing to guilt from so many directions," which left no room for reasonable doubt, even though many of the aspects of the crime remained unexplained. As in the sciences, so in law: it is the cumulative power of an hypothesis to explain many different and apparently independent facts, which would otherwise remain mysterious, that gives it overwhelming convincingness. When consequences which are unlikely if the hypothesis is false are found to be true, its probability is increased. But these principles hold for the defense as well as for the prosecution — something which the Lowell Committee in reviewing the Sacco-Vanzetti case unfortunately forgot.[5]

TESTIMONIAL EVIDENCE

Just as the best proof of a scientific proposition is an approximate coincidence observation many times repeated under controlled conditions, so the simplest evidence for a legal hypothesis is the direct testimony, maintained under cross-examination, of a credible eye-witness. There is nothing much more impressive than the flat statement of a normal observer, of good character, that by means of his own senses he saw and heard the striking of a blow by a person whom he confronts and identifies. Juries traditionally attach great importance to such first-hand ("That is the man, and I saw him do it") testimony by an "eyeball witness," as if it was inevitably free from erroneous inferences. But the analysis of perception in Section 9 of Chapter 4 should have warned us against the physical, physiological, and psychological sources of error in translating sensations into perceptions, to which must be added all those of memory and testimony also.

To remember correctly, we must not only have some reason to have retained

[5] Cohen and Nagel, *op. cit.*, p. 350. See also Lee Loevinger, "Facts, Evidence, and Legal Proof" in Ray D. Henson, ed., *Landmarks of Law* (New York, 1960), pp. 422–41.

our original experiences, but we must also be able to recall them, unmixed with other similar events, and to recognize them for what they were. Now it is a commonplace of psychology, already pointed out in Chapter 5, Section 4, that our memories are not filing cases, but workshops in which we reorganize and "logify" our past experiences, largely in terms of their dominant emotional tones. From the pleasant memory of a party, for example, a single unpleasant episode drops out; while from the unpleasant memory of a childhood humiliation, one bright but incongruous note will be similarly omitted. In short, "a perfectly correct remembrance is not the rule but the exception."[6]

Personal identifications, which rest upon similarities of general pattern filled out by perception, are notoriously tricky, since the indistinct image carried in memory is both reinforced and overlaid by the much more vivid optical image supplied by the person to be identified. The police line-up, offering a multiple choice of possible identifications does not entirely overcome this difficulty. When the witness comes to put his testimony into words in response to the legally admissible questions of an examining lawyer, many new opportunities for error crop up. Not only may he lie, or willfully misrepresent what he saw or remembers in whole or in part; he may also, in all good faith, be unable to find words which will convey to others exactly what he correctly recalls. If, as is usually the case, he is emotionally interested in the outcome of his testimony, he will color it with the values which are genuinely present in the facts as they appear to him. In spite of the vast amount of perjury which is believed by many to afflict the courts, it is the conclusion of an experienced New York City lawyer, Arthur Garfield Hays, that "most lawsuits arise through honest differences of opinion where people see things from a different point of view."[7]

Even with "subjective sincerity," however, a witness may be led to falsify by adroit questioning, especially if he is made to tell his story over and over. Stern believes that the first words which a witness uses in describing anything (usually to the police or to his lawyer) fixate his perceptions and are often more vividly remembered than the original events. A witness is easily placed on the defensive, and thus encouraged to justify the version he has already given. Being reluctant to admit ignorance, he begins to embroider it in various ways. There are, therefore, almost innumerable ways of weakening direct testimony by skillful cross-examination, and relatively few means of strengthening it. There are literally dozens of points of attack upon an eyewitness, at the levels of his original sensations, his perceptions, his retention, recall, and recognition in sequence, and his reproduction of the past in linguistic terms. On the other side, there is usually little more than the loose "character" testimony concerning the witness's good intentions and lack of prejudice, together with some indication of his ability to testify correctly to parallel instances (although the latter is greatly abused by the sudden "Where were you on the night of June 5, 1961?" sort of heckling).

6 William Stern, "The Psychology of Testimony," *Journal of Abnormal and Social Psychology*, vol. 34 (1939), p. 5.
7 In his Foreword to Percival E. Jackson, *op. cit.*, p. 7.

CIRCUMSTANTIAL EVIDENCE

Since the first concern of the criminal is to avoid direct witnesses by committing his crime unobserved, society would be helpless if convictions could be obtained only upon direct testimonial evidence. A legal hypothesis can, therefore, be proved beyond a reasonable doubt by the offering of a sufficient number of facts from which its probability may be inferred. A multitude of circumstances are established by exhibits (articles produced in court and identified) or by testimony, which are then woven together in accordance with the principle of convergence of evidence in such a way that they point unmistakably to the probability of guilt or innocence. The critics of circumstantial evidence, who are likely to refer to it as "merely circumstantial," point to the admitted element of inference in the logical building-up of the case, and stress the fallacies of inference. But what they do not notice is that the foundation upon which the inferences are built may be a great deal more solid than that which is supplied by direct testimony. The reason for this is that "circumstances do not lie; witnesses can and do." The person who testifies to the finding of an article on the street, not knowing what inferences may be drawn from his testimony by either side, is far less tempted to color his story than a witness who gives direct testimony with full awareness of its probable effects. The dogmatic preference for direct over circumstantial evidence in all cases is founded on the misconception that testimonial evidence does not involve inference, while circumstantial does. The actual difference is that circumstantial evidence usually rests on a *lesser* amount of unconscious inference in its observation-memory-testimony stages than does testimonial. If great care is taken in safeguarding logical inferences which are drawn from circumstantial evidence in building up a case, the result may be superior to testimonial evidence. Most cases are composed of both kinds.

There is a sharp reminder of the fallibility of human testimony in the volume entitled *Convicting the Innocent* by Professor Edwin M. Borchard of the Yale Law School,[8] which contains the records of sixty-five erroneous convictions in court, thirty-five of which were based upon mistaken identifications by eyewitnesses. One of the most sensational cases of this sort occurred in Salem, Massachusetts, in February, 1934, when two innocent Brighton taxi-drivers, Clement F. Molway, twenty-two, and Louis Berrett, twenty-eight, were "snatched from the shadow of the electric chair" while the members of a jury before whom they had just been tried for first-degree murder of a janitor in the Lynn Paramount Theater holdup were "leaning toward conviction." Eight eyewitnesses, several of whom had a good look at the hold-up men under the powerful electric light used in cleaning the theater, had positively identified one or both of them in a somewhat informal police line-up and in court. There was, however, no circumstantial evidence against them except their natural confusion on being suddenly arrested. No guns were found; and no motive

---

[8] (New Haven, 1932.) For an excellent example of circumstantial evidence faked almost successfully by a murderer to throw suspicion on an innocent person, see "The Perry-Palm Case, 1937" by Edward D. Radin in *New York Murders*, edited by T. Collins (New York, 1944).

was established. Yet they might easily have been executed, had it not been for the last-minute discovery of a piece of circumstantial evidence miles away in Norwood, Massachusetts, where an alert detective managed to decipher an almost defaced battery number in a burned automobile. The trail led to a garage in Dorchester rented by the Millen brothers and Abraham Faber, in which was discovered a black money bag marked "Paramount Theater, Lynn." The Millens and Faber, when arrested, promptly confessed to the hold-up murder and other crimes, and were re-identified by the chagrined eyewitnesses, while Berrett and Molway were released with apologies.

7. Scientific Evidence and the Expert Witness

In 1925, the Supreme Court of Wisconsin affirmed the conviction of John Magnuson for first-degree murder by the sending of a home-made bomb through the mails, killing one person and injuring another. The only clues were some remains of the bomb and a fragment of the wrapper bearing a word misspelled in Swedish style. The only Swede in the vicinity with any assignable motive was Magnuson. The case was remarkable for the number of different kinds of scientific identifications of materials: the paper, the ink, the glue, the pen point, the handwriting, the sawdust, the steel — all were connected with similar items found at the home of the defendant. The court concluded that "the guilt of the defendant is as conclusively established as it is possible for it to be,"[9] and on the basis of purely circumstantial evidence. As more and more laboratories of crime detection are established by police departments, the American public is becoming familiarized with what has long been known to Europeans as *police scientifique*, or the application to crime of the methods of proof which prevail in the physical and biological sciences. At the same time there has grown up a wide distrust of some kinds of technical testimony because of the so-called "battles of the experts" which have marred the legal scene for at least a century.

In spite of some opposition from the courts, scientific evidence from physics and chemistry has become generally admissible and effective in proofs of the identity of materials, hair, nail-scrapings, and so on. Fingerprint and firearms identification are now full-fledged empirical sciences; but handwriting identification is still "in its infancy" as far as judicial recognition is concerned, being characterized in the Hauptmann case appeal decision (quoting Moore) as "most unsatisfactory, very inconclusive, most unreliable, and of the lowest probative force." This is because of the great number of differing inferences which handwriting experts are still able to draw from the same materials. But another cause is the large number of unqualified persons who have successfully

[9] 187 Wis. 122; 203 N.W. 749 (1925). Cited by Fred E. Inbau, "The Admissibility of Scientific Evidence in Criminal Cases," *Law and Contemporary Problems*, vol. II (1935), pp. 496–97. The entire number is devoted to the subject of Expert Testimony. For the history of the gradual admission of scientific evidence of many varieties, see the chapter "The Detection of Crime" in Christopher Hibbert, *The Roots of Evil* (Boston, 1963), pp. 289–316.

posed as experts before judges who were careless or incapable of challenging their qualifications. This has created the impression that opposing experts are far from impartial, being "paid to disagree"; when actually the number of agreements of truly qualified persons is much larger than the public supposes.

It is in the field of psychiatry, however, that our "inexpert use of experts" has been most notorious. But battles of experts over answers to hypothetical questions and insanity pleas in criminal cases have become less and less numerous as automatic hospital commitment and examination precede public trials in more and more states. Devices for determining the genuineness of verbal statements, known as "lie detectors," based on supposed correlations between intentional deceptions and changes in a witness' systolic blood pressure, pulse wave, or respiration, have been slow in gaining judicial recognition, partly no doubt because of the possibilities of "prostitution by unethical and incompetent examiners." What such instruments record is not lying as such, but emotional disturbances supposed to accompany guilt; and it takes a person highly trained in physiology and psychology to read the wavy lines on the polygraph chart with any confidence. The feeling of guilt is too complex to be tested by a single device. Even the staunch advocates of the use of lie detectors in court cases do not claim more than a 75 or 80 per cent accuracy for them, and they acknowledge that the machines can be "beaten" by individuals who are able to "control their responses by certain mental sets or attitudes."[10] If the method of lie detection should ever come close to being infallible, a suspect would certainly be entitled to refuse a test on the ground of self-incrimination.

Two chemical substances, sodium amytal and sodium pentothal, have become known as varieties of "truth serum" in the belief that persons under their influence cannot lie. But this is not so, according to Dr. Paul H. Hoch, chief of research at the New York Psychiatric Institute. He has found that such persons are still able to withhold information and to lie, especially those who are psychopathic.

There are some criminal investigators who are impatient at the slowness of judges to admit these "advanced" scientific methods of investigation and proof, alleging that antiquated antiscientific prejudices bar the way. But it is quite apparent that many sorts of scientific evidence: blood analyses, fingerprints, and microscopic details of objects, have already made their way into the courtroom. The hesitancy of men of the law to try cases on the basis of the polygraph or the truth serum springs from serious doubts that their uniformities are recognized by the great majority of scientists in the fields concerned.

8. Decisions in Terms of Law

To this point we have been considering only one phase of the process of trial in court, that of the establishment of the facts of a case by a jury on the basis of evidence leading to a probability judgment of guilt or innocence. It

[10] Fred E. Inbau, *Lie Detection and Criminal Interrogation* (Baltimore, Md., 1948), pp. 47, 77–8, 86.

is commonly said that it is the province of the jury to decide the facts-in-law, and for the judge to determine the future legal effects of their decision. It is not the function of the judge, in other words, to be a "trier of the facts," or to comment in any way upon the degree of credence to be given to the testimony of a witness. It is not the function of the jury, save in cases of criminal libel in some states, to determine the law, or the legal consequences of the established facts. This formula is good enough as a rule of thumb; yet there are numerous exceptions, since some questions are unavoidably mixtures of the legal and the factual, such as those concerning the sufficiency of evidence to warrant the submission of a case to a jury, or a directed verdict.

We know that laws, as general rules of allowable conduct, must be framed to deal with exceptional and unusual cases in terms of classes, such as murder or manslaughter or assault in varying degrees. Yet every individual crime is "historically" unique, and might conceivably be accorded individual treatment by the court. As a matter of "equality" and convenience, however, all offenses are grouped somewhat arbitrarily into classes, much as hats are made only in a limited number of sizes. Custom establishes the norm of human conduct; and laws are framed to deal with manageable classes of important deviations. There might be four degrees of murder, or forty, or four hundred; but it is found impracticable to explain to a jury the differences between too many of such classes. So the number is limited to two or three. Legal definitions of offenses, as we observed in Chapter 8, Section 5, are therefore provisional stipulations which lend themselves to the process of reaching "rough justice" in the form of a verdict. If adhered to slavishly, they are bound to produce injustices in individual cases, so they have to be tempered by judicial discretion in the final stages of the legal process. In the "hard" cases, such as those which arise when the technical definitions of murder and abortion are applied to instances of euthanasia and prevention of the result of a rape, both judges and juries have a way, as Professor Radin has pointed out, of altering the official syllogism by substituting a milder premise derived directly from experience.[11]

One of the most serious misconceptions of the judge's functions is the belief that, once the facts-in-law have been established, his task is merely one of classification and syllogistic deduction, technically known as *subsumption*. If this were true, justice could be dispensed by a large bookkeeping machine in the courthouse, with the foreman of the jury merely pressing a button for "guilty" or "not guilty," and the defendant receiving a small printed card with his fate inscribed thereon. What a judge does in terms of logic is to bring to bear upon the accepted facts the full extent of his familiarity with the hierarchy of ordinances, statutes, common-law principles, and constitutions which prevail in his jurisdiction plus an immense mass of traditional practices in the form of general rules and their past applications to unusual cases. Let us suppose that, out of the endless variety of human behavior, a jury has before it convincing evidence, both testimonial and circumstantial, of the fact that a Mr. X has quarreled with his neighbor Mr. Y over the location of the latter's garage close to his own garage, to which he (Mr. X) has set fire in such a way as to burn down that of his neighbor. Has Mr. X committed the crime of

11 Max Radin, *Law as Logic and Experience* (New Haven, 1940), pp. 112–13.

arson, and if so, in what degree? Or is it a case of malicious mischief? The judge must charge the jury in terms of the law. But frequently a law framed to meet "average" conditions will not exactly "fit" an exceptional case, or there may be no law at all which will cover an act which no one had foreseen. Only in the most commonplace of routine cases is the task of the judge a simple matter of stating the classifications of crimes and reciting their legal definitions. Usually he must make a careful study of the individual characteristics of the particular case before him, and instruct the jury in terms of tradition and past legal practice as well as in terms of the statute book.

Broadly speaking, there are two main ways of dealing with the complexity of human acts in legal terms. They may be called tradition and legislation, or the *common law* and *codes*. In the civil-code countries of continental Europe, attempts have been made to provide in advance for the settlement of almost every foreseeable human dispute, thereby reducing to a minimum the discretionary power of the judge in interpreting the law. Such codes must be constantly recodified by legislation in order to keep up with the new conditions which their authors did not foresee. Then there are the common-law countries, notably Great Britain and the United States, where a body of traditional principles derived from the *mores* is supplemented by an immense number of individual instances of their past applications called *precedents*. The contrast, however, is more apparent than real: for, even in the most complicated code system, as Justice Cardozo pointed out, "the law leaves many things unsaid . . . and turns over to the judge the task of filling the gaps",[12] while in the common-law countries the constant pressure for "uniform laws" tends to introduce the equivalent of codes.

In all countries where the law is more than the will of a dictator, it consists of an effort to bring organized past experience to bear upon the unraveling of present and future social difficulties. This has never been successfully accomplished by writing all the rules of allowable or forbidden conduct in a simple manual accessible to all in such a way that every new contingency was covered in advance. The most complex code, supplemented by a legislature grinding out new statutes day and night, could not supply a judge with the means of deciding every case that came before him by means of mere classification and deduction. There is no way, in other words, of eliminating case or judge-made law in the form of judicial interpretations which establish useful precedents. The important thing is to combine enough rigidity to furnish a basis for reasonably accurate predictions about the ways in which future cases will be decided, with enough flexibility to take care of the vast variety of possible human behavior. Justice Holmes once wrote, "The prophecies of what the courts will do in fact, and nothing more pretentious, are what I mean by the law."[13] Such prophecies can be made in two main ways: by reading the language of the existing laws, aided perhaps by a law dictionary containing upwards of sixty thousand judicial definitions, or by acquainting oneself with what the courts have done by way of interpreting the laws in similar cases in the past.

[12] Benjamin N. Cardozo, *The Paradoxes of Legal Science* (New York, 1928), p. 28.
[13] Oliver Wendell Holmes, *Collected Legal Papers* (New York, 1920), p. 173.

THE ANALOGOUS PRECEDENT

It so happens that Anglo-Saxon law resisted logical codification, and in the absence of specific statutes covering everything, it developed in the direction of a reliance upon reason as exhibited in particular precedents. The much-criticized doctrine of *stare decisis* bids the court adhere inflexibly to the most nearly analogous previous decision, especially of a higher court, which can be discovered by a searching of past records. This presupposes that all the millions of past disputes and their outcomes have been recorded and are available as possible "authorities," and that there is some speedy way of locating cases which are similar to the one in question. But, in the first place, while the disposition of every case before an established court is made a matter of record, indexed, and made accessible to the public, it is not true that every one of them is "reported" — that is, selected and printed in a form that is usable by judges everywhere. A case is reportable only if it adds something new to "the edifice of legal doctrine." Yet the English Reports issued in the three hundred and fifty years from the reign of Elizabeth I through that of George V numbered over four thousand volumes; while the American Reports from 1783 through 1939 totaled sixteen thousand volumes for less than half that number of years.

But the reported cases are a mere trickle compared with the flood of those recorded. In 1935, it was estimated that British courts decided more than a million and a quarter recorded cases, of which less than five hundred were reported; while American courts reached an output of fifteen million recorded cases, of which about thirty thousand were reported, or about one precedent *per annum* for each of the thirty thousand members of the American Bar Association. Stated another way, in one year more than five times as many cases are recorded in England than have been *reported* since the dawn of the English Reports, more than four and a half centuries ago; in one year more than ten times as many are recorded in America than have been *reported* since the genesis of the American Reports, a century and a half ago. Thus the reported judicial precedents upon which a judge might be able to draw in making a decision of his own are believed to number many more than 2,000,000; but they are only a tiny, "unrepresentative, unrandom, and unreliable sample" of the recorded decisions, "millions upon millions of cases that are not enshrined in the Reports, but relegated to the morgue and soon forgotten by all but the litigants themselves." Yet it is these unreported cases, which do not happen to raise points of interest to the legal profession, which are, "the sources of the sources" of judicial doctrine.

Merely in order to make manageable the American Reports to 1896 required a digest of fifty volumes of about two thousand five hundred pages each, with twenty-four more in 1916, and twenty-nine in 1926. A single rule of Section 347 of the New York Civil Practice Act "has been explained, interpreted, and analyzed no less than one thousand times, by one thousand judges. . . . We have so much law that we cannot keep abreast of it." Judges and lawyers are swamped by the ever-rising flood, and not even legislators can keep track of their own prolific lawmaking, Congress on occasion having enacted the same amendment twice, once in 1916, and again in 1926.[14] In addition, there are the vast numbers of semi-legal regulations and decisions made by administrative tribunals of many sorts.

But, to return to the judge who proposes to stand upon precedent in the form of a "ruling" or "controlling" case in making his decision: what he must look for in the maze of previous decisions is a case as similar as possible to the one before him, which may serve as his authority. He seeks to reason from one particular configuration of events, the past case, to another particular configuration in the present, in deciding what legal generalization is to apply. But there is nothing in the doctrine of the analogous precedent to tell him in what, or in how many respects, the two cases must be analogous. Analogies, as we have seen already in Chapter 5, Section 5, vary enormously in depth. On the surface some are very close, but relatively trivial in any structural sense; others are the reverse. Historical analogies, of which legal analogies are one type, are far more dangerous than those which science uses in the making of its hypotheses, since there are so many more factors involved which may constitute decisive differences. There is little, then, in the doctrine of precedent itself to restrain a judge from a blind and slavish adherence to superficial similarities, even in the face of far more important differences. He may use what Professor Radin calls the "mountain-goat sort of logic which leaps from particular to particular without examination of the intervening generalization." But the abler the judge, the more he will be guided by the spirit or principle of the precedent rather than by its letter.

Furthermore, a strict adherence to precedent assumes several states of affairs in the realm of law which cannot easily be shown to prevail: (1) that no analogous decisions are contradictory; and (2) that the decision selected as a precedent was necessarily "good law" in the first place. As for contradictions, it would be amazing if they did not abound in the millions of reported decisions of thousands of independent tribunals. Not only do courts in different countries, different states, and different counties disagree; but judges in the same court disagree with one another, and sometimes with their own previous decisions.[15] That means that two judges facing exactly the same determined facts under the same laws (or even the same judge on different occasions) may find perfectly good precedents for contradictory decisions. All of which casts a good deal of doubt also upon the generalization that whatever has been decided by a court anywhere in the past must have been decided correctly. This skepticism is confirmed by the number of precedents which are flatly overruled. To suppose that mankind learns nothing by experience or education is to accept what Jeremy Bentham called "The Wisdom of Our Ancestors, or the Chinese Argument."

---

[14] Percival E. Jackson, *op. cit.*, pp. 32, 40. Relief is in sight (and unemployment for law clerks) in the form of Univac III, a computer which can scan 100,000 legal citations per minute, with results deliverable to subscribing law offices by teletype in a matter of hours.

[15] For numerous examples, see *Ibid.*, pp. 66–78. It should be pointed out that the U.S. Supreme Court is not "bound by precedent," and frequently reverses itself.

Yet the reverential attitude of the law toward past decisions could hardly have survived as pure ancestor worship, unless it had something in its favor besides economy of thinking. As Justice Cardozo has said, "What has once been settled by a precedent will not be unsettled overnight, for certainty and uniformity are gains not lightly to be sacrificed. Above all is this true when honest men have shaped their conduct upon the faith of the pronouncement." Precedent is a powerful stabilizing force in social life, so vital in the eyes of some that it has even been said that "certainty is more important than justice"; yet by its accumulated weight it can "petrify" principles which once were malleable, and by its towering presence it tends to make the legal mind cautious, self-contained, suspicious of all innovations, and trustful of the power of words to determine facts. The lawyer is constantly tempted to sit "with his back to the future," to substitute the searching of musty documents for thinking about present problems, and to terminate his thinking in some ancient classification.

9. The Science of Law and Sociological Jurisprudence

So far we have been considering legal thinking largely in its own terms. The tests which lawyers and judges habitually apply are derived from within the structure of the law itself, in spite of the fact that most of it was built up in terms of a wholly antiquated psychology and economics. On the whole, the profession has shunned questions about the consequences of laws as none of its concern; and has unwittingly made itself the defender of past interests and values accepted and certified as legal facts, while present and future interests and values are excluded as hypothetical and "subjective."

But these tendencies have been challenged on two fronts. The first is represented by the growth of a science of the formation of laws and their social effects, similar to the study of other varieties of customary behavior. The genetic description of customs and how they become laws is followed by comparative studies of their operation and social consequences. Instead of picking a few cases here and there, the legal scientist makes statistical studies of the great masses of recorded but unreported instances. During the Great Depression, the number of dispossess cases brought by New York City landlords in order to evict tenants shot up from 125,826 in 1921 to 203,271 in 1931 and 334,171 in 1933. Such extraordinary increases plainly indicated the need of a remedy for the working of a particular law under radically changed conditions. But they did not prescribe what the remedy should be, or enable a decision about which of the many possible causal factors was the principal one.

Along with this tendency to supplement the study of "law as law" by a scientific appraisal of its growth and consequences, has gone a parallel movement in the direction of what has been called *sociological jurisprudence*, associated with the names of Justices Holmes, Cardozo, and Frankfurter, and former Dean Roscoe Pound of the Harvard Law School. "The sociological jurist," writes Professor M. J. Aronson, "wishes to indicate the necessity for jurisprudence of recognizing an extra-legal norm or standard derived from a sociological analysis of the *mores*."[16] In the writings of most of the leaders of this school of thought, the standard turns out to be philosophical, a weighing of moral values in the light of the findings of the social studies. The law, as Cardozo pointed out, is closer to Jellinek's "minimum ethics" than to any attempt to "hold the crowd to the morality of saints and seers." But its guiding ideal is justice, which is unavoidably a philosophical conception; and the judge should aim at "giving effect to the scale of values revealed to him in his readings of the social mind" by the illumination of all the social studies. This view demands that legal thinking not only embrace the future in its purview, but also accept some of the responsibility which goes along with its power over the destinies of men. Some have taken this to mean that the law should undertake to transform society into Utopia single-handed, but that is not a necessary corollary of the position. For one thing, lawyers and judges already have their hands full in trying to regulate society in its "marginal" aspects in terms of its past ideals and practices, without endeavoring in addition to set its future goals and guide it to their attainment.

Both sociological jurisprudence and a behavioristic science of law have encountered much conservative opposition, because they seem to be upsetting to established practices and values. Often their champions have seemed to advocate a revolutionary abolition of tradition, when actually they were only pleading for a supplementing of legalistic thinking by additional methods. The legal mind, especially in times of rapid change, when it becomes most essential to adapt the slow-moving processes of law to the swirling currents of altered values, is likely to be more than ever concerned about social stability, and less than ever attracted by the uncertainties of unproved hypotheses. The older members of any society like to be able to count on the stability of their environments; and there is a solidity and familiarity about precepts which have endured through the centuries. Lawyers are reluctant to concede that any degree of probability established at so great a price in litigation is to be brushed aside on specious pleas of temporary expediency, or merely to forward feverish projects of reform. A few of the more timid still deprecate anything which might impair a superstitious reverence for the "majesty of the law" among the ignorant, but that view loses force as enlightenment spreads.

The law, then, only appears to escape from the uncertainties of the social studies by setting up a closed logical domain and vocabulary of its own. It is true that lawyers can claim to have an almost "infallible method" for determining whether a pronouncement is legal. The law is whatever a judge has said or can be predicted to say; and there is in existence an immense and partly organized body of knowledge which enables trained lawyers to make fairly accurate predictions about the decisions of judges, especially of those with whom they are acquainted. But there remain a good many unplugged leaks in the system. It is not always possible to be sure who is a judge. What about the rulings and "directives" of semi-legal administrative bodies? And

---

[16] Moses J. Aronson, "Cardozo's Doctrine of Sociological Jurisprudence," *Journal of Social Philosophy*, vol. IV (1938–39), p. 10. For a historian's comments, see Denis W. Brogan, "Law and Social Change in a Democratic Society," in Ray D. Henson, *op. cit.*, pp. 83–93.

it is obvious that authentic judges make mistakes, which are law just as much as anything else they decide, until overruled by a wiser judge. Finally, the whole enterprise of the law is itself to be judged like any other social mechanism which works well or badly in promoting the wider interests of the good life for man.

10. A Science of Government?

When a professional man of the law widens his vision to include the weighing of social consequences, he enters the broader field of political science or government. Here the focus of attention is upon the state in its law-making and law-enforcing activities, viewed in the larger setting of politics as a whole. Any state exists, no doubt, to provide a cumulative past for its society by winnowing human experiences and conserving the valuable lessons. But it also performs the function of attempting to provide a calculable future in the form of a set of "rules for changing the rules" that will permit its citizens to count, not necessarily on any fixed degree of permanence, but on a fair amount of normal continuity and consistency in the making of fundamental alterations. A state, in other words, always assumes its own immortality, although it cannot guarantee it. Both law and government are concerned with maintaining what Dean Karl N. Llewellyn called "the groupness of the group," the underlying cement of the community. Time was when men shaped their own schemes for the future with comparatively little attention to governmental planning. But as the world has become increasingly knit together in interdependent relationships, its peoples have come to look more and more to their political leaders for the broad master blueprints of the things to come. To what extent can these be claimed to rest upon reliable knowledge? Are there laws, either mechanical or historical, from which political conclusions may be deduced?

We have seen that some economists have sought to make their discipline partly mathematical and deductive on the mechanical pattern by assuming a psychological constant known as *economic man*, a creature resembling actual human beings in the mass sufficiently to give economic equations a rough applicability to some of the simpler aspects of existing market situations. Should government attempt to become "scientific" by the same kind of abstraction, setting up a psychologically constant *homo politicus*, or political man? Some attempts to do so have been made and defended; but they encounter one or the other of two great obstacles: either the type of man selected as political is too narrow to be representative of all men and women; or else it is described so formally (in the effort to be universal) that it is empty of content. Suppose, for example, that we say that political man is a power-seeker engaged in "making secure the way of his future desire" (Hobbes) by negotiation with his like-natured fellows. Immediately it becomes obvious that different men at different times, and the same men at different times, seek different kinds of power through an endless variety of activities, some of which are remote from those ordinarily described as political. The member of the Peace Corps and the gangster can both be depicted as in search of power; but one wants "power over" his rivals, while the other may be seeking "power for" all mankind. The content of what they are after, and the purpose for which the power will be used, are far more significant for predicting their future behavior than the form which their aspirations have in common. From that content, considerations of value cannot be excluded with profit.

Furthermore, the reduction of politics to equations of group pressures summed up in votes or polls is far too "atomistic" to fit our existing knowledge, scanty as it is, of social psychology. Men do not behave in groups in ways that can be adequately explained by measuring and adding up their individual power-urges. This is not to deny that group behavior in the field of politics can be usefully measured, and correlations established between sectional, occupational, religious, and party groupings, provided we do not mistake interesting leads for complete scientific analyses. Such methods will work best where political conditions have become stabilized over a considerable period of time, so that a degree of solidarity and discipline can be counted upon. But such circumstances rarely allow the investigator to set up a comparable control group, since the latter would have to be equal in political maturity and stability, yet lacking in the *single* factor under inquiry. Nor can measurement cope with "the perpetual surd of genius," the rise of the unpredictable "great man," who gives a new twist to old tendencies by his keen perception of hidden possibilities.

These criticisms of the mechanical pattern do not apply with equal force to the vast areas of detail comprised in the fields of public administration. Once policies, or ends, have been decided upon, the devising and utilization of means is largely a scientific matter which is open to experimental testing. "There is," as Dean Woodbridge used to remark, "no Republican or Democratic way of laying a sidewalk," once the laying of a sidewalk has been voted by the electorate. But, on the other hand, one cannot find out whether or not one's neighbors want a new sidewalk (much less whether they "ought" to want one) by consulting a manual on highway construction. For that is a question of relative values which they alone can decide.

GOVERNMENT AS FUTURE HISTORY

To detach a science of politics from history by any sort of mechanical abstraction, therefore, seems to promise little in the way of fruitfulness, at least until psychology, both individual and social, can provide some means of cutting down the boundless variety of inner motivations to be found behind political behavior. Political science has more to learn about method from history than from mathematical economics. If the proverb is correct in describing history as "past politics," then politics may be best understood as future history. Does human political experience, historically considered, yield any "laws" which would enable us to forecast the future? The sociological historian encounters manifold difficulties in constructing any such laws, such as the fewness of the instances, the excessive degree of abstraction required, and the likelihood of disregarding too many important differences. Most of the "laws" which have been offered are cyclical or rhythmical, purporting to show how the pendulum of politics swings back and forth between radicalism and conservatism, or else they are organismic à la Aristotle or Spengler or Toynbee, portraying the ways in which a régime may grow strong, only to degenerate and decay. Then there are the great numbers of platitudes which have been uttered about the art of ruling and the use of myths. But such generalizations must always be bounded by qualifications when they are applied to a particular cultural-historical context. Nothing is more short-sighted than the attempt to interpret in parliamentary terms the political behavior of a people totally without a long tradition of self-government by methods of free debate and vote.

The comparative method is sometimes urged as the surest pathway to a science of politics, but it is of little value if it means no more than the measuring of all other governments upon the yardstick of one's own, or if it consists of the forms of political structures in abstraction from their historical settings. The politics of a country cannot be fully understood without an intimate acquaintance with the genius of the people and their history. "The historical approach and the historical method of assembling and organizing facts is just as necessary to the political scientist who is studying modern political institutions as if he were studying the bureaucracy of the Byzantine or of the Chinese Empires. . . ."[17] But to study a people's history is to become acquainted with their various philosophies of life, from which (in part at least) originate those choices of values that constitute the determining factors in much of their political activity. Thus, any alleged science of politics which professes to get along without considerations of value is either a superficial sort of political engineering, which accepts its values ready-made from other sources; or else it is an abstract system of concepts from which all the vital human elements have been omitted.

The student of government is thus in need of political history and political philosophy, as well as of political science. In addition to everything which the social studies on the mechanical pattern can teach him about the similarities in human behavior, he should avail himself of the resources of history, biography, and literature in general. The songs of a country, as well as its laws, are grist for his mill. He should cultivate the technique, as Professor Postan recommends, of seeing, in concrete historical incidents, the reflections of "worlds larger than themselves. It is in this reflected flicker of truth, the revelations of the general in the particular, that the contribution of the historical method to social science will be found."[18] If the tests of historical thinking on the highest levels are philosophical, as we have contended, so are the tests of similar thinking in the field of government.

[17] Joseph P. Chamberlain, "Co-operation in the Study of Political Science" in *Studies in the History of Culture* (Menasha, Wis., 1942), p. 324.
[18] M. M. Postan, *op. cit.*, p. 34

FOR CLASS DISCUSSION

A. That law may be set down as good which is certain in meaning, just in precept, convenient in execution, agreeable to the form of government, and productive of virtue in those that live under it. — *Francis Bacon* (2)

B. A town that can't support one lawyer can always support two. — *Anon.*

C. Let those, and those only, who participate in sense and reason, and know clearly what true justice is, exercise straight vision in their judgments, and without passion apportion to each his deserts. — Instructions of *Emperors Leo III and Constantine V* to their judges, 726 A.D. (3)

> Fill the seats of justice
> With good men, not so absolute in goodness
> As to forget what human frailty is.
>
> — *T. N. Talfourd*

D. A fox should not be of the jury at a goose's trial. — *Thomas Fuller*

E. What we want is a government of laws administered by the right sort of men. — *John Chamberlain*

F. . . . in a court of law all that we can deal with is the law of the land as we find it. — *Justice North, In re Gregson,* 1887 (8)
We are under a Constitution, but the Constitution is what the judges say it is. — *Justice Charles E. Hughes*

G. Laws should be made by legislators, not by judges.
— *C. B. Beccaria,* 1764
The best law leaves the least discretion to the judge. — *Latin Proverb*

H. All laws are promulgated for this end: that every man may know his duty; and therefore the plainest and most obvious sense of the words is that which must be put on them. — *Sir Thomas More,* 1516

I. Legal enactments govern all subjects which they concern either in express words or by interpretation. When there is no statutory rule applicable to the case, the judge ought to decide according to customary law. In the absence of a custom bearing on the point he ought to decide in conformity with a rule which he would have formulated if he had been a lawgiver. In doing so he ought to follow the views established by jurisprudence and legal precedents. — *Swiss Civil Code of 1907*

J. A judge looking at a constitutional decision may have compulsions to revere past history and accept what was once written. But he remembers above all else that it is the Constitution which he swore to support and defend, not the gloss which his predecessors may have put on it. . . . (Otherwise) he lets men long dead and unaware of the problems of the age in which he lives do his thinking for him. — *Justice William O. Douglas*

K. What are twenty acts of Parliament among friends? — *John Selden*

L. The law does not consist in particular instances, though it is explained by particular instances and rules, but the law consists of principles which govern specific and individual cases as they happen to arise.
— *Lord Justice Mansfield in Rex vs. Bembridge,* 1783

M. Almost every legal concept or principle is found to be but the terminal of a scale which shades at its opposite extremity into another of exactly contrary tendency, and the line between the two oscillates from specific case to case according to the context. Thus the law of nuisance plays between the principle that every person is entitled to use his property for any purpose that he sees fit, and the opposing principle that every man is bound to use his property in such a manner as not to injure the property of his neighbor. — *John Dickinson*

N. All the sentences of precedent judges that have ever been cannot altogether make a law contrary to natural equity. — *Thomas Hobbes*

O. It usually takes a hundred years to make a law; and then, after it has done its work, it usually takes a hundred years to get rid of it.
— *Henry Ward Beecher*

P. It would be better to have no laws at all than it is to have as many as we have. — *Montaigne, 1588.*

Q. Reason is the life of the law. — *Sir Edward Coke*
The language of judicial decision is mainly the language of logic. And the logical method and form flatter that longing for certainty and for repose which is in every human mind. But certainty generally is an illusion. The actual life of the law has not been logic; it has been experience. The felt necessities of the times, the prevalent moral and political theories, intuitions of public policy, avowed or unconscious, even the prejudices which the judges share with their fellow-men, have had a good deal more to do than the syllogism in determining the rules by which men should be governed. — *Justice Oliver Wendell Holmes*

R. A good deal of the wisdom of life is apt to appear foolishness to a narrow logic. We urge our horse downhill and yet put the brake on the wheel — clearly a contradictory process to a logic too proud to learn from experience. But a genuinely scientific logic would see in this humble illustration a symbol of that measured straining in opposite directions which is the essence of the homely wisdom that makes life livable. — *Morris R. Cohen*

S. It is the province of the judge to expound the law only — the written from the statute, the unwritten or common law from the decisions of our predecessors and of our existing courts — from the text writers of acknowledged authority, and upon the principles to be clearly deduced from them by sound reason and just inference — not to speculate upon what is best, in his opinion, for the advantage of the community.
— *Lord Justice Coleridge in Brownlow vs. Egerton, 1854*

T. No law perfectly suits the convenience of every member of the community; the only consideration is, whether upon the whole it be profitable to the greater part. — *Livy*

U. Knowing that religion does not furnish grosser bigots than law, I expect little from old judges. — *Thomas Jefferson*
There are no more reactionary people in the world than judges.
— *Nicolai Lenin*

Law and arbitrary power are in eternal enmity. — *Edmund Burke*

V. What is law in the book is largely determined by history. What is law in action is largely determined by public opinion. — *Roscoe Pound*

396

W. A highly developed machine has been turned over to our keeping, a machine with intricate cogs and weights and balances, the work of many minds. Small wonder that we lie awake at nights in fear that some new apprentice, who was supposed to lubricate the joints, may turn out in the end to be either a bungler or an enemy, and set the whole appliance out of gear. — *Justice Benjamin N. Cardozo*

X. A lawyer without history or literature is a mechanic, a mere working mason; if he possesses some knowledge of these, he may venture to call himself an architect. — *Sir Walter Scott*

No truly great piece of fiction has been written by a lawyer who has practiced for any appreciable length of time, and no great novel has been written with the law as a background. I believe that the major reason is that legal training and experience tend to destroy freedom of imaginative expression, which becomes paralyzed by legal terminology. The lawyer becomes as tautological as a cuckoo clock.

— *Arthur Train*, lawyer and novelist

The best way to prepare for the law is to come to the study of the law as a well-read person. — *Justice Felix Frankfurter*

EXAMPLES IN THE LAW

Evidence: Testimonial and Circumstantial

1. In the case of *Temperance Hall Association vs. Giles*, 33 N.J.L. 260, the plaintiff claimed that he was injured by falling into a cellarway that was left unguarded at night. The defendant offered to prove that ten thousand persons had passed the spot every year without previous accident. The court excluded all such negative evidence on the ground that "it would lead to the trial of a multitude of distinct issues, involving a profitless waste of time of the court, and tending to distract the attention of the jury from the real point at issue, without possessing the slightest force as proof of the matters of fact involved. . . . The offer to show that ten thousand persons passed without accident . . . would carry with it the right to cross-examine as to the circumstances under which each individual of the multitude passed, and the degree of caution and circumspection used by each, etc., etc."

2. Despite the fact that he had allegedly swallowed the evidence, a policy slip encased in a gelatine capsule, William Rugoff of 194 Reid Avenue, Brooklyn, was held on charges of possessing policy slips by Magistrate Charles Solomon in August, 1941. Detective Marker of the Snyder Avenue Station testified that he saw Rugoff swallow the capsule on his approach, and produced a bag of similar capsules found in a compartment of Rugoff's car. The magistrate ruled that, while direct evidence of a policy slip was lacking, there was sufficient "evidence of evidence" that the slip had been swallowed.

3. In July, 1934, Walter Foster was killed in Harlem, and when the police asked two witnesses who did it, they replied: "Jesse Carrington." The pic-

ture of Jesse Carrington in the Rogues' Gallery they quickly identified as the guilty man. In August, Jesse Carrington, a Negro ex-convict with no regular home, was picked up in Toms River, New Jersey, and brought to New York, where the two witnesses identified him personally. Only one thing puzzled the prosecutor: the accused had on his person receipts for merchandise purchased in South Boston, Virginia, dated the day of the murder. Careful investigation revealed that there was another Jesse Carrington, a cousin of the accused man, who resembles him closely, even to the scars on his face. The accused Jesse was freed; and his counsel commented: "This is the first time in my experience that a district attorney ever took the time and trouble to ascertain the true facts despite the identifications of the defendant by two people."

4. Judge Samuel Leibowitz, before his elevation to the bench, was famous for his ingenuity in cross-examination. One of his cases involved the defense of Tony Romano, accused of shooting a policeman, whose alibi consisted of the claim that he was working at a fish market at the time the shooting occured. The prosecutor brought into the courtroom a basket of twenty different kinds of fish, such as halibut, bluefish, perch, and so on, asking Romano to identify each. The defendant guessed wrong twenty times. Leibowitz then reminded the jury that the fish market in question was in a Jewish neighborhood, and asked why Romano had not been confronted with pike, carp, pickerel and other varieties used in making *gefüllte* fish. "Why," asked Leibowitz, "did the prosecutor try to confuse him by showing him only *Christian* fish?" Romano was acquitted.

5. At the trial of Tom Mooney for the bombing of the 1916 Preparedness Day parade in San Francisco, the defense introduced photographs taken by Wade Hamilton showing Mooney and his wife Rita watching the parade on the roof of the Eilers Building, with a clock in the distance showing 2:01 P.M. The explosion took place ten blocks away at 2:06 P.M. The State intimated that the hands on the clock, enlarged two hundred times, might have been altered; and Mooney was convicted. About twenty years later, a photograph taken by a newsreel cameraman was found which shows the same clock at the same hour with exactly the same section of the parade passing the spot, a group of nurses, and the only section of its kind in the parade. On the basis of this and other evidence, Mooney was finally released.

Legal Reasoning on Points of Law and Precedent

6. From the opinion of Chief Justice Crane in *Salomone vs. Yellow Taxi Corporation*, 242 N.Y. 251, dealing with the mysterious plunging into the East River of a taxi driven by Nick Caniano, with Frank Salomone and Billy Mossioli inside, on the night of February 7, 1923:

"The justice charged the doctrine of *res ipsa loquitur* [the thing speaks for itself] as applicable to this case. He in substance told the jury that if the chauffeur drove the car off the dock, and the defendant [Yellow Taxi Corporation] could not explain it, the plaintiff (estate of Frank Salomone) was entitled to recover. . . . [The lower court jury had awarded the estate $12,000.]

"Here also we think the judge trespassed upon the province of the jury and decided matters which the law must leave to them. . . . The defendant . . . cannot offer any explanation. Yet the fact is that its Yellow Taxicab, of which Caniano was chauffeur, at some time and under some circumstances went into the East River, and Caniano and the two with him were drowned. Does this in and of itself raise the presumption of negligence . . . because the defendant cannot give an explanation of the accident or show that Caniano was not negligent? I for one do not think so." . . . [Judgments reserved.]

7. A young woman in Providence, R. I., twenty-two years old, eloped to Nova Scotia and married the forty-four-year-old brother of her mother, which would be forbidden by Rhode Island law. It was possible in Nova Scotia because that province is governed solely by precedent found in 32 Henry VIII 38, which cites prohibitions in the book of Leviticus against boys marrying their aunts and girls marrying their father's brothers, but which says nothing about nieces marrying their mother's brothers.

8. From the dissenting opinion of Justice Oliver Wendell Holmes in *Motion Picture Patents Company vs. Universal Film Manufacturing Company,* 243 U.S. 502, 519: "For fifteen years . . . the public has been encouraged by this Court to believe that the law is as it was laid down in *Heaton-Peninsular Button-Fastener vs. Eureka Specialty Company,* 77 Fed. Rep. 288, and numerous decisions of the lower courts. I believe that many and important transactions have taken place on the faith of those decisions, and for that reason [also] . . . the rule . . . should be maintained."

9. Not until 1951 was an unborn child in New York State entitled to sue, after birth, for injuries suffered before birth by the negligence of someone other than his or her mother. A Mrs. Woods of the Bronx, when nine months pregnant, fell on what she charged was a "defective cellar stairway" in the house rented from a Mr. Lancet, a landlord, with the result that her son Robert C. Woods, Jr., was subsequently born "sick, sore, lame and disabled with permanent injuries." In a 5–2 decision, her right to sue was upheld by the Court of Appeals, even though the only New York precedent, a case in 1921, was adverse. "Shall we," asked Judge Desmond, "bring the common law of this state on this question, into accord with justice?" He noted that courts in other states: California, Ohio, Minnesota and Georgia had done so; and concluded: "I think we should make the law conform to the right."

≥ Index

408

Social studies, definition in, 192–194; facts in, 103–104; hypothesis-making in, 153–155; and language, 171–174; proof in, 336f.
Sociological jurisprudence, 389f.
Sociology of knowledge, 360–362
Socrates, 65, 68, 69–70, 341
Spearman, C., 175
Spencer, Herbert, 366
Spengler, Oswald, 366, 393
Sprat, Thomas, 174
Stanhope, Earl (Charles), 82
Stanton, Edwin M., 13–16
Stare decisis, 387
Statistics, 277–293; and proof, 277–278; questions to ask about, 292–293; regularity in, 308–312, 327–328
Stebbing, L. Susan, 91
Stern, William, 381
Stevenson, Charles L., 161–162, 169n.
Strauss, Lewis L., 278
Structural classification, 181–182
Subject matter, access to, 116; differences in, 336f.; in social studies, 339
Subsumption, 385
Sumner, William Graham, 140
Swing, Raymond, 175
Syllogism, categorical, 69f.; exercises in, 92; figures of, 75f.; moods of, 75f.; rules of, 78f.; terms of, 73–75
Symbols and signs, 163f.
Systematic simplicity, 151–152
Systems, "closed," 236f.

T

Talfourd, T. N., 394
Tannenbaum, Frank, 216n.
Tennyson, Alfred, 163n.
Tensions and drives, 30–32
Testability of hypotheses, 148–149
Testimonial evidence, 380–383
Thales, 201
Theory and facts. 125f.; of games, 320; probability of, 323f.; scope of, 149–150; in science, 332–333; of sets, 80–81
Thomas, Benjamin P., 16n.

Thomas, Dorothy S., 342n.
Thompson, Ralph, 12
Thorndike, Edward L., 64, 110n.
Thorndike, Lynn, 293
"Thought, Laws of," 80
Thurber, James, 126, 350
Time, 229
Tocher, J. F., 330
Toscanini, Arturo, 26
Toynbee, Arnold J., 393
Tozzer, Alfred M., 372
Train, Arthur, 396
Trevor-Roper, Hugh, 370
Truth-tables, 81–82
Tyndall, John, 125

U

Ullmann, Stephen, 161n., 175
Uniformities, in causal analysis, 211f.; of Nature, 204
Use of knowledge, 61–63

V

Valéry, Paul, 147
Validity, formal, 84–85
Variables, 265f.; basic, 341f.; dependent and independent, 344f.
Value, judgments of, 107–108
Velikovsky, I., 204
Venn, John, 75; diagrams, 77–78
Vincent, John M., 356n.
Virgil, P., 200
Voltaire, v, 185, 370

W

Wagman, N. E., 322
Wagner-Jauregg, Julius, 144–145
Wallace, Henry A., 288
Wallas, Graham, 140–142, 144
Walpole, Horace, 165n.
Walpole, Hugh R., 170n., 187
Ward, James, 52
Ware, Caroline F., 367n.
Warren, Howard C., 208
Washington, George, 352
Watt, James, 136
Weather Bureau, U.S., 219–222
Wecter, Dixon, 143

57107

DATE DUE
